Beginning Algebra with Critical Thinking

Second Edition

Bernard Kolman
emeritus, Drexel University

Arnold Shapiro
emeritus, Temple University

Zia Khwaja, Ph.D.
California State University, Dominguez Hills

Nazim Khawaja, Ph.D.
California State University, Northridge

Eui Y. Chung, MS
Allan Hancock College

BVT
PUBLISHING

P.O. Box 492831 • Redding, CA 96049-2831

Managing Editor: Suzanne Morse
Project Editor: Paul Bedard, St. Clair County Community College
Contributing Editor: Connie Massey
Manager of Art and Design: Lisa Paul, Archetype Book Composition
Art Creation: Lisa Paul, Archetype Book Composition; Peggi Rodgers and Ben Rodgers,
    Misty Canyon Design
Text Layout: Archetype Book Composition
Cover Designer: BVT Publishing

Printed in the United States of America

Beginning Algebra with Critical Thinking, Second Edition

ISBN: 978-1-60229-986-3

To the memory of my mother, Eva.

— B K

To the memory of my parents.

— A S

To the memory of our parents.

— Z K , N K

To the memory of my father, Chan Do.

— E C

Contents

What Is Algebra?

Where did algebra come from?

There are about 100,000 different stories regarding algebra. The origin of algebra dates back to the ancient Babylonians. They developed mathematical systems that enabled them to calculate by applying their own formulas rather than utilizing geometric methods as most Egyptians, Greek, Indian, and Chinese mathematicians of that era did to solve problems.

The word "algebra" is of Arabic origin. It comes from the word *al-jar*, meaning reunion. Al-jar comes from the title of the book *ilm al-jebr wa'l-muqabala* written in 820 by the Persian mathematician Mahommed ben Musa al-Khwarizmi. The English translation of the title is *The book of Summary Concerning Calculating by Transposition and Reduction.*

Studying algebra will is very useful because it allows the general formulation of arithmetical laws, equations, and functional relationships. Generally, algebra is the study of the properties of operations on real numbers. Before we use the general formulation of arithmetical laws, we will learn about the properties of the real number system.

You may think that algebra is so difficult it will cause you headaches. Algebra is not easy; but once you learn it, you will find it useful in everyday situations. For example, if you have 5 apples in your refrigerator and you need 8 apples to make a pie, how many more apples do you need to purchase at the store? With such simple numbers, you easily come up with the answer 3 apples. However, in algebra we would use an equation to solve for an unknown number—in this case the number of additional apples you need. We write the unknown number as x. So I can write

$$5 + x = 8$$

We call x the variable which represents the unknown number of apples. Solving this equation means finding the unknown number x.

By substituting $x = 3$, we have

$$5 + 3 = 8 \text{ apples}$$

Isn't it fun to find the unknown number? Math is like magic.

Theses are the kinds of things that we will learn throughout this textbook. Let's start learning some fantastic mathematical magic!

To the Instructor

The authors are indebted to the faculty at those institutions that have adopted and have steadfastly continued to use the earlier editions of this text. Your letters and comments are genuinely appreciated and will always receive a prompt response.

Objectives of This Text

This second edition of *Beginning Algebra with Critical Thinking* maintains our objective of providing a textbook designed for *use by the college student*. We have adopted an informal, supportive style to encourage the student to read the book and to develop confidence under its guidance. We introduce concepts first by example with accompanying diagrams and illustrations that bolster the "reasonableness" of the resulting rules. We immediately reinforce every new mathematical technique or result with fully worked-out examples and captions clarifying their purpose. After each example, the student is presented with the opportunity to tackle a parallel problem, called a **Progress Check**, with the answer following it in the text.

New in This Edition

Although the structure of earlier editions has been retained, we have made significant additions and improvements in this edition.

- Completely new chapter openers with motivational applications and references to many websites of mathematical interest.

- Brand new chapter projects at the end of each chapter.

- Many new exercises, most of which emphasize the use of graphing calculators.

- New explanatory material for graphing calculator use.

Pedagogic Devices

We have continued to employ those pedagogic devices that instructors have found useful in the earlier editions.

Split Screens

Many algebraic procedures are described with the aid of a "split screen" that displays simultaneously both the steps of an algorithm and a worked-out example.

> ### ✔ Progress Checks
> A problem (with answers) accompanies every numbered example in the text to enable the student to test his or her understanding of the material just described.

Warnings

To help eliminate misconceptions and prevent bad mathematics habits, we have inserted numerous **Warnings** that point out the incorrect practices most commonly found in homework and exam papers.

Vignettes

In each chapter we have inserted one or more vignettes, elements that are independent of the text yet are often related to the mathematical concepts. The vignettes are intended to catch the attention of the student and heighten interest in the material. (We hope they will provide interesting reading for the instructor as well.)

Exercises

Abundant, carefully graded exercises provide practice in the mechanical and conceptual aspects of algebra. Exercises requiring the use of a calculator or graphing calculator are indicated by the calculator icons shown to the left. Exercises of a more challenging nature are indicated by a *. Answers to odd-numbered exercises, review exercises, and progress tests appear in an appendix at the back of the book.

End-of-Chapter Material

Every chapter contains a summary that includes the following:

Terms and Symbols with appropriate page references

Key Ideas for Review to stress the concepts

Review Exercises to provide additional practice

Progress Tests to provide self-evaluation and reinforcement

Chapter Projects

This edition has added chapter openers and related projects at the end of each chapter. These emphasize additional applications and demonstrate the widening relevance of algebra in many areas. Some feature a "look ahead" to topics of future courses, like polynomial curve fitting or Calculus applications. Students may be excited by the career possibilities suggested by some of these sections. Instructors may wish to review the projects first; they provide one possible means of selecting which material and which exercises to emphasize. Some of the projects include essay components; the increasing importance of communication skills in scientific careers and upper-level courses seems to make this new emphasis advisable. Projects could be modified or expanded to involve students working in groups. Significant opportunities for Internet research and graphing calculator exploration are also offered.

Answers

The answers to all **Review Exercises** and **Progress Tests** appear in the back of the book.

Solutions

Worked-out solutions to selected **Review Exercises** appear in a separate section at the back of the book. The solved problems provide one more level of reassurance to the student using the **Review Exercises** in preparation for the **Progress Tests**.

A Note on the Use of Calculators

Some of the new exercises in this edition call for the use of a graphing calculator. It is recommended that all students have one, and read the manual in order to become proficient in its use. Many instructors view graphing calculators as essential tools for students of algebra, and their use becomes even more pronounced in more advanced courses. The aid they provide in visualization, rapid evaluation of functions, using graphs to discover unsuspected relationships between concepts, and offering new approaches and a greater variety of problem-solving methods, more than balances the additional challenge in becoming skilled and comfortable with them.

Many models of graphing calculator are now available, and most offer the additional benefit of links which can be used to share programs and applications between students, from instructor to student, or from the Internet.

Supplementary Material

Student Solutions Manual by Jorge Cossio

Instructor's Manual with Tests by Gail Edinger

Acknowledgments

We thank the following for their review of the manuscript and for their helpful comments in this edition: Ken Klopfenstein, Colorado State University; C. Donald Smith, Louisiana State University at Shreveport; Kim Luna, Eastern New Mexico University; David Rearick, University of Colorado at Denver. We would like to acknowledge the following reviewers of the previous edition: David Lunsford, Grossmont College; Donald W. Bellairs, Grossmont College; Neil S. Dickson, Weber State College; Wayne Bishop, California State University, Los Angeles; and Patricia Martin, University of Illinois.

The staff at BVT Publishing has provided us with extensive and unflagging support. We also wish to express our appreciation to Paul Bedard, Project Editor.

To the Student

This book was written for you. It gives you every possible chance to succeed—if you use it properly.

We would like to have you think of mathematics as a challenging game—but not as a spectator sport. This wish leads to our primary rule: *Read this textbook with pencil and paper handy.* We illustrate every new idea or technique with fully worked-out examples. As you read the text, carefully follow the examples and then do the **Progress Checks**. The key to success in a math course is working problems, and the **Progress Checks** are there to provide immediate practice with the material you have just learned.

Your instructor will assign homework from the extensive selection of exercises that follows each section in the book. *Do the assignments regularly, thoroughly, and independently.* By doing many problems, you will develop the necessary skills in algebra, and your confidence will grow. Since algebraic techniques and concepts build on previous results, you can't afford to skip any of the work.

To help prevent or eliminate improper habits and to help you avoid the errors that we see each semester as we grade papers, we have interspersed **Warnings** throughout the book. The **Warnings** point out common errors and emphasize the proper method. They are summarized at the end of the chapter under the heading **Common Errors**.

We provide important review material at the end of each chapter. The **Terms and Symbols** should all be familiar by the time you reach them. If your understanding of a term or symbol is hazy, go back and read the definition.

It is possible to become so involved with the details of techniques that you lose track of the broader concepts. The list of **Key Ideas for Review** at the end of each chapter will help you focus on the principal ideas.

The **Review Exercises** at the end of each chapter can be used as part of your preparation for examinations. The section covering each exercise is indicated so that, if needed, you can go back to restudy the material. If you get stuck on a problem, see if the problem that is giving you difficulty or a similar problem is numbered in bold, indicating that a worked-out solution appears in the back of the book in the Solutions appendix. You are then ready to try **Progress Test A**. You will soon pinpoint your weak spots and can go back for further review and more exercises in those areas. Only then should you proceed to **Progress Test B**.

We believe that the eventual "payoff" in studying mathematics is an improved ability to tackle practical problems in your field of interest. To that end, this book places special emphasis on word problems, which recent surveys show often trouble students. Since algebra is the basic language of the mathematical techniques used in virtually all fields, the mastery of algebra is well worth your effort.

CHAPTER 1

The Real Number System

God made integers, all else is the work of man.

—Leopold Kronecker

The weather phenomena most studied by meteorologists are hurricanes; the main goal is to predict their occurrences and effects. Like all scientists, they use numbers to measure, compare, and classify their information. For example, the Saffir-Simpson Hurricane Scale uses small *natural numbers* (1, 2, 3, 4, and 5) to classify hurricanes according to the amount of damage they are likely to cause. The recent Hurricane Katrina reached category 5 status. Scales like this often employ natural numbers, because (as their name suggests) these are the types of numbers with which most people are comfortable. *Inequalities* may be used to express the range of wind speeds in miles per hour; for a category 5 storm, the speeds are >155 mph ("greater than 155 mph"). For a category 1 hurricane, the speeds are between 74 and 95 mph, which can be written as $74 \leq$ wind speed ≤ 95.

http://www.noaa.gov/

Scientists require other types of numbers too—for instance, **rational numbers** like 28.92 inches (the smallest central pressure for a category 1 hurricane). Many more examples of the uses of numbers and inequalities to describe hurricanes and other meteorological phenomena can be found at http://www.noaa.gov/.

What other uses do meteorologists and other specialists make of the real number system, number lines, inequalities, and operations with real numbers? The chapter project will suggest some ideas.

■ ■ ■

Arithmetic teaches us that the rule "two plus two equals four" is truly independent of the kind of objects to which the rule applies; it doesn't matter whether the objects are apples or ants, countries or cars. Observations such as this one led to the study of the properties of numbers in an abstract sense, that is, the study of those properties that apply to *all* numbers, regardless of what the numbers represent.

Since we will be dealing in much of our work with the *real numbers*, our studies will begin with a review of the *real number system*. We will then introduce symbols to denote arbitrary numbers, a practice characteristic of algebra. The remainder of the chapter will be devoted to explaining some of the fundamental properties of the real number system.

1.1   The Real Number System

Although this text will not stress the set approach to algebra, the concept and notation of sets will at times be useful.

Sets

A **set** is a collection of objects or numbers, which are called the **elements** or **members** of the set. The elements of a set are written within braces, so that

$$A = \{4, 5, 6\}$$

tells us that the set A consists of the numbers 4, 5, and 6. The set

$$B = \{\text{Squibb, Ford, Honeywell}\}$$

consists of the names of these three corporations. We also write $4 \in A$, which we read as "4 is a member of the set A" or "4 belongs to the set A." Similarly, Ford $\in B$ is read as "Ford is a member of the set B," and I.B.M. $\notin B$ is read as "I.B.M. is not a member of the set B."

If every element of a set A is also a member of a set B, then A is a **subset** of B. For example, the set of all robins is a subset of the set of all birds.

Example 1   Working with Sets
The set C consists of the names of all coins whose denomination is less than 50 cents.

(a) Write C in set notation.   (b) Is dime $\in C$?

(c) Is half-dollar $\in C$?   (d) Is $H = \{\text{nickel, dime}\}$ a subset of C?

Solution
(a) We have

$$C = \{\text{penny, nickel, dime, quarter}\}$$

(b) yes   (c) no   (d) yes

The Real Number System

Much of our work in algebra deals with the set of real numbers. Let's review the composition of this number system.

The numbers 1, 2, 3, . . . , used for counting, form the set of **natural numbers**. If we had only these numbers to use to show the profit earned by a company, we would have no way to indicate that the company had no profit or had a loss. To indicate no profit we introduce 0, and for losses we need to introduce negative numbers. The numbers

$$\ldots, -2, -1, 0, 1, 2, \ldots$$

form the set of **integers**. Thus, every natural number is an integer. However, not every integer is a natural number.

When we try to divide two apples equally among four people we find no number in the set of integers that will express how many apples each person should get. We need to introduce the **rational numbers**, which are numbers that can be written as a ratio of two integers,

$$\frac{p}{q} \quad \text{with } q \text{ not equal to zero}$$

Examples of rational numbers are

$$0 \qquad \frac{2}{3} \qquad -4 \qquad \frac{7}{5} \qquad \frac{-3}{4}$$

Thus, when we divide two apples equally among four people, each person gets half, or $\frac{1}{2}$, an apple. Since every integer n can be written as $n/1$, we see that every integer is a rational number. The number 1.3 is also a rational number, since $1.3 = \frac{13}{10}$.

We have now seen three fundamental number systems: the natural number system, the system of integers, and the rational number system. Each system we have introduced includes the previous system or systems, and each is more complicated than the one before. However, the rational number system is still inadequate for sophisticated uses of mathematics, since there exist numbers that are not rational, that is, numbers that cannot be written as the ratio of two integers. These are called

irrational numbers. It can be shown that the number a that satisfies $a \cdot a = 2$ is such a number. The number π, which is the ratio of the circumference of a circle to its diameter, is also such a number.

The decimal form of a rational number will either terminate, as

$$\frac{3}{4} = 0.75 \qquad -\frac{4}{5} = -0.8$$

or will form a repeating pattern, as

$$\frac{2}{3} = 0.\underset{\smile}{6}6\underset{\smile}{6}\ldots \qquad \frac{1}{11} = 0.\underset{\smile}{0909}09\ldots \qquad \frac{1}{7} = 0.\underset{\smile}{1428571}\ldots$$

Remarkably, the decimal form of an irrational number *never* forms a repeating pattern. Although we sometimes write $\pi = 3.14$, this is only an approximation, as is

$$\pi = 3.1415926536\ldots$$

Similarly, the decimal form of $\sqrt{2}$ can be approximated by $1.4142136\ldots$, which goes on forever and never forms a repeating pattern.

The rational and irrational numbers together form the **real number system** (Figure 1).

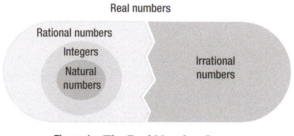

Figure 1   The Real Number System

The Real Number Line

To obtain a simple and useful geometric description of the set of real numbers we can draw a horizontal straight line, which we will call the **real number line**; pick a point, label it with the number 0, call it the **origin**, and denote it by O; and choose the **positive direction** to the right of the origin and the **negative direction** to the left of the origin. An arrow indicates the positive direction.

Now we select a unit of length for measuring distance. With each positive real number r we associate the point that is r units to the right of the origin, and with each negative number $-s$ we associate the point that is s units to the left of the origin. We can now show some points on the real number line.

Mnemonic Math

> How I want a drink
> Alcoholic of course
> After the heavy lectures
> Involving quantum mechanics!

This "poem" appeared in the *Science Times* on July 5, 1988. The same article contained yet another creative gem:

> How I wish I could
> Enumerate pi easily,
> Since all these (censored) mnemonics
> Prevent recalling any of pi's sequence
> More simply

This second poem gives you a hint as to the "meaning" of these words. If you list the number of letters in each word you have the sequence

3-1-4-1-5-9-2-6-5-3-5-8-9-7-9-3-2-3-8-4-5

Now, stick a decimal point after the first digit and you have

3.14159265358979323845

which should look vaguely familiar. This is the value of π accurate to 20 decimal places, and the "poems" are mnemonics recalling the value of this famous irrational number.

For centuries mathematicians have been fascinated by the challenge of calculating π. Gregory and David Chudnovsky of Columbia University recently became the first mathematicians to push the calculation of π to better than one billion places. And, should your interest run to poetry, π mnemonics exist in French, German, Greek, and Spanish.

Conversely, let P be a point on the real number line. If P is to the right of the origin and r units from the origin, we associate the real number r with P. If P is to the left of the origin and s units from the origin, we associate the real number $-s$ with P.

Thus, the set of all real numbers is identified with the set of all points on a straight line. Every point on the line corresponds to a real number, called its **coordinate**, and for every real number there is a point on the line. We often say that the set of real numbers and the set of points on the real number line are in **one-to-one correspondence**. The numbers to the right of the origin are called **positive**. The numbers to the left of the origin are called **negative**. The positive numbers and zero together are called the **nonnegative** numbers, whereas the negative numbers and zero together are called the **nonpositive** numbers.

Example 2   Points on a Real Number Line

Draw a real number line and plot the following points: $-\dfrac{3}{2}, 2, \dfrac{13}{4}$.

Solution

✔ **Progress Check 2**

Determine the real numbers denoted on the real number line as $A, B, C,$ and D.

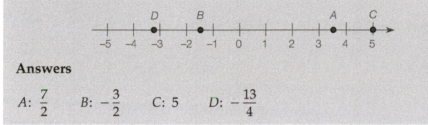

Answers

$A: \dfrac{7}{2}$ $B: -\dfrac{3}{2}$ $C: 5$ $D: -\dfrac{13}{4}$

Exercise Set 1.1

In Exercises 1−12 choose the correct answer(s) from the following: (a) rational number, (b) natural number, (c) real number, (d) integer, (e) irrational number.

1. The number 2 is

2. The number -3 is

3. The number $-\frac{2}{3}$ is

4. The number 0.8 is

5. The number 3 is

6. The numbers $-1, -2,$ and -3 are

7. The numbers 0, 1, and 2 are

8. The numbers $0, \frac{1}{2}, 1, \frac{2}{3},$ and $-\frac{4}{5}$ are

9. The numbers $\sqrt{2}$ and π are

10. The numbers 0.5 and 0.8 are

11. The numbers $\frac{\pi}{3}$ and 2π are

12. The numbers $0, \frac{1}{2}, \sqrt{2}, \pi, 4,$ and -4 are

In Exercises 13−21 determine whether the given statement is true (T) or false (F).

13. -14 is a natural number.

14. $-\frac{4}{5}$ is a rational number.

15. $\frac{\pi}{3}$ is a rational number.

16. 2.5 is an integer.

17. 1.75/18.6 is an irrational number.

18. 0.75 is an irrational number.

19. $\frac{4}{5}$ is a real number.

20. 3 is a rational number.

21. $\sqrt{2}$ is a real number.

22. Draw a real number line and plot the following points.

   (a) 4   (b) -2 (c) $\dfrac{5}{2}$ (d) -3.5 (e) 0

23. Draw a real number line and plot the following points.

   (a) -5 (b) 4   (c) -3.5 (d) $\dfrac{7}{2}$ (e) $-\pi$

24. Estimate the real number associated with the points $A, B, C, D, O,$ and E on the accompanying real number line.

25. Represent each of the following by a positive or negative integer.

   (a) a profit of \$10

   (b) a loss of \$20

   (c) a temperature of 20° above zero

   (d) a temperature of 5° below zero

In Exercises 26–31 indicate which of the two given numbers appears first, viewed from left to right, on the real number line.

26. 4, 6

27. 2, 0

28. −2, 3

29. 0, −4

30. −5, −2

31. 4, −5

In Exercises 32–37 indicate which of the two given numbers appears second, viewed from left to right, on the real number line.

32. 9, 8

33. 0, 3

34. −4, 2

35. −4, 0

36. −3, −4

37. −2, 5

In Exercises 38–40 indicate the given set of numbers on the real number line.

38. The natural numbers less than 8.

39. The natural numbers greater than 4 and less than 10.

40. The integers that are greater than 2 and less than 7.

41. Your graphing calculator can convert a decimal number to a fraction. However, when we input pi, we get a decimal back:

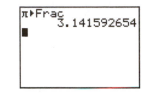

Explain in your own words why this is the case.

42. A hurricane with a central pressure of 27.25 inches might be classified as a category 4 storm. What subset of the real numbers does this number belong to? Can you verify this using your graphing calculator (see Exercise 41)?

1.2   Arithmetic Operations: Fractions

The vocabulary of arithmetic will carry over to our study of algebra. In multiplying two real numbers, each of the numbers is called a **factor** and the result is called the **product**.

$$6 \cdot 5 = 30$$

factors   product

Terminology and Order of Operations

In this text we will indicate multiplication by a dot, as in the example just given, or by parentheses.

$$(6)(5) = 30$$

We will avoid use of the multiplication sign ×, since it may be confused with other algebraic symbols.

Let's look at the terminology of division.

$$30 \div 6 = 5$$

dividend divisor quotient

Most of the time we will write division this way:

$$\frac{30}{6} = 5$$

Numbers to be multiplied have the same name (factors), whereas in division the numbers have different names (dividend, divisor). This suggests that we can interchange the factors in multiplication without altering the product, but that interchanging the dividend and divisor in division will alter the quotient. In general:

> Addition can be performed in any order.
> Multiplication can be performed in any order.
> Subtraction must be performed in the given order.
> Division must be performed in the given order.

What happens when more than one operation appears in a problem? To avoid ambiguity, we adopt this simple rule.

> Always do multiplication and division before addition and subtraction.

Example 1   Order of Arithmetic Operations
Perform the indicated operations.

(a) $2 + (3)(4) - 5 = 2 + 12 - 5 = 9$

(b) $\dfrac{10}{5} + 7 + 3 \cdot 6 = 2 + 7 + 18 = 27$

✔ Progress Check 1

Perform the indicated operations.

(a) $2 \cdot 4 - 6 + 3$ (b) $(3)(4) - 2 + \dfrac{9}{3}$

Answers

(a) 5   (b) 13

We will provide complete rules for the order of operations in the next section.

Fractions

It is important to master the *arithmetic* of fractions since this serves as background for the *algebra* of fractions. We prefer to write $10 \div 5$ in the form $\frac{10}{5}$, which we call a **fraction**. The number above the line is called the **numerator**; that below the line is called the **denominator**.

$$\text{numerator} \longrightarrow \frac{10}{5} \longleftarrow \text{denominator}$$

Multiplication of fractions is straightforward.

Multiplication of Fractions

> *Step 1.*   Multiply the numerators of the given fractions to find the numerator of the product.
>
> *Step 2.*   Multiply the denominators of the given fractions to find the denominator of the product.

Example 2   Multiplication of Fractions

Multiply.

(a) $\dfrac{3}{5} \cdot \dfrac{7}{2}$

(b) $\dfrac{2}{9} \cdot \dfrac{5}{3} \cdot 4$

Solution

(a) $\dfrac{3}{5} \cdot \dfrac{7}{2} = \dfrac{3 \cdot 7}{5 \cdot 2} = \dfrac{21}{10}$

(b) $\dfrac{2}{9} \cdot \dfrac{5}{3} \cdot 4 = \dfrac{2}{9} \cdot \dfrac{5}{3} \cdot \dfrac{4}{1} = \dfrac{2 \cdot 5 \cdot 4}{9 \cdot 3 \cdot 1} = \dfrac{40}{27}$

✔ **Progress Check 2**

Multiply.

(a) $\dfrac{4}{3} \cdot \dfrac{7}{3}$

(b) $\dfrac{5}{12} \cdot \dfrac{7}{3} \cdot \dfrac{1}{2}$

Answers

(a) $\dfrac{28}{9}$

(b) $\dfrac{35}{72}$

Reciprocal

The **reciprocal** of $\frac{3}{4}$ is found by inverting $\frac{3}{4}$ to obtain $\frac{4}{3}$. Thus, $\frac{4}{3}$ is the reciprocal of $\frac{3}{4}$. Similarly, $\frac{1}{5}$ is the reciprocal of 5, and $\frac{1}{\pi}$ is the reciprocal of π. Note that the product of a real number and its reciprocal is always equal to 1. The number 0 does not have a reciprocal, since the product of 0 and any number is 0.

> • Every real number, except 0, has a reciprocal such that the product of the number and its reciprocal is equal to 1.
>
> • The number 0 does not have a reciprocal and *division by 0 is not permitted.*

Division of fractions can always be converted into a multiplication problem by forming the reciprocal.

<table>
<tr><td rowspan="2">**Division of Fractions**</td><td>*Step 1.*   Invert the divisor.</td></tr>
<tr><td>*Step 2.*   Multiply the resulting fractions.</td></tr>
</table>

Since 0 has no reciprocal, division by 0 is not defined.

Example 3   Division of Fractions

Divide.

(a) $\dfrac{4}{9} \div \dfrac{3}{5}$ (b) $\dfrac{\frac{2}{3}}{\frac{5}{7}}$

Solution

(a) $\dfrac{4}{9} \div \dfrac{3}{5} = \dfrac{4}{9} \cdot \dfrac{5}{3} = \dfrac{4 \cdot 5}{9 \cdot 3} = \dfrac{20}{27}$ (b) $\dfrac{\frac{2}{3}}{\frac{5}{7}} = \dfrac{2}{3} \div \dfrac{5}{7} = \dfrac{2}{3} \cdot \dfrac{7}{5} = \dfrac{14}{15}$

✔ **Progress Check 3**

Divide.

(a) $\dfrac{8}{7} \div \dfrac{3}{2}$ (b) $\dfrac{\frac{1}{2}}{3}$ (c) $\dfrac{2}{11} \div \dfrac{5}{3}$

Answers

(a) $\dfrac{16}{21}$ (b) $\dfrac{1}{6}$ (c) $\dfrac{6}{55}$

The same fractional value can be written in many ways. Thus,

$$\frac{3}{2} = \frac{6}{4} = \frac{18}{12} = \frac{72}{48}$$

are four forms of the same fractional value.

<table>
<tr><td rowspan="2">**Equivalent Fractions**</td><td>The value of a fraction is not changed by multiplying or dividing *both* the numerator and denominator by the same number (other than 0). The result is called an **equivalent fraction**.</td></tr>
</table>

If we multiply a fraction, say $\frac{5}{2}$ by $\frac{3}{3}$, we are really multiplying by a "disguised," equivalent form of 1, since $\frac{3}{3} = 1$. Thus,

$$\frac{5}{2} = \frac{5}{2} \cdot \frac{3}{3} = \frac{15}{6}$$

Example 4   Finding an Equivalent Fraction
Find the equivalent fraction.

$$\frac{7}{3} = \frac{?}{12}$$

Solution
Since $12 = 3 \cdot 4$, we multiply the original denominator by 4 to obtain the new denominator. Then we must also multiply the numerator by 4.

$$\frac{7}{3} \cdot \frac{4}{4} = \frac{7 \cdot 4}{3 \cdot 4} = \frac{28}{12}$$

✔ **Progress Check 4**
Find the equivalent fraction.

(a) $\frac{5}{4} = \frac{?}{20}$ (b) $6 = \frac{?}{4}$ (c) $\frac{2}{3} = \frac{8}{?}$

Answers

(a) $\frac{25}{20}$ (b) $\frac{24}{4}$ (c) $\frac{8}{12}$

Now let's reverse the process. We saw that $\frac{7}{3}$ can be written as

$$\frac{7}{3} \cdot \frac{4}{4} = \frac{28}{12}$$

which is equivalent to $\frac{7}{3}$. Beginning with $\frac{28}{12}$, we can write the numerator and denominator as a product of factors:

$$\frac{28}{12} = \frac{7 \cdot 4}{3 \cdot 4} = \frac{7}{3} \cdot \frac{4}{4} = \frac{7}{3} \cdot 1 = \frac{7}{3}$$

We say that $\frac{7}{3}$ is the **reduced form** of $\frac{28}{12}$. This illustrates the **cancellation principle**.

Cancellation Principle

> Common factors appearing in both the numerator and denominator of a fraction can be canceled without changing the value of the fraction. When a fraction has no common factors in its numerator and denominator, it is said to be in reduced form.

Example 5   Obtaining Reduced Form
Write $\frac{15}{27}$ in reduced form.

Solution

$$\frac{15}{27} = \frac{5 \cdot 3}{9 \cdot 3} = \frac{5}{9} \cdot \frac{3}{3} = \frac{5}{9} \cdot 1 = \frac{5}{9}$$

Finding all the Primes up to *N*: The Sieve of Eratosthenes

An integer $p > 1$ is called a **prime** if the only positive integers that divide p are p and 1. For example, 3, 5, 11, and 2 are primes. The number 2 is the only even prime, since every even integer greater than 2 is divisible by 2. A positive integer that is not a prime is said to be a **composite**. For example, 4, 10, and 15 are composite integers.

A method for listing all the primes up to a given integer *N* was developed by the Greek scientist and mathematician Eratosthenes (275–194 B.C.), who was a friend of Archimedes. We will describe this method, called the **Sieve of Eratosthenes**, and apply it to the accompanying table, which lists the positive integers less than or equal to 100.

Prime Integers Less Than or Equal to 100

2   3   4   5   6   7   8
9   10   11   12   13   14   15
16   17   18   19   20   21   22
23   24   25   26   27   28   29
30   31   32   33   34   35   36
37   38   39   40   41   42   43
44   45   46   47   48   49   50
51   52   53   54   55   56   57
58   59   60   61   62   63   64
65   66   67   68   69   70   71
72   73   74   75   76   77   78
79   80   81   82   83   84   85
86   87   88   89   90   91   92
93   94   95   96   97   98   99
100

Step 1. Make a list of all integers from 2 to *N*.

Step 2. Since 2 is the first prime, cross out all multiples of 2. The next integer in the list that has not been crossed out is 3, which is a prime. Now cross out all multiples of 3. The next integer in the list that has not been crossed out is 5, which is a prime. Next, cross out all multiples of 5. Repeat the process until the list is exhausted.

Step 3. The numbers that have not been crossed out are the primes less than *N*.

You probably noticed that no additional cross-outs occurred after you crossed out the multiples of 7. In general, you can stop when you reach a number *K* such that *K* times *K* is at least *N*.

The number of computations required for executing the "sieve" rises dramatically as *N* increases. For this reason, the "sieve" has become a favorite benchmark program for comparing computer hardware and software.

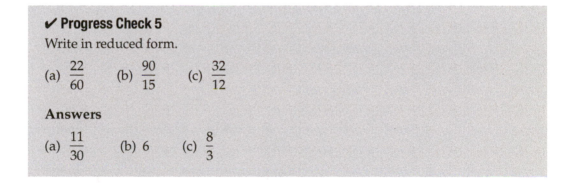

✔ Progress Check 5

Write in reduced form.

(a) $\dfrac{22}{60}$ (b) $\dfrac{90}{15}$ (c) $\dfrac{32}{12}$

Answers

(a) $\dfrac{11}{30}$ (b) 6   (c) $\dfrac{8}{3}$

Warning

Only multiplicative factors common to both the *entire* numerator and the *entire* denominator can be canceled. *Don't* write

$$\frac{6+5}{3} = \frac{\overset{2}{\cancel{6}}+5}{\cancel{3}} = \frac{7}{1} = 7$$

Since 3 is not a multiplicative factor common to the *entire* numerator, we may not cancel.

The addition and subtraction of fractions can sometimes be more complicated than their multiplication. We begin by stating the key idea for adding and subtracting fractions.

Addition and Subtraction Principle

> We can add or subtract fractions directly only if they have the same denominator.

When fractions do have the same denominator, the process is easy: Add or subtract the numerators and keep the common denominator. Thus,

$$\frac{3}{4} + \frac{15}{4} = \frac{3 + 15}{4} = \frac{18}{4} = \frac{9}{2}$$

Least Common Denominator

If the fractions we wish to add or subtract do not have the same denominator, we must rewrite them as equivalent fractions that do have the same denominator. There are easy ways to find the **least common denominator (LCD)** of two or more fractions, that is, the smallest number that is divisible by each of the given denominators.

To find the LCD of two or more fractions, say, $\frac{1}{2}$, $\frac{5}{6}$, and $\frac{4}{9}$, we first write each denominator as a product of prime numbers. Recall that a **prime number** is a natural number greater than 1 whose only factors are itself and 1. For example, 5 is a prime number, since it is divisible only by 5 and 1. Other examples of numbers written as a product of primes are:

$$2 = 2$$
$$6 = 2 \cdot 3$$
$$9 = 3 \cdot 3$$

We then form a product in which each distinct prime factor appears the greatest number of times that it occurs in any single denominator. This product is the LCD. In our example, the prime factor 2 appears at most once in any denominator, while the prime factor 3 appears twice in a denominator. Thus, the LCD is $2 \cdot 3 \cdot 3 = 18$.

The LCD is the tool we need to add or subtract fractions with different denominators. Here is an example of the process.

Example 6   Using the LCD in the Addition of Fractions

Find the following sum:

$$\frac{2}{5} + \frac{3}{4} - \frac{2}{3}$$

Solution

| **Addition and Subtraction of Fractions** | |

Step 1. Find the LCD of the fractions.

Step 1. $\text{LCD} = 5 \cdot 2 \cdot 2 \cdot 3 = 60$

Step 2. Convert each fraction to an equivalent fraction with the LCD as its denominator.

Step 2.

$$\frac{2}{5} = \frac{2}{5} \cdot \frac{12}{12} = \frac{24}{60}$$

$$\frac{3}{4} = \frac{3}{4} \cdot \frac{15}{15} = \frac{45}{60}$$

$$\frac{2}{3} = \frac{2}{3} \cdot \frac{20}{20} = \frac{40}{60}$$

Step 3. The fractions now have the same denominator. Add and subtract the numerators as indicated.

Step 3.

$$\frac{2}{5} + \frac{3}{4} - \frac{2}{3} = \frac{24}{60} + \frac{45}{60} - \frac{40}{60}$$

$$= \frac{24 + 45 - 40}{60}$$

$$= \frac{29}{60}$$

Step 4. Write the answer in reduced form.

Step 4.

$$\text{Answer: } \frac{29}{60}$$

✔ **Progress Check 6**

Find the sum $\dfrac{2}{3} + \dfrac{4}{7}$.

Answer

$\dfrac{26}{21}$

Example 7   Adding and Subtracting Fractions

Perform the indicated operations and simplify.

(a) $\dfrac{1}{2} - \dfrac{1}{6} + \dfrac{1}{3}$ (b) $\dfrac{\dfrac{4}{3} - \dfrac{1}{1}}{\dfrac{1}{3} + \dfrac{3}{4}}$

Solution

(a) We see that the LCD is 6 and

$$\frac{1}{2} = \frac{1}{2} \cdot \frac{3}{3} = \frac{3}{6}$$

$$\frac{1}{6} = \frac{1}{6} \cdot \frac{1}{1} = \frac{1}{6}$$

$$\frac{1}{3} = \frac{1}{3} \cdot \frac{2}{2} = \frac{2}{6}$$

Thus,

$$\frac{1}{2} - \frac{1}{6} + \frac{1}{3} = \frac{3}{6} - \frac{1}{6} + \frac{2}{6} = \frac{3 - 1 + 2}{6} = \frac{4}{6} = \frac{2}{3}$$

(b) The LCD of the fractions in the numerator is 6 and hence the numerator is

$$\frac{4}{3} - \frac{1}{2} = \frac{4}{3} \cdot \frac{2}{2} - \frac{1}{2} \cdot \frac{3}{3} = \frac{8}{6} - \frac{3}{6} = \frac{5}{6}$$

The LCD of the fractions in the denominator is 12 and hence the denominator is

$$\frac{1}{3} + \frac{3}{4} = \frac{1}{3} \cdot \frac{4}{4} + \frac{3}{4} \cdot \frac{3}{3} = \frac{4}{12} + \frac{9}{12} = \frac{13}{12}$$

Then the given fraction is

$$\frac{\dfrac{5}{6}}{\dfrac{13}{12}} = \frac{5}{6} \cdot \frac{\cancel{12}^{2}}{13} = \frac{10}{13}$$

✔ **Progress Check 7**
Perform the indicated operations and simplify.

(a) $\dfrac{3}{2} + \dfrac{5}{9} - \dfrac{1}{3}$ (b) $\dfrac{\dfrac{2}{3} + \dfrac{5}{6}}{\dfrac{1}{2} + \dfrac{2}{3}}$

Answers

(a) $\dfrac{31}{18}$ (b) $\dfrac{9}{7}$

Percent

Percent is a way of writing a fraction whose denominator is 100. The percent sign, %, following a number means "place the number over 100." Thus, 7% means $\frac{7}{100}$.

A fraction whose denominator is 100 is converted to decimal form by moving the decimal point in the numerator two places to the left and eliminating the denominator.

$$\frac{65}{100} = 0.65$$

Since a percent is understood to mean a fraction whose denominator is 100, we see that

$$7\% = 0.07$$

Similarly, we change a decimal to a percent by moving the decimal point two places to the right and adding the percent sign.

$$0.065 = 6.5\%$$

To write a fraction as a percent, we multiply the fraction by 100 and divide the new fraction by its denominator. For example, to write $\frac{1}{20}$ as a percent, we form

$$\frac{100}{20} = 5$$

so $\frac{1}{20} = 5\%$. Similarly, to write $\frac{1}{7}$ as a percent, we form

$$\frac{100}{7} = 14.28$$

so $\frac{1}{7} = 14.28\%$.

Example 8   Converting Percents, Decimals, and Fractions
Write each percent as a decimal and as a fraction, and each decimal or fraction as a percent.

(a) 25%   (b) 142%   (c) 0.06   (d) 2.1   (e) $\frac{3}{4}$ (f) $\frac{21}{5}$ (g) $\frac{1}{6}$

Solution

(a) $25\% = 0.25$; $25\% = \frac{25}{100} = \frac{1}{4}$ (b) $142\% = 1.42$; $142\% = \frac{142}{100} = \frac{71}{50}$

(c) $0.06 = 6\%$ (d) $2.1 = 210\%$

(e) $\frac{3}{4} = \frac{75}{100} = 75\%$ (f) $\frac{21}{5} = \frac{420}{100} = 420\%$

(g) $\frac{1}{6} = 0.167$ (rounded) $= 16.7\%$

✔ **Progress Check 8**
Write each percent as a decimal and as a fraction, and each decimal or fraction as a percent.

(a) 62.5%   (b) $\frac{1}{2}\%$ (c) 0.26   (d) 3.475

(e) $\frac{1}{8}$ (f) $\frac{5}{2}$ (g) $\frac{1}{9}$

Answers

(a) $0.625, \frac{5}{8}$ (b) $0.005, \frac{1}{200}$ (c) 26%   (d) 347.5%

(e) 12.5%   (f) 250%   (g) 11.1%

It is common practice to state business problems in terms of percent. You have heard and read statements such as:

> Ms. Smith was promised an 8% salary increase.
> The Best Savers Bank pays 5.75% interest per year.
> Automobile prices will increase 4.62% on July 1.
> During the sale period, all merchandise is reduced by 20%.

To find the **percent of a number**, we must convert the percent to a decimal or fraction and then *multiply* by the number.

Example 9   Finding the Percent of a Number

(a) What is 30% of 15?   (b) What is 5% of 400?

(c) A bank pays 6.75% interest per year. What will the annual interest be on a deposit of $500?

(d) The price of a refrigerator selling at $600 is to be reduced by 20%. What is the sale price?

Solution

(a) 30% = 0.3 and (0.3)(15) = 4.5

(b) 5% = 0.05 and (0.05)(400) = 20

(c) 6.75% = 0.0675 and (0.0675)($500) = $33.75

(d) 20% = 0.2 and (0.2)($600) = $120 = amount of discount

$$\text{Sale price} = \text{original price} - \text{discount}$$
$$= \$600 - \$120$$
$$= \$480$$

✔ Progress Check 9

(a) What is 40% of 60?

(b) What is 2% of 1200?

(c) How much interest will be earned during one year on a deposit of $2500 at 7.5% per year?

(d) The price of an automobile selling at $6800 will be increased by 4%. What is the new price?

Answers

(a) 24   (b) 24   (c) $187.50   (d) $7072

Decimals

We can use decimals to represent fractions and mixed numbers. We often use decimals in measurement because it is easier to write them in order and compare them than it is when using fractions.

For the decimal 345.674:

> 3 is placed for the hundreds place
> 4 is placed for the tens place
> 5 is placed for the ones place
> 6 is placed for the tenths place
> 7 is placed for the hundredths place
> 4 is placed for the thousandths place

We can write this decimal in expanded notation:

$$345.674 = 300 + 40 + 5 + \frac{6}{10} + \frac{7}{100} + \frac{4}{1000}$$

Decimals are composed of three parts: the whole number part, the decimal point, and the fractional part.

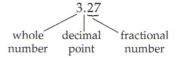

Let's write 3.27 in words: "Three and twenty-seven hundredths."

We can write decimals as fractions or as mixed numbers. For example, the decimal 3.27 can also be written as

$$3\frac{27}{100}$$

Example 1   Writing Decimals as Fractions

Write each decimal in words, and then as a fraction or mixed number.

(a) 65.739   (b) 0.43

Solution

(a) 65.739: "Sixty-five and seven hundred thirty-nine thousandths"

$$65.739 = 65\frac{739}{1000}$$

(b) 0.43: "Forty-three hundredths"

$$0.43 = \frac{43}{100}$$

Example 2   Writing Fractions as Decimals

Write each fraction or mixed number as a decimal.

(a) $\dfrac{13}{100}$ (b) $\dfrac{47}{1000}$

(c) $23\dfrac{9}{10,000}$ (d) $-127\dfrac{6}{10}$

Solution

(a) $\dfrac{13}{100} = 0.13$ (b) $\dfrac{47}{1000} = 0.047$

(c) $23\dfrac{9}{10,000} = 23.0009$ (d) $-127\dfrac{6}{10} = -127.6$

Decimal numbers can be negative or positive. We can graph decimal numbers on the number line to compare values. We can also compare the digits of each decimal, column by column, working from left to right.

Example 3   Comparing Decimals

(a) Which is greater: 23.56 or 23.6?

(b) Which is greater: -40.09 or -40.18?

Solution

(a) 23.56

Write a 0 after the 6 in 23.6 so that both decimals have the same number of digits to the right of the decimal point: 23.60. Then compare digits from left to right: 6 is greater than 5. Thus we conclude that 23.60 is greater than 23.56 (23.60 > 23.56).

(b) -40.09

Working from left to right, 0 is less than 1. Thus we conclude that -40.09 is greater than -40.18 ($-40.09 > -40.18$).

Exercise Set 1.2

In Exercises 1−14 perform the indicated operations.

1. $\dfrac{2(6+2)}{4}$

2. $\dfrac{(4+5)6}{18}$

3. $\dfrac{6(3+1)}{2}+3\cdot 5$

4. $\dfrac{8(6-1)}{4}-3\cdot 2$

5. $\dfrac{(4+5)(2+3)}{3}-3\cdot 5$

6. $\dfrac{(7-2)(8-2)}{3}+7\cdot 4$

7. $\dfrac{2}{11}\cdot\dfrac{10}{3}\cdot\dfrac{2}{5}$

8. $\dfrac{7}{5}\cdot\dfrac{4}{3}\cdot 2$

9. $\dfrac{\frac{2}{3}}{\frac{1}{5}}$

10. $\dfrac{\frac{3}{4}}{\frac{4}{3}}$

11. $\dfrac{\frac{2}{5}}{\frac{3}{10}}$

12. $\dfrac{\frac{1}{2}}{\frac{5}{6}}$

13. $\dfrac{2}{3}\div\dfrac{4}{9}$

14. $\dfrac{3}{5}\div\dfrac{9}{25}$

In Exercises 15−20 find the number that makes the fractions equivalent.

15. $\dfrac{4}{3}=\dfrac{?}{9}$

16. $\dfrac{3}{4}=\dfrac{15}{?}$

17. $1=\dfrac{7}{?}$

18. $2=\dfrac{?}{14}$

19. $\dfrac{5}{4}=\dfrac{?}{20}$

20. $\dfrac{4}{7}=\dfrac{12}{?}$

In Exercises 21−24 find the least common denominator of the given fractions.

21. $\dfrac{1}{4},\dfrac{1}{2},\dfrac{2}{15}$

22. $\dfrac{1}{3},\dfrac{1}{9},\dfrac{1}{5}$

23. $\dfrac{1}{20},\dfrac{1}{30},\dfrac{1}{45}$

24. $2,\dfrac{1}{4},\dfrac{5}{36}$

In Exercises 25−32 perform the indicated operations and simplify.

25. $\dfrac{3}{4}+\dfrac{2}{3}$

26. $\dfrac{2}{3}+\dfrac{5}{6}$

27. $\dfrac{1}{4}+\dfrac{2}{3}-\dfrac{1}{2}$

28. $\dfrac{1}{5}-\dfrac{1}{2}+\dfrac{1}{3}$

29. $\dfrac{\frac{1}{6}+\frac{1}{2}}{\frac{5}{4}+\frac{2}{3}}$

30. $\dfrac{\frac{1}{2}-\frac{3}{8}}{\frac{1}{3}+\frac{1}{4}}$

31. $\dfrac{2-\frac{1}{3}}{3+\frac{1}{4}}$

32. $\dfrac{\frac{3}{5}-\frac{1}{10}}{1+\frac{1}{2}}$

In Exercises 33−42 change the given percent to both fractional and decimal forms.

33. 20%

34. 60%

35. 65.5%

36. 32.5%

37. 4.8%

38. 5.5%

39. 120%

40. 160%

41. $\frac{1}{5}$%

42. $\frac{1}{10}$%

In Exercises 43−54 convert each number to a percent.

43. 0.05

44. 0.03

45. 0.425

46. 0.345

47. 6.28

48. 7.341

49. $\frac{3}{5}$

50. $\frac{5}{6}$

51. $\frac{9}{4}$

52. $\frac{6}{5}$

53. $\frac{2}{7}$

54. $\frac{4}{3}$

55. What is 35% of 60?

56. What is 60% of 80?

57. What is 140% of 30?

58. What is 160% of 50?

59. What is $\frac{1}{2}$% of 40?

60. What is $\frac{2}{5}$% of 20?

In Exercises 61−64 use a calculator to convert each number to decimal form and then determine the smallest number.

61. $\frac{5}{32}, \frac{11}{64}, \frac{8}{50}$

62. $\frac{20}{27}, \frac{28}{39}, \frac{78}{103}$

63. $\frac{150}{171}, \frac{78}{88}, \frac{125}{144}$

64. $\frac{814}{653}, \frac{910}{731}, \frac{3875}{3107}$

In Exercises 65−68 use a calculator to convert each number to a percent and determine the largest number.

65. $\frac{32}{55}, \frac{15}{27}, \frac{52}{89}$

66. $\frac{75}{61}, \frac{941}{765}, \frac{66}{54}$

67. $\frac{137}{49}, \frac{850}{304}, \frac{267}{96}$

68. $\frac{999}{1077}, \frac{67}{73}, \frac{297}{321}$

69. A bank pays 7.25% interest per year. If a depositor has $800 in a savings account, how much interest will the bank pay him at the end of one year?

70. Suppose that you buy a $5000 General Motors bond that pays 9.3% interest per year. What will be the amount of the dividend when mailed to you by G.M. at the end of the year?

71. A savings bank pays 8% interest per year. If a depositor has $6000 in a savings account, what will be the amount in the account at the end of one year, assuming that no withdrawals are made?

72. A student has borrowed $3000 at a rate of 7% per year. How much interest is owed to the bank at the end of one year?

73. A record store embarks on an advertising campaign to raise its profits by 20%. If this year's profits were $96,000, what will next year's profits be if the campaign succeeds?

*74. An $800 stereo system will be sold at a 25% reduction. What will be the new price?

*75. In order to cope with rising costs, an oil producer plans to raise prices by 15%. If a barrel of oil now sells for $28.00, what will be the new price?

*76. A boat that originally sold for $600 is now on sale for $540. What is the percentage of discount?

*77. The holder of an $8000 savings certificate gets a $640 check at the end of the year. What is the annual rate of simple interest?

*78. A department store runs the following sale on a brand of stereo equipment. During the first week of the sale, the merchandise is discounted by 10%. If the merchandise is not sold by the second week, it is discounted by 20% of the sale price that was in effect during the first week. (This is called **chain discount**.) What is the price during the second week of a receiver that originally sold for $400?

*79. On September 1 an automobile manufacturer introduces the new model of a car and increases by 6% the price that was in effect for the car on August 31. Since demand for the new model exceeds supply, on October 1 the manufacturer raises the price by 2% of the price in effect on September 30. What is the new price of a car that on August 31 sold for $8000? (This is known as **chain percent increase**.)

80. Use your graphing calculator to convert each number to a fraction in lowest terms (see your manual for instructions): 0.12, 0.1278, 0.$\overline{63}$ (this is 0.636363 . . . ; how many repetitions must you enter before your calculator will interpret this as a repeating decimal?)

81. According to the Bipartisan Task Force on Funding Disaster Relief (1995), hurricanes accounted for 39.9% of insurance payouts for the period 1984–1993. For every million dollars paid out in this period, how many dollars were paid out for hurricanes?

82. Agricultural damages accounted for 1.52 billion dollars out of a total of 30 billion dollars of damages related to hurricane Andrew, which struck Florida in August 1992. What percentage of the total damages were agricultural?

Source for data in Exercises 81–82: Pielke Jr., Roger A., and Roger A. Pielke Sr. *Hurricanes: Their Nature and Impacts on Society.* Chichester: John Wiley & Sons, 1997.

In Exercises 83–88, write the decimals as fractions or mixed numbers.

83. 0.00003

84. 0.234

85. 32.37

86. 2.108

87. −54.02

88. 0.41

In Exercises 89–94, write the fractions or mixed numbers as decimals.

89. $\dfrac{1}{10}$

90. $3\dfrac{45}{100}$

91. $121\dfrac{7}{10,000}$

92. $-25\dfrac{1234}{10,000}$

93. $79\dfrac{3}{100}$

94. $-\dfrac{99}{1000}$

1.3 Algebraic Expressions

A rational number is one that can be written as p/q where p and q are integers (and q is not zero). These symbols can take on more than one distinct value. For example, when $p = 5$ and $q = 7$, we have the rational number $\frac{5}{7}$; when $p = -3$ and $q = 2$, we have the rational number $\frac{-3}{2}$. The symbols p and q are called **variables**, since various values can be assigned to them.

If we invest P dollars at an interest rate of 6% per year, we will have $P + 0.06P$ dollars at the end of the year. We call $P + 0.06P$ an **algebraic expression**. Note that an algebraic expression involves **variables** (in our case, P), **constants** (such as 0.06), and **algebraic operations** (such as $+, -, \times, \div$). Virtually everything we do in algebra involves algebraic expressions, sometimes as simple as our example and sometimes very complicated.

When we assign a value to each variable in an algebraic expression and carry out the indicated operations, we are "evaluating" the expression.

Example 1   Evaluating an Algebraic Expression
Evaluate.

(a) $2x + 5$ when $x = 3$

(b) $\dfrac{3m + 4n}{m + n}$ when $m = 3, n = 2$

Solution
(a) Substituting 3 for x, we have

$$2(3) + 5 = 6 + 5 = 11$$

(b) Substituting, we have

$$\frac{3(3) + 4(2)}{3 + 2} = \frac{9 + 8}{3 + 2} = \frac{17}{5}$$

✔ **Progress Check 1**
Evaluate.

(a) $\dfrac{r + 2s}{s - r}$ when $r = 1, s = 3$

(b) $4x + 2y - z$ when $x = 1, y = 4, z = 2$

Answers

(a) $\dfrac{7}{2}$

(b) 10

Order of Operations

If we want to evaluate

$$3 + 5y/2 \quad \text{when } y = 4$$

in what order should we perform the operations? The interpretation

$$\frac{3 + 5y}{2}$$

doesn't produce the same result as the interpretation

$$3 + \frac{5y}{2}$$

Fortunately, most calculators and computer languages use the same convention for determining the order of operations. This order or **hierarchy of operations** is shown below.

Hierarchy of Operations

1. Perform all operations within parentheses.
2. Compute any squares or powers (see Section 1.4).
3. Perform multiplication and division, working from left to right.
4. Perform addition and subtraction, working from left to right.

To evaluate an expression, substitute the given values for the variables and then apply the rules for the hierarchy of operations.

Example 2   Evaluating an Algebraic Expression

Evaluate the expression

$$\frac{3(x - 1)}{y + 2} + (x - y)(x + y) \quad \text{when } x = 5, y = 2$$

Solution

Substituting, we have

$$\frac{3(5 - 1)}{(2 + 2)} + (5 - 2)(5 + 2) = \frac{3(4)}{4} + (3)(7) \qquad \text{Operations in parentheses}$$

$$= 3 + 21 \qquad \text{Multiplication and division}$$

$$= 24 \qquad \text{Addition}$$

✔ **Progress Check 2**

Evaluate.

(a) $\dfrac{2(x-1)}{(x+1)+(x+3)}$ when $x = 2$

(b) $1 + (2-x) + \dfrac{y}{y-1}$ when $x = 1, y = 2$

Answers

(a) $\dfrac{1}{4}$ (b) 4

Exercise Set 1.3

In Exercises 1–4 determine whether the given statement is true (T) or false (F).

1. $3x + 2 = 8$ when $x = 2$

2. $5x - 1 = 11$ when $x = 2$

3. $2xy = 12$ when $x = 2, y = 3$

4. $\dfrac{2x + y}{7} = 7$ when $x = 3, y = 1$

In Exercises 5–12 evaluate the given expression when $x = 4$.

5. $2x + 3$

6. $3x - 2$

7. $\dfrac{1}{2}x$

8. $3(x - 1)$

9. $(2x)(2x)$

10. $(2x + 1)x$

11. $\dfrac{1}{2x + 3}$

12. $\dfrac{x}{2x - 4}$

In Exercises 13–20 evaluate the given expression when $a = 3, b = 4$.

13. $2a + b$

14. $3a - b$

15. $2b - a$

16. ab

17. $3(a + 2b)$

18. $\dfrac{1}{3a + b}$

19. $\dfrac{2a - b}{b}$

20. $\dfrac{a + b}{b - a}$

In Exercises 21–28 evaluate the given expression when $r = 2, s = 3, t = 4$.

21. $r + 2s + t$

22. rst

23. $\dfrac{rst}{r + s + t}$

24. $(r + s)t$

25. $\dfrac{r + s}{t}$

26. $\dfrac{r + s + t}{t}$

27. $\dfrac{t - r}{rs}$

28. $\dfrac{3(r + s + t)}{s}$

29. Evaluate $2\pi r$ when $r = 3$. (Recall that π is approximately 3.14.)

30. Evaluate $\frac{9}{5}C + 32$ when $C = 37$.

31. Evaluate $0.02r + 0.314st + 2.25t$ when $r = 2.5$, $s = 3.4$, and $t = 2.81$.

32. Evaluate $10.421x + 0.821y + 2.34xyz$ when $x = 3.21$, $y = 2.42$, and $z = 1.23$.

In Exercises 33–36 evaluate the given expression when $x = -3.25$ and $y = 0.75$.

33. $3 + x \div 6 \cdot x - 1$

34. $3 \div (x + y) - y$

35. $2 \cdot y + 1 \div (x + 1)$

36. $-1 + (2x - y) \div 2 + y \div (1 - x)$

*37. If P dollars are invested for t years at a simple interest rate of r percent per year, the amount on hand at the end of t years is $P + Prt$. Suppose \$2000 is invested at 8% per year ($r = 0.08$). How much money is on hand after

(a) one year? (b) three years?

(c) half a year? (d) eight months?

(*Hint:* Express eight months as a fraction of a year.)

*38. The perimeter of a rectangle is given by the formula $P = 2(L + W)$, where L is the length and W is the width of the rectangle. Find the perimeter if

(a) $L = 2$ feet, $W = 3$ feet.

(b) $L = \frac{1}{2}$ meter, $W = \frac{1}{4}$ meter.

(c) $L = 13$ inches, $W = 15$ inches.

39. Al purchases 3 boxes of cereal at \$1.25 per box, 2 bottles of soda at \$1.10 per bottle, and $1\frac{1}{2}$ pounds of salad at \$2.29 per pound. Write an expression for the total cost.

40. If apples cost a cents per pound, pears cost p cents per pound, and cucumbers cost c cents each, write an expression for the total bill when Joan purchases 2 pounds of apples, $3\frac{1}{2}$ pounds of pears, and 6 cucumbers.

41. The campus cafeteria sells hamburgers for \$1.35, hot dogs for 85¢, and french fries for 80¢ per order. Write an expression for the total cost when Jim purchases d hot dogs, h hamburgers, and f orders of french fries.

42. Hi-Fi house is offering a 10% discount on all record and cassette purchases. Write an expression for the total cost when a student purchases N cassettes at \$5.99 each, M cassettes at \$6.99 each, and K records at \$6 each.

43. Use your calculator to evaluate the expression

$$\frac{140x - 319y}{500y}$$

for $x = 200, y = 200$. First, store the values under variable names. Then, enter the expression using those variable names. Now you can store new values and retrieve the expression you entered (it should not be necessary to enter it again). Evaluate the same expression for $x = 210$ and $y = 199$.

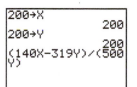

1.4   Operating with Signed Numbers; Exponents

Let's review the rules for operating with signed numbers before using them in more complicated problems.

We say that $-a$ is the **opposite** of a if a and $-a$ are equidistant from the origin and lie on opposite sides of the origin.

Since $-a$ is opposite in direction to a, then $-(-a)$ must have the same direction as a. We see that

$$-(-a) = a$$

We also refer to $-a$ as the **negative** of a. Of course, the negative of a number need not be negative: $-(-5) = 5$.

Here are the rules for addition with signed numbers:

Addition with Like Signs

Ignoring the signs, add the numbers. The sign of the answer is the same as the common sign of the original numbers.

$$5 + 2 = 7$$
$$(-5) + (-2) = -7$$

Addition with Unlike Signs

Ignoring the signs, find the difference of the numbers. The sign of the answer is the sign of the number that is larger in absolute value.

$$6 + (-4) = 2 \qquad 3 + (-5) = -2$$
$$(-7) + 3 = -4 \qquad (-5) + 8 = 3$$

Example 1   Adding Signed Numbers

(a) $2 + 4 = 6$ 　　　　(b) $2 + (-4) = -2$ 　　(c) $(-2) + (-4) = -6$

(d) $(-2) + 4 = 2$ 　　　(e) $3 + [(-5) + (-2)] = 3 + (-7) = -4$

(f) $[(-4) + (-7)] + 3 = -11 + 3 = -8$ 　　　　(g) $8 + 0 = 8$

✔ Progress Check 1

Add.

(a) $(-3) + (-7)$ 　　　(b) $(-5) + 1$ 　　　　(c) $2 + (-6)$

(d) $-2 + [5 + (-4)]$ 　(e) $0 + (-8)$ 　　　　(f) $[3 + (-6)] + (-1)$

Answers

(a) -10 　　　　　　(b) -4 　　　　　　(c) -4

(d) -1 　　　　　　 (e) -8 　　　　　　 (f) -4

Subtraction problems can be converted into addition of signed numbers.

Subtraction

Change $a - b$ to $a + (-b)$ and follow the rules for addition of signed numbers.

$$5 - 2 = 5 + (-2) = 3$$
$$-3 - 4 = -3 + (-4) = -7$$
$$2 - (-6) = 2 + (+6) = 8$$
$$-6 - (-5) = -6 + (+5) = -1$$

Example 2   Subtracting Signed Numbers

(a) $7 - 4 = 7 + (-4) = 3$ 　　　　 (b) $10 - (-6) = 10 + (+6) = 16$

(c) $-8 - 2 = -8 + (-2) = -10$ 　 (d) $-5 - (-4) = -5 + (+4) = -1$

(e) $-7 - (-7) = -7 + (+7) = 0$ 　 (f) $(-2 - 5) + 6 = [-2 + (-5)] + 6 = -1$

✔ Progress Check 2

Perform the operations.

(a) $3 - 8$ 　　　 (b) $-6 - 7$ 　　　 (c) $-9 - (-5)$ 　　　 (d) $16 - (-9)$

(e) $(14 - 5) - 4$ 　 (f) $(-11 + 2) - 4$ 　 (g) $(-6 - 4) - 2$

Answers

(a) -5 　　　 (b) -13 　　　 (c) -4 　　　 (d) 25

(e) 5 　　　 (f) -13 　　　 (g) -12

The rules for determining the sign in multiplication and division are straightforward.

If both numbers have the same sign, the result is positive. If the numbers have opposite signs, the result is negative.

$$3 \cdot 4 = 12 \qquad\qquad \frac{6}{3} = 2$$

$$(-2)(-5) = 10 \qquad\qquad \frac{-8}{-4} = 2$$

$$(-4)(6) = -24 \qquad\qquad \frac{-10}{2} = -5$$

$$(7)(-3) = -21 \qquad\qquad \frac{12}{-3} = -4$$

Multiplication and Division

Example 3   Multiplying and Dividing Signed Numbers

(a) $4 \cdot \left(-\frac{1}{5}\right) = -\frac{4}{5}$ 　 (b) $\left(-\frac{2}{3}\right)(-3) = 2$ 　 (c) $\frac{-4}{8} = -\frac{1}{2}$

(d) $\frac{-16}{-24} = \frac{2}{3}$ 　 (e) $(-5) \cdot \frac{1}{4} = -\frac{5}{4}$ 　 (f) $\frac{18}{-2} = -9$

✔ Progress Check 3

(a) $(-3)\left(\dfrac{2}{-7}\right)$ (b) $\left(\dfrac{2}{3}\right)\left(\dfrac{-3}{4}\right)$ (c) $\dfrac{20}{-6-4}$

(d) $\dfrac{4-5}{3-6}$ (e) $(-4)\left(\dfrac{2-3}{4}\right)$ (f) $\left(\dfrac{1}{5}\right)\left(\dfrac{5-6}{4}\right)$

Answers

(a) $\dfrac{6}{7}$ (b) $-\dfrac{1}{2}$ (c) -2

(d) $\dfrac{1}{3}$ (e) 1 (f) $-\dfrac{1}{20}$

Let's apply the rules for operating with signed numbers to the evaluation of algebraic expressions.

Example 4   Evaluating an Algebraic Expression

Evaluate the given expression when $x = -1, y = -1$.

(a) $2x + \dfrac{x-1}{y+2}$ (b) $-3(2x-y) + (-4)(2y-x)$

Solution

(a) Substituting, we have

$$2(-1) + \frac{(-1-1)}{-1+2} = -2 + \frac{-2}{1} = -2 + (-2) = -4$$

(b) Substituting, we have

$$-3[2(-1) - (-1)] + (-4)[2(-1) - (-1)]$$
$$= -3(-2+1) + (-4)(-2+1)$$
$$= -3(-1) + (-4)(-1) = 3 + 4 = 7$$

✔ Progress Check 4

Evaluate the given expression when $x = 2, y = -1$.

(a) $-(-y)$ (b) $2 - 3x + y$ (c) $\dfrac{2-2x}{2-2y}$ (d) $\dfrac{x+y}{x-y}$

Answers

(a) -1 (b) -5 (c) $-\dfrac{1}{2}$ (d) $\dfrac{1}{3}$

Mathematicians use a special notation to indicate a product of repeated factors. For example, the product

$$3 \cdot 3 \cdot 3 \cdot 3 \cdot 3$$

is written as

$$3 \cdot 3 \cdot 3 \cdot 3 \cdot 3 = 3^5$$

We call 3 the **base** and 5 the **exponent**. We can generalize this notation by the following definition.

Exponent Notation

> For any real number a and natural number n,
>
> $$a^n = a \cdot a \cdot a \cdots a$$

Example 5   Working with Exponent Notation

Evaluate.

(a) 2^6 (b) 0.1^3 (c) $(-2)^4$ (d) $(-5)^3$

Solution

(a) $2^6 = 2 \cdot 2 \cdot 2 \cdot 2 \cdot 2 \cdot 2 = 64$ (b) $0.1^3 = (0.1)(0.1)(0.1) = 0.001$

(c) $(-2)^4 = (-2)(-2)(-2)(-2) = 16$ (d) $(-5)^3 = (-5)(-5)(-5) = -125$

✔ Progress Check 5

Evaluate.

(a) 10^3 (b) $(-4)^4$ (c) $(-2)^5$ (d) 3^4 (e) $\left(\dfrac{2}{3}\right)^3$

Answers

(a) 1000 (b) 256 (c) -32 (d) 81 (e) $\dfrac{8}{27}$

Exercise Set 1.4

In Exercises 1–54 simplify the given expression by carrying out the indicated operations.

1. $3 + 5$

2. $-2 + (-3)$

3. $(-3) + (-4)$

4. $2 + (-3)$

5. $4 + (-2)$

6. $-4 + 6$

7. $-4 + 2$

8. $0 + (-2)$

9. $3 + 0$

10. $3 + (-3)$

11. $5 - 3$

12. $5 - 8$

13. $5 - (-3)$

14. $4 - (-4)$

15. $-8 - (-3)$

16. $-6 - (-7)$

17. $5 - (-6)(-3)$

18. $4 - (-1)(2)$

19. $[-3 - (-2)] - 1$

20. $[-8 - (-4)] - 5$

21. $(-4 - 2) - (-3)$

22. $2\left(\dfrac{3}{4}\right)$

23. $(-2)(-5)$

24. $(-3)\left(-\dfrac{8}{6}\right)$

25. $\left(-\dfrac{5}{6}\right)\left(\dfrac{9}{15}\right)$

26. $\left(\dfrac{3}{5}\right)\left(-\dfrac{10}{4}\right)$

27. $\dfrac{8}{2}$

28. $\dfrac{-10}{-2}$

29. $\dfrac{-15}{5}$

30. $\dfrac{20}{-4}$

31. $\dfrac{-15}{25}$

32. $\dfrac{15}{-\dfrac{3}{4}}$

33. $\dfrac{-12}{-\dfrac{2}{3}}$

34. $(-4)\left(-\dfrac{5}{2}\right)$

35. $\dfrac{3}{5}\left(-\dfrac{15}{2}\right)$

36. $\left(-\dfrac{3}{4}\right)0$

37. $\left(-\dfrac{4}{5}\right)\left(-\dfrac{15}{2}\right)$

38. $-(-2)$

39. $\dfrac{4-4}{2}$

40. $\dfrac{14+1}{-5-(-2)}$

41. $\dfrac{5+(-5)}{3}$

42. $\dfrac{-18}{-3-6}$

43. $\dfrac{15}{2-7}$

44. $\dfrac{24}{2-8}$

45. $\dfrac{-8-4}{3}$

46. $-5(2-4)$

47. $-4(4-1)$

48. $\dfrac{3(-5+1)}{-4(2-6)}$

49. $-(-2x+3y)$

50. $(-x)(-y)$

51. $\dfrac{-x}{-y}$

52. $\dfrac{-x}{\dfrac{1}{2}}$

53. $\dfrac{2}{\dfrac{x}{-2}}$

54. $\dfrac{-a}{(-b)(-c)}$

In Exercises 55–57 evaluate the given expression when $x = -2$.

55. $x - 5$

56. $-2x$

57. $\dfrac{x}{x-1}$

In Exercises 58–60 evaluate the given expression when $x = -3$, $y = -2$.

58. $x + 2y$

59. $x - 2y$

60. $\dfrac{4x-y}{y}$

In Exercises 61–68 evaluate a^n for the given values of a and n.

61. $a = -1, n = 5$

62. $a = 4, n = 2$

63. $a = 6, n = 3$

64. $a = -2, n = 4$

65. $a = \dfrac{2}{5}, n = 3$

66. $a = 0.2, n = -3$

67. $a = \dfrac{5}{3}, n = 4$

68. $a = -1, n = 100$

69. Subtract 3 from -5.

70. Subtract -3 from -4.

71. Subtract -5 from -2.

72. Subtract -2 from 8.

73. At 2 P.M. the temperature is 10°C above zero and at 11 P.M. it is 2°C below zero. How many degrees has the temperature dropped?

74. Repeat the previous exercise if the temperature at 2 P.M. is 8°C and it is -4°C at 11 P.M.

75. A stationery store had a loss of $400 during its first year of operation and a loss of $800 during its second year. How much money did the store lose during the first two years of its existence?

76. A bicycle repair shop had a profit of $150 for the month of July and a loss of $200 for the month of August. How much money did the shop gain or lose over the two-month period?

*77. E. & E. Fabrics had a loss of x dollars during its first business year and a profit of y dollars its second year. Write an expression for the net profit or loss after two years.

*78. S. & S. Hardware had a profit of x dollars, followed by a loss that exceeded twice the profit by $200. Write an expression for the net loss.

*79. The Student Stereo Shoppe had a loss of $200 during its first year of business, a profit of $800 during its second year, and a profit of $900 during its third year. What was the average profit (or loss) over the three-year period?

80. Use your calculator to evaluate the expression

$$3200x - 2900y$$

for $x = -2900$, $y = 3200$. First, store the values under variable names. Then, enter the expression using those variable names. Now you can store new values and retrieve the expression you entered (it should not be necessary to enter it again). Evaluate the same expression for $x = -3200$ and $y = -2900$.

1.5 Properties of the Real Numbers

The real numbers obey laws that enable us to manipulate algebraic expressions with ease. We'll use the letters $a, b,$ and c to denote real numbers.

To begin, note that the sum of two real numbers is a real number and the product of two real numbers is a real number. These are known as the **closure properties**.

Closure Properties

> *Property 1.* The sum of a and b, denoted by $a + b$, is a real number.
>
> *Property 2.* The product of a and b, denoted by $a \cdot b$ or ab, is a real number.

We say that the set of real numbers is **closed** with respect to the operations of addition and multiplication, since the sum and product of two real numbers are also real numbers.

We know that

$$3 + 4 = 7 \qquad \text{and} \qquad 3 \cdot 4 = 12$$
$$4 + 3 = 7 \qquad\qquad 4 \cdot 3 = 12$$

That is, we may *add or multiply real numbers in any order*. Writing this in algebraic symbols, we have the following.

Commutative Properties

> *Property 3.* $a + b = b + a$ \qquad Commutative property of addition
>
> *Property 4.* $ab = ba$ \qquad\qquad Commutative property of multiplication

Example 1   Using the Commutative Properties
(a) $5 + 7 = 7 + 5;\ 5 \cdot 7 = 7 \cdot 5$
(b) $3 + (-6) = -6 + 3;\ 3 \cdot (-6) = (-6) \cdot 3$
(c) $3x + 4y = 4y + 3x;\ (3x)(4y) = (4y)(3x)$

✔ Progress Check 1

Use the commutative properties to write each expression in another form.

(a) $(-3) + 6$ \qquad (b) $(-4) \cdot 5$ \qquad (c) $-2x + 6y$ \qquad (d) $\left(\dfrac{3}{2}x\right)\left(\dfrac{1}{2}y\right)$

Answers

(a) $6 + (-3)$ \qquad (b) $5 \cdot (-4)$ \qquad (c) $6y + (-2x)$ \qquad (d) $\left(\dfrac{1}{2}y\right)\left(\dfrac{3}{2}x\right)$

When we add $2 + 3 + 4$, does it matter in what order we group the numbers? No. We see that

$$(2 + 3) + 4 = 5 + 4 = 9$$

and

$$2 + (3 + 4) = 2 + 7 = 9$$

Similarly, for multiplication of $2 \cdot 3 \cdot 4$ we have

$$(2 \cdot 3) \cdot 4 = 6 \cdot 4 = 24$$

and

$$2 \cdot (3 \cdot 4) = 2 \cdot 12 = 24$$

Clearly, *when adding or multiplying real numbers, we may group them in any order.* Translating into algebraic symbols, we have the following.

Associative Properties

Property 5. $(a + b) + c = a + (b + c)$	Associative property of addition
Property 6. $(ab)c = a(bc)$	Associative property of multiplication

Example 2 Using the Associative Properties

(a) $5 + (2 + 3) = (5 + 2) + 3 = 10$ (b) $5 \cdot (2 \cdot 3) = (5 \cdot 2) \cdot 3 = 30$

(c) $(3x + 2y) + 4z = 3x + (2y + 4z)$ (d) $3(4y) = (3 \cdot 4)y = 12y$

(e) $(-2)[(-5)(-x)] = [(-2)(-5)](-x) = 10(-x) = -10x$

✔ **Progress Check 2**

Use the associative properties to simplify.

(a) $3 + (2 + x)$ (b) $6 \cdot 2xy$

Answers

(a) $5 + x$ (b) $12xy$

We can combine the commutative and associative properties to simplify algebraic expressions.

Example 3 Simplifying an Expression

Use the commutative and associative properties to simplify.

(a) $(3 + x) + 5$ (b) $\left(\frac{2}{3}y\right)\left(\frac{3}{4}\right)$ (c) $(2x - 4) + 7$

Solution

(a) $(3 + x) + 5 = (x + 3) + 5$ Commutative property of addition

$= x + (3 + 5)$ Associative property of addition

$= x + 8$

(b) $\left(\frac{2}{3}y\right)\left(\frac{3}{4}\right) = \frac{3}{4} \cdot \left(\frac{2}{3}y\right)$ Commutative property of multiplication

$= \left(\frac{3}{4} \cdot \frac{2}{3}\right)y$ Associative property of multiplication

$= \frac{1}{2}y$

(c) $(2x - 4) + 7 = [2x + (-4)] + 7$

$\qquad\qquad\qquad = 2x + [(-4) + 7]$ Associative property of addition

$\qquad\qquad\qquad = 2x + 3$

✔ **Progress Check 3**

Use the commutative and associative properties to simplify.

(a) $4 + (2x + 2)$ (b) $\left(\dfrac{4}{5}x\right)\left(\dfrac{10}{2}\right)$ (c) $(5 - 3x) + 6$

Answers

(a) $6 + 2x$ (b) $4x$ (c) $11 - 3x$

The **distributive properties** deal with both addition and multiplication. For instance,

$$2(3 + 4) = 2(7) = 14 \quad \text{and} \quad (1 + 2)5 = (3)5 = 15$$

We may notice that

$$2(3) + 2(4) = 6 + 8 = 14$$

and

$$1(5) + 2(5) = 5 + 10 = 15$$

produce the same results as the first two equations. The distributive properties tell us that this is not an accident; rather, it is a rule that we may always use.

Distributive Properties

> *Property 7. $a(b + c) = ab + bc$*
>
> *Property 8. $(a + b)c = ac + bc$*

The distributive properties can be extended to factors that are a sum of more than two terms. Thus,

$$3(5x + 2y - 4z) = 3(5x) + 3(2y) + 3(-4z)$$
$$= 15x + 6y - 12z$$

Example 4   Using the Distributive Properties

(a) $4(2x + 3) = 4(2x) + 4(3) = 8x + 12$

(b) $(4x + 2)6 = (4x)(6) + (2)(6) = 24x + 12$

(c) $2(x + 5y - 2z) = 2x + 2(5y) + 2(-2z)$

$\qquad\qquad\qquad\quad = 2x + 10y - 4z$

(d) $-(2y - x) = (-1)(2y - x) = (-1)(2y) + (-1)(-x) = -2y + x$

Note that a negative sign in front of parentheses is treated as multiplication by -1.

> ✔ **Progress Check 4**
> Simplify, using the distributive properties.
>
> (a) $5(3x + 4)$ (b) $(x + 3)7$ (c) $-2(3a - b + c)$
>
> **Answers**
> (a) $15x + 20$ (b) $7x + 21$ (c) $-6a + 2b - 2c$

It is easy to show that the commutative and associative properties *do not* hold for subtraction and division. For example,

$$2 - 5 = -3 \quad \text{but} \quad 5 - 2 = 3$$

and, in general,

$$a - b = -(b - a) \neq b - a$$

Similarly, $12 \div 3 \neq 3 \div 12$ shows that the commutative property does not hold for division.

The student is encouraged to provide counterexamples to show that the associative property does not hold for subtraction and division (see Exercise 19 in Exercise Set 1.5.)

Table 1 summarizes some of the important properties of real numbers.

Table 1   **Properties of Real Numbers**

For all real numbers a, b, and c:

Closure properties
$a + b$ is a real number
ab is a real number

Commutative properties
$a + b = b + a$
$ab = ba$

Associative properties
$(a + b) + c = a + (b + c)$
$(ab)c = a(bc)$

Distributive properties
$a(b + c) = ab + ac$
$(a + b)c = ac + bc$

Identity properties
There is a unique real number 0 called the **additive identity** such that
$$a + 0 = a \quad \text{and} \quad 0 + a = a$$
There is a unique real number 1 called the **multiplicative identify** such that
$$a \cdot 1 = a \quad \text{and} \quad 1 \cdot a = a$$

Inverse properties
For every real number a there is a unique number $-a$ called the **additive inverse** or **opposite** of a such that
$$a + (-a) = 0$$
For every real number a (other than 0) there is a unique real number $\frac{1}{a}$ called the **multiplicative inverse** or **reciprocal** such that
$$a \cdot \frac{1}{a} = 1$$

Exercise Set 1.5

In Exercises 1–18 justify the given equation by using one or more properties of real numbers.

1. $2 + 5 = 5 + 2$

2. $(3 \cdot 2)(-4) = 3[(2)(-4)]$

3. $-2 \cdot 5 = 5(-2)$

4. $2(4 + 5) = 2 \cdot 4 + 2 \cdot 5$

5. $(4 + 3)2 = 4 \cdot 2 + 3 \cdot 2$

6. $3(2 - 4) = 3 \cdot 2 - 3 \cdot 4$

7. $-2(4 - 5) = (-2)(4) - 2(-5)$

8. $(3 + 2) + 4 = 3 + (2 + 4)$

9. $-3 + (2 + 5) = (-3 + 2) + 5$

10. $(2 - 5) + 8 = 2 + (-5 + 8)$

11. $3 + a = a + 3$

12. $2(x + 2) = 2x + 4$

13. $2(ab) = (2a)b$

14. $5(a + b) = 5(b + a)$

15. $2(xy) = x(2y)$

16. $4(a + b) = 4b + 4a$

17. $5 + (a + 2) = 2 + (5 + a)$

18. $(5x)y = 5(yx)$

19. Give examples showing that the commutative and associative properties do not hold for the operation of subtraction.

In Exercises 20–25 find and correct the mistake.

20. $a + 2a = 2a^2$

21. $2(a + 2) = 2a + 2$

22. $3(x - 2) = x - 6$

23. $(a - b)2 = 2a - b$

24. $3(ab) = (3a)(3b)$

25. $(2a + 3) + a = 3(a + 2)$

In Exercises 26–54 simplify the given expression.

26. $(2 + x) + 4$

27. $(2 - x) + 2$

28. $(x - 3) - 4$

29. $(x - 5) - 2x$

30. $(2x)(-5)$

31. $(-3x)(-4)$

32. $2(-3x)$

33. $a(2b)(3c)$

34. $4\left(\dfrac{3}{2}a\right)$

35. $\dfrac{2}{3}(9 + 12a - 6b)$

36. $\dfrac{4x}{-2}$

37. $\dfrac{-2}{4x}$

38. $\dfrac{-8x}{-4}$

39. $(3x)\left(-\dfrac{4}{9}y\right)$

40. $\dfrac{1}{4}(4a)$

41. $\dfrac{1}{5}(10ab)$

42. $\dfrac{4(b + 2)}{3}$

43. $\dfrac{3(5x - y)}{12}$

44. $6x + \dfrac{(y - 1)4}{2}$

45. $3a + \dfrac{(b - 3c)}{2}(-5)$

46. $3(a - 2) - 2(b + 4)$

47. $4(x + y) - 2(z - 2w)$

48. $3\left(\dfrac{2u + v}{6}\right) + \dfrac{1}{2}(4w)$

49. $2\left(\dfrac{x}{2} + y - 2\right) - (-2u + 4)$

50. $4\left(\dfrac{a - 2b + 4}{2}\right) + \dfrac{1}{3}(6c + 9)$

51. $-3.65\left(\dfrac{0.47 - 2.79}{6.44}\right)$

52. $\dfrac{6.92}{4.7}\left(\dfrac{2.01}{1.64 - 3.53}\right)$

53. $0.40\left(\dfrac{17.52 - 6.48 + 2.97}{3.60}\right) - 0.25(-4.75 + 2.92)$

54. $16.33\left(\dfrac{14.94}{3.87} - \dfrac{2.22 + 7.46}{2.96}\right)$

In Exercises 55–58 find a counterexample for each given statement; that is, find real values for the variables that make the statement false.

*55. $a(b + c) = ab + c$

*56. $\dfrac{a}{b} = \dfrac{b}{a}$

*57. $(b - c)a = b - ca$

*58. $(a + b)(c + d) = ac + bd$

1.6   Absolute Value and Inequalities

When we introduced the real number line we pointed out that positive numbers lie to the right of the origin and negative numbers lie to the left of the origin.

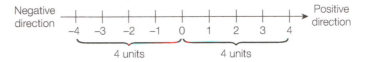

Suppose we are interested in the *distance* between the origin and the points labeled 4 and −4. Each of these points is four units from the origin, that is, the *distance is independent of the direction.*

When we are interested in the size of a number *a* and don't care about the direction or sign, we use the notation of **absolute value**, which we write as $|a|$. Thus,

$$|4| = 4$$
$$|-4| = 4$$

Example 1   Working with Absolute Value

(a) $|-6| = 6$ (b) $|17.4| = 17.4$ (c) $|0| = 0$

(d) $|4 - 9| = |-5| = 5$ (e) $\left|\dfrac{2}{5} - \dfrac{6}{5}\right| = \left|-\dfrac{4}{5}\right| = \dfrac{4}{5}$

✔ **Progress Check 1**

Find the values.

(a) $|22|$ (b) $\left|-\dfrac{2}{7}\right|$ (c) $|4 - 4|$ (d) $|6 - 8|$ (e) $\left|\dfrac{1}{7} - \dfrac{3}{7}\right|$

Answers

(a) 22 (b) $\dfrac{2}{7}$ (c) 0 (d) 2 (e) $\dfrac{2}{7}$

The absolute value bars act as grouping symbols. We must work *inside* these grouping symbols before we can remove them.

Example 2   Order of Operations with Absolute Value

(a) $|-3| + |-6| = 3 + 6 = 9$

(b) $|3 - 5| - |8 - 6| = |-2| - |2| = 2 - 2 = 0$

(c) $\dfrac{|4 - 7|}{|-6|} = \dfrac{|-3|}{|-6|} = \dfrac{3}{6} = \dfrac{1}{2}$

(d) $\left|\dfrac{2 - 8}{3}\right| = \left|\dfrac{-6}{3}\right| = |-2| = 2$

✔ **Progress Check 2**

Find the values.

(a) $|-2| - |-4|$ (b) $\dfrac{|2-5|}{-3}$ (c) $\left|\dfrac{1-5}{2-8}\right|$ (d) $\dfrac{|-3| - |-6|}{4 - |-10|}$

Answers

(a) -2 (b) -1 (c) $\dfrac{2}{3}$ (d) $\dfrac{1}{2}$

The absolute value of a number is, then, always nonnegative. But what can we do with the absolute value of a variable, say, $|x|$? We don't know whether x is positive or negative, so we can't write $|x| = x$. For instance, when $x = -4$, we have

$$|x| = |-4| = 4 \neq x$$

and when $x = 4$, we have

$$|x| = |4| = 4 = x$$

We must define absolute value so that it works for both positive and negative values of a variable.

Absolute Value

$$|a| = \begin{cases} a & \text{when } a \text{ is 0 or positive} \\ -a & \text{when } a \text{ is negative} \end{cases}$$

When a is positive, say, $a = 4$, the absolute value is the number itself; when a is negative, say, $a = -4$, the absolute value is the negative of a, or $+4$. Thus, the absolute value is always nonnegative.

The following properties of absolute value follow from the definition.

Properties of Absolute Value

For all real numbers a and b,

1. $|a|$ is nonnegative
2. $|a| = |-a|$
3. $|a - b| = |b - a|$

We began by showing how absolute value can be used to denote distance from the origin without regard to direction. We will conclude by demonstrating the use of absolute value to denote the distance between *any* two points a and b on the real number line. In Figure 2, the distance between the points labeled 2 and 5 is 3 units and can be obtained by evaluating either $|5 - 2|$ or $|2 - 5|$. Similarly, the distance between the points labeled -1 and 4 is given by either $|4 - (-1)| = 5$ or $|-1 - 4| = 5$. Using the

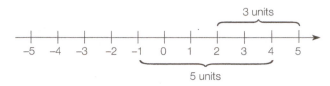

Figure 2   Distance Expressed by Absolute Value

notation to denote the distance between the points A and B, we provide the following definition.

Distance on the Real Number Line

> The distance $\overline{AB}$ between points A and B on the real number line, whose coordinates are a and b, respectively, is given by
>
> $$\overline{AB} = |b - a|$$

Property 3 then tells us that $\overline{AB} = |b - a| = |a - b|$. Viewed another way, Property 3 states that the distance between any two points on the real number line is independent of the direction.

Example 3   Absolute Value and Distance

Let points A, B, and C have coordinates -4, -1, and 3, respectively, on the real number line, and let the origin, with coordinate 0, be denoted by O. Find the following distances.

(a) $\overline{AB}$ (b) $\overline{CB}$ (c) $\overline{OB}$

Solution

Using the definition, we have

(a) $\overline{AB} = |-1 - (-4)| = |-1 + 4| = |3| = 3$

(b) $\overline{CB} = |-1 - 3| = |-4| = 4$

(c) $\overline{OB} = |-1 - 0| = |-1| = 1$

✔ Progress Check 3

The points P, Q, and R on the real number line have coordinates -6, 4, and 6, respectively. Find the following distances.

(a) $\overline{PR}$ (b) $\overline{QP}$ (c) $\overline{PQ}$ (d) $\overline{PO}$

Answers

(a) 12   (b) 10 ·   (c) 10   (d) 6

Inequalities

If a and b are real numbers, we can compare their positions on the real number line by using the relations of **less than**, **greater than**, **less than or equal to**, and **greater than or equal to**, denoted by the **inequality symbols** $<$, $>$, $\leq$, and $\geq$, respectively. Table 2 describes both algebraic and geometric interpretations of the inequality symbols.

Here is a helpful way to remember the meaning of the symbols $>$ and $<$. We can think of the symbols $>$ and $<$ as pointers that always point to the lesser of the two numbers.

Example 4   Using the Inequality Symbols

(a) $2 < 5$ (b) $-1 < 3$ (c) $6 > 4$

✔ Progress Check 4

Make a true statement by replacing the square with the symbol $<$ or $>$.

(a) $7 \,\square\, 10$ (b) $16 \,\square\, 8$ (c) $4 \,\square\, -2$

Answers

(a) $<$ (b) $>$ (c) $>$

We can use the real number line to illustrate the relations $<$ and $>$. For example, in Figure 3 we show that the inequality $x < 3$ is satisfied by *all* points to the left of 3.

Table 2   Inequalities and the Real Number Line

Algebraic Statement	Equivalent Statement	Location on the Number Line
$a > b$	a is greater than b or b is less than a	a lies to the right of b
$a > 0$	a is greater than zero or a is positive	a lies to the right of the origin
$a < b$	a is less than b or b is greater than a	a lies to the left of b
$a < 0$	a is less than zero or a is negative	a lies to the left of the origin
$a \geq b$	a is greater than or equal to b or b is less than or equal to a	a coincides with b or lies to the right of b
$a \geq 0$	a is greater than or equal to zero or a is nonnegative	a coincides with or lies to the right of the origin
$a \leq b$	a is greater than or equal to b or b is greater than or equal to a	a coincides with b or lies to the left of b
$a \leq 0$	a is less than or equal to zero or a is nonpositive	a coincides with or lies to the left of the origin

$$x < 3$$

Figure 3   Graph of $x < 3$

Similarly, in Figure 4 we show that the inequality $x \geq -1$ is satisfied by *all* points to the right of (and including) -1.

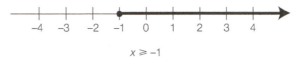

$$x \geq -1$$

Figure 4   Graph of $x \geq -1$

For $x < 3$, the point labeled 3 does not satisfy the inequality; we indicate this by an open circle.

3

For $x \geq -1$, the point labeled -1 does satisfy the inequality; we indicate this by a solid circle.

-1

In Figures 3 and 4 the shading indicates the "set" of all points whose coordinates satisfy the given inequality. The set of all such coordinates is called the **solution set** of the inequality, and we are said to have **graphed** the solution set of the inequality or to have graphed the inequality.

Example 5   Inequalities and the Real Number Line

In the following figure,

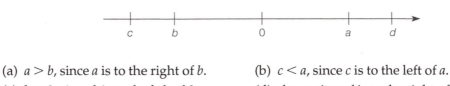

(a) $a > b$, since a is to the right of b.   (b) $c < a$, since c is to the left of a.
(c) $b < 0$, since b is to the left of 0.   (d) $d > a$, since d is to the right of a.

✔ **Progress Check 5**

For the figure in Example 5, make a true statement by replacing each square with the symbol $<$ or $>$.

(a) $b \;\square\; d$ (b) $a \;\square\; c$ (c) $d \;\square\; 0$ (d) $b \;\square\; a$

Answers

(a) $<$ (b) $>$ (c) $>$ (d) $<$

Example 6 Graphing an Inequality

Graph the solution set of the inequality on the real number line.

(a) $x \geq 2$ (b) $x < 2$

Solution

(a)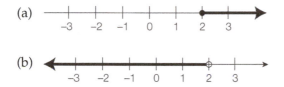

(b)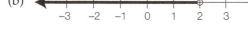

✔ **Progress Check 6**

Graph the inequality on the real number line.

(a) $x < 0$ (b) $x \geq -1$ (c) $x < -2$

Answers

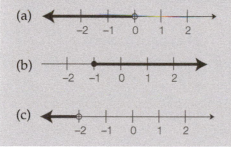

We also write compound inequalities, such as

$$-1 \leq x < 2$$

The solution set to this inequality consists of all real numbers that satisfy

$$-1 \leq x \quad \text{and} \quad x < 2$$

that is, all numbers between -1 and 2 and including -1 itself. We can easily graph the solution set on a real number line.

$$-1 \leq x < 2$$

Example 7　Graphing a Compound Inequality

Graph $-3 < x < -1$, x a real number.

Solution

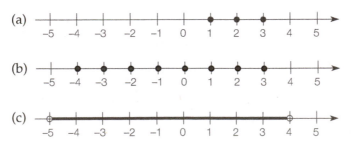

We can also graph the solution set to the inequality

$$-1 \leq x < 2, \ x \text{ an integer}$$

that is, the set of integers greater than or equal to -1 and less than 2. The solution set is $\{-1, 0, 1\}$.

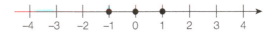

Example 8　Graphing a Compound Inequality

Graph the given inequality on the real number line.

(a) $-5 < x < 4$, x a natural number

(b) $-5 < x < 4$, x an integer

(c) $-5 < x < 4$, x a real number

Solution

(a)
![number line graph]

(b)
![number line graph]

(c)
![number line graph]

✔ **Progress Check 8**

Graph the given inequality on the real number line.

(a) $-3 \le x \le 2$, x a natural number

(b) $-2 \le x < 3$, x an integer

(c) $-4 \le x \le 0$, x a real number

Answers

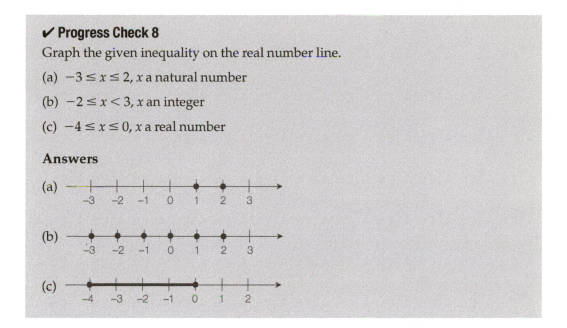

It is sometimes convenient to use **set-builder notation** as a way of writing statements such as "A is the set of integers between -3 and 2." If we let I represent the set of integers, we write

$$A = \{x \in I \mid -3 < x < 2\}$$

Each part of this symbolic expression has an explicit meaning.

{ }	*read*	the set of all
$x \in I$	*read*	integers x
|	*read*	such that
$-3 < x < 2$	*read*	x is between -3 and 2

Example 9   Working with Set-Builder Notation

If N is the set of natural numbers, write the statement "the set A of all natural numbers less than 10" in set-builder notation. List the elements of A.

Solution

$A = \{x \in N \mid x < 10\} = \{1, 2, 3, 4, 5, 6, 7, 8, 9\}$

✔ **Progress Check 9**

If N is the set of natural numbers, write the statement "A is the set of all odd natural numbers less than 12" in set-builder notation. List the elements of A.

Answer

$A = \{x \in N \mid x < 12 \text{ and } x \text{ is odd}\} = \{1, 3, 5, 7, 9, 11\}$

Exercise Set 1.6

In Exercises 1–24, find the value of the given expression.

1. $|2|$

2. $\left|-\dfrac{2}{3}\right|$

3. $|1.5|$

4. $|-0.8|$

5. $-|2|$

6. $-\left|-\dfrac{2}{5}\right|$

7. $|2-3|$

8. $|2-2|$

9. $|2-(-2)|$

10. $|2|+|-3|$

11. $\dfrac{|14-8|}{|-3|}$

12. $\dfrac{|2-12|}{|1-6|}$

13. $\dfrac{|3|-|2|}{|3|+|2|}$

14. $\dfrac{|4|-2|4||-3|}{|4-3|}$

15. $|x|-|y|$ when $x=-1, y=-2$

16. $|x|-|x\cdot y|$ when $x=-3, y=4$

17. $|x+y|+|x-y|$ when $x=-3, y=2$

18. $\dfrac{|a-2b|}{2a}$ when $a=1, b=2$

19. $\dfrac{|x|+|y|}{|x|-|y|}$ when $x=-3, y=4$

20. $\dfrac{|-|2a+b||}{|a-b|}$ when $a=-3, b=2$

21. $\dfrac{|-|3a-2b|+c|}{|a-b|}$ when $a=1, b=3, c=1$

22. $\dfrac{|a-b|-2|c-a|}{|a-b+c|}$ when $a=-2, b=3, c=-5$

23. $\dfrac{|2a-b|-|c+a|}{a|a+b-2c|}$ when $a=1.69, b=-7.43$, $c=2.98$

24. $\dfrac{|-b|c-a||}{c|b-a|}$ when $a=12.44, b=4.74, c=-5.83$

In Exercises 25–30 the coordinates of points A and B are given. Find $\overline{AB}$.

25. $2, 5$

26. $-3, 6$

27. $-3, -1$

28. $-4, \dfrac{11}{2}$

29. $-\dfrac{4}{5}, \dfrac{4}{5}$

30. $2, 2$

In Exercises 31–36, write each given statement using the symbols $<, >, \le, \ge$.

31. 4 is greater than 1.

32. -2 is less than -1.

33. 2 is not greater than 3.

34. 3 is not less than 1.

35. 3 is nonnegative.

36. -2 is nonpositive.

In Exercises 37–51 make a true statement by replacing the square with the symbol $<$ or $>$.

37. $3 \square 5$

38. $8 \square 2$

39. $4 \square -3$

40. $4 \square -6$

41. $-3 \square -2$

42. $-5 \square -4$

43. $-\dfrac{1}{2} \square \dfrac{1}{3}$

44. $\dfrac{1}{2} \square -\dfrac{1}{4}$

45. $-\dfrac{1}{5} \square -\dfrac{1}{3}$

46. $|-3| \square |5|$

47. $-|3| \square |4|$

48. $|-4| \square |-3|$

49. $|-2| \square 1$

50. $|4| \square 0$

51. $-|4| \square 0$

In Exercises 52–57 replace the square with the symbol $<$ or $>$ to make a true statement, referring to the number line below.

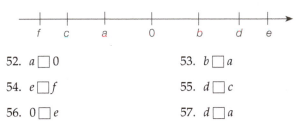

52. $a \square 0$

53. $b \square a$

54. $e \square f$

55. $d \square c$

56. $0 \square e$

57. $d \square a$

In Exercises 58–61 state the inequality represented on the given number line.

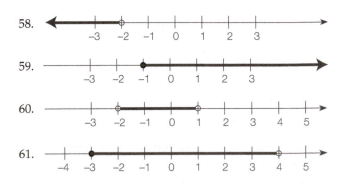

58.

59.

60.

61.

In Exercises 62−73 graph the inequality.

62. $x \leq -2$

63. $x \geq -3$

64. $x < 4$

65. $x > 1$

66. $-3 \leq x \leq 2$

67. $-4 < x < -2$

68. $-2 < x < 0$

69. $1 < x < 3$

70. $-2 < x \leq 3$, x an integer

71. $1 < x < 5$, x a natural number

72. $-3 \leq x \leq -1$, x an integer

73. $-3 \leq x < 2$, x a natural number

In Exercises 74−77 I is the set of integers, N is the set of natural numbers, and R is the set of real numbers. Write each statement in set-builder notation.

74. The set of natural numbers between -3 and 4, including -3.

75. The set of integers between 2 and 4, including 4.

76. The set of negative integers.

77. The set of even natural numbers less than 6.

In Exercises 78−83 list the elements of the given set. I is the set of integers, and N is the set of natural numbers.

78. $\{x \in I \mid -5 < x \leq -1\}$

79. $\{x \in I \mid -4 \leq x < 0\}$

80. $\{x \in N \mid -2 \leq x < 4\}$

81. $\{x \in N \mid 0 \leq x \leq 6\}$

82. $\{x \in I \mid -4 \leq x \leq 10 \text{ and } x \text{ is even}\}$

83. $\{x \in N \mid 1 < x \leq 6 \text{ and } x \text{ is odd}\}$

*84. Using the indicated values for a and b, verify the following properties of absolute value.

(a) $|a| \geq 0$ $a = 2; a = -4$

(b) $|a| = |-a|$ $a = -5; a = 3; a = 0$

(c) $|a - b| = |b - a|$ $a = 3, b = 1; a = -2, b = -1$

(d) $|ab| = |a||b|$ $a = -2, b = -4$

(e) $\left|\dfrac{a}{b}\right| = \dfrac{|a|}{|b|}$ $a = 3, b = -5$

*85. Let a and b be the coordinates of two distinct points on the real number line. What does property (c) in the previous exercise say about measuring the distance between the two points?

*86. Verify that

$$|a + b| \leq |a| + |b|$$

using the following values of a and b:

$$a = 3, b = 2; a = -3, b = 2;$$
$$a = 3, b = -2; a = -3, b = -2$$

1.7 Critical Thinking Problems

In this section, we will apply some of the properties we learned in previous sections.

We learned that we can find the distance between two points on the real number line. Since distances, dimensions, time, weight, etc. may only be positive numbers, we use the absolute value sign to indicate the distance between two points.

The distance between two points a and b is $|a - b| = |b - a|$.

Regardless of the signs of two numbers a and b, the distance between any two points will always be positive.

Example 1 Finding the Distance between Two Points

Tom and Bob were climbing the stairs in K-building at Allan Hancock College. Tom can climb the stairs much faster than Bob. When Tom was climbing the 18th step, Bob was on the 9th step. How many steps away was Tom from Bob?

Solution

Tom was on the 18th step while Bob was on the 9th step. To find the distance between Tom and Bob in terms of steps, we need to find the number of steps between Tom and Bob.

Using the distance formula between the two points, 18th step and 9th step, we write

$$|18 - 9| = |9 - 18| = 9$$

Therefore, Tom was 9 steps away from Bob.

✔ Progress Check 1

Find the distance between two points A and B on the number line.

$$A = 3 \quad \text{and} \quad B = -3$$

Answer

6

Example 2   Finding Balance

Suppose you had a balance of $825.36 in your checking account. Then, you deposited $1,000 on Monday. The next day you wrote a check for $725, and you spent $120.73 at a grocery store. How much money would you have remaining in your checking account?

Solution

Since deposit means plus, we write

$$\$825.36 + \$1,000 = \$1,825.36$$

You have a balance of $1,825.36 in your account. You wrote a check for $725 and spent $120.73. So, we need to subtract $725 and $120.73 from the balance in your checking account.

$$
\begin{aligned}
\text{Balance} &= \$825.36 + \$1,000 - \$725 - \$120.73 \\
&= (\$825.36 + \$1,000) - \$725 - \$120.73 \qquad \text{By the order of operation} \\
&= \$1,825.36 - \$725 - \$120.73 \\
&= (\$1,825.36 - \$725) - \$120.73 \qquad \text{By the order of operation} \\
&= \$1,100.36 - \$120.73 \\
&= \$979.63
\end{aligned}
$$

Therefore, you have a new balance of $979.63 in your checking account.

✔ Progress Check 2

You had $120 in your pocket. You spent $35.63 at Macy's, $25.39 at Denny's, and $3.50 at the Yogurt Shop. How much money is left in your pocket?

Answer

$55.48

Example 3   Discount and Sales Price

You want to buy a $1,200 T.V. that is on sale. If you get a 20% discount, find the amount of discount and the sales price.

Solution

You get a 20% discount of $1,200 so

$$\text{discount} = 20\% \text{ of } \$1,200$$

We convert 20% to a decimal 0.2; "of" means "product"

so

$$= (0.2) \cdot (\$1,200)$$
$$= \$240$$

To find the sales price, we write

$$\textbf{Sales Price} = \textbf{Original Price} - \textbf{Discount Amount}$$

So,

$$\text{Sales Price} = \$1,200 - \$240$$
$$= \$960$$

Therefore, the amount of the discount is $240, and the sales price is $960.

✔ **Progress Check 3**

Bob wants to buy a new printer that costs $300. If he gets a 15% discount, what is the amount he needs to pay?

Answer

$255

■ ■ ■

Terms and Symbols

$<, >, \leq, \geq$	equivalent fraction	percent, %
$\in, \notin$	exponent	prime number
absolute value, $\vert\,\vert$	factor	product
algebraic expression	fraction	quotient
associative properties	graph of an inequality	rational number
base	hierarchy of operations	real number line
cancellation principle	identity properties	real number system
closure properties	inequality symbols	reciprocal
common factor	integer	reduced form
commutative properties	inverse properties	set
constant	irrational number	set-builder notation
denominator	LCD	set notation
distributive properties	member	solution set
dividend	natural number	subset
divisor	numerator	variable
element	origin	

Key Ideas for Review

Topic	Key Idea
Fractions	
multiplication	Find the product of the numerators and then divide by the product of the denominators.
division	Multiply the numerator by the reciprocal of the denominator.
addition and subtraction	If the denominators are the same, add or subtract the numerators and keep the common denominator.
	If the denominators are different, find the LCD and convert each fraction to an equivalent with the LCD as the denominator.
Percent	Percent is a fraction whose denominator is 100.
Conversions	Fractions, decimals, and percents are different ways of writing the same thing; you can always convert any form to any other form.
Rational number	A rational number is a quotient of two integers, p/q, with $q \neq 0$. The decimal form of a rational number either terminates or forms a repeating pattern.
Irrational number	An irrational number cannot be written as a quotient of two integers; the decimal equivalent never forms a repeating pattern.
Real number system	The real number system consists of the rational numbers and the irrational numbers.
Hierarchy of operations	Operations within parentheses are done *before* multiplication and division; addition and subtraction are done last.
Properties of the real numbers	See Table 2.
Absolute value	Absolute value is defined by $$\|a\| = \begin{cases} a & \text{when} & a \geq 0 \\ -a & \text{when} & a < 0 \end{cases}$$
Distance from origin	Absolute value represents distance and is always nonnegative. The distance from the origin to a point whose coordinate is a on the real number line is $\|a\|$.
Distance between points	The distance between points A and B, whose coordinates on the real number line are a and b, respectively, is $$\overline{AB} = \|b - a\| = \|a - b\|$$

Common Errors

1. $2x - y \neq 2(x - y)$. *Don't* assume grouping where it isn't indicated.

2. $3(a - b) = 3a - 3b$. *Don't* write $3(a - b) = 3a - b$.

3. $(-2)(-3)(-4) = -24$, not $+24$. When the number of negative factors is odd, the product is negative.

4. To evaluate an expression such as
$$\frac{3x + 2y}{x + 3y} \quad \text{when } x = 2 \text{ and } y = 1$$
work independently on the numerator and denominator before dividing.
$$\frac{3(2) + 2(1)}{2 + 3(1)} = \frac{6 + 2}{2 + 3} = \frac{8}{5}$$

Don't write
$$\frac{3(2) + 2(1)}{2 + 3(1)} = \frac{3 + 1}{1 + 3} = \frac{4}{4} = 1$$

5. The absolute value bars act as grouping symbols. We must work *inside* these grouping symbols before we can remove them.

6. The number π is irrational; therefore, we cannot say $\pi = \frac{22}{7}$ or $\pi = 3.14$. These are approximations for computational use only. We write $\pi \approx 3.14$ where the symbol $\approx$ is read as "is approximately equal to."

Review Exercises

Solutions to exercises whose numbers are in bold are in the Solutions section in the back of the book.

1.1 In Exercises 1–3 write each set by listing its elements within braces.

1. The set of natural numbers between -5 and 4, inclusive.

2. The set of integers between -3 and -1, inclusive.

3. The subset of $x \in S$, $S = \{0.5, 1, 1.5, 2\}$, such that x is an even integer.

In Exercises 4–7 determine whether the statement is true (T) or false (F).

4. $\sqrt{7}$ is a real number.

5. -35 is a natural number.

6. -14 is not an integer.

7. 0 is an irrational number.

8. Draw a real number line and plot the following points.
   (a) 3 (b) -5 (c) $\frac{1}{2}$ (d) -1.5

In Exercises 9–11 determine which of the two numbers appears second when viewed from left to right on the real number line.

9. $3, 2$ 10. $-4, -5$ 11. $0, -2$

1.2 In Exercises 12–17 perform the indicated operations.

12. $\dfrac{(2 + 3)4}{10} + 4 \cdot 3$ 13. $\dfrac{(3 - 5)(4 - 16)}{(3 + 1)(-2)} + \dfrac{1}{2}$

14. $\dfrac{2}{3} \cdot \dfrac{4}{5} \cdot \dfrac{6}{7}$ 15. $\dfrac{3}{4} \div \dfrac{5}{8}$

16. $1 + \dfrac{1}{2}$ 17. $\dfrac{2}{3} + \dfrac{1}{6}$

   $\dfrac{3}{4} + \dfrac{1}{2}$ $\dfrac{2}{9} - \dfrac{3}{2}$

In Exercises 18 and 19 change the given percent to both fractional and decimal forms.

18. 7% **19.** 2.25%

In Exercises 20 and 21 convert the given number to percent.

20. 4.52 21. 0.021

22. Suppose that your school tax bill reads: "$800 in taxes due Nov 1, reduced to $784 if paid by Oct 15." What is the percent of the discount?

1.3 In Exercises 23–26 determine whether the given statement is true (T) or false (F).

23. $2x + 4 = 10$ when $x = 3$

24. $3x - 2 = 6$ when $x = 3$

25. $3x - 4y = 6$ when $x = 1, y = 2$

26. $2x + 5y = 11$ when $x = -2, y = 3$

27. A salesperson receives $3.25x + 0.15y$ dollars, where x is the number of hours worked and y is the number of miles of automobile usage. Find the amount due the salesperson if $x = 12$ hours and $y = 80$ miles.

1.4 In Exercises 28−33 simplify.

28. $3 + (-5)$

29. $6 - 8$

30. $(-5) + (-3)$

31. $(-3) - (-2)$

32. $(-2)\left(-\dfrac{1}{2}\right)$

33. $\dfrac{-16}{-2}$

34. Evaluate $x - 3y$ when $x = 2, y = -3$.

35. A stereo shop had the following financial history during its first three years of operation. It lost x dollars during the first year and made a profit of y dollars during the second year. Its profit during the third year was $1000. Write an expression for the net profit or loss after three years.

1.5 In Exercises 36−39 identify the property (or properties) that justifies the given statement.

36. $(3 + 4)x = 3x + 4x$

37. $a + (b + c) = c + (a + b)$

38. $c(a + b) = bc + ac$

39. $3(ab) = b(3a)$

In Exercises 40−43 find and correct the mistake.

40. $2(a + 3) = 2a + 3$

41. $\dfrac{4 + a}{2} = 2 + a$

42. $-2(a - 3) = -2a - 6$

43. $2(ab) = (2b)(2a)$

1.6 In Exercises 44 and 45 find the value of the expression.

44. $\dfrac{|3| - |4|}{|2| + |-5|}$

45. $\dfrac{|2 - 2b| + |a - b|}{|ab|}$ when $a = -2, b = 3$

46. Provide a counterexample for the following statement:

If a and b are real numbers such that $|a| = |b|$, then $a = b$.

In Exercises 47 and 48 the coordinates of points A and B are given. Find $\overline{AB}$.

47. $-3, 2$

48. $-4, -8$

In Exercises 49 and 50 state the inequality represented on the given number line.

49.
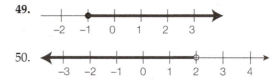

50.

In Exercises 51 and 52 graph the inequality on the real number line.

51. $x > -2$

52. $-2 \leqslant x < 5$

Progress Test 1A

1. The numbers $3, -\frac{2}{3}$, and 0.72 are all

   (a) natural numbers   (b) rational numbers
   (c) irrational numbers   (d) none of these

2. The numbers $-\frac{\pi}{2}, \sqrt{3}$, and $-\frac{4}{5}$ are all

   (a) irrational numbers   (b) rational numbers
   (c) real numbers   (d) none of these

3. On a real number line, indicate the integers that are greater than -3 and less than 4.

4. Evaluate $\dfrac{3a - 4b}{2a - b}$ when $a = 3, b = 2$.

5. Evaluate $\dfrac{2x - 6y}{x - y}$ when $x = -1, y = 1$.

6. Evaluate $\dfrac{3[(a + 2b) - (2b - a)]}{c}$ when $a = -2$, $b = -1, c = -6$.

7. Simplify $5(x - y) - 3(2x - y)$.

8. Simplify $2\left(\dfrac{a + b}{4}\right) + \left(\dfrac{b - a}{2}\right)$.

9. Evaluate $\dfrac{|2 - 8|}{|2| + |-8|}$.

10. Evaluate $3\,|x| - 2\,|2y|$ when $x = -2, y = -3$.

11. Evaluate $\left|\dfrac{-2\,|3x| + 3\,|-y|}{|x + y|}\right|$ when $x = -2, y = 1$.

12. Evaluate $|x| \cdot |y| - 2\,|x \cdot y|$ when $x = -1, y = 2$.

13. Graph the inequality $-1 \leqslant x < 3$.

14. Graph the inequality $-4 \leqslant x \leqslant 1$, x an integer.

15. Give the inequality represented on the following number line.

Progress Test 1B

1. The numbers $-2, 0.45$, and $\frac{7}{9}$ are all

   (a) integers   (b) irrational numbers
   (c) rational numbers   (d) none of these

2. The numbers $-\sqrt{7}, 2\pi$, and -0.49 are all

   (a) natural numbers   (b) irrational numbers
   (c) real numbers   (d) none of these

3. On a real number line, indicate the integers that are greater than -5 and less than -1.

4. Evaluate $\dfrac{2m - 5n}{3m - n}$ when $m = 2, n = 4$.

5. Evaluate $\dfrac{x + 2y}{2x - y}$ when $x = 3, y = -5$.

6. Evaluate $\dfrac{-2[(p - 2q) - 2r - p]}{p \cdot q}$ when $p = 2, q = -3$, $r = \frac{1}{2}$.

7. Simplify $7(x + 2y) - 2(3x - y)$.

8. Simplify $3\left(\dfrac{a - 2b}{6}\right) - \left(\dfrac{b - 2a}{2}\right)$.

9. Evaluate $\dfrac{|-3| - |4 - 7|}{|-4| + |-2|}$.

10. Evaluate $\dfrac{|x|}{2} - 3\,|3y|$ when $x = -4, y = -5$.

11. Evaluate $\dfrac{3\,|2y| - 3\,|x|}{-|x - 2y|}$ when $x = -2, y = 1$.

12. Evaluate $\left|\dfrac{x}{3} \cdot \dfrac{y}{2}\right| - 3\,|2x \cdot y|$ when $x = -6, y = 4$.

13. Graph the inequality $-2 < x \leqslant 5$.

14. Graph the inequality $-5 \leqslant x \leqslant -1$, x an integer.

15. Give the inequality represented on the following number line.

Chapter 1 Project

To study the nature and impact of hurricanes, from a scientific as well as a human standpoint, it is necessary to use and understand real numbers. In the chapter opener, you read about the Saffir-Simpson Hurricane Scale. What subset of the real numbers does this scale use?

Look at Exercise 42 in Section 1.1, and Exercises 81 and 82 in Section 1.2. Now do some additional research on hurricanes. Use percents, inequalities, and number lines to make a report on the data you discover. For example, what percentage of deaths due to weather were caused by hurricanes in your area last year? What range of wind speeds are associated with a category 3 hurricane?

CHAPTER 2

Linear Equations and Inequalities

Neglect of mathematics works injury to all knowledge since he who is ignorant of it cannot know the other sciences or the things of this world.

—Roger Bacon

Nutritionists and dietitians use algebra to determine an appropriate balance of amounts and types of food in a healthy diet. To any mathematician, the word "balance" immediately suggests equations! Metaphorically, the operations we perform to solve an equation are a "balancing act." For example, we must never add more to one side of an equation than we do to the other.

How does a dietitian determine the correct number of calories for a person who wants to maintain a certain weight? Actually, this determination should be made on an individual basis and must include details about the individual other than just the desired weight. However, in this chapter's project we will look at a simple way of answering this question using a linear equation.

http://www.bls.gov

(By the way, the U.S. Department of Labor's Bureau of Labor Statistics suggests that courses in mathematics are a healthy part of a balanced dietitian's background! See how many careers require algebra at www.bls.gov.)

■ ■ ■

Finding solutions to equations has long been a major concern of algebra. Recent work in inequalities, much of it since World War II, has elevated the importance of solving inequalities as well. Oil refining and steel producing are among the major industries using computers daily to solve problems involving thousands of inequalities. The solutions enable these companies to optimize their "product mix" and their profitability.

In this chapter we will learn to solve the most basic forms of equations and inequalities. But even this rudimentary capability will prove adequate to allow us to tackle a wide range of applications in both this and the following chapter.

2.1   Linear Equations in One Variable

Here are some examples of equations in the variable x.

$$x - 2 = 0 \qquad\qquad x(x - 3) = 10$$
$$3(2x - 5) = 3 \qquad\qquad 2x + 5 = x - 7$$
$$\frac{1}{2x + 3} = 5 \qquad\qquad \frac{x + 2}{x - 3} = -1$$

An **equation** states that two algebraic expressions are equal. The expression to the left of the equal sign is called the **left-hand side** of the equation and the expression to the right of the equal sign is called the **right-hand side**.

Our task is to find values of the variable for which the equation holds true. These values are called **solutions** or **roots** of the equation, and the set of all solutions is called the **solution set**. For example, the equation

$$x - 5 = 3$$

is a true statement only when $x = 8$. Then 8 is a solution of the equation, and $S = \{8\}$ is the solution set.

Solving an Equation

When we say that we want to "solve an equation," we mean that we want to find all the solutions, or roots. If we can replace an equation by another, simpler, equation that has the same roots, we will have an approach to solving equations. Equations having the same roots are called **equivalent equations**. There are two important rules that allow us to replace an equation by an equivalent equation.

Simplifying Equations

> The solutions of a given equation are not affected by the following operations:
>
> - Addition or subtraction of a number or expression on both sides of the equation.
> - Multiplication or division of both sides of the equation by a number other than 0.

Let's solve the equation

$$2x + 5 = 13$$

By the rules for the order of equations, we see that x has first been multiplied by 2 and then 5 has been added to the result. To return to the original value of x, we need to subtract 5 and then divide by 2. Since these operations are permitted by the rules for simplifying equations, we begin by *subtracting +5 from both sides of the equation.*

$$2x + 5 - 5 = 13 - 5$$
$$2x + 0 = 8$$
$$2x = 8$$

Now, *dividing both sides of the last equation by 2* yields

$$\frac{2x}{2} = \frac{8}{2}$$
$$x = 4$$

We have arrived at the solution $x = 4$. It is a good idea to check that 4 does indeed satisfy the original equation.

$$2x + 5 = 13$$
$$2(4) + 5 \stackrel{?}{=} 13$$
$$13 \stackrel{\checkmark}{=} 13$$

Then 4 is a root, or solution, of the equation $2x + 5 = 13$.

In simplifying equations we often reach a point at which the equation looks like this:

$$5x + 4x = -18$$

Here, simplification of the left-hand side relies on the distributive property of the real numbers:

$$5x + 4x = (5 + 4)x$$
$$= 9x$$

We say that $5x$ and $4x$ are **like terms** and we see that the distributive property allows us to combine like terms. You may think of this as "adding apples and apples." For example, the expression

$$3x + 2y - x + 6y$$

becomes

$3x - x + 2y + 6y$	Commutative property
$= 2x + 8y$	Distributive property

Why can't we simplify further? Because we cannot add "apples and oranges"!

Example 1   Solving an Equation

Solve the equation $3x - 1 = x + 9$.

Solution

We gather the terms involving x on one side of the equation and the constant terms on the other. Here are the steps.

$$3x - 1 = x + 9$$
$$3x - 1 + 1 = x + 9 + 1 \qquad \text{Add 1 to both sides.}$$
$$3x = x + 10 \qquad \text{Simplify.}$$
$$3x - x = x + 10 - x \qquad \text{Subtract } x \text{ from both sides.}$$
$$2x = 10 \qquad \text{Combine like terms.}$$

Now it is easy to solve for x.

$$\frac{2x}{2} = \frac{10}{2} \qquad \text{Divide both sides by 2.}$$
$$x = 5$$

Check:

$$3(5) - 1 \overset{?}{=} 5 + 9$$
$$15 - 1 \overset{?}{=} 5 + 9$$
$$14 \overset{\checkmark}{=} 14$$

✔ Progress Check 1

Solve and check.

(a) $4x + 7 = 3$ 　　　　　　　(b) $x - 6 = 5x - 26$

Answers

(a) -1 　　　　　　　　　　　(b) 5

When the equation we seek to solve involves fractions we can eliminate the fractions to ease the solution process.

Example 2   **Solving an Equation with Fractions**

Solve $\frac{5}{6}x - \frac{4}{3} = \frac{3}{5}$.

Solution

The LCD of all fractions appearing in the equation is 30. We multiply both sides of the equation by the LCD to clear the equation of fractions.

$$30\left(\frac{5}{6}x - \frac{4}{3}\right) = 30\left(\frac{3}{5}\right)$$

$$30\left(\frac{5}{6}x\right) + 30\left(-\frac{4}{3}\right) = 30\left(\frac{3}{5}\right) \qquad \text{Distributive property}$$

$$25x - 40 = 18$$

$$25x = 58 \qquad \text{Add 40 to both sides.}$$

$$x = \frac{58}{25} \qquad \text{Divide both sides by 25.}$$

Verify that $\frac{58}{25}$ is a solution of the original equation!

✔ Progress Check 2

Solve and check.

(a) $-\frac{2}{3}(x - 5) = \frac{3}{2}(x + 1)$

(b) $\frac{1}{3}x + 2 - 3\left(\frac{x}{2} + 4\right) = \left(\frac{x}{4} - 1\right)$

Answers

(a) $\frac{11}{13}$

(b) $-\frac{24}{5}$

Solving a Linear Equation

The equations we have solved are all of the first degree and involve only one unknown. Such equations are called **first-degree equations in one unknown** or, more simply, **linear equations**. By rearranging and collecting like terms, any such equation can be put into the general form

$$ax + b = 0$$

where a and b are any real numbers and $a \neq 0$. Let's see how we would solve this equation.

$$ax + b = 0$$

$$ax + b - b = 0 - b \qquad \text{Subtract } b \text{ from both sides.}$$

$$ax = -b$$

$$\frac{ax}{a} = \frac{-b}{a} \qquad \text{Divide both sides by } a.$$

$$x = -\frac{b}{a}$$

Substituting in Equation (1) shows that $-\frac{b}{a}$ is indeed a solution and leads to the following:

Roots of a Linear Equation

> The linear equation $ax + b = 0$, $a \neq 0$, has exactly one solution: $-\dfrac{b}{a}$.

Identities and Conditional Equations

Does every equation have a solution? Can an equation have multiple solutions? No solutions? We will explore these questions in depth throughout this text as we develop more sophisticated tools for tackling these problems.

We can, however, begin our exploration with some simple observations. Some equations, such as

$$3x = 2x + x$$

are true for all values of x and are called **identities**. (It's not always possible to establish that an equation is an identity by just looking at it.) Those equations that are true for only certain values of the unknown (namely, the solutions) are called **conditional equations**. Every linear equation

$$ax + b = 0, a \neq 0$$

is a conditional equation since it has precisely one solution.

Finally, we point out that some equations have no solutions. For example, consider the equation

$$3x = 3x + 1$$

Adding $-3x$ to both sides we have

$$3x - 3x = 3x + 1 - 3x$$
$$0 = 1$$

Since this last equation is a contradiction, we conclude that the given equation has no solution. (Write the given equation in the form $ax + b = 0$ and carefully note the value of a.)

Example 3   Identities and Conditional Equations

Determine whether each of the following is a conditional equation, an identity, or has no solution.

(a) $4(x - 1) = 3x - 1$

(b) $5(x + 2) + x = 6x + 10$

(c) $4(x - 3) = 4x - 3$

Solution

We'll let the student supply a reason for each step.

(a)

$$4(x - 1) = 3x - 1$$
$$4x - 4 = 3x - 1$$
$$4x - 4 + 4 = 3x - 1 + 4$$
$$4x = 3x + 3$$
$$4x - 3x = 3x + 3 - 3x$$
$$x = 3$$

Since the original equation is true only for $x = 3$, it is a conditional equation.

(b)

$$5(x + 2) + x = 6x + 10$$
$$5x + 10 + x = 6x + 10$$
$$6x + 10 = 6x + 10$$

Since the left- and right-hand sides of the last equation are identical, substituting any real value for x will make the equation true. We conclude: the equation is an identity.

(c)

$$4(x - 3) = 4x - 3$$
$$4x - 12 = 4x - 3$$
$$4x - 12 - 4x = 4x - 3 - 4x$$
$$-12 = -3$$

Since this is a contradiction, the original equation has no solution.

> ✔ **Progress Check 3**
>
> Determine whether each of the following is a conditional equation (C), an identity (I), or has no solution (N).
>
> (a) $-2(x - 5) + 2 = -2(x - 6)$ (b) $3(2x + 1) = -4(x + 1) + 10x$
>
> (c) $-5(x - 2) = 2x + 17$
>
> **Answers**
>
> (a) I   (b) N   (c) C

Exercise Set 2.1

In Exercises 1–8 determine whether the given statement is true (T) or false (F).

1. $x = 2$ is a solution to $3x = 6$.

2. $x = -2$ is a solution to $4x = -6$.

3. $x = 3$ is a solution to $3x - 1 = 10$.

4. $x = -5$ is a solution to $2x + 3 = -7$.

5. $x = \frac{3}{2}$ is a solution to $2x + 1 = 4$.

6. $x = \frac{5}{2}$ is a solution to $3x - 4 = \frac{5}{2}$.

7. $x = 6/(4 - k)$ is a solution to $kx + 6 = 4x$.

8. $x = 7/3k$ is a solution to $2kx + 7 = 5x$.

In Exercises 9–42 solve the given linear equation and check your answer.

9. $2x = 8$

10. $3x = -6$

11. $2x = -\dfrac{5}{2}$

12. $2x + 3 = 7$

13. $3x + 5 = -1$

14. $5r + 10 = 0$

15. $3s - 1 = 2$

16. $4 - x = 2$

17. $2 - 3a = 6$

18. $2 = 3x + 4$

19. $3 = 2x - 1$

20. $\dfrac{1}{2}s + 2 = 4$

21. $\dfrac{3}{2}t - 2 = 7$

22. $-\dfrac{2}{3}x + 3 = 2$

23. $-1 = -\dfrac{2}{3}x + 1$

24. $0 = -\dfrac{1}{2}a - \dfrac{2}{3}$

25. $2x + 2 = x + 6$

26. $4r + 3 = 3r - 2$

27. $-5x + 8 = 3x - 4$

28. $2x - 1 = 3x + 2$

29. $-2x + 6 = -5x - 4$

30. $6x + 4 = -3x - 5$

31. $2(3b + 1) = 3b - 4$

32. $-3(2x + 1) = -8x + 1$

33. $4(2x - 1) = 5x + 5$

34. $-3(3x - 1) = -4x - 2$

35. $4(x - 1) = 2(x + 3)$

36. $-3(x - 2) = 2(x + 4)$

37. $2(x + 4) - 1 = 0$

38. $3a + 2 - 2(a - 1) = 3(2a + 3)$

39. $-2(x - 1) + 3(x - 1) = 4(x + 5)$

40. $2(y - 1) + 3(y + 2) = 8$

41. $-4(2x + 1) - (x - 2) = -11$

42. $3(a + 2) - 2(a - 3) = 0$

In Exercises 43–46 solve for x.

43. $kx + 8 = 5x$

44. $8 - 2kx = -3x$

45. $2 - k + 5(x - 1) = 3$

46. $3(2 + 3k) + 4(x - 2) = 5$

In Exercises 47–52 determine whether the equation is an identity (I), a conditional equation (C), or has no solution (N).

47. $3x + 5 = 2(x - 4)$

48. $3x - 4 = 4(x - 3) - x$

49. $-5(x + 2) = -2(x + 5) - 3x$

50. $\dfrac{2}{3}x + 1 = x - \dfrac{x - 1}{3} + \dfrac{2}{3}$

51. $\dfrac{1}{2}x - 1 = \dfrac{3}{4}x - 2$

52. $\dfrac{x + 1}{2} = \dfrac{x - 1}{2}$

*53. If $x = 2$ is a solution to the equation $2a + 3x = 14$, find a.

*54. If $x = -3$ is a solution to the equation $5a - 2x = 3a - 10$, find a.

*55. If $y = 4$ is a solution to the equation $40 - 4y = 2b - 6y + 8$, find b.

*56. If $z = -\frac{1}{2}$ is a solution to the equation $-4b + 2z = -4$, find b.

*57. After many hours of work, an analyst for the Safety Lock Company finds that the equation

$$0.5(2x - 5) = -x + 18$$

can be used to determine (in thousands of units) the manufacturing capacity x of a plant. Find the manufacturing capacity.

*58. A business consultant tells the board of directors of the Super Computer Corporation that the profit or loss (in thousands of dollars) for the current year can be found by solving the equation

$$2x - 23 = 2(5 - 0.5x)$$

(a) Solve the equation for x.

(b) Will the board of directors announce a profit or a loss for the year?

59. You can use a graphing calculator to determine whether an equation is an identity. When a mathematical statement like an equation is entered, using symbols like "=," "<," or ">," the calculator will return a "1" if the statement is true, and "0" if it is false. (Look under TEST for the equality and inequality symbols, or check your manual.) An identity must be true for any value of the variable, so you should store one value, test the equation, then try again with a different value.

Use this method to verify your answers to Exercises 47–52.

60. A simple rule of thumb for determining a healthy body weight W for a man of a given height h in inches is given by the equation

$$W = 6(h - 60) + 106$$

According to this formula, how tall should a man who weighs 148 pounds be? (Note that in the real world other factors like body type and muscle mass affect healthy weights.)

61. Another rule of thumb relates desired weight to number of calories consumed each day. For a person with a moderately active lifestyle, this formula suggests that the daily intake of calories should be fifteen times the desired weight in pounds. To lose one pound in one week, a person who weighs 170 pounds would need to consume x calories each day, according to the equation

$$7(170(15) - x) = 3500$$

Solve for x. (The 3500 on the right-hand side of this equation suggests that cutting 3500 calories out of one's diet results in a loss of one pound. Do some research to determine how accurate this simplified model is.)

Now explain in your own words what each number and symbol in this equation refers to, and why the equation "works."

2.2 Problem Solving: From Words to Algebra

The larger of two numbers is 1 more than the smaller. Five times the larger exceeds four times the smaller by 12. Find the numbers.

How do you go about solving a word problem? The words are your clues. But you must translate these clues into algebraic expressions and then form an equation or inequality that you can solve. In this section we're going to show you how to attack a word problem and how to recognize the "code words" that appear time and again in applications.

These are the typical steps used in solving word problems.

Step 1. Read the problem until you understand what is required.

Step 2. Isolate what is known and what is to be found.

Step 3. In many problems, the unknown quantity is the answer to a question such as "how much" or "how many." Let an algebraic symbol, say, x, represent the unknown.

Step 4. Represent other quantities in the problem in terms of x.

Step 5. Find the relationship in the problem that lets you write an equation (or an inequality).

Step 6. Solve. Check your answer to see that it

(a) satisfies the original question, and

(b) satisfies the equation (or inequality).

Words and Phrases

Some students have trouble with word problems because they are unfamiliar with the mathematical interpretation of certain words and phrases. Practice, of course, will help; we also suggest that you read the problem very carefully. Table 1 may be helpful; it has a list of words and phrases you will come across, with examples of how they are used.

Let's apply our steps to the problem that we stated at the outset of this section.

Example 1   Solving a Word Problem

The larger of two numbers is 1 more than the smaller. Five times the larger exceeds four times the smaller by 12. Find the numbers.

Solution

After reading the problem, it is clear that the unknown may represent either the larger or smaller number. If we let

$$n = \text{the smaller number} \qquad \text{Step 3}$$

then

$$n + 1 = \text{the larger number} \qquad \text{Step 4}$$

Table 1   Translating Words and Phrases to Algebra

Word or phrase	Algebraic Symbol	Example	Algebraic Expression
Sum	+	Sum of two numbers	$a + b$
Difference	−	Difference of two numbers	$a - b$
		Difference of a number and 3	$x - 3$
Product	× or ·	Product of two numbers	$a \cdot b$
Quotient	÷ or /	Quotient of two numbers	$\dfrac{a}{b}$ or a/b
Exceeds		a exceeds b by 3.	$a = b + 3$
More than		a is 3 more than b.	or
More of		There are 3 more of a than of b.	$a - 3 = b$
Twice		Twice a number	$2x$
		Twice the difference of x and 3	$2(x - 3)$
		3 more than twice a number	$2x + 3$
		3 less than twice a number	$2x - 3$
Is or equals	=	The sum of a number and 3 is 15.	$x + 3 = 15$
Percent of	%	30% of a number	$0.3x$

The relationship between these numbers specified in the problem is

$$5 \times \text{larger} = (4 \times \text{smaller}) + 12$$

Step 5

or, in terms of our unknowns,

$$5(n + 1) = 4n + 12$$

Step 5a

Solving,

$$5n + 5 = 4n + 12$$

Step 6

$$n = 7 = \text{the smaller number}$$

$$n + 1 = 8 = \text{the larger number}$$

You can verify that the solution (a) answers the original question and (b) satisfies the equation of Step 5a.

✔ Progress Check 1

Write the number 30 as the sum of two numbers such that twice the larger is 3 less than 7 times the smaller.

Answer

$7 + 23$

Example 2   A Word Problem in Geometry

The length of a rectangle is 2 feet more than twice its width. If the perimeter is 22 feet, find the dimensions of the rectangle.

Solution

Drawing a figure is a necessity when dealing with geometric applications. In Figure 1, we let

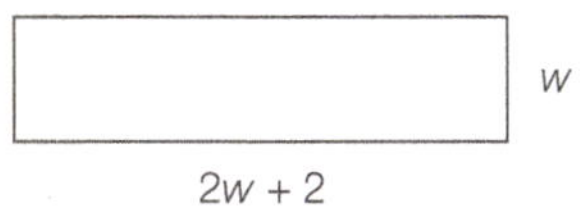

$$w = \text{the width of the rectangle}$$

w

$2w + 2$

Figure 1   Diagram for Example 2

since the length is expressed in terms of the width. The problem states that

$$\text{length} = 2(\text{width}) + 2$$

$$= 2w + 2$$

From Figure 1, we see that

$$\text{perimeter} = 2(\text{length} + \text{width})$$

or, in terms of our problem,

$$22 = 2[(2w + 2) + w]$$
$$22 = 2(3w + 2)$$
$$22 = 6w + 4$$
$$18 = 6w$$
$$w = 3$$

We conclude: The width w is 3 feet and the length is $2w + 2$ or 8 feet. The rectangle has dimensions 3 feet by 8 feet.

> ✔ **Progress Check 2**
> One side of a triangle is 3 cm longer than the shortest side; the third side is 1 cm more than twice the shortest side. If the perimeter of the triangle is 20 cm, find the dimensions of the three sides.
>
> **Answer**
> 4, 7, and 9 cm

Example 3   A Word Problem in Business
A department store advertises that all appliances are on sale at a 20% discount. If the sale price of a microwave oven is $160, what was its original price?

Solution
It's clear that

$$\boxed{\text{sale price} = \text{original price} - \text{discount}}$$

where *discount* is the reduction in dollars and not in percent. If we let

$$p = \text{original price}$$

then the discount is 20% of the original price or

$$\text{discount} = 0.2p$$

Substituting in the equation above,

$$160 = p - 0.2p$$
$$160 = 0.8p$$
$$200 = p$$

The oven was originally priced at $200.

Example 4   A Word Problem in Integers

Find three consecutive integers whose sum is 54.

Solution

Let's have the unknown represent the first of the three consecutive integers. Then

$$n = \text{the first integer}$$
$$n + 1 = \text{the second integer}$$

and

$$n + 2 = \text{the third integer}$$

But the sum of these three integers is to be 54, that is,

first integer + second integer + third integer = 54

or, in terms of the unknown n,

$$n + (n + 1) + (n + 2) = 54$$
$$3n + 3 = 54$$
$$3n = 51$$
$$n = 17$$

Then 17, 18, and 19 are the three consecutive integers we seek.

- -

Warning

Don't be fooled into thinking that every problem has a solution. For example, try to find three consecutive integers whose sum is 23. You will have a very frustrating experience—there simply are no such numbers.

- -

Example 5   A Word Problem Using Average

John has taken two quizzes in algebra and has received scores of 90 and 96. What score must he receive on his third quiz to achieve an average of 92?

Solution

We let the unknown represent the third quiz score:

$$x = \text{score on the third quiz}$$

Since

$$\text{average} = \frac{\text{sum of scores}}{\text{number of scores}}$$

we must have

$$92 = \frac{90 + 96 + x}{3}$$

We then multiply both sides of the equation by 3, the denominator of the fraction. This will clear the equation of fractions.

$$(92)(3) = 90 + 96 + x$$
$$276 = 186 + x$$
$$90 = x$$

John must achieve a grade of 90 on his third quiz.

✔ Progress Check 5

A golf pro has an average of 71 in the last four tournaments. If the scores were 68, 70, and 72 in three of the events, what was the score in the fourth tournament?

Answer

74

Example 6   A Word Problem in Geometry

A right triangle whose area is 12 square feet has a base that measures 3 feet. What is the altitude?

Solution

It is a good idea to draw a figure for problems of this type (see Figure 2). We have labeled the figure to indicate that the base measures 3 feet and the altitude is our unknown h. Since

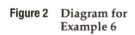

Figure 2   Diagram for Example 6

$$\text{area} = \frac{1}{2}(\text{base})(\text{height})$$

$$12 = \frac{1}{2}(3)(h)$$

$$12(2) = 3h$$

$$\frac{24}{3} = h$$

$$8 = h$$

We have found that the altitude is 8 feet.

✔ **Progress Check 6**

A carpenter is instructed to build a rectangular room with a perimeter of 18 meters. If one side of the room measures 5 meters, what are the dimensions of the room?

Answer

4 meters by 5 meters

Exercise Set 2.2

1. A vacation club charters an airplane to carry its 200 members to Rome. If the airline charges the club $50,000 for the round trip, how much will each member pay for the trip?

2. Suppose that a camp director needs to provide each camper with a small portable radio that sells for $4. The director has been given $900 for the purchase of the radios. How many campers will receive a radio?

3. How many $7 transistor radios can a dealer buy with $350?

4. Suppose that 12.5 gallons of special fuel are required to fill the tank of a tractor. If it costs $7.50 to fill the tank, what is the price per gallon?

5. If a dozen rolls cost $1.02, what is the price per roll?

6. A school district tries to give each of 110 typewriters a routine maintenance check, which costs $12 per typewriter once a year. This year the school has $960 on hand for the typewriter maintenance program. Will all typewriters be checked? If not, how many will not be checked?

7. 78 is 30% of what number?

8. 24 is 60% of what number?

9. 96 is 120% of what number?

10. 2 is $\frac{1}{2}$% of what number?

11. A car dealer advertises a $5400 sedan at a "30% discount" for $4000. Is the dealer telling the truth?

12. The local discount store sells a camera for $180, which is a 25% discount from the suggested retail price. What is the suggested retail price?

13. A stationery store sells a dozen ballpoint pens for $3.84, which represents a 20% discount from the price charged when a dozen pens are bought individually. How much does it cost to buy three pens?

14. A copying service advertises as follows: " cents per copy for 4 or fewer copies per page; 12 cents per copy, a 20% reduction, for 5 or more copies per page." Since the typesetter forgot to set the original prediscount price per copy, calculate it.

15. The sum of a certain number and 4 is 12. Find the number.

16. The difference between two numbers is 16. If one of the numbers is 16, find the other number or numbers.

17. The difference between two numbers is 24. If one of the numbers is 14, find the other number or numbers.

18. Find a number that when subtracted from 4 times itself yields 36.

19. Find a number that when added to 3 times itself gives 24.

20. Find three consecutive integers whose sum is 21.

21. A certain number is 3 more than another number. If their sum is 21, find the numbers.

22. A certain number is 5 less than another number. If their sum is 11, find the numbers.

23. A certain number is 2 more than 3 times another number. If their sum is 14, find the numbers.

24. A certain number is 5 less than twice another number. If their sum is 19, find the numbers.

25. A young man is 3 years older than his brother. Thirty years from now the sum of their ages will be 111. Find the current ages of the brothers.

26. An elderly man is 22 years older than his daughter. Fifty years ago, the sum of their ages was 34. Find the current age of the man.

27. Joan is 3 times as old as Anne. Fifteen years from now Joan will be twice as old as Anne will be then. How old is each now?

28. The sum of the ages of a woman and her son is 36 years. Six years from now the woman will be twice as old as her son. How old is each now?

29. John is presently 12 years older than Joseph. Four years ago John was twice as old as Joseph. How old is each now?

30. At the present time Albert is 20 years old and Steven is 16 years old. How many years ago was Albert $1\frac{1}{2}$ times as old as Steven?

31. At the present time Lisa is 24 years old and Erica is 16 years old. How many years ago was Lisa twice as old as Erica?

32. A certain number is 3 more than twice another. If their sum is increased by 8, the result is 41. Find the numbers.

33. The larger of two numbers is 3 more than twice the smaller. If the sum is 18, find the numbers.

34. Separate 36 into two parts so that 4 times the smaller minus 3 times the larger is 11.

35. A resort guarantees that the average temperature over the period Friday, Saturday, and Sunday will be exactly 80°F, or else each guest pays only half price for the facilities. If the temperatures on Friday and Saturday were 90°F and 82°F respectively, what must the temperature be on Sunday so that the resort does not lose half of its revenue?

36. A patient's temperature was taken at 6 A.M., 12 noon, 3 P.M., and 8 P.M. The first, third, and fourth readings were 102.5°, 101.5°, and 102°F, respectively. The nurse forgot to write down the second reading but remembered that the average of the four readings was 101.5°F. What was the second temperature reading?

37. Suppose that an investor buys 100 shares of stock on each of four successive days at $10 per share on the first day, $10.50 per share on the second day, and $12 per share on the fourth day. If the average price of the stock is $11.20 per share, what was the price per share on the third day?

38. In an election for president of a local volunteer organization there were 84 votes cast. If candidate A received 24 votes more than candidate B, how many votes did each candidate receive?

39. A 12-meter-long steel beam is to be cut into two pieces so that one piece will be 4 meters longer than the other. How long will each piece be?

40. A rectangular grazing field whose length is 10 meters longer than its width is to be enclosed with 100 meters of fencing material. What are the dimensions of the field?

41. The perimeter of a rectangle is 36 meters. If the width is 3 times the length, find the dimensions.

42. The length of a rectangle is 4 meters more than 3 times its width. If the perimeter is 24 meters, find the dimensions.

43. A triangle whose area is 36 square centimeters has an altitude that measures 8 centimeters. What is the length of the base?

44. The perimeter of an isosceles triangle is 32 centimeters. The two equal sides are each 2 centimeters shorter than the base. Find the dimensions of the triangle.

45. In an isosceles triangle, the two equal angles are each 15° more than the third angle. Find the measure of each angle. (Recall that the sum of the angles of a triangle is 180°.)

46. An investor invested $4000 at 5% per year. How much additional money should be invested at 8% per year so that the total invested will pay 6% per year?

47. The length of a rectangle is 5 feet more than twice its width. If the perimeter is 40 feet, find the dimensions of the rectangle.

48. The length of rectangle is 3 cm less than four times its width. If the perimeter is 34 cm, find the dimensions of the rectangle.

49. A farmer plans to enclose a rectangular field, whose length is 16 meters more than its width, with 140 meters of chain-link fencing. What are the dimensions of the field?

50. Suppose that one angle of a triangle is 20° larger than the smallest angle, while the third angle is 10° larger than the smallest angle. Find the number of degrees in each angle.

51. One side of a triangle is 1 meter more than twice the shortest side, while the third side is 3 meters more than the shortest side. If the perimeter is 24 meters, what is the length of each side?

2.3   Formulas

We can think of a **formula** (sometimes called a **literal equation**) as a rule that expresses a relationship between two or more variables. For example, the familiar formula from geometry

$$A = \frac{1}{2}bh$$

allows us to calculate the area A of a right triangle if we know the length of both the base b and the altitude h. In the next example we'll use a formula to convert between different temperature scales.

Example 1   Using a Formula for Temperature Conversion
The formula

$$C = \frac{5}{9}(F - 32)$$

tells us how to obtain the temperature C in Celsius if we know the temperature F in Fahrenheit. If the thermostat in a room reads 68° Fahrenheit, what is the equivalent Celsius temperature?

Solution
Substituting $F = 68$ in the formula, we have

$$C = \frac{5}{9}(F - 32) = \frac{5}{9}(68 - 32) = \frac{5}{9}(36) = 20$$

and we see that the corresponding Celsius temperature is 20°.

✔ Progress Check 1
The formula for simple interest I is $I = Prt$, where P is the amount invested, r is the rate of interest, and t is the time (in years). Find the interest earned if $1500 is invested at 8% for 3 years.

Answer
$360

The formula of Example 1 is adequate for converting from the Fahrenheit scale to the Celsius scale. But what if we know the Celsius temperature C and want to find the corresponding Fahrenheit temperature F? It would appear worthwhile to *turn the formula around*, that is, to solve for F in terms of C. We can do this by using the familiar steps of algebraic manipulation. Thus,

$$C = \frac{5}{9}(F - 32)$$

$$\frac{9}{5}C = F - 32 \qquad \qquad \text{Multiply by } \frac{9}{5}$$

$$\frac{9}{5}C + 32 = F \qquad \qquad \text{Add } +32$$

Now, given a value of C we can determine the value of F, that is, we can convert from temperature on the Celsius scale to temperature on the Fahrenheit scale.

Example 2   Solving a Formula in Finance

If an amount P is invested at the simple annual interest rate r, then the amount A available at the end of t years is

$$A = P + Prt$$

Solve for P.

Solution

$$A = P + Prt$$

$$A = P(1 + rt) \qquad \qquad \text{Distributive property}$$

$$\frac{A}{1 + rt} = \frac{P(1 + rt)}{1 + rt} \qquad \qquad \text{Divide both sides by } 1 + rt.$$

$$\frac{A}{1 + rt} = P$$

✔ **Progress Check 2**

Solve for t:

$$d = v + 0.5at$$

Answer

$$t = \frac{2d - 2v}{a}$$

The steps in solving a formula for another variable are the same as those you would use in obtaining a numerical solution. We always seek to consolidate the variable we are solving for on one side of the equals sign and then isolate this variable.

Example 3   Solving a Formula with Fractions
Solve for a:

$$c = \frac{1}{a} + \frac{1}{b}$$

Solution
We first multiply by the LCD, ab, obtaining

$$cab = b + a$$

Putting all the terms that contain the unknown a on one side, we have

$$cab - a = b$$

Applying the distributive property to the left-hand side,

$$(cb - 1)a = b$$

then

$$a = \frac{b}{cb - 1}$$

✔ **Progress Check 3**
Solve for a:

$$\frac{1}{a} + \frac{1}{y} = \frac{1}{c}$$

Answer

$$a = \frac{cy}{y - c}$$

Sometimes we need to know a specific formula in order to solve a problem. Chapter 3 presents a range of problems of this type; an example follows.

Example 4   Applying a Formula in Finance
A student wins $1000 in a state lottery and decides to invest this sum in a bank that pays 8% simple interest. How long will it take for the original investment to double?

Solution
The formula needed to handle this problem was presented in Example 2. The sum A available when P dollars is invested at a simple interest rate r for a period of t years is

$$A = P + Prt$$

We are told that $P = 500$ dollars and that $r = 8\%$. Since the investment P is to double, we must have $A = 1000$ dollars. We then substitute in the formula above

$$1000 = 500 + 500(0.08)t$$

being careful to use the decimal value 0.08 for the rate $r = 8\%$. Solving for t,

$$500 = 500(0.08)t \qquad \text{Subtract 500.}$$
$$500 = 40t \qquad \text{Simplify.}$$
$$12.5 = t \qquad \text{Divide by 40.}$$

Conclusion: It takes 12.5 years for an investment to double in value at an 8% simple interest rate.

✔ **Progress Check 4**

How long does it take for an investment to double at a simple interest rate of 10%?

Answer

10 years

Exercise Set 2.3

In Exercises 1–20 solve the formula for the specified variable.

1. $C = 2\pi r$ for r (geometry: circumference of a circle)

2. $I = Prt$ for t (finance: simple interest)

3. $S = 2\pi rh$ for h (geometry: lateral surface area of a right circular cylinder)

4. $E = IR$ for I (physics: electricity, Ohm's law)

5. $A = \dfrac{1}{2}h(b + b')$ for b (geometry: area of a trapezoid)

6. $P = 2L + 2W$ for W (geometry: perimeter of a rectangle)

7. $A = P + Prt$ for t (finance: simple interest)

8. $y - y_1 = m(x - x_1)$ for x_1 (analytic geometry: point-slope form)

9. $a_n = a_1 + (n - 1)d$ for n (nth term of an arithmetic sequence)

10. $S = \dfrac{n}{2}(a_1 + a_n)$ for a_1 (sum of an arithmetic series)

11. $S = \dfrac{a_1}{1 - r}$ for r (sum of an infinite geometric series)

12. $\dfrac{1}{f} = \dfrac{1}{a} + \dfrac{1}{b}$ for f (physics: optics, focal length)

13. $A = 2\pi r(r + h)$ for h (geometry: surface area of a right circular cylinder)

14. $d = v + 0.5at$ for a (physics: motion of a falling body)

15. $V = \dfrac{1}{3}\pi r^2 h$ for h (geometry: volume of a cone)

16. $E = mc^2$ for m (physics: energy in terms of mass and the speed of light)

17. $s = \dfrac{1}{2}gt^2$ for g (physics: distance of a falling body)

18. $A = \dfrac{1}{3}h(y_0 + 4y_1 + y_2)$ for h (mathematics: Simpson's Rule)

19. $S = P(1 + r)^t$ for P (finance: compound interest)

20. $x^2 = 4py$ for y (geometry: equation of a parabola)

21. Solve the equation $A = bt + c$ for t.

22. Solve the equation $S = 3abt + 2ab$ for b.

23. Solve the equation $5Av + 3bvt + 2kt = 0$ for v.

24. Solve $F = \dfrac{9}{5}C + 32$ for C.

25. For the linear equation $A = P + Prt$
    (a) solve for r.
    (b) solve for t.

*26. Solve the equation for a:

$$\frac{1}{a-1} + \frac{1}{b} = c$$

*27. Solve the equation for b:

$$A = \frac{b-a}{b+a}$$

*28. Solve the equation for s:

$$R = \frac{gs}{g+s}$$

*29. Solve the equation for r:

$$S = \frac{rt-a}{r-t}$$

2.4 Linear Inequalities

To solve an inequality such as

$$2x + 5 > x - 3$$

means to find its solution set, that is, to find *all* values of x that make it true. We need to know what operations we can perform on inequalities to simplify the expressions and allow us to isolate the variable.

Let's see if we can deduce the rules for inequalities. If we begin with

$$8 > 3$$

and add a positive number, say, $+12$, to both sides, we have

$$8 + 12 \overset{?}{>} 3 + 12$$

$$20 > 15$$

Similarly, if we add a negative number, say, -4, to both sides, we have

$$8 + (-4) \overset{?}{>} 3 + (-4)$$

$$4 > -1$$

We can say that

Any number can be added to or subtracted from both sides of
an inequality without affecting the inequality.

Now let's see what happens when we multiply both sides of the inequality

$$8 > 3$$

by a positive number, say, $+6$. We see that

$$8 \cdot 6 \overset{?}{>} 3 \cdot 6$$

$$48 > 18$$

If we multiply both sides by a negative number, say, -4, we have

$$(8)(-4) \overset{?}{>} (3)(-4)$$

$$-32 < -12$$

Look at what happened! Multiplication by a negative number changed the direction of the inequality sign. We can summarize the rules for handling inequalities in this way:

Rules for Inequalities

> The same operations can be performed with inequalities as with equations, except that multiplication or division by a *negative* number reverses the inequality sign.

Example 1   Solving an Inequality

Solve the inequality $2x + 5 \geq x - 3$ and graph the solution set.

Solution

We will perform addition and subtraction to collect terms in x just as we did for equations.

$$2x + 5 \geq x - 3$$

$$2x + 5 - 5 \geq x - 3 - 5$$

$$2x \geq x - 8$$

$$2x - x \geq x - 8 - x$$

$$x \geq -8$$

The graph of the solution set consists of -8 and all points to the right of -8.

The circle at -8 has been filled in to indicate that -8 belongs to the solution set. The arrow indicates that the solution set includes all points to the right of -8.

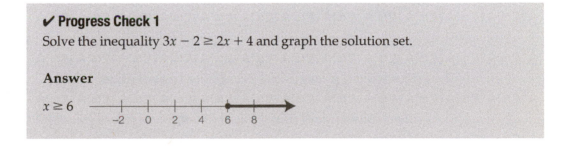

✔ **Progress Check 1**

Solve the inequality $3x - 2 \geq 2x + 4$ and graph the solution set.

Answer

$x \geq 6$

Example 2   Solving an Inequality

Solve the inequality $5x < 2(x - 1)$ and graph the solution set.

Solution

We proceed just as if we were dealing with an equation.

$$5x < 2(x - 1)$$
$$5x < 2x - 2$$
$$3x < -2$$

To solve for x we must divide by $+3$. Our rules say we may divide by a positive number without affecting the direction of the inequality sign.

$$\frac{3x}{3} < \frac{-2}{3}$$
$$x < -\frac{2}{3}$$

The graph of the solution set looks like this:

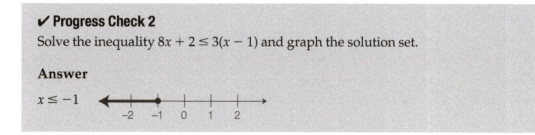

The circle at $-\frac{2}{3}$ has been left open to indicate that $-\frac{2}{3}$ does not belong to the solution set. The arrow indicates that the solution set consists of all points to the left of $-\frac{2}{3}$.

✔ Progress Check 2

Solve the inequality $8x + 2 \le 3(x - 1)$ and graph the solution set.

Answer

$x \le -1$

Applications

Word problems can also result in a linear inequality. An example follows.

Example 3   A Word Problem Using Inequalities

A taxpayer may choose to pay a 20% tax on the gross income or to pay a 25% tax on the gross income less \$4000. Above what income level should the taxpayer elect to pay at the 20% rate?

Solution

If we let $x =$ gross income, then the choice available to the taxpayer is

(a) pay at the 20% rate on the gross income, that is, pay $0.02x$, or

(b) pay at the 25% rate on the gross income less \$4000, that is, pay $0.25(x - 4000)$.

To determine when (a) produces a lower tax than (b), we must solve

$$0.20x < 0.25(x - 4000)$$
$$0.20x < 0.25x - 1000$$
$$-0.05x < -1000$$

This time we must divide by -0.05. Our rule says that division by a negative number will change the direction of the inequality, so that $<$ becomes $>$. Thus,

$$\frac{-0.05x}{-0.05} > \frac{-1000}{-0.05}$$
$$x > 20{,}000$$

The taxpayer should choose to pay at the 20% rate if the income exceeds $20,000.

✔ Progress Check 3

A customer is offered the following choice of telephone services:

(a) unlimited local calls at a $20 monthly charge, or

(b) a base rate of $8 per month plus 6 cents per message unit.

When does it cost less to choose the unlimited service?

Answer

It costs less when the anticipated use exceeds 200 units.

Compound Inequalities

We can solve compound inequalities such as

$$1 < 3x - 2 \le 7$$

by operating on all three parts at the same time.

$$3 < 3x \le 9 \qquad \text{Add } +2 \text{ to all three parts.}$$
$$1 < x \le 3 \qquad \text{Divide each part by 3.}$$

Example 4 Solving a Compound Inequality

Solve the inequality

$$-3 \le 1 - 2x < 6$$

Solution

Operating on both inequalities, we have

$$-4 \le -2x < 5 \qquad \text{Add } -1 \text{ to all three parts.}$$
$$2 \ge x > -\frac{5}{2} \qquad \text{Divide each part by } -2.$$

✔ **Progress Check 4**

Solve the inequality $-5 < 2 - 3x < -1$.

Answer

$\dfrac{7}{3} > x > 1$

Exercise Set 2.4

In Exercises 1–4 select the values of x that satisfy the given inequality.

1. $x < 3$
   (a) 4   (b) 5   (c) −2   (d) 0   (e) 1.2

2. $x > 4$
   (a) 8   (b) 4   (c) 6   (d) −3   (e) 9.1

3. $x \le 5$
   (a) 3   (b) 7   (c) 5   (d) 4.3   (e) −5

4. $x \ge -1$
   (a) 0   (b) −4   (c) 1   (d) −2   (e) −1

In Exercises 5–44 solve the given inequality and graph the solution set.

5. $x + 4 < 8$
6. $x + 5 < 4$
7. $x + 3 < -3$
8. $x - 2 \le 5$
9. $x - 3 \ge 2$
10. $x + 5 \ge -1$
11. $2 < a + 3$
12. $-5 > b - 3$
13. $2y < -1$
14. $3x < 6$
15. $2x \ge 0$
16. $-\dfrac{1}{2}y \ge 4$
17. $2r + 5 < 9$
18. $3x - 2 > 4$
19. $3x - 1 \ge 2$
20. $4x + 3 \le 11$
21. $\dfrac{1}{2}y - 2 \le 2$
22. $\dfrac{3}{2}x + 1 \ge 4$
23. $3 \le 2x + 1$
24. $4 \ge 3b - 2$
25. $-3x - 2 \le 4$
26. $-5x + 2 > -8$
27. $4(2x + 1) < 16$
28. $3(3r - 4) \ge 15$
29. $2(x - 3) < 3(x + 2)$
30. $4(x - 3) \ge 3(x - 2)$
31. $3(2a - 1) < 4(2a - 3)$
32. $2(3x - 1) + 4 < 3(x + 2) - 8$

33. $3(x + 1) + 6 \ge 2(2x - 1) + 4$
34. $4(3x + 2) - 1 \le -2(x - 3) + 15$
35. $-2 < 4x \le 5$
36. $3 \le 6x < 12$
37. $4 < -3x < 0$
38. $-5 < -2x < 9$
39. $-4 \le 2x + 2 \le -2$
40. $5 \le 3x - 1 \le 11$
41. $3 \le 1 - 2x < 7$
42. $5 < 2 - 3x \le 11$
43. $-8 < 2 - 5x \le 7$
44. $-10 < 5 - 2x < -5$

45. You can rent a compact car from firm A for $160 per week with no charge for mileage, or from firm B for $100 per week plus 20 cents for each mile driven. Above what mileage does it cost less to rent from firm A?

46. An appliance salesperson is paid $30 per day plus $25 for each appliance sold. How many appliances must be sold for the salesperson's income to exceed $130 per day?

47. A pension trust invests $6000 in a bond that pays 5% interest per year. It also wishes to invest additional funds in a more speculative bond paying 9% interest per year so that the return on the total investment will be at least 6%. What is the minimum amount that must be invested in the more speculative bond?

48. A book publisher spends $25,000 on editorial expenses and $6 per book for manufacturing and other expenses in the course of publishing a psychology textbook. If the book sells for $25.00, how many copies must be sold to show a profit?

*49. Suppose that the base of a right triangle is 10 inches. If the area is to be at least 20 square inches and is not to exceed 80 square inches, what values may be assigned to the altitude h?

*50. A total of 70 meters of fencing material is available with which to enclose a rectangular area whose width is 15 meters. If the area must be at least 180 square meters, what values can be assigned to the length L?

2.5   Absolute Value in Equations and Inequalities

Let's review the definition of absolute value given in Chapter 1.

$$|x| = \begin{cases} x & \text{when } x \geq 0 \\ -x & \text{when } x < 0 \end{cases}$$

For example,

$$|5| = 5 \qquad |-5| = 5 \qquad |0| = 0$$

Equations

We can apply the definition of absolute value to solving the equation

$$|x - 3| = 5 \tag{1}$$

From the definition of absolute value, we then have

$$x - 3 = 5 \quad \text{or} \quad -(x - 3) = 5$$

which can be rewritten as

$$x - 3 = 5 \quad \text{or} \quad x - 3 = -5$$

This last pair of equations says that the *quantity $x - 3$* in Equation (1) can have the values 5 or −5, which is exactly what we mean by absolute value. Solving, we have

$$x = 8 \quad \text{or} \quad x = -2$$

It's a good idea to check the answers by substituting.

$$|8 - 3| \stackrel{?}{=} 5 \qquad |-2 - 3| \stackrel{?}{=} 5$$

$$|5| \stackrel{?}{=} 5 \qquad |-5| \stackrel{?}{=} 5$$

$$5 \stackrel{\checkmark}{=} 5 \qquad 5 \stackrel{\checkmark}{=} 5$$

Example 1   Absolute Value in an Equation

Solve the equation $|2x - 7| = 11$.

Solution

We have to solve two equations.

$$2x - 7 = 11 \quad \text{or} \quad -(2x - 7) = 11$$
$$2x = 18 \qquad\qquad -2x + 7 = 11$$
$$x = 9 \qquad\qquad\qquad x = -2$$

✔ Progress Check 1

Solve and check.

(a) $|x + 8| = 9$ (b) $|3x - 4| = 7$

Answers

(a) $1, -17$ (b) $\dfrac{11}{3}, -1$

By focusing on the definition of absolute value as the distance of a point on the real number line from the origin, we can provide a slightly different way to solve equations involving absolute value.

Example 2   Absolute Value as Distance

Solve the equation $|2 - x| = 6$.

Solution

The *point* on the real number line whose coordinate is $2 - x$ must lie precisely 6 units from the origin, that is,

$$2 - x = 6 \quad \text{or} \quad 2 - x = -6$$
$$-x = 4 \qquad\qquad -x = -8$$
$$x = -4 \qquad\qquad x = 8$$

✔ Progress Check 2

Solve as in Example 2 and check: $\left|\dfrac{x}{2} - 4\right| = 5$

Answer

$18, -2$

Here's a trick question: Does the equation

$$|x + 2| = -3$$

have a solution? The answer is an emphatic "No!" since the absolute value of a quantity is always greater than or equal to 0.

Inequalities

To solve inequalities involving absolute value, we again recall that $|x|$ is the distance between the origin and x on the real number line. We can then easily graph the solution set for each of the inequalities $|x| < a$ and $|x| > a$.

$|x| < a$

$|x| > a$

We can summarize the result this way:

> For a given positive number a,
>
> $|x| < a$ is equivalent to $-a < x < a$
>
> $|x| > a$ is equivalent to $x > a$ or $x < -a$

Example 3   Absolute Value in an Inequality

Solve the inequality $|2x - 5| \leq 7$ and graph the solution set.

Solution

We must solve the equivalent compound inequality.

$$-7 \leq 2x - 5 \leq 7$$

$$-2 \leq 2x \leq 12 \qquad \text{Add } +5 \text{ to each part.}$$

$$-1 \leq x \leq 6 \qquad \text{Divide each part by 2.}$$

The graph of the solution set is then

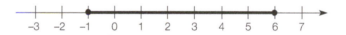

✔ **Progress Check 3**

Solve, and graph the solution set.

(a) $|x| < 3$ (b) $|3x - 1| \leq 8$ (c) $|x| < -2$ (d) $|x| > -5$

Answers

(a) $-3 < x < 3$

(b) $-\dfrac{7}{3} \leq x \leq 3$

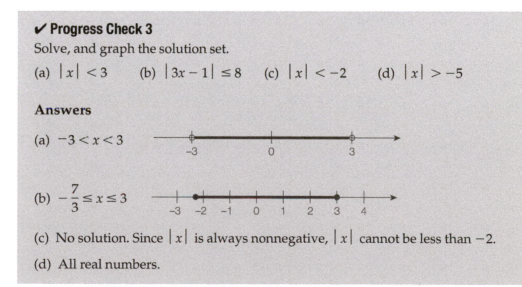

(c) No solution. Since $|x|$ is always nonnegative, $|x|$ cannot be less than -2.

(d) All real numbers.

Example 4   Absolute Value in an Inequality

Solve the inequality $|2x - 6| > 4$ and graph the solution set.

Solution

We must solve the equivalent inequalities.

$$2x - 6 > 4 \quad \text{or} \quad 2x - 6 < -4$$
$$2x > 10 \qquad\qquad 2x < 2$$
$$x > 5 \qquad\qquad\quad x < 1$$

The graph of the solution set is then

✔ **Progress Check 4**

Solve, and graph the solution set.

(a) $|5x - 6| > 9$ (b) $|2x - 2| \geq 8$

Answers

(a) $x < -\dfrac{3}{5}, x > 3$

(b) $x \leq -3, x \geq 5$

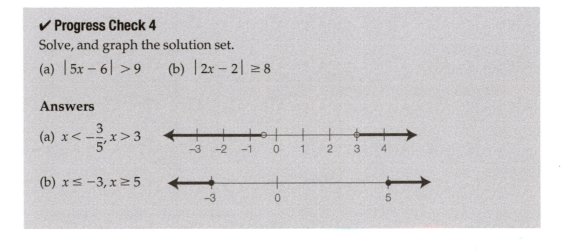

Warning

Don't write

$$1 > x > 5$$

When written this way, the notation requires that x be *simultaneously* less than 1 and greater than 5, which is impossible. Write this as

$$x < 1 \quad \text{or} \quad x > 5$$

The answer must always be written this way when the graph consists of disjoint segments. This will occur every time you solve an inequality of the form $|x \pm b| \geq a$ (or $|x \pm b| > a$), where x, a, and b are real numbers.

Exercise Set 2.5

1. Which of the following are solutions to $|x - 3| = 5$?
   (a) −8   (b) 8   (c) 2   (d) −2
   (e) none of these

2. Which of the following are solutions to $|2x + 5| = 6$?
   (a) $\frac{1}{2}$ (b) $-\frac{1}{2}$ (c) $-\frac{11}{2}$ (d) $\frac{11}{2}$
   (e) none of these

3. Which of the following are solutions to $|3a + 5| < 20$?
   (a) 5   (b) 4   (c) −10   (d) −8
   (e) none of these

4. Which of the following are solutions to $|2b - 3| \le 6$?
   (a) −1   (b) 0   (c) 5   (d) 4   (e) −2

5. Which of the following are solutions to $|-3x + 2| > 11$?
   (a) −3   (b) −4   (c) 5   (d) 2   (e) 4

6. Which of the following are solutions to $|3x - 5| \ge 7$?
   (a) $-\frac{1}{2}$ (b) 4   (c) 1   (d) 6   (e) −1

7. Which of the following are solutions to $|x - 3| < -5$?
   (a) −2   (b) 1   (c) 8   (d) 0
   (e) none of these

8. Which of the following are solutions to $|3x + 1| > -2$?
   (a) $\frac{1}{3}$ (b) −1   (c) 0   (d) 1
   (e) all of these

In Exercises 9−20 solve and check.

9. $|x + 2| = 3$ 10. $|x - 3| = 5$

11. $|r - 5| = \frac{1}{2}$ 12. $|2r - 4| = 2$

13. $|2x + 1| = 3$ 14. $|3x - 1| = 5$

15. $|3y - 2| = 4$ 16. $|5y + 1| = 11$

17. $|-3x + 1| = 5$ 18. $|-4x - 3| = 9$

19. $|2t + 2| = 3$ 20. $|2t + 2| = 0$

In Exercises 21−46 solve and graph.

21. $|x| < 5$ 22. $|x| \le 3$

23. $|x| > 4$ 24. $|x| \ge 8$

25. $|x| > -3$ 26. $|x| > 0$

27. $|x + 3| < 5$ 28. $|x - 2| \le 4$

29. $|x + 1| > 3$ 30. $|x + 2| > -3$

31. $|x - 3| \ge 4$ 32. $|2x + 1| < 5$

33. $|3x + 6| \le 12$ 34. $|4x - 1| > 3$

35. $|3x + 2| \ge -1$ 36. $|2x + 3| \ge 7$

37. $|1 - 2x| \le 3$ 38. $\left|\frac{1}{3} - x\right| < \frac{2}{3}$

39. $|1 - 3x| > 4$ 40. $|1 + 2x| < 0$

41. $\left|\frac{1}{2} + x\right| > \frac{1}{2}$ 42. $|1 - 2x| < 0$

43. $\left|\frac{x - 1}{2}\right| < 3$ 44. $\frac{|2x + 1|}{3} < 0$

45. $\frac{|2x - 1|}{4} < 2$ 46. $\frac{|3x + 2|}{2} < 4$

47. A machine that packages 100 vitamin pills per bottle can make an error of 2 pills per bottle. If x is the number of pills in a bottle, write an inequality using absolute value that indicates a maximum error of 2 pills per bottle. Solve the inequality.

48. The weekly income of a worker in a manufacturing plant differs from $300 by no more than $50. If x is the weekly income, write an inequality using absolute value that expresses this relationship. Solve the inequality.

*49. If $x = 2$ is a solution to $|a + x| = 5$, find all possible values of a.

*50. If $x = -3$ is a solution to $|2a - 3x| = 2$, find all possible values of a.

*51. If $x = 3$ is a solution to the inequality $|2a - x| < 3$, find all possible values of a.

*52. If $x = 4$ is a solution to the inequality $|3a + x| \le 5$, find all possible values of a.

*53. If $x = -2$ is a solution to the inequality $|2a + 5x| > 4$, find all possible values of a.

*54. If $x = 4$ is a solution to the inequality $|3a - 2x| \ge 3$, find all possible values of a.

■ ■ ■

2.6   Critical Thinking Problems

We can apply what we have learned so far in Chapter 2 to real-life situations. Let's try some problems, and then you can check yourself doing **Progress Check** problems.

Example 1   Finding Ages of Children

Mrs. Jones has three children. The youngest two children are twins. Find the ages of each of the three children if the difference between the oldest and youngest is three years and the sum of the ages of all three children is 30.

Solution

We need to find the age of the twins and the oldest child. Since we don't know the age of the twins, let x represent the age of one of the twins.

The difference between the youngest and oldest is 3 years, so we can write

$$x + 3 = \text{the age of the oldest child}$$

The sum of the ages of all three children is 30. Follow the equation below.

$$\text{age of one of the twins} + \text{age of the other twin} + \text{age of the oldest child} = 30$$
$$x + x + (x + 3) = 30$$

Now let's solve this linear equation in one variable. We can write

$$x + x + x + 3 = 30$$

$3x + 3 = 30$	By combining like terms
$3x = 27$	By subtracting 3 from both sides
$x = \dfrac{27}{3}$	Divide both sides by 3
$x = 9$	

Since $x = 9$ represents the age of one of the twins, the age of the oldest child is $x + 3 = 12$. Before you confirm your answer, check your solution.

The age of one of the twins + the age of the other twin + the age of the oldest child = 30.

$9 + 9 + 12 = 30$.

Therefore, the ages of the three children are 9, 9, and 12 years old.

✔ Progress Check 1

The sum of the ages of a father and a son is 59. Find the age of each if the father's age is 3 more than three times the age of his son.

Answer

Father's age: 45
Son's age: 14

The next example involves determining how long it takes for an amount to double. Suppose that an amount P is invested at the simple annual interest rate r. To find the time that it takes for P to double or triple, we generalize the formula.

Use $A = P + Prt$ (A represents the amount after t years).

Twice the amount of P is $2P$.

By substituting $A = 2P$, we have

$2P = P + Prt$

Let's solve this equation for t, since we want to find the doubling time.

$$2P = P + Prt$$
$$2P - P = Prt \qquad \text{Subtracting both sides by } P$$
$$P = Prt$$
$$1 = rt \qquad \text{Dividing both sides by } P\left(\frac{P}{P} = \frac{Prt}{P}\right)$$
$$t = \frac{1}{r} \qquad \text{Dividing both sides by } r$$

Therefore, we find the doubling time as shown below.

Doubling Time

> Suppose that the amount P is invested at the simple annual interest rate r. Then the doubling time is
> $$t = \frac{1}{r} \quad (r \text{ is in decimal form})$$

In a similar way, we can find the time it takes to triple the original amount when we invest the amount of P into a savings account paying the annual simple interest r.

The tripling time is

$$t = \frac{2}{r}$$

Example 2   Finding Doubling Time

Jamie put \$5,000 into a savings account that pays an 8% simple interest rate annually. How long will it take for Jamie to have \$10,000 in her account?

Solution

By applying the formula

$$t = \frac{1}{r}$$

we have

$$t = \frac{t}{0.08} \qquad 8\% \text{ is } 0.08 \text{ in decimal form}$$

$$t = 12.5 \text{ years}$$

Therefore, it will take 12.5 years for Jamie's \$5,000 to double in value at an 8% simple interest rate.

> ✔ **Progress Check 2**
>
> Bob invested $1,000 at a 10% annual simple interest rate.
>
> a. How long will it take for the original investment to double?
>
> b. How long will it take for the original investment to triple?
>
> **Answers**
> a. 10 years   b. 20 years

Example 3   Which One Is the Better Offer?

You would like to have internet service at your home. Company A offers a special rate of $24.99 for the first six months and $59.99 after that promotion period. The company charges a $60 installation fee. Company B charges $42.99 a month with an installation fee of $50. If you plan to have internet service for at least two years, which company has the better offer?

Solution

Let's compare the total cost for each company over a two-year period.

For two years, Company A charges

$$\text{Total Cost} = \$60 + \$24.99(6) + \$59.99(18)$$
$$= \$1{,}289.76$$

For two years, Company B charges

$$\text{Total Cost} = \$50 + \$42.99(24)$$
$$= \$1{,}081.76$$

Company B offers the better deal if you plan to have internet service for at least two years.

> ✔ **Progress Check 3**
>
> You want to rent a car. There are two different plans. For Plan A, the basic cost is $40 for the first 100 miles and $0.15 for each additional mile. Plan B does not have any basic fee but it charges $0.20 per mile. If you plan to drive at least 600 miles, which plan offers the better deal?
>
> **Answer**
> Plan A

For the next example, we will use some geometric formulas.

To find the area of a rectangle or a square, we multiply the width and the length.

$$the\ area\ of\ a\ rectangle = width \cdot length$$

In short, we write

$$A = lw$$

To find the perimeter of a rectangle, we need to add the dimensions of all four sides.

$$\textit{the perimeter of a rectangle} = \textit{width} + \textit{length} + \textit{width} + \textit{length}$$

In short, we write

$$P = 2l + 2w$$

Using these formulas, let's try this example.

Example 4   Finding the Area of Walls

Suppose you want to paint three walls of your dining room burgundy. To determine how much paint you need, you must find out the areas of the walls. If one wall has dimensions of 10 ft by 10 ft and the two other walls both have dimensions of 8 ft by 10 ft, find the total area you need to paint.

Solution

You need to find the area of all three walls. Using the formula for area of a rectangle,

$$
\begin{aligned}
\text{Total Area} \;=\;& \text{Area of the wall (10 ft by 10 ft) } + \\
& \text{Areas of two walls (8 ft by 10 ft)}
\end{aligned}
$$

$$
\begin{aligned}
\text{Total Area} \;=\;& (10\text{ ft} \cdot 10\text{ ft}) + 2(8\text{ ft} \cdot 10\text{ ft}) \\
=\;& 100\text{ ft}^2 + 2(80\text{ ft}^2) \quad \text{Since you multiply ft twice you will have the area} \\
& \qquad\qquad\qquad\qquad\;\; \text{unit ft} \cdot \text{ft} = (\text{ft})^2 = \text{ft}^2 \\
=\;& 100\text{ ft}^2 + 160\text{ ft}^2 \\
=\;& 260\text{ ft}^2
\end{aligned}
$$

Therefore, you need to paint a total area of 260 ft^2.

> ✔ **Progress Check 4**
>
> Mrs. Murphy wants to put new tiles in her kitchen. If her kitchen is 12 ft by 8 ft, how many 1 foot by 1 foot tiles does she need?
>
> **Answer**
> 96 tiles

■ ■ ■

Terms and Symbols

absolute value	formula	literal equation
compound inequality	identity	right-hand side
conditional equations	left-hand side	root
equation	like terms	solution
equivalent equation	linear equation	solution set
first-degree equation	linear inequality	

Key Ideas for Review

Topic	Key Idea
Solving an equation	
equivalent equations	Solutions of an equation are found by changing the equation into a succession of simpler equivalent equations that have the same roots.
linear equation	The linear equation $ax + b = 0, a \neq 0$, has exactly one solution.
formula	A formula is an equation giving the relationship between two or more variables. You can "solve" a formula for any variable using the usual steps of algebra.
Solving an inequality	
caution on multiplication by negative numbers	Linear inequalities are solved in a manner very similar to that of linear equations, except that multiplication or division by a negative number reverses the direction of the inequality sign.
solution set	Assuming $a > 0$, the solution set to the inequality $\lvert x \rvert < a$ is the interval $-a < x < a$, whereas the solution set to the inequality $\lvert x \rvert > a$ consists of two disjoint intervals: $x < -a$ or $x > a$.
Absolute value	
equations and inequalities	Linear equations and inequalities involving absolute value can be solved using the definition of absolute value.

Common Errors

1. When multiplying an equation or inequality by a constant, remember to multiply both sides by the constant. This requires that each term of each side be multiplied by the constant, and the constant must never be zero.

2. When multiplying or dividing an inequality by a negative number, remember to change the direction of the inequality sign. Write

$$-3x \leq 6$$
$$x \geq -2$$

Don't write

$$-3x \leq 6 \qquad \text{or} \qquad -3x \leq 6$$
$$x \geq 2 \qquad\qquad\qquad x \leq -2$$

Both of these are wrong!

3. Inequalities of the form

$$\lvert x - 4 \rvert \geq 9$$

will result in the two disjoint segments $x \leq -5$ or $x \geq 13$. This result must be written as shown; *don't* write $-5 \geq x \geq 13$, since this notation makes no sense.

Review Exercises

Solutions to exercises whose numbers are in bold are in the Solutions section in the back of the book.

2.1 In Exercises 1−6 solve the given linear equation and check your answer.

1. $3x = 5$

2. $5x = 15$

3. $2x + 3 = 15$

4. $5a + 2 = 12$

5. $2(x - 1) = 4x - 3$

6. $3(2b - 1) = 4b - 2$

2.2 7. The XYZ company consists of two divisions: the foreign division and the domestic division. A stockbroker tells her mathematically minded client that the domestic division's annual profit (in millions of dollars) was 4 more than twice the profit of the foreign division, and that the total annual profit of the XYZ company was $19 million. Find the annual profit of each division.

8. In a certain sociology course there are two textbooks. If one book costs $6 less than the other book, and the total book expense for the course is $44, what is the cost of each book?

9. A photographer working in the darkroom makes four test prints before deciding on the proper exposure time for the final print. If the first three test prints have been exposed for 5, 12, and 15 seconds, and the average of the four exposure times is 13 seconds, determine the exposure time of the fourth test print.

10. The perimeter of a parallelogram is 46 inches. If the shorter sides are one inch shorter than the longer sides, find the dimensions.

2.3 **11.** Solve the equation $r = 2s + 4tu$ for u.

12. Solve the equation $3A - 2B = C + D$ for A.

13. Solve the equation $3A - 2B + C = D$ for B.

14. Solve the equation $2a + 3cd = ef - g$ for c.

2.4 In Exercises 15−22 solve the given inequality.

15. $x + 3 < 6$

16. $x - 2 \leq 4$

17. $2x + 3 > 5$

18. $3x - 2 \geq 3$

19. $2(x + 2) < 3(x - 1)$

20. $3(2x - 3) \geq 2(3x - 4)$

21. $3 < 2x < 6$

22. $-3 < 3x + 2 \leq 4$

In Exercises 23−30 solve the given inequality and graph the solution set.

23. $x - 2 < 1$

24. $2x - 1 \leq 3$

25. $3x - 2 > -5$

26. $2x + 4 \geq 0$

27. $2x < 3(x - 1)$

28. $3(x - 1) < 2(x - 3)$

29. $-1 < 2x + 1 < 4$

30. $0 \leq 2x + 2 \leq 2$

31. An hour of exercising on machine A burns up 400 calories, while an hour on machine B burns up 300 calories. If a woman exercises one hour on machine B, how many hours should she also exercise on machine A so that a total of 1500 calories will be burned up?

32. Sportsview Rental provides a projection screen TV for a charge of $8.00 for the first day and $5.00 for each additional day. Actionview Rental provides the same equipment for $6.50 per day. If you are planning to rent a projection screen TV for t days, for what values of t would you prefer to rent from Sportsview Rental?

33. A telephone salesperson is paid a salary of $120 per week, plus $1.50 for each person who places an order. How many persons must place orders so that the salesperson's weekly income will exceed $180?

34. The author of a mathematics textbook determines that it takes 30 minutes to read a certain section and 4 minutes to solve each exercise. How many exercises should an instructor assign in addition to the reading so that the student will spend at least 70 minutes on the assignment?

2.5 In Exercises 35−40 solve and check.

35. $\left| 3x - 4 \right| = 5$

36. $\left| 2x + 3 \right| = 1$

37. $\left| -y + 3 \right| = 2$

38. $\left| -3s - 2 \right| = 4$

39. $\left| 3r + 3 \right| = 0$

40. $\left| 4t - 2 \right| = 0$

In Exercises 41−50 solve and graph.

41. $\left| 3x \right| < 3$

42. $\left| 3x \right| > 6$

43. $\left| 2x + 3 \right| \leq 2$

44. $\left| 3x - 2 \right| \geq 1$

45. $\left| 2x + 1 \right| = 2$

46. $\left| -3x + 6 \right| = 0$

47. $\left| 2 + 2x \right| < 0$

48. $\left| 2 - 2x \right| \geq 0$

49. $\dfrac{\left| 3x + 1 \right|}{2} < 2$

50. $\dfrac{\left| 4x - 2 \right|}{3} \geq 4$

Progress Test 2A

1. Solve and check: $4x - 6 = 9$.

2. Solve and check: $2(x - 2) = 3(2x + 4)$.

3. True or false: -1 is a root of $2x - 1 = 3x + 1$.

4. Solve for h: $V = \pi r^2 h$.

5. Solve for x: $-2x + 3 = 4 + kx$.

6. 28 is 40% of what number?

7. 8 is $\frac{1}{4}$% of what number?

8. The length of a rectangle is 3 meters longer than its width. If the perimeter is 36 meters, find the dimensions of the rectangle.

9. Find three consecutive even integers whose sum is 48.

10. Part of a $5000 trust fund is invested in a mutual fund yielding 6% per year in dividends, and the balance in a corporate bond yielding 7% interest per year. If the total annual interest is $320, how much is invested in each?

11. Solve and graph: $3(2 - x) < 12$.

12. Solve and graph: $5(3x - 2) \geq 2(4 - 5x) + 7$.

13. Solve: $\left| 2x - 2 \right| = 5$.

14. Solve and graph: $\left| 2 - x \right| \leq 12$.

15. Solve and graph: $\left| 2x + 5 \right| > 7$.

Progress Test 2B

1. Solve and check: $5x + 4 = -6$.

2. Solve and check: $-(x + 3) = 4(x - 7)$.

3. True or false: -2 is a root of $-3x - 5 = 2x - 3$.

4. Solve for b: $A = \frac{1}{2}h(b + c)$.

5. Solve for x: $2(3 - kx) = (5 - 2x)$.

6. 44 is 110% of what number?

7. 56 is 70% of what number?

8. The width of a rectangle is 1 centimeter less than twice its length. If the perimeter is 22 centimeters, find the dimensions of the rectangle.

9. A certain number is 4 less than another number. If their sum is 46, find the numbers.

10. An $8000 pension fund is invested in two parts yielding 5% and 8% interest per year, respectively. If the total annual interest is $520, how much is invested in each part?

11. Solve and graph: $5(4 - 2x) > 45$.

12. Solve and graph: $4(x + 2) \leq 3(2 - 3x) - 11$.

13. Solve: $\left| 3x - 4 \right| = 5$.

14. Solve and graph: $\left| 3 - 2x \right| \geq 12$.

15. Solve and graph: $\left| 3x - 1 \right| < 2$.

Chapter 2 Project

How do dietitians design healthy diets for people of different shapes and sizes? Factors like muscle mass, height, age, and gender play a role. Algebra is an important tool for solving problems that involve numerical data like these.

Do Exercises 60 and 61 in Section 2.1. Now do some research into how age, height, body shape, and other factors like these affect determinations about healthy weights and caloric intake. Remember that the formulas given here are simple examples intended to show how dietitians may use algebra; they are not proven laws! If you can, interview a real dietitian or nutritionist and ask him or her how mathematics is utilized in human health science.

Adapt the equation given in Exercise 61 for a man who wishes to lose 1.5 pounds in one week, with a starting weight of 200 pounds. If the man's goal weight is 180 pounds, how tall does the formula in Exercise 60 suggest he might be?

CHAPTER 3

Mathematical Models and Word Problems

A great discovery solves a great problem but there is a grain of discovery in the solution of any problem. Your problem may be modest; but if it challenges your curiosity and brings into play your inventive faculties, and if you solve it by your own means, you may experience the tension and enjoy the triumph of discovery.

—George Polya

Scientists and mathematicians work together to learn about, and hopefully to solve, serious problems facing all of us. One of these problems is global warming. The Earth's surface is about one degree Fahrenheit warmer than it was just 100 years ago. The presence in our atmosphere of increasing amounts of so-called greenhouse gases like methane and carbon dioxide is largely responsible.

If human activities like burning fossil fuels add methane to our air, how do scientists determine what proportion of the atmosphere is methane? One figure indicates that the concentration of methane has increased by 150% in the last 250 years. What does this figure mean? Problems dealing with the

http://www.epa.gov

concentrations of substances in combination are called **mixture problems**, and they are one of the several types of word problems that this chapter addresses. The chapter project will look at some more examples related to global warming, and you can learn more at an informative government website, www.epa.gov.

■ ■ ■

When engineers want to test a new idea, they build a model upon which to experiment. A properly constructed model is expected to behave in the same manner as the final product. In the same way, a physicist may build a model that facilitates exploration of the behavior of a natural phenomenon. Similarly, a biologist may build a model to explain the interaction between body mechanisms.

Mathematicians also build models, but they do so on paper. A **mathematical model** consists of mathematical expressions and equations that are an abstract representation of the problem. The steps in the process consist of

(a) determining the variables

(b) creating the model

(c) using the model to find a solution or solutions

(d) verifying that the solution satisfies the original problem.

The steps in the process of mathematical modeling should sound familiar. They are precisely the steps we used in Chapter 2 when we introduced you to the intriguing world of word problems. You have seen that the challenge in solving word problems lies in translating from words into mathematical equivalents, that is, in building the mathematical model.

We are now going to explore a variety of word problems in which we will show you how to build a model in an organized manner that will lead to the appropriate algebraic expressions and equations. In short, *we are going to demonstrate a method for solving word problems that is virtually foolproof.*

We pointed out in Section 2.2 that sometimes you must use a formula in order to solve a problem. This need not frighten you. For example, you already know one of the formulas we will use:

$$\text{distance} = \text{rate} \times \text{time}$$

Often, these formulas express a relationship that you use all of the time but have never written down. For example, if you have a pocketful of change and want to know how wealthy you are, you would determine the number of coins of each type (the technical term is *denomination*) and multiply each by the number of cents in that type. The formula

$$\text{value in cents} = \text{number of coins} \times \text{number of cents in each coin}$$

explicitly states the relationship that you intuitively used.

Having successfully translated from words into algebra, you must now solve the equation that you have formulated. That's the easy part: straightforward algebraic steps will lead you to a numerical solution. The final step: always check to insure that the answer "makes sense" in the context of the problem.

3.1   Coin Problems

In building a model for coin problems, you must distinguish between the *number* of coins and the *value* of the coins. For example,

$$n \text{ nickels have a value of } 5n \text{ cents}$$

$$n \text{ dimes have a value of } 10n \text{ cents}$$

$$n \text{ quarters have a value of } 25n \text{ cents}$$

If you have 8 quarters, what is their value? You find the answer by using this relationship.

For any denomination of coins,

number of coins × number of cents in each coin = value in cents

---

Since each quarter has a value of 25 cents, the total value of the quarters is

$$8 \times 25 = 200 \text{ cents}$$

Example 1   A Coin Problem
A purse contains $3.20 in quarters and dimes. If there are 3 more quarters than dimes, how many coins of each type are there?

Solution
In our model, we may let the unknown represent the number of quarters or the number of dimes. We make a choice. Let

$$n = \text{number of quarters}$$

then

$$n - 3 = \text{numbers of dimes}$$

since "there are 3 more quarters than dimes."

We can begin to build our model by gathering the data in the form of a chart, using the relationship

---

value in cents = number of coins × number of cents in each coin

---

to guide us.

	Number of coins	×	Number of cents in each coin	=	Value in cents
Quarters	n		25		$25n$
Dimes	$n - 3$		10		$10(n - 3)$
Total					320

In our problem, we are told that

total value = (value of quarters) + (value of dimes)

Substituting from the chart and solving,

$$320 = 25n + 10(n - 3)$$
$$320 = 25n + 10n - 30$$
$$350 = 35n$$
$$10 = n$$

Then

$$n = \text{number of quarters} = 10$$
$$n - 3 = \text{number of dimes} = 7$$

Now verify that the value is $3.20.

✔ Progress Check 1

(a) Solve Example 1, letting the unknown n represent the number of dimes.

(b) A class collected $3.90 in nickels and dimes. If there were 6 more nickels than dimes, how many coins were there of each type?

Answers

(a) 10 quarters, 7 dimes   (b) 24 dimes, 30 nickels

Example 2   A Coin Problem

A jar contains 25 coins worth $3.05. If the jar contains only nickels and quarters, how many coins are there of each type?

Solution

We'll choose a variable to represent the number of nickels:

$$n = \text{number of nickels}$$

Can our model represent the number of quarters in terms of n? Since there is a total of 25 coins, we must have

$$25 - n = \text{number of quarters}$$

The model can then be built in the form of a chart.

	Number of coins	×	Number of cents in each coin	=	Value in cents
Nickels	n		5		$5n$
Quarters	$25 - n$		25		$25(25 - n)$
Total					305

We know that

$$\text{total value} = (\text{value of nickels}) + (\text{value of quarters})$$
$$305 = 5n + 25(25 - n)$$
$$305 = 5n + 625 - 25n$$
$$-320 = -20n$$
$$n = 16 = \text{number of nickels}$$
$$25 - n = 9 = \text{number of quarters}$$

Verify that the coins have a total value of $3.05.

> ### ✔ Progress Check 2
> A pile of coins worth $10 consisting of quarters and half-dollars is lying on a desk. If there are twice as many quarters as half-dollars, how many half-dollars are there?
>
> **Answer**
> 10

Example 3   A Disguised Coin Problem

A man purchased 10-cent, 15-cent, and 20-cent stamps with a total value of $8.40. If the number of 15-cent stamps is 8 more than the number of 10-cent stamps and there are 10 more of the 20-cent stamps than of the 15-cent stamps, how many of each did he receive?

Solution

This problem points out two things: (a) it is possible to phrase coin problems in terms of stamps or other objects, and (b) a "wordy" problem can be attacked by the same type of analysis.

	Number of stamps	×	Denomination of each stamp	=	Value in cents
10-cent	$n - 8$		10		$10(n - 8)$
15-cent	n		15		$15n$
20-cent	$n + 10$		20		$20(n + 10)$
Total					840

We let n be the number of 15-cent stamps (since the 10-cent and 20-cent stamps are specified in terms of the 15-cent stamps). Since

$$\text{total value} = \left(\begin{array}{c}\text{value of} \\ \text{10-cent stamps}\end{array}\right) + \left(\begin{array}{c}\text{value of} \\ \text{15-cent stamps}\end{array}\right) + \left(\begin{array}{c}\text{value of} \\ \text{20-cent stamps}\end{array}\right)$$

we have

$$840 = 10(n - 8) + 15n + 20(n + 10)$$
$$840 = 10n - 80 + 15n + 20n + 200$$
$$840 = 45n + 120$$
$$720 = 45n$$
$$16 = n$$

Thus,

$$n = \text{number of 15-cent stamps} = 16$$
$$n - 8 = \text{number of 10-cent stamps} = 8$$
$$n + 10 = \text{number of 20-cent stamps} = 26$$

Verify that the total value is $8.40.

✔ Progress Check 3

The pretzel vendor finds that her coin-changer contains $8.75 in nickels, dimes, and quarters. If there are twice as many dimes as nickels and 10 fewer quarters than dimes, how many of each kind of coin are there?

Answer
15 nickels, 30 dimes, and 20 quarters

Exercise Set 3.1

1. A soda machine contains $3.00 in nickels and dimes. If the number of dimes is 5 times more than twice the number of nickels, how many coins of each type are there?

2. A donation box has $8.50 in nickels, dimes, and quarters. If there are twice as many dimes as nickels, and 4 more quarters than dimes, how many coins of each type are there?

3. A wallet has $460 in $5, $10, and $20 bills. The number of $5 bills exceeds twice the number of $10 bills by 4, while the number of $20 bills is 6 fewer than the number of $10 bills. How many bills of each type are there?

4. A traveler buys $990 in traveler's checks, in $10, $20, and $50 denominations. The number of $20 checks is 3 less than twice the number of $10 checks, while the number of $50 checks is 5 less than the number of $10 checks. How many traveler's checks were bought in each denomination?

5. A movie theater charges $5 admission for an adult and $3 for a child. If 700 tickets were sold and the total revenue received was $2900, how many tickets of each type were sold?

6. At a gambling casino a red chip is worth $5, a green one $2, and a blue one $1. A gambler buys $27 worth of chips. The number of green chips is 2 more than 3 times the number of red ones, while the number of blue chips is 3 less than twice the number of red ones. How many chips of each type did the gambler get?

7. A student buys 5-cent, 10-cent, and 15-cent stamps, with a total value of $6.70. If the number of 5-cent stamps is 2 more than the number of 10-cent stamps, while the number of 15-cent stamps is 5 more than one half the number of 10-cent stamps, how many stamps of each denomination did the student obtain?

8. A railroad car, designed to carry containerized cargo, handles crates that weigh 1, $\frac{1}{2}$, and $\frac{1}{4}$ ton. On a certain day, the railroad car carries 17 tons of cargo. If the number of $\frac{1}{2}$-ton containers is twice the number of 1-ton containers, while the number of $\frac{1}{4}$-ton containers is 8 more

than 4 times the number of 1-ton containers, how many containers of each type are in the car?

9. An amateur theater group is converting a large class-room into an auditorium for a forthcoming play. The group will sell $3, $5, and $6 tickets. They want to receive exactly $503 from the sale of the tickets. If the number of $5 tickets to be sold is twice the number of $6 tickets, and the number of $3 tickets is 1 more than 3 times the number of $6 tickets, how many tickets of each type are there?

10. An amusement park sells 25-cent, 50-cent, and $1 tick-ets and a teacher purchases $32.50 worth of tickets. A student remarks that there are twice as many 50-cent tickets as there are $1 tickets and that the number of 25-cent tickets is 30 more than the number of 50-cent tickets. How many tickets of each type are there?

11. During its annual picnic, a company supplies lemonade for all employees and their families. The picnic commit-tee has purchased twice as many pint jugs as quart jugs and 8 fewer gallon jugs than quart jugs. How many jugs of each type are there if 22 gallons of lemonade were purchased? (*Hint*: There are 2 pints to a quart and 4 quarts to a gallon.)

12. A gym offers a variety of weights for use by its mem-bers. If there are 6 more 50-pound weights than 100-pound weights and three times as many 20-pound weights as 50-pound weights, for a total of 3180 pounds, how many of each weight are there?

3.2   Investment Problems

The class of investment problems that we are going to solve involves simple interest. As an example, assume that you invest $500 (called the **principal**) at an annual interest rate of 6%. Then the interest I available at year's end is

$$I = (0.06)(500) = 30$$

In this example, you have earned $30 in interest. We can generalize and develop a formula that will form the basis for our modeling of these investment problems.

simple annual interest = principal × annual rate
or
$I = P \cdot r$

This formula will be used in all investment problems.

Example 1   Investing at Simple Interest
A part of $7000 is invested at 6% annual interest and the remainder at 8%. If the total amount of annual interest is $460, how much was invested at each rate?

Solution
Let

$$n = \text{amount invested at 6\%}$$

then

$$7000 - n = \text{amount invested at 8\%}$$

since the total amount is $7000. The model can then be built in the form of a chart.

	Principal	×	Rate	=	Interest
6% portion	n		0.06		$0.06n$
8% portion	$7000 - n$		0.08		$0.08(7000 - n)$
Total					460

Since the total interest is the sum of the interest from the two parts,

$$460 = 0.06n + 0.08(7000 - n)$$
$$460 = 0.06n + 560 - 0.08n$$
$$0.02n = 100$$
$$n = \$5000 = \text{portion invested at 6\%}$$
$$7000 - n = \$2000 = \text{portion invested at 8\%}$$

✔ **Progress Check 1**

A club decides to invest a part of $4600 in stocks earning 4.5% annual dividends, and the remainder in bonds paying 7.5%. How much must the club invest in each to obtain a net return of 5.4%?

Answer
$3220 in stocks, $1380 in bonds

Example 2   Investing at Simple Interest
A part of $12,000 is invested at 5% annual interest, and the remainder at 9%. The annual income on the 9% investment is $100 more than the annual income on the 5% investment. How much is invested at each rate?

Solution
Let

$$n = \text{amount invested at 5\%}$$

then

$$12,000 - n = \text{amount invested at 9\%}$$

We can then model the information in the form of a chart.

	Principal	×	Rate	=	Interest
5% investment	n		0.05		$0.05n$
9% investment	$12,000 - n$		0.09		$0.09(12,000 - n)$

Since the interest on the 9% investment is $100 more than the interest on the 5% investment,

$$0.09(12{,}000 - n) = 0.05n + 100$$
$$1080 - 0.09n = 0.05n + 100$$
$$980 = 0.14n$$
$$n = 7000$$

Thus, $7000 is invested at 5% and $5000 at 9%.

✔ Progress Check 2

$7500 is invested in two parts yielding 5% and 15% annual interest. If the interest earned on the 15% investment is twice that earned on the 5% investment, how much is invested in each?

Answer
$4500 at 5%, $3000 at 15%

Example 3   An Inventory Investment Problem

A shoe store owner had $6000 invested in inventory. The profit on women's shoes was 35%, while the profit on men's shoes was 25%. If the profit on the entire stock was 28%, how much was invested in each type of shoe?

Solution

Let

$$n = \text{amount invested in women's shoes}$$

then

$$6000 - n = \text{amount invested in men's shoes}$$

In chart form, the model now looks like this:

	Principal	×	Rate	=	Profit
Women's shoes	n		0.35		$0.035n$
Men's shoes	$6000 - n$		0.25		$0.25(6000 - n)$
Total stock	6000		0.28		$0.28(6000)$

The profit on the entire stock was equal to the sum of the profits on each portion:

$$0.28(6000) = 0.35n + 0.25(6000 - n)$$
$$1680 = 0.35n + 1500 - 0.25n$$
$$180 = 0.1n$$
$$n = 1800$$

The store owner had invested $1800 in women's shoes and $4200 in men's shoes.

> ✔ **Progress Check 3**
>
> An automobile dealer has $55,000 invested in compacts and midsize cars. The profit on sales of the compacts is 10%, and the profit on sales of midsize cars is 16%. How much did the dealer invest in compact cars if the overall profit on the total investment is 12%?
>
> **Answer**
>
> $36,666.67

Exercise Set 3.2

1. A part of $8000 was invested at 7% annual interest, and the remainder at 8%. If the total annual interest is $590, how much was invested at each rate?

2. A $20,000 scholarship endowment fund is to be invested in two ways: part in a stock paying 5.5% annual interest in dividends and the remainder in a bond paying 7.5%. How much should be invested in each to obtain a net yield of 6.8%?

3. To help pay for his child's college education, a father invests $10,000 in two separate investments: part in a certificate of deposit paying 8.5% annual interest, the rest in a mutual fund paying 7%. The annual income on the certificate of deposit is $200 more than the annual income on the mutual fund. How much is invested in each type of investment?

4. A bicycle store selling 3-speed and 10-speed models has $16,000 in inventory. The profit on a 3-speed is 11%, while the profit on a 10-speed model is 22%. If the profit on the entire stock is 19%, how much was invested in each type of bicycle?

5. A film shop carrying black-and-white film and color film has $4000 in inventory. The profit on black-and-white film is 12%, and the profit on color film is 21%. If the annual profit on color film is $150 less than the annual profit on black-and-white film, how much was invested in each type of film?

6. A widow invested one third of her assets in a certificate of deposit paying 6% annual interest, one sixth of her assets in a mutual fund paying 8%, and the remainder in a stock paying 8.5%. If her total annual income from these investments is $910, what was the total amount invested by the widow?

7. A trust fund has invested $8000 at 6% annual interest. How much additional money should be invested at 8.5% to obtain a return of 8% on the total amount invested?

8. A businessman invested a total of $12,000 in two ventures. In one he made a profit of 8% and in the other he lost 4%. If his net profit for the year was $120, how much did he invest in each venture?

9. A retiree invested a certain amount of money at 6% annual interest; a second amount, which is $300 more than the first amount, at 8%; and a third amount, which is 4 times as much as the first amount, at 10%. If the total annual income from these investments is $1860, how much was invested at each rate?

10. A finance company lends a certain amount of money to Firm A at 7% annual interest; an amount $100 less than that lent to Firm A is lent to Firm B at 8%; and an amount $200 more than that lent to Firm A is lent to Firm C at 8.5%. If the total annual income is $126.50, how much was lent to each firm?

11. A prospective bridegroom wants to buy an engagement ring. Two jewelry stores each show him a ring at a cost of $2400. One jeweler requires a 20% down payment with the balance to be paid at the end of one year at 11% simple interest. The other jeweler requires a 25% down payment with the balance to be paid at the end of one year at 12% simple interest. What is the difference in total cost?

12. Because payment is one month overdue, a customer receives a department store bill for $332.92 that includes a 1.5% interest charge for late payment. What was the original amount of the bill?

13. An art dealer is ready to sell a Goya drawing and a Monet watercolor for which he paid a total of $45,000. If the Goya appreciated 83% and the Monet appreciated 72%, how much profit will he realize on each if he is offered $80,700 for both?

14. A small firm borrows $1000 from a stockholder at a simple interest rate of 7.5%. The company secretary lends the firm an additional sum at a simple interest rate of 8.25%. At the end of one year, the firm repays a total of $3997.75. How much did the secretary lend the firm and what is the simple interest rate on the total loan?

15. Use your graphing calculator to investigate what happens if you calculate interest more often than once per year (this is called *compound interest*). Suppose $1000 is invested at an interest rate of 1.5 % and the interest is computed after 6 months; then this interest is added to the principal so that it may earn interest for the next 6 months. (See below.)

```
1000*.015*.5
            7.5
(Ans+1000)*.015*
.5
        7.55625
      7.556671875
```

The total interest for the year is $7.50 plus $7.56, or $15.06, rather than the $15.00 we would expect from simple interest.

Repeat the procedure above for quarterly (four times per year) and monthly compounding. Put your findings in a table.

3.3   Distance (Uniform Motion) Problems

Here is the basic formula for solving distance problems:

$$\text{distance} = \text{rate} \times \text{time}$$
$$\text{or}$$
$$d = r \cdot t$$

For instance, an automobile traveling at an average speed of 50 miles per hour for 3 hours will travel a distance of

$$d = r \cdot t$$
$$= 50 \cdot 3 = 150 \text{ miles}$$

The relationships that permit you to write an equation are sometimes obscured by the words. Here are some questions to ask as you set up a distance problem:

(a) Are there two distances that are equal? Will two objects have traveled the same distance? Is the distance on a return trip the same as the distance going?

(b) Is the sum (or difference) of two distances equal to a constant? When two objects are traveling toward each other, they meet when the sum of the distances traveled by each equals the original distance between them.

Example 1   A Distance Problem
Two trains leave New York for Chicago. The first train travels at an average speed of 60 miles per hour, while the second train, which departs an hour later, travels at an

average speed of 80 miles per hour. How long will it take the second train to overtake the first train?

Solution

Since we are interested in the time the second train travels, we choose to let

$$t = \text{number of hours second train travels}$$

then

$$t + 1 = \text{number of hours first train travels}$$

since the first train departs one hour earlier. In chart form, the model now looks like this:

	Rate	×	Time	=	Distance
First train	60		$t + 1$		$60(t + 1)$
Second train	80		t		$80t$

At the moment the second train overtakes the first, they must both have traveled the *same* distance.

$$60(t + 1) = 80t$$
$$60t + 60 = 80t$$
$$60 = 20t$$
$$3 = t$$

It will take the second train 3 hours to catch up with the first train.

✔ Progress Check 1

A light plane leaves the airport at 9 A.M. traveling at an average speed of 200 miles per hour. At 11 A.M. a jet plane departs and follows the same route. If the jet travels at an average speed of 600 miles per hour, at what time will the jet overtake the light plane?

Answer

12 noon

Warning

The units of measurement of rate, time, and distance must be consistent. If a car travels at an average speed of 40 miles per hour for 15 minutes, then the distance covered is

$$d = r \cdot t$$

$$d = 40 \cdot \frac{1}{4} = 10 \text{ miles}$$

since 15 minutes $= \frac{1}{4}$ hour.

Example 2   A Distance Problem

A jogger running at the rate of 4 miles per hour takes 45 minutes more than a car traveling at 40 miles per hour to cover a certain course. How long does it take the jogger to complete the course and what is the length of the course?

Solution

Notice that time is expressed in both minutes and hours. Let's choose hours as the unit of time and let

$$t = \text{time for the jogger to complete the course}$$

then

$$t - \frac{3}{4} = \text{time for the car to complete the course}$$

since the car takes 45 minutes (= $\frac{3}{4}$ hour) less time. We can then model the information in the form of a chart.

	Rate	×	Time	=	Distance
Jogger	4		t		$4t$
Car	40		$t - \frac{3}{4}$		$40\left(t - \frac{3}{4}\right)$

Since the jogger and car travel the same distance,

$$4t = 40\left(t - \frac{3}{4}\right) = 40t - 30$$

$$30 = 36t$$

$$\frac{5}{6} = t$$

The jogger takes $\frac{5}{6}$ hour or 50 minutes. The distance traveled is

$$4t = 4 \cdot \frac{5}{6} = \frac{20}{6} = 3\frac{1}{3} \text{ miles}$$

✔ Progress Check 2

The winning horse finished the race in 3 minutes; a losing horse took 4 minutes. If the average rate of the winning horse was 5 feet per second more than the average rate of the slower horse, find the average rates of both horses.

Answer

Winner: 20 feet per second; loser: 15 feet per second

Example 3   A Distance Problem

At 2 P.M. a plane leaves Boston for San Francisco, traveling at an average speed of 500 miles per hour. Two hours later a plane departs from San Francisco to Boston traveling at an average speed of 600 miles per hour. If the cities are 3200 miles apart, at what time do the planes pass each other?

Solution

Let

t = the number of hours after 2 P.M. at which the planes meet

Let's piece together the information that we have. The model can then be built in the form of a chart.

	Rate	×	Time	=	Distance
From Boston	500		t		$500t$
From San Francisco	600		$t - 2$		$600(t - 2)$

At the moment that the planes pass each other, the sum of the distances traveled by both planes must be 3200 miles.

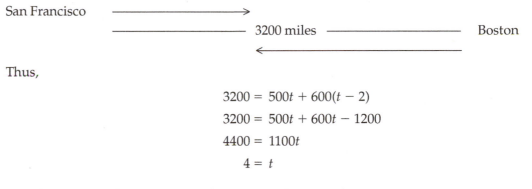

Thus,

$$3200 = 500t + 600(t - 2)$$
$$3200 = 500t + 600t - 1200$$
$$4400 = 1100t$$
$$4 = t$$

The planes meet 4 hours after the departure of the plane from Boston.

> ✔ **Progress Check 3**
>
> Two cyclists start at the same time from the same place and travel in the same direction. If one cyclist averages 16 miles per hour and the second averages 20 miles per hour, how long will it take for them to be 12 miles apart?
>
> **Answer**
>
> 3 hours

Exercise Set 3.3

1. Two trucks leave Philadelphia for Miami. The first truck to leave travels at an average speed of 50 kilometers per hour. The second truck, which leaves 2 hours later, travels at an average speed of 55 kilometers per hour. How long will it take the second truck to overtake the first truck?

2. Jackie either drives or bicycles from home to school. Her average speed when driving is 36 miles per hour, and her average speed when bicycling is 12 miles per hour. If it takes her $\frac{1}{2}$ hour less to drive to school than to bicycle, how long does it take to drive to school, how long does it take to bicycle to school, and how far is the school from her home?

3. Professors Roberts and Jones, who live 676 miles apart, are exchanging houses and jobs for four months. They start out for their new locations at exactly the same time, and they meet after 6.5 hours of driving. If their average speeds differ by 4 miles per hour, what is each professor's average speed?

4. Steve leaves school by moped for spring vacation. Forty minutes later his roommate, Frank, notices that Steve forgot to take his camera, so Frank decides to try to catch up with Steve by car. If Steve's average speed is 25 miles per hour and Frank averages 45 miles per hour, how long does it take Frank to overtake Steve?

5. A tour boat makes the round trip from the mainland to a fishing village in 6 hours. If the average speed of the boat going to the village is 15 miles per hour and the average speed returning is 12 miles per hour, how far from the mainland is the island?

6. Two cars start out from the same point at the same time and travel in opposite directions. If their average speeds are 36 and 44 miles per hour, respectively, after how many hours will they be 360 miles apart?

7. An express train and a local train start out from the same point at the same time and travel in opposite directions. The express train travels twice as fast as the local train. If after 4 hours they are 480 kilometers apart, what is the average speed of each train?

8. Two planes start out from the same place at the same time and travel in the same direction. One plane has an average speed of 400 miles per hour and the other plane has an average speed of 480 miles per hour. After how many hours will they be 340 miles apart?

9. Two cyclists start out at the same time from points that are 395 kilometers apart and travel toward each other. The first cyclist travels at an average speed of 40 kilometers per hour, and the second travels at an average speed of 50 kilometers per hour. After how many hours will they be 35 kilometers apart?

10. It takes a student 8 hours to drive from her home back to college, a distance of 580 kilometers. Before lunch her average speed is 80 kilometers per hour and after lunch it is 60 kilometers per hour. How many hours does she travel at each rate?

3.4   Mixture Problems

One type of mixture problem involves mixing commodities, say, two or more types of nuts, to obtain a mixture with a desired value. To form a suitable model, we will need to use a number of "common sense" relationships. If the commodities are measured in pounds, these are

> number of pounds × price per pound = value of commodity
>
> pounds in mixture = sum of pounds of each commodity
>
> value of mixture = sum of values of individual commodities

Example 1   A Coffee Mixture

How many pounds of Brazilian coffee worth $5 per pound must be mixed with 20 pounds of Colombian coffee worth $4 per pound to produce a mixture worth $4.20 per pound?

Solution

Let

$$n = \text{number of pounds of Brazilian coffee}$$

The model can then be built in the form of a chart.

Type of coffee	Number of pounds	×	Price per pound	=	Value in cents
Brazilian	n		500		$500n$
Colombian	20		400		8000
Mixture	$n + 20$		420		$420(n + 20)$

(Note that the weight of the mixture equals the sum of the weights of the Brazilian and Colombian coffees going into the mixture.) Since the value of the mixture is the sum of the values of the two types of coffee, we have

$$420(n + 20) = 500n + 8000$$
$$420n + 8400 = 500n + 8000$$
$$400 = 80n$$
$$5 = n$$

We must add 5 pounds of Brazilian coffee.

✔ Progress Check 1

How many pounds of macadamia nuts worth $4 per pound must be mixed with 4 pounds of cashews worth $2.50 per pound and 6 pounds of pecans worth $3 per pound to produce a mixture that is worth $3.20 per pound?

Answer

5 pounds

Example 2   A Mixture of Chocolates

Caramels worth $1.75 per pound are to be mixed with cream chocolates worth $2 per pound to make a 5-pound mixture that will be sold at $1.90 per pound. How many pounds of each are needed?

Solution

Let n = number of pounds of caramels. Displaying all of the information, we have

Type of candy	Number of pounds	×	Price per pound	=	Value in cents
Caramels	n		175		$175n$
Cream chocolates	$5 - n$		200		$200(5 - n)$
Mixture	5		190		950

(Note that the number of pounds of cream chocolates is the weight of the mixture less the weight of the caramels.) Since the value of the mixture is the sum of the values of the two components, we have

$$950 = 175n + 200(5 - n)$$
$$950 = 175n + 1000 - 200n$$
$$25n = 50$$
$$n = 2$$

We must have 2 pounds of caramels and 3 pounds of cream chocolates.

✔ Progress Check 2

How many gallons of oil worth 55¢ per gallon and how many gallons of oil worth 75¢ per gallon must be mixed to obtain 40 gallons of oil worth 60¢ per gallon?

Answer

30 gallons of the 55-cent oil and 10 gallons of the 75-cent oil

---

Liquid Mixtures

A second type of mixture problem involves solutions containing different concentrations of materials. For instance, a 40-gallon drum of a solution that is 75% acid contains $(40)(0.75) = 30$ gallons of acid. If the solutions are measured in gallons, the relationship we need is

number of gallons of solution	×	% of component A	=	number of gallons of component A

The other relationships we need are really the same as in our first type of mixture problem.

	number of gallons in mixture	=	sum of the number of gallons in each solution
	number of gallons of component A in mixture	=	sum of the number of gallons of component A in each solution

Example 3 A Liquid Mixture

A 40% acid solution is to be mixed with a 75% acid solution to produce 140 gallons of a solution that is 50% acid. How many gallons of each solution must be used?

Solution

For our model, we let

$$n = \text{number of gallons of the 40\% acid solution}$$

Then

$$140 - n = \text{number of gallons of the 75\% acid solution}$$

since the number of gallons in the mixture is the sum of the number of gallons in each contributing solution. We can then model the information in the form of a chart.

	Number of gallons	×	% acid	=	Number of gallons of acid
40% solution	n		40		$0.40n$
75% solution	$140 - n$		75		$0.75(140 - n)$
Mixture	140		50		70

Since the number of gallons of acid in the mixture is the sum of the number of gallons of acid in each solution (see Figure 1), we have

$$70 = 0.40n + 0.75(140 - n)$$
$$70 = 0.40n + 105 - 0.75n$$
$$-35 = -0.35n$$
$$n = 100 \text{ gallons}$$
$$140 - n = 40 \text{ gallons}$$

Thus, we mix 100 gallons of the 40% solution with 40 gallons of the 75% solution to produce 140 gallons of the 50% solution.

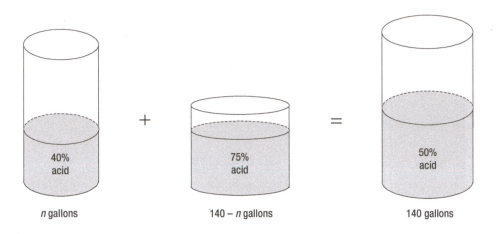

Figure 1   Concentration of Acid

✔ **Progress Check 3**

How many gallons of milk that is 22% butterfat must be mixed with how many gallons of cream that is 60% butterfat to produce 19 gallons of a mixture that is 40% butterfat?

Answer

10 gallons of milk and 9 gallons of cream

Example 4   A Mixture of Alloys

How many ounces of an alloy that is 30% tin must be mixed with 15 ounces of an alloy that is 12% tin to produce an alloy that is 24% tin?

Solution

Let n = number of ounces of the 30% tin alloy. The alloy may be treated as a solution, and we can display the information for our model.

	Number of ounces	×	% tin	=	Number of ounces of tin
30% alloy	n		30		$0.30n$
12% alloy	15		12		1.8
Mixture	$n + 15$		24		$0.24(n + 15)$

(Note that the number of ounces in the mixture is the sum of the number of ounces in the alloys going into the mixture.) Since the number of ounces of *tin* in the mixture is the sum of the number of ounces of tin in each alloy, we have

$$0.24(n + 15) = 0.30n + 1.8$$
$$0.24n + 3.6 = 0.30n + 1.8$$
$$1.8 = 0.06n$$
$$n = 30$$

Thus, we need to add 30 ounces of the 30% alloy to 15 ounces of the 12% alloy.

✔ **Progress Check 4**

How many pounds of a 25% copper alloy must be added to 50 pounds of a 55% copper alloy to produce an alloy that is 45% copper?

Answer
We need to add 25 pounds of 25% copper alloy.

Example 5   Reducing a Mixture

A tank contains 40 gallons of water and 10 gallons of alcohol. How many gallons of water must be removed if the remaining solution is to be 30% alcohol?

Solution

Let n = number of gallons of water to be removed. This problem is different since we are removing water. We can model the information in the form of a chart.

	Number of gallons	×	% alcohol	=	Gallons of alcohol
Original solution	50		20		10
Water removed	n		0		0
New solution	$50 - n$		30		$0.3(50 - n)$

(Note that the water removed has 0% alcohol!) The number of gallons of alcohol in the new solution is the same amount as in the original solution, since only water has been removed.

$$0.3(50 - n) = 10$$
$$15 - 0.3n = 10$$
$$5 = 0.3n$$
$$n = 16\frac{2}{3}$$

Thus, we must remove $16\frac{2}{3}$ gallons of water.

✔ **Progress Check 5**

A tank contains 90 quarts of an antifreeze solution that is 50% antifreeze. How much water should be removed to raise the antifreeze level to 60% in the new solution?

Answer

15 quarts of water should be removed.

Exercise Set 3.4

1. How many pounds of raisins worth $1.50 per pound must be mixed with 10 pounds of peanuts worth $1.20 per pound to produce a raisin-peanut mixture worth $1.40 per pound?

2. How many ounces of Ceylon tea worth $1.50 per ounce and how many ounces of Formosa tea worth $2.00 per ounce must be mixed to obtain a mixture of 8 ounces that is worth $1.85 per ounce?

3. A copper alloy that is 40% copper is to be combined with a copper alloy that is 80% copper to produce 120 kilograms of an alloy that is 70% copper. How many kilograms of each alloy must be used?

4. How many liters of an ammonia solution that is 20% ammonia must be mixed with 20 liters of an ammonia solution that is 48% ammonia to produce a solution that is 36% ammonia?

5. A vat contains 60 gallons of a 15% saline solution. How many gallons of water must be evaporated so that the resulting solution will be 20% saline?

6. How many grams of pure silver must be added to 30 grams of an alloy that is 50% silver to obtain an alloy that is 60% silver?

7. How much water must be added to dilute 10 quarts of a solution that is 18% iodine so that the resulting solution will be 12% iodine?

8. A vat contains 27 gallons of water and 9 gallons of acetic acid. How many gallons of water must be evaporated if the remaining solution is to be 40% acetic acid?

9. How many pounds of a fertilizer worth $3 per pound must be combined with 12 pounds of a weed killer worth $6 per pound and 18 pounds of phosphate worth $6 per pound to produce a mixture worth $4.80 per pound?

10. A producer of packaged frozen vegetables wants to market the product at $1.20 per kilogram. How many kilograms of green beans worth $1 per kilogram must be mixed with 100 kilograms of corn worth $1.30 per kilogram and 90 kilograms of peas worth $1.40 per kilogram to produce the required mixture?

3.5   Critical Thinking Problems

In previous sections of this chapter, we discussed how to solve problems involving coins, interest, mixtures, and distance. We will now use what we have learned to solve additional critical thinking problems. It is best to utilize the following general steps in order to solve problems more easily and consistently:

General Steps for Problem Solving

> 1. Understand the problem.
>
> 2. Translate the problem into an algebraic equation.
>
> 3. Solve the resulting equation.
>
> 4. Interpret the result.

Now let's try some examples. The first example involves percentages.

You may be surprised at how often we use percentages in our everyday lives. For example, if items are on sale, we get certain amounts of discount. It is easier to say that we get a 15% discount rather than give the exact cost. You may also notice that realtors usually speak in terms of percentages. For example, they say house prices increased by 10% last year or house prices are dropping by 5% this year.

It is important to know how to calculate the percent of increase or decrease.

Example 1   Calculating Home Prices

The average price of a home in Santa Maria was $200,000 in 1999. The average home price increased to $450,000 in 2005. Find the percent increase.

Solution

Step 1. Understand the Problem. First, let's read the problem. The average home price has increased from $200,000 to $450,000 in Santa Maria. Now we need to find the percent increase. Since we don't know by what percent the average home price has increased, we let x = the percent increase.

Step 2. Translate the Problem into an Equation. Let's write the problem in words first and then translate the words into an algebraic equation.

> Increase = New average home price − Old average home price
> Increase = $450,000 − $200,000
> Increase = $250,000

$250,000 is the amount of increase. To find the percent increase, we write the problem in words first.

$250,000 = x \cdot \$200,000$

Step 3. Solve the Equation.

$$250,000 = x \cdot 200,000$$ Since "of" represents "multiplication"

$$\frac{250,000}{200,000} = x$$ Dividing both sides by 200,000

$$x = 1.25$$

$$x = 125\%$$ Write as a percent

Step 4. Interpret the Results. Finally, check the proposed solution. The percent increase in average home prices is 125%.

✔ Progress Check 1

If the price of a certain computer decreases from $2,000 to $1,200, find the percent decrease.

Answer

40%

Example 2   Finding the Number of Tickets

For the musical called "The Company," tickets cost $8 for children and $12 for adults. Altogether 172 tickets were sold and $1,824 was collected. Find the number of child and adult tickets sold.

Solution

After carefully reading the problem, we see that we need to find the number of child and adult tickets sold. Since we don't know theses two values, let's write one of them as an unknown.

Step 1. Understand the Problem.

Let x = the number of child tickets that were sold.

Then $172 - x$ = the number of adult tickets that were sold.

Because

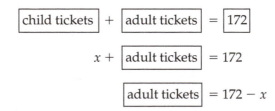

Since each child ticket costs $8,

$$\text{Revenue from child tickets} = 8 \cdot x$$

Since each adult ticket costs $12,

$$\text{Revenue from adult tickets} = 12 \cdot (172 - x)$$

Step 2. Translate the Problem into an Equation. Now, write the equation in words.

$$\boxed{\text{total revenue}} = \boxed{\text{revenue from child tickets}} + \boxed{\text{revenue from adult tickets}}$$

Then we can translate the words into the algebraic equation.

$$\$1{,}824 = 8 \cdot x + 12 \cdot (172 - x)$$

Step 3. Solve the Equation.

Next, solve the equation for x.

$$1{,}824 = 8 \cdot x + 12 \cdot (172 - x)$$

$1{,}824 = 8 \cdot x + 2{,}064 - 12 \cdot x$ By distributing 12 to $(172 - x)$

$1{,}824 = -4x + 2{,}064$ Combining like terms on the right-hand side

$1{,}824 - 2{,}064 = -4x$ Subtracting 2,064 from both sides

$-240 = -4x$

$\dfrac{-240}{-4} = x$ Dividing both sides by -4

$x = 60$

The number of adult tickets $= 172 - x$

$= 172 - 60$

$= 112$

Step 4. Interpret the Result. Let's check the solution before we state the conclusion.

Check: By substituting $x = 60$ into the equation $\$1{,}824 = 8 \cdot x + 12 \cdot (172 - x)$,

$$\$1{,}824 = 8 \cdot (60) + 12 \cdot (172 - 60)$$
$$\$1{,}824 = 480 + 12 \cdot (112)$$
$$\$1{,}824 = 480 + 1{,}344$$
$$\$1{,}824 = \$1{,}824$$

Finally, we state the conclusion.

State: There were 60 child tickets and 112 adult tickets sold.

✔ Progress Check 2

a. The sum of two numbers is 60 and their difference is 24. Find the two numbers.

b. Ms. Chung purchased 64 stamps, some 41-cent stamps and some 3-cent stamps. Find the number of each type purchased if she spent $8.00 total.

Answers

a. 18 and 42

b. 16 41-cent stamps and 48 3-cent stamps

■ ■ ■

Key Ideas for Review

Topic	Key Idea
Mathematical model	When you convert a word problem into mathematical expressions, equations, and inequalities, you create a mathematical model for the problem.
Formulas associated with word problems	
coin problems	number of coins $\times$ number of cents in each coin $=$ value in cents
investment problems	principal $\times$ rate $=$ interest
distance (uniform motion) problems	rate $\times$ time $=$ distance
mixture problems	number of pounds $\times$ price per pound $=$ value
	amount of solution $\times$ % of component A $=$ amount of component A

Review Exercises

Solutions to exercises whose numbers are in bold are in the Solutions section in the back of the book.

3.1 1. A church collection box contains $5.35 in dimes, quarters, and half-dollars. If the number of dimes is twice the number of quarters, and the number of half-dollars is one less than three times the number of quarters, how many coins of each denomination are there?

2. A certain electronic device consists of 16-transistor, 48-transistor, and 64-transistor components. The number of 48-transistor components is two less than the number of 16-transistor components, and the number of 64-transistor components is three less than twice the number of 16-transistor components. If the device contains a total of 480 transistors, how many components of each type are required?

3. A freighter carries a load of 2-ton, 5-ton, and 8-ton slabs of steel. The number of 5-ton slabs is 20 fewer than the number of 2-ton slabs and the number of 8-ton slabs is one more than twice the number of 2-ton slabs. If the load being carried weighs 575 tons, how many slabs of each type are being carried?

4. Suppose that you receive a package with a total postage of $5.60 that is made up of 20-cent, 40-cent, and 1-dollar stamps. If the number of 40-cent stamps is three more than the number of 20-cent stamps, and the number of 1-dollar stamps is two fewer than the number of 20-cent stamps, how many stamps of each denomination are there on the package?

3.2 5. Part of a lump-sum death payment of $40,000 was invested at 10% annual interest, and the rest was invested at 8% annual interest. If the total annual interest is $3500, how much was invested at each rate?

6. A record shop selling classical and popular music has $12,000 worth of music in inventory. The profit on classical music is 15%, while the profit on popular music is 20%. If the annual profit on classical music is $1000 less than the annual profit on popular music, how much inventory does the shop carry in each type of music? (Assume that the entire inventory is sold.)

7. An investment club invested a total of $7000 in two real estate limited partnerships. In one partnership they make a profit of 10% for the year and in the other they have a loss of 5% for the year. If the net annual profit is $325, how much was invested in each limited partnership?

8. A finance company lent a certain amount of money to the AB company at 8% annual interest. An amount $500 more than that lent to the AB company was lent to the CD company at 10% annual interest, and an amount $400 less than the amount lent to the AB company was lent to the EF company at 12% annual interest. If the total annual interest received by the finance company is $1502, how much was lent to each borrower?

3.3 **9.** Two aircraft start from the same point at the same time flying in opposite directions. The faster aircraft travels twice as fast as the other one. After 5 hours of travel they are 1500 miles apart. Find the average speed of each aircraft.

10. Two joggers start to run toward each other at the same time from points that are 12 miles apart, at average speeds of 10 miles per hour and 9 miles per hour, respectively. After how many hours will they be 0.6 mile apart?

11. Two buses, traveling at average speeds of 50 and 55 miles per hour, respectively, leave Los Angeles for Chicago at the same time. After how many hours are they 60 miles apart?

12. Two airplanes leave at the same time from points 3150 miles apart, traveling toward each other, and they pass each other after 3.5 hours of flying. If their average speeds differ by 100 miles per hour, what is the average speed of each airplane?

3.4 **13.** How many pounds of cashews worth $4.00 per pound must be mixed with 6 pounds of walnuts worth $2.00 per pound to yield a mixture worth $2.50 per pound?

14. A vat contains 100 gallons of a 20% potassium solution. How many gallons of water must be evaporated to get a 25% solution?

15. How many pounds of ground beef that is 25% fat must be blended with 10 pounds of ground veal that is 10% fat to produce a mixture that is 15% fat?

16. How many pounds of Colombian coffee worth $4.00 per pound must be mixed with how many pounds of Jamaican coffee worth $5.00 per pound to produce 25 pounds of a mixture that will be sold at $4.80 per pound?

17. Atmospheric concentrations are usually measured in parts per billion, by volume (ppbv). So, a concentration of carbon dioxide equal to 13 ppbv means that, for every billion volume units (say, milliliters) of the atmosphere, there are 13 units of carbon dioxide.

   Convert an atmospheric concentration of carbon dioxide of 13 ppbv to a percent (that is, what percent of this atmosphere would be carbon dioxide?)

18. In 2002 the atmospheric concentration of the greenhouse gas methane was about 1751 parts per billion by volume (ppbv). This means that in a one-billion liter volume of the atmosphere, we should find about 1751 liters of methane gas.

   Suppose we had a 100 L sample of gas with this concentration of methane. How much methane, in mL, would have to be added to increase the concentration to 150% of its current level? (Hint: We want to increase the concentration to 1.5×1751, or 2626.5 ppbv.)

19. Store the following values in your graphing calculator as A and B: $A = 0.1$, $B = 0.3$ (see the calculator screen below). Then, enter the expression

$$\frac{112A + (172 - 112)B}{172}$$

   Suppose the 112 in the above expression represents liters of CO_2, and the values of A and B represent 10% and 30%, respectively.

```
.1→A
                          .1
.3→B
                           3
(112A+(172-112)B
)/172
           .1697674419
```

   a. What might the 172 represent? What about the 0.17?

   b. Experiment with changing the values of A and B. How can this expression help you solve certain mixture problems?

Progress Test 3A

1. Translate into algebra: "The number of chairs is 3 less than 4 times the number of tables."

2. Steve is presently 6 years younger than Lisa. If the sum of their ages is 40, how old is each?

3. The width of a rectangle is 4 cm less than twice its length. If the perimeter is 12 cm, find the dimensions of the rectangle.

4. A donation box contains 30 coins consisting of nickels, dimes, and quarters. The number of dimes is 4 more than twice the number of quarters. If the total value of the coins is $2.60, how many coins of each type are there?

5. A fruit grower ships crates of oranges that weigh 30, 50, and 60 pounds each. A certain shipment weighs 1140 pounds. If the number of 30-pound crates is 3 more than one half the number of 50-pound crates, and the number of 60-pound crates is 1 less than twice the number of 50-pound crates, how many crates of each type are there?

6. A college fund has invested $12,000 at 7% annual interest. How much additional money must be invested at 9% to obtain a return of 7.8% on the total amount invested?

7. A businessperson invested a certain amount of money at 6.5% annual interest; a second amount, which is $200 more than the first amount, at 7.5%; and a third amount, which is $300 more than twice the first amount, at 9%. If the total annual income from these investments is $1962, how much was invested at each rate?

8. A moped and a car leave from the same point at the same time and travel in opposite directions. The car travels 3 times as fast as the moped. If after 5 hours they are 300 miles apart, what is the average speed of each vehicle?

9. A bush pilot in Australia picks up mail at a remote village and returns to home base in 4 hours. If the average speed going is 150 miles per hour and the average speed returning is 100 miles per hour, how far from the home base is the village?

10. An alloy that is 60% silver is to be combined with an alloy that is 80% silver to produce 120 ounces of an alloy that is 75% silver. How many ounces of each alloy must be used?

11. A beaker contains 150 cubic centimeters of a solution that is 30% acid. How much water must be evaporated so that the resulting solution will be 40% acid?

Progress Test 3B

1. Translate into algebra: "The number of Democrats is 4 more than one third the number of Republicans."

2. Separate 48 into two parts so that the larger part plus 3 times the smaller is 80.

3. One side of a triangle is 2 cm shorter than the third side, while the second side is 3 cm longer than one half the third side. If the perimeter is 15 cm, find the length of each side.

4. An envelope contains 20 discount coupons in $1, $5, and $10 denominations. The number of $5 coupons is twice the number of $10 coupons. If the total value of the coupons is $54, how many coupons of each type are there?

5. A cheese sampler with a total weight of 25 ounces of cheese contains 1-ounce, 2-ounce, and 3-ounce samples. If the number of 1-ounce samples is 3 more than the number of 3-ounce samples, and the number of 2-ounce samples is 1 less than twice the number of 3-ounce samples, how many samples of each weight are there?

6. Part of an $18,000 trust fund is to be invested in a stock paying 6% in dividends, and the remainder in a bond paying 7.2% annual interest. How much should be invested in each to obtain a net yield of 7%?

7. A woman invested a certain amount of money at 8% annual interest, and a second amount of money, $2000 greater than the first amount, at 6%. If the annual incomes on the two investments are equal, how much was invested at each rate?

8. Two trains start out at 10 A.M. from stations that are 1120 kilometers apart, and travel toward each other at

average speeds of 80 and 60 kilometers per hour, respectively. At what time will they pass each other?

9. Two charter buses leave New York for Los Angeles. The first one travels at an average speed of 40 miles per hour. The second one leaves 3 hours later and travels at an average speed of 50 miles per hour. How long will it take the second bus to overtake the first one?

10. How many pounds of lawn seed worth $4.00 per pound must be mixed with 15 pounds of fertilizer worth $3.00 per pound to produce a mixture worth $3.20 per pound?

11. A vat contains 12 gallons of acid and 48 gallons of water. How much acid must be added to make a solution that is 40% acid?

Chapter 3 Project: Greenhouse Gas Concentrations and Global Warming

The atmosphere of the Earth is a mixture of gases. The relative proportions of the major components of the atmosphere (nitrogen and oxygen) don't change very much over time, but there are small amounts of other gases that can have a big effect on the planet's climate, and on its inhabitants (us!).

Greenhouse gases like carbon dioxide and methane trap heat that would otherwise be radiated out into space. A little of this is a good and necessary thing, but some human activities (like burning of fossil fuels) release these gases and increase the concentration of greenhouse gases. This has the world's scientists concerned that we may have too much of a good thing!

In this chapter project, you will learn about how concentrations of these gases are measured, and how to use the notion of percent to get an idea of what proportion of our atmosphere is composed of greenhouse gases. You will try to determine how much this proportion can change with the addition of greater quantities of these atmospheric components. Start by reading more at www.epa.gov, and then do Exercises 17, 18, and 19 in Section 3.4.

Create a table showing how much the composition of the atmosphere changes with the addition of different amounts of CO_2 and methane. (You might want to use scientific notation to express small percents more compactly.) Explain how you can use your calculator to carry out these computations more quickly. (Hint: See Exercise 19 in Section 3.4.)

Using the information at the website listed above, or other sources, make a graph of the changes in quantities of methane in our atmosphere over the past 200 years.

CHAPTER 4

Polynomials

Algebra is generous: she often gives more than is asked of her.

—Jean le Rond D'Alembert

Mathematics is required in unexpected places. The United States Postal Service considers a package to have a combined length and girth of up to 84 inches. (The girth is the perimeter around the widest part of the package.) A "large package" may have a combined length and girth of up to 130 inches. Suppose I created a package by cutting squares out of the sides of a rectangle of cardboard, then folding up the sides. How can we write an algebraic expression that gives the volume of such a package? We would call this expression a polynomial—in this case, a cubic polynomial.

The facts about package volume discussed above suggest how useful mathematics is in many careers, including packaging. The chapter project will explore these ideas more fully.

Are you fascinated by numbers, patterns, and statistics? Learn more about them (and some careers in mathematics) at http://www.amstat.org/.

http://www.amstat.org

■ ■ ■

Much of the work that is carried out in algebra involves expressions of a special form that are called polynomials. Since you will be dealing with polynomials throughout this book, we will devote this chapter to making sure that you can handle basic operations with polynomials.

4.1   Polynomials

Exponents

Let's review the notation of exponents that we introduced in Chapter 1. We write

$$a^1 = a$$
$$a^2 = a \cdot a$$
$$a^3 = a \cdot a \cdot a$$
$$\vdots \qquad \vdots$$
$$a^n = \underbrace{a \cdot a \cdot \cdots \cdot a}_{n \text{ factors}}$$

where n is a natural number and a is a real number. The notation a^n means "a is used as a **factor** n times" and is read as "a to the nth **power**" or simply as "a to the n." We call a the **base** and n the **exponent**. When $n = 1$, we simply write a rather than a^1. When $n = 2$, a^2 is referred to as "a squared." And when $n = 3$, a^3 is referred to as "a cubed."

Definition of a^n

If n is a natural number, then

$$a^n = a \cdot a \cdot \cdots \cdot a$$

for every real number a.

Example 1   Exponent Notation

Expand (write without exponents).

(a) $\left(\dfrac{1}{2}\right)^3$ (b) x^4 (c) $2x^3$ (d) $-3x^2y^3$ (e) $(3x)^2$

Solution

(a) $\left(\dfrac{1}{2}\right)^3 = \dfrac{1}{2} \cdot \dfrac{1}{2} \cdot \dfrac{1}{2} = \dfrac{1}{8}$ Base is $\dfrac{1}{2}$, exponent is 3

(b) $x^4 = x \cdot x \cdot x \cdot x$ Base is x, exponent is 4

(c) $2x^3 = 2 \cdot x \cdot x \cdot x$

(d) $-3x^2y^3 = -3 \cdot x \cdot x \cdot y \cdot y \cdot y$

(e) $(3x)^2 = 3x \cdot 3x$

Note that, as demonstrated in (c) and (d) of Example 1, the exponent applies only to the factor *immediately* preceding it.

✔ Progress Check 1

Write without using exponents.

(a) 2^4 　　　　(b) $\left(\dfrac{1}{3}\right)^2$ 　　　　(c) $x^3 y$ 　　　　(d) $\dfrac{1}{2} x y^3$

Answers

(a) $2 \cdot 2 \cdot 2 \cdot 2$ 　(b) $\dfrac{1}{3} \cdot \dfrac{1}{3}$ 　　(c) $x \cdot x \cdot x \cdot y$ 　(d) $\dfrac{1}{2} \cdot x \cdot y \cdot y \cdot y$

Warning

Note the difference between

$$(-3)^2 = (-3)(-3) = 9$$

and

$$-3^2 = -(3 \cdot 3) = -9$$

There is a rule of exponents that we will need later in this chapter. We see that

$$a^2 \cdot a^3 = \underbrace{(a \cdot a)}_{2 \text{ factors}} \cdot \underbrace{(a \cdot a \cdot a)}_{3 \text{ factors}}$$

$$= \underbrace{(a \cdot a \cdot a \cdot a \cdot a)}_{2 + 3 = 5 \text{ factors}} = a^5$$

We can generalize this rule as follows:

Product Rule for Exponents

> If *m* and *n* are natural numbers and *a* is a real number, then
>
> $$a^m \cdot a^n = a^{m+n}$$

Example 2　The Product Rule for Exponents

Multiply.

(a) $x^2 \cdot x^3$ 　　　(b) $(3x)(4x^4)$

Solution

(a) $x^2 \cdot x^3 = x^{2+3} = x^5$

(b) $(3x)(4x^4) = 3 \cdot 4 \cdot x \cdot x^4 = 12x^{1+4} = 12x^5$

Polynomials

When we combine exponent forms in one or more variables, as in

$$2x^2 + 3xy - x + 4$$

each part connected by addition is called a **term** and the entire expression is called a **polynomial**. The constants 2, 3, -1, and 4 are also given a special name: **coefficients**. Thus,

$2x^2$	$+$ $3xy$	$-$ x	$+$ 4	Polynomial
$2x^2,$	$3xy,$	$-x,$	4	Terms
2,	3,	$-1,$	4	Coefficients

We'll state these observations in a formal manner.

Definition of a Polynomial

A **polynomial** is a sum of terms in which

(a) the exponent of each variable must be a nonnegative integer, and

(b) no variables appear in the denominator.

Example 3   The Terms and Coefficients of a Polynomial

Find the terms and coefficients.

(a) $x^2y - y^2 + 3xy$ (b) $\frac{1}{2}x^3 - \frac{2}{3}y^3$

Solution

(a)

Term	x^2y	$-y^2$	$3xy$
Coefficient	1	-1	3

(b)

Term	$\frac{1}{2}x^3$	$-\frac{2}{3}y^3$
Coefficient	$\frac{1}{2}$	$-\frac{2}{3}$

✔ Progress Check 3

Find the terms and coefficients.

(a) $\frac{1}{4}x^7$ (b) $2x^2y^2 + 4xy - y^2$

Answers

(a) Term: $\frac{1}{4}x^7$; coefficient: $\frac{1}{4}$ (b) Terms: $2x^2y^2, 4xy, -y^2$; coefficients: $2, 4, -1$

Here are some examples of polynomials:

$$2x \qquad \frac{1}{2}x^3 \qquad xy^2 \qquad 3x - 2 \qquad x^3 + 6x^2$$
$$4x^2 - 2x + 1 \qquad 3x^2 + 4x^2y - xy^2 - 5y^3$$

We will later see that the product of two polynomials, such as

$$(2x + 1)(x^2 - 2x + 1)$$

is also a polynomial. Be careful, however, when dealing with the quotient of polynomials.

> The quotient of two polynomials, such as
> $$\frac{2x + 1}{x^2 - 2x + 1}$$
> is not always a polynomial.

Example 4   Recognizing Polynomials

Which of the following are not polynomials?

(a) $3x^{1/2} + xy^2 + 2y$ (b) $2x^2y - 5$ (c) $x^5 - x^{-1} + 2$ (d) $-2x^3 + \frac{1}{x}$

Solution

Every exponent of a variable in a polynomial must be a nonnegative integer. Thus, (a) is not a polynomial since x appears with the fractional exponent $\frac{1}{2}$; (c) is not a polynomial, since x appears with the negative exponent -1. Further, no variable may appear in the denominator of a polynomial, which rules out (d).

✔ Progress Check 4

Which of the following are not polynomials?

(a) $-2xy + 3x - 3y$ (b) $xy^{2/5} - 2x^2$ (c) $-3xy + 3x^{-3}y$

Answer

(b) and (c)

Degree of a Polynomial

The **degree of a term** of a polynomial is found by adding the exponents of all the variables in that term. (The degree of a constant term is zero.) For instance, the terms of

$$2x^3 - 3xy^2 + 5x^2y^2 + xy - 7$$

have the following degrees:

$2x^3$	is of degree 3
$-3xy^2 = -3x^1y^2$	is of degree $1 + 2 = 3$
$5x^2y^2$	is of degree $2 + 2 = 4$
$xy = x^1y^1$	is of degree $1 + 1 = 2$
-7	is of degree 0 and is often called the **constant term**

The **degree of a polynomial** is the degree of the term with nonzero coefficient that has the highest degree in the polynomial. The polynomial

$$2x^3 - 3xy^2 + 5x^2y^2 + xy - 7$$

is of degree 4 since the term of highest degree, $5x^2y^2$, is of degree 4.

Example 5   Degree of a Polynomial and Its Terms

Find the degree of each term and of the polynomial.

$$4x^5 - 2x^3y + x^2y^2 - 3$$

Solution

$4x^5$	degree 5
$-2x^3y$	degree 4 (since $3 + 1 = 4$)
x^2y^2	degree 4 (since $2 + 2 = 4$)
-3	degree 0

Degree of the polynomial = 5 (degree of highest-degree term)

✔ **Progress Check 5**

Find the degree of each term and of the polynomial $2x^6y - x^3y^2 + 7xy^2 - 12$.

Answers

Degree of each term, in sequence: 7, 5, 3, 0; degree of the polynomial: 7

Applications of Polynomials

Many problems lead to algebraic expressions that are polynomials. We will now look at several simple examples; many others will occur later throughout the book.

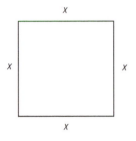

Figure 1 Diagram for Example 6

Example 6 Polynomials for Area and Perimeter

Find polynomials given the perimeter of the square and the area of the square shown in Figure 1.

Solution

Each side is of length x. The polynomial $4x$ gives the perimeter of the square. The polynomial x^2 gives the area of the square.

✔ **Progress Check 6**

Consider the rectangle in Figure 2, whose sides are x and y.

(a) Write the polynomial representing the perimeter of the rectangle.

(b) Write the polynomial representing the area of the rectangle.

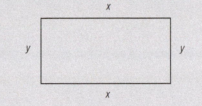

Figure 2 Diagram for Progress Check 6

Answers

(a) $2x + 2y$ (b) xy

Example 7 A Polynomial Expression for Total Cost

A grocery bag contains x apples, each costing 12 cents, and y pears, each costing 10 cents. What does the polynomial $12x + 10y$ represent?

Solution

The term $12x$ gives the total cost (in cents) of the apples in the bag and the term $10y$ gives the total cost (in cents) of the pears in the bag. Thus, the polynomial $12x + 10y$ represents the total cost of the contents of the grocery bag.

✔ **Progress Check 7**

If a car travels at the rate of r miles per hour for t hours, what does the polynomial rt represent?

Answer

the distance traveled in t hours

Exercise Set 4.1

In Exercises 1–8 identify the base(s) and exponent(s) in each expression.

1. 2^5

2. $(-2)^4$

3. t^4

4. w^6

5. $3y^5$

6. $-2t^3$

7. $3x^2y^3$

8. $-4u^3v^4$

In Exercises 9–14 write the given expression using exponents.

9. $3 \cdot 3 \cdot 3$

10. $(-5)(-5)(-5)(-5)$

11. $\left(\frac{1}{3}\right)\left(\frac{1}{3}\right)\left(\frac{1}{3}\right)\left(\frac{1}{3}\right)$

12. $x \cdot x \cdot x \cdot x \cdot x \cdot x$

13. $3 \cdot y \cdot y \cdot y \cdot y$

14. $-2 \cdot \frac{1}{p} \cdot \frac{1}{p} \cdot \frac{1}{p}$

In Exercises 15–16 evaluate each expression when $x = 3$ and $y = -2$.

15. (a) $(-xy)^2$ (b) $-(xy)^2$

16. (a) $-\left(\frac{x}{y}\right)^2$ (b) $\left(-\frac{x}{y}\right)^2$

In Exercises 17–26 carry out the indicated operations.

17. $b^5 \cdot b^2$

18. $x^3 \cdot x^5$

19. $(3x^2)(2x^4)$

20. $(6x^3)(5x)$

21. $(4y^3)(-5y^6)$

22. $(-6x^4)(-4x^7)$

23. $\left(\frac{4}{3}v^3\right)\left(\frac{5}{7}v^5\right)$

24. $\left(\frac{4}{3}w^2\right)\left(\frac{5}{2}w^4\right)$

25. $\left(\frac{3}{2}x^3\right)(-2x)$

26. $\left(-\frac{5}{3}x^6\right)\left(-\frac{3}{10}x^3\right)$

27. Which of the following expressions are not polynomials?

(a) $-3x^2 + 2x + 5$ (b) $-3x^2y$
(c) $-3x^{2/3} + 2xy + 5$ (d) $-2x^{-4} + 2xy^3 + 5$

28. Which of the following expressions are not polynomials?

(a) $4x^5 - x^{1/2} + 6$ (b) $\frac{2}{5}x^3 + \frac{4}{3}x - 2$
(c) $4x^5y$ (d) $x^{4/3}y + 2x - 3$

In Exercises 29–34 give the terms and coefficients for each given polynomial.

29. $4x^4 - 2x^2 + x - 3$

30. $\frac{1}{3}x^2 + 2x - 5$

31. $\frac{2}{3}x^3y + \frac{1}{2}xy - y + 2$

32. $2.5x^3y - 3xy^2 + 4x^2 + 8$

33. $\frac{1}{3}x^3 + \frac{1}{2}x^2y - 2x + y + 7$

34. $-4x^4 + 3x^3y - y^3 + 12$

In Exercises 35–40 find the degree of each term in the given polynomial.

35. $3x^3 - 2x^2 + 3$

36. $4x^2 + 2x - y + 3$

37. $4x^4 - 5x^3 + 2x^2 - 5x + 1$

38. $5x^5 + 2x^2y^2 + xy^3 + 3y$

39. $\frac{3}{2}x^4 + 2xy^2 + y^3 - y + 2$

40. $3x^8 - 3y^5 + 4x + 2$

In Exercises 41–46 find the degree of each of the given polynomials.

41. $2x^3 + 3x^2 - 5$ 42. $4x^5 - 8x^3 + x + 5$

43. $3x^2y + 2x^2 - y^2 + 2$ 44. $4xy^3 + xy^2 + 4y^2 - y$

45. $\frac{3}{5}x^4 + 2x^2 - x^2y + 4$ 46. $4x^5y^2 + x^3y - 2xy^2 + 7$

47. The degree of the polynomial $\frac{3}{5}x^4 + 2x^2 + 3x - 2$ is

(a) $\frac{3}{5}$ (b) 4   (c) 1   (d) none of these

48. The degree of the polynomial $-2x^3y + y^3 + x^2 + 3$ is

(a) -2 (b) 3   (c) 4   (d) none of these

49. Find the value of the polynomial $2x^2 - 2x + 1$ when $x = 3$.

50. Find the value of the polynomial $2x^3 + x^2 - x + 4$ when $x = -2$.

51. Find the value of the polynomial $3x^2y^2 + 2xy - x + 2y + 7$ when $x = 2, y = -1$.

52. Find the value of the polynomial $0.02x^2 + 0.3x - 0.5$ when $x = 0.3$.

53. Find the value of the polynomial $2.1x^3 + 3.3x^2 - 4.1x - 7.2$ when $x = 4.1$.

54. Find the value of the polynomial $0.3x^2y^2 - 0.5xy + 0.4x - 0.6y + 0.8$ when $x = 0.4, y = 0.25$.

*55. Write a polynomial giving the area of a circle of radius r.

*56. Write a polynomial giving the area of a triangle of base b and height h.

*57. Figure 3 shows a field consisting of a rectangle and a square. What does each of the following polynomials represent?

(a) $x^2 + xy$ (b) $2x + 2y$ (c) $4x$ (d) $4x + 2y$

Figure 3   Diagram for Exercise 57

*58. An investor buys x shares of G.E. stock at $55 per share, y shares of Exxon stock at $45 per share, and z shares of A.T.&T. stock at $20 per share. What does the polynomial $55x + 45y + 20z$ represent?

*59. Show that

$$-(ab)^2 = -\left| ab \right|^2 \text{ and } (-ab)^2 = \left| ab \right|^2$$

60. Store the value -3 as x in your graphing calculator. Do you think the value of the polynomial $x^5 + 3x^4 + x^3 + 2x^2 + 3$ will be positive, negative, or zero when $x = -3$? Enter the polynomial and see if you were correct.

4.2   Addition and Subtraction of Polynomials

Those terms of a polynomial that differ only in their coefficients are called **like terms**. Here are some examples of like terms:

$$
\begin{array}{ccc}
4x^2 & \text{and} & -3x^2 \\
-5xy^3 & \text{and} & 17xy^3 \\
2x^2y^2 & \text{and} & -2x^2y^2
\end{array}
$$

Once again, the distributive property makes it easy to add like terms. For example,

$$-5xy^3 + 17xy^3 = (-5 + 17)xy^3 = 12xy^3$$

This leads to a simple rule for the addition of polynomials.

> To add polynomials, combine like terms by adding their coefficients.

It is often helpful to regroup the terms before adding. For example,

$$x^2 \text{ terms} \quad x \text{ terms} \quad \text{constant terms}$$

$$(3x^2 - 2x + 5) + (x^2 + 4x - 9)$$

$$= 3x^2 + x^2 - 2x + 4x + 5 - 9$$

$$= 4x^2 + 2x - 4$$

Example 1   Addition of Polynomials

Add.

(a) $4x^2 - 3xy + 2y^2$ and $2x^2 - xy - y^2$

(b) $x^2 - 2x^2 + 6x$, $x^2 - 4$, and $2x^3 - x + 6$

Solution

(a) Grouping like terms and then adding, we see that

$$4x^2 + 2x^2 - 3xy - xy + 2y^2 - y^2 = 6x^2 - 4xy + y^2$$

(b) Grouping like terms and then adding, we have

$$x^3 + 2x^3 - 2x^2 + x^2 + 6x - x - 4 + 6 = 3x^3 - x^2 + 5x + 2$$

✔ Progress Check 1

Simplify by combining like terms.

(a) $2x^2 + x - 3 + 4x^2 - 5x - 8$

(b) $-2x^3 + 2x^2y^2 - 4y^2 + 4x^3 + 2y^2 + xy - 7$

Answers

(a) $6x^2 - 4x - 11$ (b) $2x^2 + 2x^2y^2 - 2y^2 + xy - 7$

Sometimes we must remove parentheses before we can combine terms. Again, the key is the distributive property. For example,

$$2(x - 3y) - 3(2x + 4y)$$
$$= 2x - 6y - 6x - 12y \qquad \text{Distributive property}$$
$$= -4x - 18y \qquad \text{Combine like terms}$$

The same idea permits us to subtract polynomials. For example, to subtract $x^2 - 3x + 1$ from $3x^2 - x - 5$, we have

$$(3x^2 - x - 5) - (x^2 - 3x + 1)$$
$$= 3x^2 - x - 5 - x^2 + 3x - 1$$
$$= 2x^2 + 2x - 6$$

Warning

Don't write

$$(x + 5) - (x + 2) = x + 5 - x + 2 = 7$$

The coefficient -1 in front of $(x + 2)$ is understood (but not written) and must be multiplied by each term in the parentheses:

$$(x + 5) - (x + 2) = x + 5 - x - 2 = 3$$

Example 2   Simplifying Expressions with Polynomials

Simplify.

(a) $3(x^2 - 2xy + \frac{1}{3}y^2) - 2(2y^2 + x^2 - \frac{1}{2}xy)$ (b) $2x(x - 5) + 4(x - 3)$

Solution

(a) $3(x^2 - 2xy + \frac{1}{3}y^2) - 2(2y^2 + x^2 - \frac{1}{2}xy)$

$= 3x^2 - 6xy + y^2 - 4y^2 - 2x^2 + xy$

$= 3x^2 - 2x^2 - 6xy + xy + y^2 - 4y^2$

$= x^2 - 5xy - 3y^2$

(b) $2x(x - 5) + 4(x - 3)$

$= 2x^2 - 10x + 4x - 12$

$= 2x^2 - 6x - 12$

✔ **Progress Check 2**

Simplify.

(a) $6(r^2 + 2rs - 1) - 4(-rs - 2 + 2r^2)$

(b) $4\left(\frac{1}{2}x^2 + \frac{1}{4}x + 1\right) + 5\left(2x^2 - \frac{2}{5}x - 1\right)$

Answers

(a) $-2r^2 + 16rs + 2$ (b) $12x^2 - x - 1$

Exercise Set 4.2

In Exercises 1–11 add the given polynomials.

1. $5x; 2x$

2. $5y; -3y$

3. $3x^3; -6x^2$

4. $-3x^2; -5x^2$

5. $x^2 - 3x + 1; 3x^2 + 2x + 3$

6. $2x^2 + \frac{5}{2}x + 2; -3x^2 - \frac{5}{3}x + 7$

7. $2x^3 + 2x^2 - x + 1; -2x^3 + 5x^2 + x + 2$

8. $3xy; 4xy$

9. $2rs; -5rs$

10. $2x^2y^2 - xy + 2x + 3y + 3; x^2y^2 + 3xy + 2x + 7$

11. $\frac{2}{5}rs^3 + 4r^2s^2 + 2r^2 + 2; \frac{4}{5}rs^3 - 6r^2s^2 - r^2s + 5$

In Exercises 12–15 find the mistake(s) in each statement. Obtain the correct answer.

12. $(x + 3) - (x + 5) = 8$

13. $(x^2 + 2x + 4) - 2(x^2 + 3x - 5) = -x^2 + 5x - 1$

14. $(x^2y^2 + 2x^2 + y) - (3x^2y^2 + x^2 - y + 2) =$
     $-x^2y^2 + x^2 - 2$

15. $(y^2 + xy + y) - 2(x^2 + xy - 3y) = y^2 - 2x^2 - xy - 2y$

In Exercises 16–25 subtract the second polynomial from the first.

16. $8x; 3x$

17. $18y; -6y$

18. $3x^2; 4x^2$

19. $3x^2 + 2x - 5; -3x^2 + 2x - 2$

20. $\frac{3}{2}x^3 + 2x^2 + 5; \frac{5}{2}x^3 - x^2 - \frac{1}{2}x + 3$

21. $3x^2y^2 + 2xy - y; 2x^2y^2 - xy + x + 2y + 3$

22. $4x^2 + 2x - 5; 3x^2 - 3x + 5$

23. $\frac{5}{2}x^3 - 2x^2 + x - 2; \frac{3}{5}x^3 + x^2 - 4$

24. $2xy^2 + xy + x - 3; 2x^2y - xy^2 + y + x - 2$

25. $3rs^3 - 2rs^2 + rs + 3; -2rs^2 + 3rs - r + s$

In Exercises 26–35 simplify by combining like terms.

26. $(4x^2 + 3x + 2) + (3x^2 - 2x - 5)$

27. $5x^2 + 2x + 7 - 3x^2 - 8x + 2$

28. $(2x^2 + 3x + 8) - (5 - 2x + 2x^2)$

29. $3xy + 2x + 3y + 2 + (1 - y - 2x + xy)$

30. $4xy^2 + 2xy + 2x + 3 - (-2xy^2 + xy - y + 2)$

31. $(3r^2s^2 + rs^2 - rs + r) + (2r^2s^2 - r^2s + s + 1)$

32. $3a^2b - ba^2 + 2a - b + 2a^2b - 3ba^2 + b + 1$

33. $(2s^2t^3 - st^2 + st - s + t) - (3s^2t^2 - 2s^2t - 4st^2 - t + 3)$

34. $3xy^2z - 4x^2yz + xy + 3 - (2xy^2z + x^2yz - yz + x - 2)$

35. $a^2bc + ab^2c + 2ab^3 - 3a^2bc - 4ab^3 + 3$

36. On Monday morning an investor buys x shares of Honeywell stock at $60 per share and y shares of Sears stock at $50 per share. On Monday afternoon the same investor buys x shares of G.E. stock at $55 per share and y shares of Bethlehem Steel stock at $20 per share. Write polynomials to answer the following questions:

 (a) How much money was invested during the morning transactions?
 (b) How much money was invested during the afternoon transactions?
 (c) How much money was invested by the end of Monday?

37. At Thursday's opening of the stock market, an investor buys x shares of I.B.M. stock at $110 per share. Later in the day, he sells y shares of Kindercare stock at $13 per share and z shares of Lotus stock at $17 per share. Write a polynomial that expresses the net of his transactions for the day.

38. To obtain a mat for a painting, an artist takes a rectangular piece of cardboard with sides x and y and cuts out a square of side $x/2$ (see Figure 4). Write a polynomial giving the area of the mat; that is, what is the area of the remaining figure?

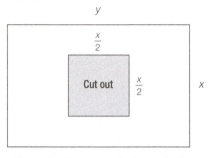

Figure 4   Diagram for Exercise 38

*39. The polynomial all of whose coefficients are zero is called the **zero polynomial** and is denoted by O. By use of an example, show that if P is a polynomial of degree n, then

$$P + O = O + P = P$$

*40. Let P be a polynomial and let $-P$ be the polynomial obtained from P by negating the sign of the coefficient of each term in P. By use of an example, show that

$$P + (-P) = O$$

where O is the zero polynomial (see Exercise 39).

4.3   Multiplication of Polynomials

We have already dealt with multiplication of some simple polynomial forms such as

$$3x^2 \cdot x^4 = 3x^6$$

and

$$2x(x + 4) = 2x^2 + 8x$$

By using the rule for exponents

$$a^m \cdot a^n = a^{m+n}$$

and the distributive properties

$$a(b + c) = ab + ac$$
$$(a + b)c = ac + bc$$

we can handle the product of any two polynomials.

Example 1 Multiplying Polynomials
Multiply.

(a) $3x^3(2x^3 - 6x^2 + 5)$ (b) $-x^2y(x^3 - 4xy^2 + 6y^3)$

Solution

(a) $3x^3(2x^3 - 6x^2 + 5)$

$= (3x^3)(2x^3) + (3x^3)(-6x^2) + (3x^3)(5)$

$= (3 \cdot 2)x^{3+3} + 3(-6)x^{3+2} + 3 \cdot 5x^3$

$= 6x^6 - 18x^5 + 15x^3$

(b) $-x^2y(x^3 - 4xy^2 + 6y^3)$

$= (-x^2y)(x^3) + (-x^2y)(-4xy^2) + (-x^2y)(6y^3)$

$= -x^5y + 4x^3y^3 - 6x^2y^4$

✔ Progress Check 1
Multiply.

(a) $2x^2\left(\dfrac{1}{2}x^2 - 3x - 4\right)$ (b) $-xy(x^2 - 2x^2y - 3xy^2)$

Answers

(a) $x^4 - 6x^3 - 8x^2$ (b) $-x^3y + 2x^3y^2 + 3x^2y^3$

Let's try to find the product

$$(x + 2)(3x^2 - x + 5)$$

The key here is to "rename" terms and groups of terms to fit into the alternate form of the distributive property $(a + b)c = ac + bc$. Here is how we can do it.

$$(x + 2)(3x^2 - x + 5) = x(3x^2 - x + 5) + 2(3x^2 - x + 5)$$

$(a + b) \quad c \qquad = \qquad ac \qquad + \qquad bc$

$$= 3x^3 - x^2 + 5x + 6x^2 - 2x + 10$$
$$= 3x^3 + 5x^2 + 3x + 10$$

In general, we can multiply two polynomials by multiplying one polynomial by each term of the other polynomial and adding the resulting products.

Example 2 Multiplying Polynomials
Multiply.

(a) $(3x - 2)(x + 4)$ (b) $(2x - 3)(-4x^2 + x + 5)$

Solution

(a) $(3x - 2)(x + 4)$

$\quad = 3x(x + 4) - 2(x + 4)$

$\quad = 3x^2 + 12x - 2x - 8$

$\quad = 3x^2 + 10x - 8$

(b) $(2x - 3)(-4x^2 + x + 5)$

$\quad = 2x(-4x^2 + x + 5) - 3(-4x^2 + x + 5)$

$\quad = -8x^3 + 2x^2 + 10x + 12x^2 - 3x - 15$

$\quad = -8x^3 + 2x^2 + 12x^2 + 10x - 3x - 15$

$\quad = -8x^3 + 14x^2 + 7x - 15$

✔ Progress Check 2

Multiply.

(a) $(3x - 1)(x - 3)$ (b) $(x^2 + 2)(x^2 - 3x + 1)$

Answers

(a) $3x^2 - 10x + 3$ (b) $x^4 - 3x^3 + 3x^2 - 6x + 2$

Long Form

The work done in multiplying polynomials can be arranged in a "long multiplication" format. Here is an example.

Example 3   **"Long Multiplication" Form**

Find the product of $2x - 3$ and $-4x^2 + x + 5$.

Solution

We arrange the work as follows:

$$-4x^2 + x + 5$$

$$\underline{\, 2x - 3}$$

$$-8x^3 + 2x^2 + 10x \qquad = 2x(-4x^2 + x + 5)$$

$$\underline{\, 12x^2 - 3x - 15} \qquad = -3(-4x^2 + x + 5)$$

$$-8x^3 + 14x^2 + 7x - 15$$

✔ Progress Check 3

Repeat Progress Check 2(b) using long multiplication.

Mental Multiplication

Products of the form $(2x + 3)(5x - 2)$ are so important that we must learn to handle them mentally. Let's work through this problem:

$$(2x + 3)(5x - 2) = 2x(5x - 2) + 3(5x - 2)$$
$$= (2x)(5x) + 2x(-2) + 3(5x) + 3(-2)$$
$$= 10x^2 - 4x + 15x - 6$$

We have stopped just short of the last step because we want to show the relationships between the factors and the products. If we take the product of the first term of each expression

$$(2x + 3)(5x - 2)$$
$$10x^2$$

we have the term containing x^2. Similarly, taking the product of the last term of each expression

$$(2x + 3)(5x - 2)$$
$$-6$$

we have the constant term. The term containing x can be found by adding the product of the "inners" and the product of the "outers":

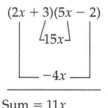

$$(2x + 3)(5x - 2)$$
$$15x$$
$$-4x$$
$$\text{Sum} = 11x$$

Thus, $(2x + 3)(5x - 2) = 10x^2 + 11x - 6$.

Example 4   Mental Multiplication
Multiply.

(a) $(x - 1)(2x + 3)$ (b) $(2x + 2)(2x - 2)$

Solution
(a) We diagram the process so that you can learn to do these mentally.

$$(x - 1)(2x + 3) \qquad (x - 1)(2x + 3) \qquad (x - 1)(2x + 3)$$
$$2x^2 \qquad\qquad \begin{matrix}-2x \\ 3x\end{matrix} \qquad\qquad -3$$
$$\text{Sum} = +x$$

Thus, $(x - 1)(2x + 3) = 2x^2 + x - 3$.

(b) Once more, we have

$$(2x + 2)(2x - 2)$$
$$\underbrace{\qquad}$$
$$4x^2$$

$$(2x + 2)(2x - 2)$$
$$\overbrace{\qquad}$$
$$4x$$
$$-4x$$
$$\text{Sum} = + 0x$$

$$(2x + 2)(2x - 2)$$
$$\overbrace{\qquad}$$
$$-4$$

Thus, $(2x + 2)(2x - 2) = 4x^2 - 4$.

✔ Progress Check 4

Multiply mentally.

(a) $(x + 2)(x + 1)$ 　　　　 (b) $(t - 2)(2t + 3)$

(c) $(2x - 3)(3x - 2)$ 　　　 (d) $(3x + 2)(3x - 2)$

Answers

(a) $x^2 + 3x + 2$ 　 (b) $2t^2 - t - 6$ 　 (c) $6x^2 - 13x + 6$ 　 (d) $9x^2 - 4$

In Examples 2 and 3, the product of polynomials of degrees one and two is seen to be a polynomial of degree three. From the multiplication process it is easy to derive the following useful rule.

Degree of a Product

> The degree of the product of two nonzero polynomials is the sum of the degrees of the polynomials.

Special Forms

Here are three forms that occur frequently and are worthy of special attention.

$$(x + y)^2 = (x + y)(x + y) = x^2 + 2xy + y^2$$
$$(x - y)^2 = (x - y)(x - y) = x^2 - 2xy + y^2$$
$$(x + y)(x - y) = x^2 - y^2$$

Example 5   Multiplying with Special Forms

Multiply mentally.

(a) $(x + 2)^2$ 　　 (b) $(x - 3)^2$ 　　 (c) $(x + 4)(x - 4)$

Solution

(a) $(x + 2)^2 = (x + 2)(x + 2) = x^2 + 4x + 4$

(b) $(x - 3)^2 = (x - 3)(x - 3) = x^2 - 6x + 9$

(c) $(x + 4)(x - 4) = x^2 - 16$

✔ **Progress Check 5**
Multiply mentally.

(a) $(x-4)^2$

(b) $(x+1)^2$

(c) $(2x-3)^2$

(d) $(2x+3)(2x-3)$

Answers

(a) $x^2-8x+16$

(b) x^2+2x+1

(c) $4x^2-12x+9$

(d) $4x^2-9$

Exercise Set 4.3

In Exercises 1–16 perform the indicated multiplication.

1. $(2x^3)(3x^2)$
2. $(6x^2)(-5x^4)$
3. $(3ab^2)(2ab)$
4. $(-3s^2t)(4s)$
5. $2x(x^2+3x-5)$
6. $6x^2(2x^3-2x^2+5)$
7. $-2s^3(2st^2-2st+6)$
8. $a^3(-3a^2-a+2)$
9. $4a^2b^2(2a^2+ab-b^2)$
10. $4y(2y^3-3y+3)$
11. $(x+2)(x-3)$
12. $(x-1)(x+4)$
13. $(y+5)(y+2)$
14. $(a-3)(a-4)$
15. $(x+3)^2$
16. $(y-2)(y-2)$

In Exercises 17–30 perform the indicated multiplication mentally.

17. $(s+3)(s-3)$
18. $(t+6)(t-6)$
19. $(3x+2)(x-1)$
20. $(2x-3)(x+1)$
21. $(a-2)(2a+5)$
22. $(a+3)(3a-2)$
23. $(2y+3)(3y+2)$
24. $(3x-2)(2x+3)$
25. $(2a+3)(2a+3)$
26. $(3x+2)(3x+2)$
27. $(2y+5)(2y-5)$
28. $(4t+3)(4t-3)$
29. $(3x-4)(3x+4)$
30. $(5b-2)(5b+2)$

In Exercises 31–54 perform the indicated multiplication. Use long multiplication where convenient.

31. $(x^2+2)(x^2+2)$
32. $(y^2-3)(y^2-3)$
33. $(x^2-2)(x^2+2)$
34. $(2x^2-5)(2x^2+5)$
35. $(x+1)(x^2+2x-3)$
36. $(x-2)(2x^3+x-2)$
37. $(2s-3)(s^3-s+2)$
38. $(-3s+2)(-2s^2-s+3)$
39. $(a+2)(3a^2-a+5)$
40. $(b+3)(-3b^2+2b+4)$
41. $(x^2+3)(2x^2-x+2)$
42. $(2y^2+y)(-2y^3+y-3)$
43. $(x^2+2x-1)(2x^2-3x+2)$
44. $(a^2-4a+3)(4a^3+2a+5)$
45. $(3x^2-2x+2)(2x^3-4x+2)$
46. $(-3y^3+3y-4)(2y^2-2y+3)$
47. $(2a^2+ab+b^2)(3a-b^2+1)$
48. $(-3a+ab+b^2)(3b^2+2b+2)$
49. $5(2x-3)^2$
50. $2(3x-2)(2x+3)$
51. $x(2x-1)(x+2)$
52. $3x(2x+1)^2$
53. $(x-1)(x+2)(x+3)$
54. $(3x+1)(2x-4)(3x+2)$
55. In the product $(x-1)(x^2-2x+3)$ give the coefficient of
    (a) x^2 (b) x
56. In the product $(3x-2)(2x^2+3x-4)$ give the coefficient of
    (a) x^2 (b) x
57. In the product $(x^2-2x+1)^2$ give the coefficient of
    (a) x^4 (b) x^2
58. In the product $(x^2-2x+3)(x^2-3x-5)$ give the coefficient of
    (a) x^3 (b) x^2

In Exercises 59–66 simplify the expression.

59. $3x(yx^2+xy)+xy(x^2-x)$
60. $(x-y)(x+y)-x(x+y)$

61. $(x - 1)(x + 3) - x^2$

62. $(2x - 1)(3x + 2) - (x - 2)(x + 3)$

63. $2x(x - 3) - 4(x^2 - 4)$ 64. $x(-x - 3) + (-x + 4)^2$

65. $(x + 4)(x - 4) - (x - 2)^2$ 66. $(x - 2)^2 - x(x - 1)$

67. When a polynomial of degree 3 is multiplied by a polynomial of degree 4, the degree of the product is

(a) 12   (b) 1   (c) 7   (d) $\dfrac{4}{3}$

68. When a polynomial of degree 6 is multiplied by a polynomial of degree 3, the degree of the product is

(a) 18   (b) 3   (c) 2   (d) 9
(e) none of these

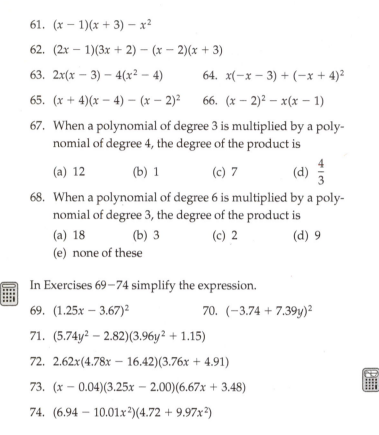

In Exercises 69–74 simplify the expression.

69. $(1.25x - 3.67)^2$ 70. $(-3.74 + 7.39y)^2$

71. $(5.74y^2 - 2.82)(3.96y^2 + 1.15)$

72. $2.62x(4.78x - 16.42)(3.76x + 4.91)$

73. $(x - 0.04)(3.25x - 2.00)(6.67x + 3.48)$

74. $(6.94 - 10.01x^2)(4.72 + 9.97x^2)$

*75. If P and Q are nonzero polynomials, can their product be the zero polynomial?

In Exercises 76–78 give a counterexample that disproves each statement.

*76. $(a + b)^2 = a^2 + b^2$

*77. $(a + b)(a^2 + b^2) = a^3 + b^3$

*78. $(a + b)(a^2 + b^2) = (a + b)^3$

79. Construct a polynomial expression to model the situation described in the chapter opener. A square piece of cardboard measuring 60 inches on each side is made into a rectangular box by cutting identical squares from the four corners, then folding up the flaps. Let x represent the length of the side of each discarded square. Write an expression for the length, width, and height of the open-top box. Now multiply these binomials together to get a cubic polynomial in standard form. This polynomial represents the volume of the box.

80. Evaluate the polynomial you found in Exercise 79 using your graphing calculator by selecting various values of x and storing them, as you did in Exercise 60 in section 4.1. For what value of x does the volume seem to be largest? Would a package designed this way satisfy the postal requirements discussed in the chapter opener?

4.4 Factoring

Now that we can find the product of two polynomials, let's consider the reverse problem: Given a polynomial, can we find factors whose product will yield the given polynomial? This process is known as **factoring**. We will approach factoring by learning to recognize the situations in which factoring is possible.

Common Factors

Look at the polynomial

$$x^2 + x$$

Is there some factor common to *both* terms? Yes—each term contains the variable x. If we remove x and write

$$x^2 + x = x(\ \ +\ \ )$$

we can see that we must have

$$x^2 + x = x(x + 1)$$

Example 1   Removing Common Factors

Factor.

(a) $15x^3 - 10x^2$ (b) $4x^2y - 8xy^2 + 6xy$

Solution

(a) Both 5 and x^2 are common to *both* terms.

$$15x^3 - 10x^2 = 5x^2(3x - 2)$$

(b) Here, we see that 2, x, and y are common to all three terms.

$$4x^2y - 8xy^2 + 6xy = 2xy(2x - 4y + 3)$$

✔ **Progress Check 1**

Factor.

(a) $4x^2 - x$ (b) $3x^4 - 9x^2$

Answers

(a) $x(4x - 1)$ (b) $3x^2(x^2 - 3)$

Example 2   Removing Common Factors

Factor.

(a) $2ab - 8bc$ (b) $2x(x + y) - 5y(x + y)$

Solution

(a) We see that both 2 and b are found in each term. Don't be misled by the position of b to the right of the first term and to the left in the second term. Remember, multiplication is commutative!

$$2ab - 8bc = 2b(a - 4c)$$

(b) Here, $(x + y)$ is found in both terms. Factoring, we have

$$2x(\underbrace{x + y}) - 5y(\underbrace{x + y}) = (x + y)(2x - 5y)$$
$$\text{common factor}$$

✔ **Progress Check 2**

Factor.

(a) $3r^2t - 15t^2u + 6st^3$ (b) $3m(2x - 3y) - n(2x - 3y)$

Answers

(a) $3t(r^2 - 5tu + 2st^2)$ (b) $(2x - 3y)(3m - n)$

Factoring by Grouping

It is sometimes possible to discover common factors by first grouping terms. The best way to learn the method is by studying some examples.

Example 3   Factoring by Grouping

Factor.

(a) $2ab + b + 2ac + c$ (b) $2x - 4x^2y - 3y + 6xy^2$

Solution

(a) Begin by grouping those terms containing b and those terms containing c.

$$2ab + b + 2ac + c = (2ab + b) + (2ac + c) \qquad \text{Grouping}$$
$$= b(2a + 1) + c(2a + 1) \qquad \text{Factoring out } b \text{ and } c$$
$$= (2a + 1)(b + c) \qquad \text{Factoring out } 2a + 1$$

(b) $2x - 4x^2y - 3y + 6xy^2$
$$= (2x - 4x^2y) + (-3y + 6xy^2) \qquad \text{Grouping}$$
$$= 2x(1 - 2xy) + (-3y)(1 - 2xy) \qquad \text{Factoring out } 2x \text{ and } -3y$$
$$= (1 - 2xy)(2x - 3y) \qquad \text{Factoring out } 1 - 2xy$$

✔ **Progress Check 3**

Factor.

(a) $2m^3n + m^2 + 2mn^2 + n$ (b) $2a^2 - 4ab^2 - ab + 2b^3$

Answers

(a) $(2mn + 1)(m^2 + n)$ (b) $(a - 2b^2)(2a - b)$

Factoring Second-Degree Polynomials

Another type of factoring involves second-degree polynomials. We now know that

$$(x + 2)(x + 3) = x^2 + 5x + 6$$

and can do the multiplication mentally. We will need these mental gymnastics to allow us to reverse the process.

Let's look at

$$x^2 + 5x + 6$$

and think of this in the form

$$x^2 + 5x + 6 = (\qquad)(\qquad)$$

If we restrict ourselves to positive integer coefficients, then the term x^2 can only have come from $x \cdot x$, so we can write

$$x^2 + 5x + 6 = (x \qquad)(x \qquad)$$

The constant 6 can be the product of either two positive numbers or two negative numbers. (If we choose one positive factor and one negative factor, we can't produce a positive product.) But the middle term is positive and results from adding two terms. Then the signs must both be positive.

$$x^2 + 5x + 6 = (x + \quad)(x + \quad)$$

Finally, the number 6 can be written as the product of two positive integers in just two ways:

$$1 \cdot 6 \quad \text{or} \quad 2 \cdot 3$$

The factors of 6 whose sum is 5 are 2 and 3, so that

$$x^2 + 5x + 6 = (x + 2)(x + 3)$$

Example 4   Factoring a Second-Degree Polynomial

Factor.

(a) $x^2 - 7x + 10$ (b) $x^2 - 3x - 4$

Solution

(a) Since the constant term is positive and the middle term is negative, we must have

$$x^2 - 7x + 10 = (x - \quad)(x - \quad)$$

The possible positive integer factors of 10 are

$$1 \cdot 10 \quad \text{and} \quad 2 \cdot 5$$

The factors of 10 whose sum is 7 are 2 and 5, so that

$$x^2 - 7x + 10 = (x - 2)(x - 5)$$

(b) Since the constant term is negative, we must have

$$x^2 - 3x - 4 = (x + \quad)(x - \quad)$$

The positive integer factors of 4 are

$$1 \cdot 4 \quad \text{and} \quad 2 \cdot 2$$

The factors of 4 whose difference is 3 are 1 and 4. Associating 4 with the negative sign, we have

$$x^2 - 3x - 4 = (x + 1)(x - 4)$$

✔ Progress Check 4

Factor.

(a) $x^2 - 11x + 24$ (b) $x^2 + 6x + 9$ (c) $x^2 - 2x - 8$

Answers

(a) $(x - 3)(x - 8)$ (b) $(x + 3)(x + 3)$ (c) $(x + 2)(x - 4)$

Irreducible Polynomial

Before you get the impression that every second-degree polynomial with integer coefficients can be factored as a product of polynomials of lower degree with integer coefficients, try your hand at factoring

$$x^2 + x + 1$$

There are no polynomials with integer coefficients that allow us to factor $x^2 + x + 1$. Such polynomials are said to be **irreducible** over the integers.

Leading Coefficient Other Than One

Now we will try something a bit more difficult, for example,

$$2x^2 - x - 6$$

When the coefficient of x^2 is a number other than 1, we can use the same approach but the number of possible combinations increases.

First, we see that $2x^2$ can only result from the factors $2x$ and x if we restrict ourselves to positive integer coefficients. Thus, we write

$$2x^2 - x - 6 = (2x\quad)(x\quad)$$

Since the constant term is negative, we must have

$$2x^2 - x - 6 = (2x +\quad)(x -\quad)$$

or

$$2x^2 - x - 6 = (2x -\quad)(x +\quad)$$

The possible positive integer factors of 6 are

$$1 \cdot 6 \quad \text{and} \quad 2 \cdot 3$$

We need factors of 6 such that the difference between one factor and two times the other factor is -1. We thus find that the correct factorization is

$$2x^2 - x - 6 = (2x + 3)(x - 2)$$

Example 5   Factoring a Second-Degree Polynomial

Factor.

(a) $3x^2 + 7x + 4$ (b) $6x^2 + 5x - 4$

Solution

(a) We start with

$$3x^2 + 7x + 4 = (3x +\quad)(x +\quad) \quad \text{(Why?)}$$

The possible positive integer factors of 4 are

$$1 \cdot 4 \quad 4 \cdot 1 \quad 2 \cdot 2$$

We need factors of 4 such that one factor plus three times the other is 7. Thus,

$$3x^2 + 7x + 4 = (3x + 4)(x + 1)$$

(b) The coefficient of x^2 is 6, and the only positive integer factors of 6 are

$$1 \cdot 6 \quad \text{and} \quad 2 \cdot 3$$

The factorization (if it exists) must look like one of the following:

$$6x^2 + 5x - 4 = (x - \quad)(6x + \quad)$$
$$6x^2 + 5x - 4 = (x + \quad)(6x - \quad)$$
$$6x^2 + 5x - 4 = (2x - \quad)(3x + \quad)$$
$$6x^2 + 5x - 4 = (2x + \quad)(3x - \quad)$$

We next turn to the positive integer factors of 4. The possible factors are

$$1 \cdot 4 \quad \text{and} \quad 2 \cdot 2$$

By trial and error, we see that the choice that produces $+5$ for the middle term is

$$6x^2 + 5x - 4 = (2x - 1)(3x + 4)$$

✔ Progress Check 5

Factor.

(a) $3x^2 - 16x + 21$ (b) $2x^2 + 3x - 9$ (c) $4x^2 + 12x + 5$

Answers

(a) $(3x - 7)(x - 3)$ (b) $(2x - 3)(x + 3)$ (c) $(2x + 1)(2x + 5)$

No-Fuss Factoring

If you found the trial and error approach used in Example 5 to be a bit tedious, we can offer you an alternative factoring method to use when the coefficient of x^2 is a number other than 1. The steps are outlined as follows:

Factoring $ax^2 + bx + c$	Example: $6x^2 + 5x - 6$
Step 1. Find two integers whose product is $a \cdot c$ and whose sum is b.	*Step 1.* $a \cdot c = (6)(-6) = -36$. Two integers whose product is -36 and sum is 5 are 9 and -4.
Step 2. Write the middle term bx in terms of these integers.	*Step 2.* $5x = 9x - 4x$ and $6x^2 + 5x - 6 = 6x^2 + (9x - 4x) - 6$
Step 3. Group.	*Step 3.* $= (6x^2 + 9x) - (4x + 6)$
Step 4. Remove the common factors in each group.	*Step 4.* $= 3x(2x + 3) - 2(2x + 3)$
Step 5. Factor out the common linear term.	*Step 5.* $= (2x + 3)(3x - 2)$

Example 6   Factoring by the No-Fuss Method

Factor $4x^2 + 11x + 6$ by the No-Fuss Method.

Solution

The product of the coefficients of the first and last terms is

$$(4)(6) = 24$$

Two integers whose product is 24 and whose sum is 11 (the coefficient of the first-degree term) are 3 and 8, that is,

$$11x = 3x + 8x$$

Then

$$4x^2 + 11x + 6 = 4x^2 + 3x + 8x + 6$$
$$= (4x^2 + 3x) + (8x + 6)$$
$$= x(4x + 3) + 2(4x + 3)$$
$$= (4x + 3)(x + 2)$$

✔ Progress Check 6

Factor $6x^2 + x - 2$ by the no-fuss method.

Answer

$(2x - 1)(3x + 2)$

Combining Methods

We conclude with problems that combine the various methods of factoring that we have studied. Here is a good rule to follow:

> Always remove common factors before attempting any other factoring techniques.

Example 7   Combining Methods of Factoring

Factor.

(a) $x^3 - 6x^2 + 8x$

(b) $2x^3 + 4x^2 - 30x$

(c) $3y(y + 3) + 2(y + 3)(y^2 - 1)$

Solution

(a) Following our rule, we first remove the common factor x:

$$x^3 - 6x^2 + 8x = x(x^2 - 6x + 8)$$
$$= x(x - 2)(x - 4)$$

(b) Removing $2x$ as a common factor, we have

$$2x^3 + 4x^2 - 30x = 2x(x^2 + 2x - 15)$$
$$= 2x(x - 3)(x + 5)$$

(c) Removing the common factor $y + 3$, we have

$$3y(y + 3) + 2(y + 3)(y^2 - 1) = (y + 3)[3y + 2(y^2 - 1)]$$
$$= (y + 3)(3y + 2y^2 - 2)$$
$$= (y + 3)(2y^2 + 3y - 2)$$
$$= (y + 3)(2y - 1)(y + 2)$$

common factor

✔ **Progress Check 7**

Factor.

(a) $x^3 + 5x^2 - 6x$ (b) $2x^3 - 2x^2y - 4xy^2$

(c) $-3x(x + 1) + (x + 1)(2x^2 + 1)$

Answers

(a) $x(x + 6)(x - 1)$ (b) $2x(x + y)(x - 2y)$ (c) $(x + 1)(2x - 1)(x - 1)$

Exercise Set 4.4

In Exercises 1–86 factor completely.

1. $2x + 6$
2. $5x - 15$
3. $3x - 9y$
4. $\frac{1}{2}x + \frac{1}{4}y$
5. $-2x - 8y$
6. $3x + 6y + 15$
7. $4x^2 + 8y - 6$
8. $3a + 4ab$
9. $5bc + 25b$
10. $2x^2 - x$
11. $y - 3y^3$
12. $2x^4 + x^2$
13. $-3y^2 - 4y^5$
14. $-\frac{1}{2}y^2 + \frac{1}{8}y^3$
15. $3abc + 12bc$
16. $3x^2 + 6x^2y - 9x^2z$
17. $5r^3s^4 - 40r^4s^3t$
18. $9a^3b^3 + 12a^2b - 15ab^2$
19. $8a^3b^5 - 12a^5b^2 + 16$
20. $7x^2y^3z^4 - 21x^4yz^5 + 49x^5y^2z^3$
21. $x^2 + 4x + 3$
22. $x^2 + 2x - 8$
23. $y^2 - 8y + 15$
24. $y^2 + 7y - 8$
25. $a^2 - 7ab + 12b^2$
26. $x^2 - 14x + 49$
27. $y^2 + 6y + 9$
28. $a^2 - 7a + 10$
29. $25 - 10x + x^2$
30. $4b^2 - a^2$
31. $x^2 - 5x - 14$
32. $x^2 - \frac{1}{9}$
33. $4 - y^2$
34. $a^2 + ab - 6b^2$
35. $x^2 - 6x + 9$
36. $a^2 - 4ab + 4b^2$
37. $x^2 - 12x + 20$
38. $x^2 - 8x - 20$
39. $x^2 + 11x + 24$
40. $y^2 + 4y + 3$
41. $2x^2 - 3x - 2$
42. $2x^2 + 7x + 6$

43. $3a^2 - 11a + 6$

44. $4x^2 - 9x + 2$

45. $6x^2 + 13x + 6$

46. $4y^2 + 4y - 3$

47. $8m^2 - 6m - 9$

48. $9x^2 + 24x + 16$

49. $10x^2 - 13x - 3$

50. $6a^2 + ab - 2b^2$

51. $6a^2 - 5ab - 6b^2$

52. $4x^2 + 20x + 25$

53. $10r^2s^2 + 9rst + 2t^2$

54. $16 - 24xy + 9x^2y^2$

55. $6 + 5x - 4x^2$

56. $8n^2 - 18n - 5$

57. $25r^2 + 4s^2$

58. $15 + 4x - 4x^2$

59. $2x^2 - 2x - 12$

60. $3y^2 + 6y - 45$

61. $30x^2 + 28x - 16$

62. $30x^2 - 35x + 10$

63. $12x^2b^2 + 2xb^2 - 24b^2$

64. $x^4y^4 + x^2$

65. $18x^2m + 33xm + 9m$

66. $8x^3 + 14x^2 - 15x$

67. $25m^2n^3 - 5m^2n$

68. $12x^2 - 22x^3 - 20x^4$

69. $xy + \dfrac{1}{4}x^3y^3$

70. $10r^2 - 5rs - 15s^2$

71. $x^4 + 2x^2y^2 + y^4$

72. $a^4 - 8a^2 + 16$

73. $b^4 + 2b^2 - 8$

74. $4b^4 + 20b^2 + 25$

75. $6b^4 + 7b^2 - 3$

76. $4(x + 1)(y + 2) - 8(y + 2)$

77. $2(x + 1)(x - 1) + 5(x - 1)$

78. $3(x + 2)^2(x - 1) - 4(x + 2)^2(2x + 7)$

79. $3xy - 6x + 3y - 6$

80. $2ac - bc + 2a - b$

81. $2x^3y - 3x^2 - 2xy^2 + 3y$

82. $4a^2 - 4b^2 - 3a^3b + 3ab^3$

83. $4(2x - 1)^2(x + 2)^3(x + 1) - 3(2x - 1)^5(x + 2)^2(x + 3)$

84. $5(x - 1)^2(y - 1)^3(x + 2) - (3x - 1)(x - 1)^3(y - 1)$

85. $(7 - 2x)^3(2)(5x)(5) + (5x)^2(3)(7 - 2x)^2(-2)$

86. $3(4x)^2(4)(7x - 2)^2 + (4x)^3(2)(7x - 2)(6)$

*87. Show that the polynomial $x^2 + 1$ cannot be written as the product $(x + r)(x + s)$, where r and s are integers.

*88. Show that the polynomial $x^2 + x + 1$ cannot be written as the product $(x + r)(x + s)$, where r and s are integers.

In Exercises 89–92 factor the given polynomial by the "no-fuss" factoring method.

*89. $2x^2 + 5x - 12$

*90. $4x^2 - 2x - 2$

*91. $6x^2 - 7x - 3$

*92. $6x^2 + 5x - 6$

93. Using your graphing calculator, you can check whether a polynomial has been factored correctly. Consider the following possible factorings:

(a) $x^5 + x^4 + 5x^3 - x^2 + 2x - 8 =$
$(x^2 + x - 2)(x^3 + 3x + 4)$

(b) $x^5 + x^4 + 5x^3 - x^2 + 2x - 8 =$
$(x^2 + x + 2)(x^3 + 3x - 4)$

Both equations are valid for $x = 1$. But what about $x = 7.523$? Try several values of x and determine which of the two is correct.

4.5   Special Factors

There is a special case of the second-degree polynomial that occurs frequently and factors easily. Given the polynomial $x^2 - 9$, we see that each term is a perfect square. You may easily verify that

$$x^2 - 9 = (x + 3)(x - 3)$$

In general, the following rule is one that works whenever we are dealing with a difference of two squares.

Difference of Two Squares

$$a^2 - b^2 = (a + b)(a - b)$$

Example 1   Factoring a Difference of Two Squares

Factor.

(a) $x^2 - 16$ (b) $4x^2 - 25$ (c) $9x^2 - 16y^2$

Solution

(a) $x^2 - 16 = (x + 4)(x - 4)$

(b) With $a = 2x$ and $b = 5$,
$$4x^2 - 25 = (2x + 5)(2x - 5)$$

(c) With $a = 3x$ and $b = 4y$,
$$9x^2 - 16y^2 = (3x + 4y)(3x - 4y)$$

✔ Progress Check 1

Factor.

(a) $x^2 - 49$ (b) $16x^2 - 9$ (c) $25x^2 - y^2$

Answers

(a) $(x + 7)(x - 7)$ (b) $(4x + 3)(4x - 3)$ (c) $(5x + y)(5x - y)$

Warning

Don't confuse a *difference* of two squares, such as $4x^2 - 9$, and a *sum* of two squares, such as $x^2 + 25$. In the case of a difference of two squares,

$$4x^2 - 9 = (2x + 3)(2x - 3)$$

But a sum of two squares such as $x^2 + 25$ cannot be factored.

The formulas for a sum of two cubes and a difference of two cubes can be verified by multiplying the factors on the right-hand sides of the following equations.

Sum and Difference of Two Cubes

$$a^3 + b^3 = (a + b)(a^2 - ab + b^2)$$
$$a^3 - b^3 = (a - b)(a^2 + ab + b^2)$$

These formulas provide a direct means for factoring a sum and a difference of two cubes and are used in the same way as the formula for a difference of two squares. Be careful as to the placement of plus and minus signs when using these formulas.

Greek Algebra

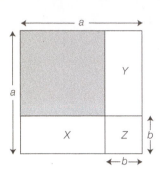

The Greek mathematicians of antiquity viewed algebra from a geometric perspective. They had no need for negative numbers since measurements of distance are positive values. From earliest times they recognized the need for (positive) rational numbers and believed that this number system was adequate for all their needs. When they discovered that the hypotenuse of a right triangle whose sides are 1 unit in length is *not* a rational number, they were forced to extend their concept of number to the (positive) real numbers. Modern mathematicians have introduced more sophisticated number systems for similar reasons: the need to represent solutions to problems.

An example of "Greek algebra" is illustrated in the accompanying figure. The Greeks used a geometric argument to establish the identity

$$(a - b)^2 = a^2 - 2ab + b^2 \qquad\qquad (1)$$

The shaded area is a square whose side is of length $a - b$ and whose area is $(a - b)^2$. The area of the entire region is obviously a^2, the area of the regions labeled X and Y are both ab, and the area of the small square Z is b^2. From the figure,

area of shaded region = area of entire region − area of region X − area of region Y − area of region Z

On substitution, we obtain the identity in (1) above.

Example 2   Factoring a Sum or Difference of Two Cubes

Factor each of the following.

(a) $x^3 + 1$ (b) $27m^3 - 64n^3$

Solution

(a) When $a = x$ and $b = 1$, the formula for a sum of two cubes yields

$$x^3 + 1 = (x + 1)(x^2 - x + 1)$$

(b) Note that $27m^3 - 64n^3 = (3m)^3 - (4n)^3$. We then use the formula for a difference of two cubes with $a = 3m$ and $b = 4n$.

$$27m^3 - 64n^3 = (3m - 4n)(9m^2 + 12mn + 16n^2)$$

✔ **Progress Check 2**

Factor.

(a) $8x^3 + y^3$ (b) $8s^3 - 27t^3$

Answers

(a) $(2x + y)(4x^2 - 2xy + y^2)$ (b) $(2s - 3t)(4s^2 + 6st + 9t^2)$

Example 3 Recognizing Special Factors

Factor each of the following.

(a) $\dfrac{1}{27}u^3 - 8v^3$ (b) $125x^6 + 8y^3$

Solution

(a) Since

$$\frac{1}{27}u^3 - 8v^3 = \left(\frac{u}{3}\right)^3 - (2v)^3$$

we may use the formula for a difference of two cubes with $a = \dfrac{u}{3}$ and $b = 2v$.

$$\frac{1}{27}u^3 - 8v^3 = \left(\frac{u}{3} - 2v\right)\left(\frac{u^2}{9} + \frac{2}{3}uv + 4v^2\right)$$

(b) Rewrite the polynomial as $(5x^2)^3 + (2y)^3$. With $a = 5x^2$ and $b = 2y$, the formula for a sum of two cubes tells us that

$$125x^6 + 8y^3 = (5x^2 + 2y)(25x^4 - 10x^2y + 4y^2)$$

✔ **Progress Check 3**

Factor each of the following.

(a) $125r^3 + \dfrac{1}{125}s^3$ (b) $27a^6 - 64b^6$

Answers

(a) $\left(5r + \dfrac{s}{5}\right)\left(25r^2 - rs + \dfrac{s^2}{25}\right)$ (b) $(3a^2 - 4b^2)(9a^4 + 12a^2b^2 + 16b^4)$

Exercise Set 4.5

In Exercises 1–10 use the formulas for the sum of two cubes and the difference of two cubes to find the given product.

1. $(2x + y)(4x^2 - 2xy + y^2)$

2. $(x + 3y)(x^2 - 3xy + 9y^2)$

3. $(x - 2y)(x^2 + 2xy + 4y^2)$

4. $(4x - y)(16x^2 + 4xy + y^2)$

5. $(3r + 2s)(9r^2 - 6rs + 4s^2)$

6. $(2a - 3b)(4a^2 + 6ab + 9b^2)$

7. $(2m - 5n)(4m^2 + 10mn + 25n^2)$

8. $(4a + 3b)(16a^2 - 12ab + 9b^2)$

9. $\left(\dfrac{x}{2} - 2y\right)\left(\dfrac{1}{4}x^2 + xy + 4y^2\right)$

10. $\left(3x - \dfrac{y}{3}\right)\left(9x^2 + xy + \dfrac{1}{9}y^2\right)$

In Exercises 11–30 factor the expression.

11. $x^2 - 49$

12. $9 - x^2$

13. $y^2 - \dfrac{1}{9}$

14. $\dfrac{1}{16} - y^2$

15. $4b^2 - a^2$

16. $16r^2 - 25s^2$

17. $x^2y^2 - 9$

18. $a^4 - 16$

19. $x^3 + 27y^3$

20. $8x^3 + 125y^3$

21. $27x^3 - y^3$

22. $64x^3 - 27y^3$

23. $a^3 + 8$

24. $8r^3 - 27$

25. $\dfrac{1}{8}m^3 - 8n^3$

26. $8a^3 - \dfrac{1}{64}b^3$

27. $(x + y)^3 - 8$

28. $27 + (x + y)^3$

29. $8x^6 - 125y^6$

30. $a^6 + 27b^6$

In Exercises 31 and 32 factor the expression as a difference of squares and as a difference of cubes. Compare answers.

31. $x^6 - y^6$

32. $64a^6 - \dfrac{1}{64}b^{12}$

33. Determine whether the following factoring is valid by storing any value of x, then entering the entire equation (refer to your calculator manual to find the equals sign).

If the calculator returns a value of "0" the equation is not an identity and the factoring is not valid. If it returns a "1" then the equation is valid for the value of x you chose. Does this mean the factoring is correct? (Refer back to Exercise 93 in Section 4.4!)

$$x^{100} - 81 = (x^{50} + 9)(x^{50} + 9)$$

```
X^100-81=(X^50+9
)(X^50-9)■
```

34. Use the method of Exercise 33 to check your answers to other exercises in this section.

4.6 Division of Polynomials

There is a procedure for polynomial division that parallels the long division process of arithmetic. In arithmetic, if we divide an integer p by an integer $d \neq 0$, we obtain a quotient q and a remainder r, so we can write

$$\frac{p}{d} = q + \frac{r}{d} \tag{1}$$

where

$$0 \leq r < d \tag{2}$$

This result can also be written in the form

$$p = qd + r, \quad 0 \leq r < d \tag{3}$$

For example,

$$\frac{7284}{13} = 560 + \frac{4}{13}$$

or

$$7284 = (560)(13) + 4$$

In the long division process for polynomials, we divide the dividend $P(x)$ by the divisor $D(x) \neq 0$ to obtain a quotient $Q(x)$ and a remainder $R(x)$. We have

$$\frac{P(x)}{D(x)} = Q(x) + \frac{R(x)}{D(x)} \tag{4}$$

where $R(x) = 0$ or where

$$\text{degree of } R(x) < \text{degree of } D(x) \tag{5}$$

This result can also be written as

$$P(x) = Q(x)D(x) + R(x) \tag{6}$$

Note that Equations (1) and (4) have the same form and that Equation (6) has the same form as Equation (3). Equation (2) requires that the remainder be less than the divisor, and the parallel requirement for polynomials in Equation (5) is that the *degree* of the remainder be less than that of the divisor.

Example 1   Dividing Polynomials

Divide $3x^3 - 7x^2 + 1$ by $x - 2$.

Solution

Polynomial Division

Step 1. Arrange the terms of both polynomials by descending powers of x. If a power is missing, write the term with a zero coefficient.

Step 1. $x - 2 \,\overline{\big)\, 3x^3 - 7x^2 + 0x + 1}$

Step 2. Divide the first term of the dividend by the first term of the divisor. The answer is written above the first term of the dividend.

Step 2.
$$\begin{array}{r} 3x^2 \\ x - 2 \,\overline{\big)\, 3x^3 - 7x^2 + 0x + 1} \end{array}$$

Step 3. Multiply the divisor by the quotient obtained in Step 2, and then subtract the product.

Step 3.
$$\begin{array}{r} 3x^2 \\ x - 2 \,\overline{\big)\, 3x^3 - 7x^2 + 0x + 1} \\ \underline{3x^3 - 6x^2 } \\ -\ x^2 + 0x + 1 \end{array}$$

Step 4. Repeat Steps 2 and 3 until the remainder is zero or the degree of the remainder is less than the degree of the divisor.

Step 4.
$$\begin{array}{r} 3x^2 -\ x\ -\ 2 \quad = Q(x)\\ x - 2 \,\overline{\big)\, 3x^3 - 7x^2 + 0x + 1} \\ \underline{3x^3 - 6x^2 } \\ -\ x^2 + 0x + 1 \\ \underline{-\ x^2 + 2x } \\ -\ 2x + 1 \\ \underline{-\ 2x + 4} \\ -\ 3 \quad = R(x) \end{array}$$

Step 5. Write the answer in the form of Equation (4) or Equation (6).

Step 5. $P(x) = 3x^3 - 7x^2 + 1$
$$= \underbrace{(3x^2 - x - 2)}_{Q(x)} \underbrace{(x - 2)}_{D(x)} + \underbrace{-3}_{R(x)}$$

✔ **Progress Check 1**

Divide $\dfrac{3x^3 - 4x + 5}{x - 2}$.

Answer

$3x^2 + 6x - 8 + \dfrac{21}{x - 2}$

Example 2 Dividing Polynomials

Divide $x^3 + 1$ by $x + 1$.

Solution

Note that there are terms missing in the dividend. We fill in these terms with zero coefficients and proceed as before.

$$
\begin{array}{r}
x^2 - x + 1 \\
x + 1 \overline{\smash{\big)}\, x^3 + 0x^2 + 0x + 1} \\
\underline{x^3 + x^2} \\
-x^2 + 0x + 1 \\
\underline{-x^2 - x} \\
x + 1 \\
\underline{x + 1} \\
0
\end{array}
$$

$$\frac{x^3 + 1}{x + 1} = x^2 - x + 1$$

We see that it is possible for the remainder to be 0. We then say that $x + 1$ is a factor of $x^3 + 1$.

✔ **Progress Check 2**

Divide $x^5 - 5x^3 + 3x^2 + 6x - 6$ by $x^2 - 2$.

Answers

$x^3 - 3x + 3$

Exercise Set 4.6

In Exercises 1–38 perform the indicated division. Be sure to write your answers in the form of Equation (4).

1. $\dfrac{10x + 25}{5}$

2. $\dfrac{8x - 4}{-2}$

3. $\dfrac{4 - 12x}{-3}$

4. $\dfrac{14 - 7x}{7}$

5. $\dfrac{12x^2 - 6x + 3}{3}$

6. $\dfrac{15x^3 + 20x^2 - 5}{5}$

7. $\dfrac{12x^2 - 8x}{2x}$

8. $\dfrac{6x - 15x^3}{3x}$

9. $\dfrac{10a^2 - 12a^4}{4a^2}$

10. $\dfrac{27a^4 - 18a^3}{9a^2}$

11. $\dfrac{4x^3 - 12x^2 + 16x}{4x}$

12. $\dfrac{-12y^4 - 18y^3 + 6y^2}{6y^2}$

13. $\dfrac{x^2 - 16}{x + 4}$

14. $\dfrac{y^2 + 2y - 3}{y + 2}$

15. $\dfrac{a^2 - 2a - 8}{a - 2}$

16. $\dfrac{x^2 + 7x + 10}{x + 2}$

17. $\dfrac{x^2 - 7x + 12}{x - 5}$

18. $\dfrac{b^2 - b - 6}{b + 4}$

19. $\dfrac{2x^2 + 5x + 3}{2x + 1}$

20. $\dfrac{6x^2 - x - 2}{2x - 3}$

21. $\dfrac{6a^2 + a - 1}{2a - 1}$

22. $\dfrac{9x^2 + 6x - 8}{3x - 2}$

23. $\dfrac{10x^2 + x - 3}{5x + 1}$

24. $\dfrac{6x^2 + 2x}{3x - 1}$

25. $\dfrac{4s^2 - 9}{2s + 3}$

26. $\dfrac{-6y^2 - 4y + 2}{4 - 2y}$

27. $\dfrac{4s^2 + 9}{2s + 3}$

28. $\dfrac{2x^3 + x^2 - 4x - 1}{x - 2}$

29. $\dfrac{3y^3 + 6y^2 - y - 2}{y + 2}$

30. $\dfrac{x^3 + x^2}{x - 1}$

31. $\dfrac{x^3 - 8}{x + 2}$

32. $\dfrac{x^3 + 8}{x + 2}$

33. $\dfrac{x^3 - x^2 - x + 1}{x + 1}$

34. $\dfrac{y^3 - 4y^2 + y + 6}{y + 3}$

35. $\dfrac{a^3 + 3a^2 - 4a + 2}{4 - a^2}$

36. $\dfrac{a^3 + 3a^2 - 10a - 24}{a^2 - a - b}$

37. $\dfrac{1.27x^3 - 22.42x + 3.05}{x^2 - 2}$

38. $\dfrac{6.49x^3 + 9.47x^2 - 7.84}{x^2 + x - 1}$

39. If a polynomial of degree 6 is divided by a polynomial of degree 2, the degree of the quotient is

(a) 3   (b) 8   (c) 4   (d) 12

(e) none of these

40. If a polynomial of degree 18 is divided by a polynomial of degree 6, the degree of the quotient is

(a) 3   (b) 108   (c) 24   (d) 12

(e) none of these

4.7   Critical Thinking Problems

In this chapter we learned to add, subtract, multiply, divide, and factor polynomials. Using what we have learned so far, we can now approach more interesting problems.

Example 1   Finding the Area of a Rectangle

The length of a rectangle is one less than twice its width. Find the polynomial that represents the area of the rectangle. Then find the area of the rectangle if its width is 3 inches.

Solution

Use the formula

$$Area\ of\ a\ rectangle = width \cdot length$$

What is the width of the rectangle? We don't know. So let

$$x = \text{the width of a rectangle}$$
$$2x - 1 = \text{the length of a rectangle}$$
$$\text{Area} = x \cdot (2x - 1)$$
$$= 2x^2 - x \qquad\qquad \text{Distributive Property}$$

The polynomial representing the area of a rectangle is $2x^2 - x$.

Now, let's find the area of this triangle when its width is 3. By substituting $x = 3$ into the expression $2x^2 - x$,

$$A = 2(3)^3 - (3)$$
$$A = 2(9) - 3 \qquad\qquad \text{By the order of operation, we}$$
$$\qquad\qquad\qquad\qquad\qquad \text{evaluate the exponent first}$$
$$A = 18 - 3$$
$$A = 15$$

Therefore, the area is 15 square inches.

✔ **Progress Check 1**

(a) You have a 4 ft by 4 ft rectangular piece of cardboard. You want to make a box with it (top is opened). Once you cut out four square corners each of width $\times$ ft, you fold each side up. Find the polynomial representing the total area of the cardboard. Write the resulting polynomial in factored form if possible.

(b) Find the perimeter of the figure before each side is folded up.

(c) What is the area of the remaining cardboard if you cut four 1 ft by 1 ft square corners?

Answers

(a) Polynomial $= -4(x - 2)(x + 2)$

(b) Perimeter $= 16$ ft

(c) Area $= 12$ ft^2

Some polynomials require using special factoring formulas. When we say we factor a polynomial, we mean factoring completely. Sometimes we get a polynomial that we can't factor; then we call it a prime polynomial. To factor polynomials, using special factor formulas or other techniques, we need to first factor out the greatest common factor **(GCF)**.

Let's try to factor a higher order polynomial.

Example 2   Factor

Factor $3x^4y - 48y^5$.

Solution

Before we attempt to use the special factor formulas, let's try to find the greatest common factor. What is the GCF ?

Correct! The GCF is $3y$. Both terms include $3y$. So

$$3x^4y - 48y^5 = 3y(x^4 - 16y^4)$$
$$= 3y(x^2 - 4y^2)(x^2 + 4y^2) \qquad \text{Using } a^2 - b^2 = (a - b)(a + b)$$
$$= 3y(x - 2y)(x + 2y)(x^2 + 4y^2) \qquad (x^2 - 4y^2) \text{ can be factored one more time}$$

Therefore,

$$3x^4y - 48y^5 = 3y(x - 2y)(x + 2y)(x^2 + 4y^2)$$

✔ **Progress Check 2**

Factor completely.

(a) $2x^6y - 18x^2y^9$ (b) $25x^4 - 100y^6$

Answers

(a) $2x^2y(x^2 - 3y^4)(x^2 + 3y^4)$ (b) $25(x^2 - 2y^3)(x^2 + 2y^3)$

Example 3   Factoring a Polynomial

Factor $x^4 + x^3 + x^2 + 2x + 1$.

Solution

It is not easy to factor this type of polynomial; however, we can do so by grouping first. Looking at the polynomial, we notice that it is possible to combine the first two terms $x^4 + x^3$ since the two terms have the common factor x^3:

$$x^4 + x^3 = x^3(x + 1)$$

Let's combine the last three terms $x^2 + 2x + 1$; we can factor this expression as a square of a binomial.

$$x^2 + 2x + 1 = (x + 1)(x + 1)$$

We now factor as shown below.

$$
\begin{aligned}
x^4 + x^3 + x^2 + 2x + 1 &= (x^4 + x^3) + (x^2 + 2x + 1) && \text{Group terms} \\
&= x^3(x + 1) + [(x + 1)(x + 1)] && \text{Because } x^4 + x^3 = x^3(x + 1) \text{ and} \\
& && x^2 + 2x + 1 = (x + 1)(x + 1) \\
&= (x + 1) \cdot [x^3 + (x + 1)] && \text{Factor out } (x + 1) \\
&= (x + 1)(x^3 + x + 1)
\end{aligned}
$$

Thus, when we factor the polynomial $x^4 + x^3 + x^2 + 2x + 1$ we get $(x + 1)(x^3 + x + 1)$.

✔ Progress Check 3

Factor completely.

(a) $p^6 - q^6$

(b) $\dfrac{1}{4}a^3 - a^2b + ab^2 - a$

Answers

(a) $(p - q)(p + q)(p^2 - pq + q^2)(p^2 + pq + q^2)$

(b) $\dfrac{1}{4}a(a - 2b - 2)(a - 2b + 2)$

■ ■ ■

Terms and Symbols

base	degree of a term	like terms
coefficient	exponent	polynomial
constant term	factoring	power
degree of a polynomial	irreducible polynomial	term

Key Ideas for Review

Topic	Key Idea
Product rule for exponents	$a^m \cdot a^n = a^{m+n}$
Degree of a term	The degree of a term is the sum of the exponents of all the variables within the term.
Polynomial	A polynomial is a sum of terms of the form $3x^2$, $-5x^2y$, and so on, where the exponent of each variable must be a nonnegative number.
degree	The degree of a polynomial is the degree of the term of highest degree.
addition	To add two polynomials, add like terms. To subtract two polynomials, subtract like terms.
multiplication	To multiply two polynomials, multiply one polynomial by each term of the other and add the products. $$(a+b)^2 = a^2 + 2ab + b^2$$ $$(a-b)^2 = a^2 - 2ab + b^2$$ $$(a+b)(a-b) = a^2 - b^2$$
Factoring	A polynomial is said to be factored when it is written as a product of two or more polynomials of lower degree.
methods	Factoring methods include the removal of common factors and grouping. To find the factors of a second-degree polynomial, you may use trial-and-error and the no-fuss factoring methods.
difference of squares	$a^2 - b^2 = (a+b)(a-b)$
sum and difference of cubes	$a^3 + b^3 = (a+b)(a^2 - ab + b^2)$ $a^3 - b^3 = (a-b)(a^2 + ab + b^2)$

Common Errors

1. *Don't* write

   $$(2x + 3) - (x + 3) = 2x + 3 - x \oplus 3 = x + 6$$

   This is probably the most common and persistent error made by algebra students! You must use the distributive law to give

   $$(2x + 3) - (x + 3) = 2x + 3 - x \ominus 3 = x$$

2. The notation $a \div b$ is read "a divided by b" and is equivalent to $\frac{a}{b}$, *not* $\frac{b}{a}$.

Review Exercises

Solutions to exercises whose numbers are in bold are in the Solutions section in the back of the book.

4.1 In Exercises 1−4 determine whether the given expression is a polynomial.

1. $-2xy^2 + x^2y$

2. $3b^2 + 2b - 6$

3. $x^{-1/2} + 5x^2 - x$

4. $7.5x^2 + 3x - \dfrac{1}{2}x^0$

In Exercises 5−8 write the terms and the coefficients of the terms.

5. $3x^3 - 4x + 2$

6. $4x^4 - x^2 + 2x - 3$

7. $-4x^2y^2 + 3x^2y - xy^2 + xy - 1$

8. $2xy^2 - 3xy + x + 3$

In Exercises 9−12 indicate the degree of the polynomial.

9. $-0.5x^7 + 6x^3 - 5$

10. $2x^2 + 3x^4 - 7x^5$

11. $3x^2 - 2x + 2$

12. $\dfrac{1}{2}x^4 - 2x + 3$

In Exercises 13−16 find the value of the given polynomial for the indicated value(s) of x (and y).

13. $3x^4 - 2x^2 + 2x - 1$, $x = -2$

14. $2x^2y^2 - 2xy^2 + x - 2y$, $x = 2, y = -1$

15. $-3x^3y + xy^2 - 2xy + 3$, $x = 1, y = -2$

16. $3x^3 - 2x^2 + x - 3$, $x = 3$

4.2/ In Exercises 17−28 perform the indicated operations.
4.3

17. $(2x^3 - 3x + 1) + (3x^3 + 2x^2 - 3)$

18. $(3a^2b^3 - 2a^2b + ab - a) - (-2a^3b^3 + ab^2 - 2ab + b)$

19. $(x^2y - xy^2 + x - 1) + (3xy^2 - 2x + y + 3)$

20. $(4x^4 - 2x^3 + x - 3) - (3x^3 - x^2 + 2x - 5)$

21. $(2x + 1)(3x - 2)$

22. $x(2x - 1)^2$

23. $(3y - 1)(2y + 2)$

24. $(3y - 1)(2y^2 + 2)$

25. $ab(a - 1)(a + 2)^2$

26. $(a^2 + 2a + 3)(a^2 - a - 1)$

27. $(x - 2)(x + 2)(x^2 - 2x + 3)$

28. $(b + 1)^2(2b - 1)^2$

29. In the product $(x^2 - 1)(x^2 + 3x - 4)$, find the coefficient of x^3.

30. In the product $(x^2 - 2x + 3)(x^3 + 2x^2 - 3x - 1)$, find the coefficient of x^4.

31. In the product $x^2(2x - 3)^2$, find the coefficient of x^3.

32. In the product $(x^2y + x - y)(x^2y - x + y)$, find the coefficient of x^3y.

4.4 In Exercises 33−46 factor completely.

33. $x^3 + x^2 - 2x$

34. $y^4 - y^3 - 6y^2$

35. $x^3 + 2x^2 - 3x$

36. $2x^2 - 5x - 3$

37. $6x^2 - 7x + 2$

38. $16x^2 - y^2$

39. $18x^2 - 24x + 6$

40. $2rs + s - 2r - 1$

41. $9a^4 + 6a^2 + 1$

42. $2x^2 + xy - 2y^2$

43. $y^2 - \dfrac{1}{4}x^2$

44. $3a^2 + 2ab - 2b - 3a$

45. $2ab + ac - 2b - c$

46. $a^4 - 2a^2 + 1$

4.5 In Exercises 47−52 factor completely.

47. $a^2 - \dfrac{1}{4}b^2$

48. $x^2y^2 - 9$

49. $8a^3 + 27b^3$

50. $8x^3 + 125y^3$

51. $8a^3 - 27b^3$

52. $8x^3 - 125y^3$

4.6 In Exercises 53−60 perform the indicated division. Be sure to write the answer in the form of Equation (4).

53. $\dfrac{16x - 8}{4}$

54. $\dfrac{6x - 18x^3}{3x}$

55. $\dfrac{4y^5 - 6y^4 + 2y^3}{2y^2}$

56. $\dfrac{4y^2 - 25}{y + 5}$

57. $\dfrac{x^3 + 27}{x + 3}$

58. $\dfrac{x^3 - 27}{x + 3}$

59. $\dfrac{y^3 - 3y + 2}{y - 2}$

60. $\dfrac{a^3 - 3a^2 - 2a + 6}{a^2 + 2}$

Progress Test 4A

1. In $\left(-\dfrac{1}{5}\right)^4$, what is the base? What is the exponent?

2. Find the degree of the polynomial.
$$-3x^5 + 2x^3 + xy^2 - 2$$

3. Find the value of the polynomial
$$3x^2y + 2xy - 3x + 1$$
when $x = -2$, $y = 3$.

4. Find a polynomial giving the volume of a cube of side s.

5. Add the polynomials.
$$2x^3 + 3x^2 + 1 \quad \text{and} \quad -5x^3 + x - 3$$

6. Simplify.
$$x - 3x^2y + 2y + 1 + 3y - 2x + 5x^2y + y - 3$$

7. Find $(2x^3 + x^2 - 2x + 1) - (3x^3 + 4x - 2)$.

8. Subtract $2xy^2 + x^2 - y + 2$ from $3x^2y + 5xy^2 + 3y$.

9. Multiply mentally $(2x - 5y)^2$.

10. Multiply $(x^2 + 2)(3x^2 - 2x + 5)$.

11. Factor $x^2 + 4x - 12$.

12. Factor completely $2x^2y - 8xy + 6y$.

13. Factor $4a^2 - 49$.

14. Factor $3x^2 - 13xy - 10y^2$.

15. Factor $\dfrac{x^3}{125} - 125y^3$.

16. Divide $\dfrac{x^3 + 2x^2 - 2x + 1}{x - 2}$.

17. Divide $2a^4 - 3a^3 - 2a^2 - 3a - 4$ by $a^2 + 1$.

18. If a polynomial of degree 12 is divided by a polynomial of degree 5, what is the degree of the quotient?

Progress Test 4B

1. State the base and exponent in $\left(-\dfrac{2}{3}\right)^5$.

2. Find the degree of the polynomial.
$$2x^4 - x^3y^2 + 4y^3 + 7$$

3. Evaluate the polynomial
$$-x^3 + 2x^2y - y + 1$$
when $x = -2$, $y = -1$.

4. Find a polynomial giving the area of a square of side s, less the area of an isosceles right triangle of side s.

5. Add the polynomials.
$$6x^5 - x^3 + x^2 \quad \text{and} \quad 4x^4 + 3x^3 - 2x^2 + 1$$

6. Simplify.
$$2x^2 - 3x^2y + y^2 - 7 + 4x^2y - 4y^2 + 4x^2 - 3$$

7. Find $(-3x^3 - 2x^2 + x - 3) - (2x^3 - 4x^2 - 2x + 5)$.

8. Subtract $2x^2y^2 - 3xy^2 - 2$ from $6x^2y^2 - 4xy^2 + xy$.

9. Multiply mentally $(3x - 4)^2$.

10. Multiply $(x + y)(2x - 3y - 2)$.

11. Factor $r^2 + 9r + 14$.

12. Factor completely $3x^2 + 6x + 3$.

13. Factor $16y^2 - 64x^2$.

14. Factor $3x^2 - 17x + 10$.

15. Factor $8a^3 + \dfrac{b^3}{8}$.

16. Divide $\dfrac{4x^3 - 2x^2 + 6x - 5}{x - 3}$.

17. Divide $r^4 - 3r^3 + 4r - 2$ by $r^2 - 1$.

18. If a polynomial of degree 17 is divided by a polynomial of degree 7, what is the degree of the quotient?

Chapter 4 Project

As discussed in the chapter opener, packages must often be designed to meet certain requirements. The United States Postal Service explains its requirements at http://postcalc.usps.gov/mailpiecedimensions.asp. As you saw in Exercises 79 and 80 in Section 4.3, cubic polynomials can be used to express the volume of packages whose dimensions must meet certain requirements.

For this project, we will use design a fourth degree (quartic) polynomial with two variables, x and y, to represent the cost of mailing a package. Suppose the variable y represents the cost per cubic inch of mailing a package. Suppose we have a package with a width 3 inches greater than the length, and a height $2\frac{1}{2}$ inches greater than the width. If the length is x inches, write a polynomial expression that represents the cost of mailing this package. Multiply it out. Is it a fourth degree polynomial?

Suppose $x = 5\frac{1}{2}$ inches, and $y = 1\frac{1}{2}$ cents. How much would it cost to mail this package? Can it be mailed more cheaply? Check out the website above and find out.

CHAPTER 5

Rational Expressions

From the intrinsic evidence of his creation, the Great Architect of the Universe now begins to appear as a pure mathematician.

—Sir James Hopwood Jeans

5.1 Simplifying Rational Expressions

5.2 Multiplication and Division of Rational Expressions

5.3 Addition and Subtraction of Rational Expressions

5.4 Complex Fractions

5.5 Equations and Inequalities with Fractions

5.6 Applications; Work Problems

5.7 Ratio and Proportion

5.8 Critical Thinking Problems

Game Theory is an exciting and ever-growing branch of mathematics. Game theorists (like John Nash, the subject of the book and film *A Beautiful Mind*) study the mathematical properties of simple conflict situations, to determine which strategies should be used to maximize gains and minimize losses. The lessons mathematicians learn from simple games with dice or coins can be of great use when applied to more complicated "games" like international finance or competitions between animal species.

Suppose you are playing a game with two possible actions at each turn. Perhaps the actions are "move" or "stand still." You might decide to move 3/5 of the time and stand still 2/5 of the time. In this case the **ratio** of "move"

http://www.awm-math
.org

turns to "stand still" turns would be 3:2 ("three to two"). If you wanted a *move* to *stand still* ratio of $x : y$ then you would stand still $\frac{x}{x+y}$ of the time. What **rational expression,** like $\frac{x}{x+y}$, would represent how often you "stand still"?

In this chapter's project you will see how rational expressions like the one above can be used to describe some basic aspects of simple games, like strategies, oddments, and payoffs.

Linda Goldway Keen is a mathematician who has worked with dynamical systems, which can be used to study the complex "game" played by predators and prey in the wild, where the payoff is survival. Learn about her and other women in mathematics at www.awm-math.org.

■ ■ ■

In algebra we are often faced with complex fractions such as

$$\frac{1 - \dfrac{1}{x}}{\dfrac{1}{x^2} + \dfrac{1}{x}}$$

that must be simplified. We also, at times, need to find the sum of expressions such as

$$\frac{x}{x - 2} + \frac{2x^2}{x - 3}$$

Our objective is to learn to handle such problems. We will study the rules for basic operations with fractions (addition, subtraction, multiplication, and division) and will see that a simple idea forms the cornerstone for much of our work: *multiplying a number or expression by a fraction equivalent to 1 does not change its value.*

We will also solve equations involving algebraic fractions, and word problems leading to such equations.

5.1 Simplifying Rational Expressions

At the start of this book we defined a **rational number** as the quotient $\frac{p}{q}$ where p and q are integers and q is not zero. In an analogous manner we define a **rational expression** as the quotient of two polynomials. Here are some examples of rational expressions (which are also called **algebraic fractions**):

$$\frac{2x}{5} \qquad \frac{x + 2}{x - 2} \qquad \frac{-2x^2 + 3x + 4}{x^2 - 4} \qquad \frac{a^3 - b^3}{a^2 + 2ab + b^2}$$

A rational expression is not defined when the denominator is zero. In subsequent chapters we will be very careful to avoid assigning values to variables that can create a zero denominator. For now, we will let you concentrate on the operations involved and will assume that all denominators represent nonzero real numbers.

We begin our study by examining the rule that enables us to simplify rational expressions.

Cancellation Principle

$$\frac{ab}{ac} = \frac{b}{c} \quad \text{if } a \neq 0$$

This is not anything new; we have used cancellation in arithmetic before.

$$\frac{2}{\cancel{3}} \cdot \frac{\cancel{3}}{5} = \frac{2}{5}$$

Why does this work? Why are we allowed to "cancel" the number 3? Because $\frac{3}{3} = 1$. In fact, for any nonzero number a, $a/a = 1$, so that if $a \neq 0$ is a factor of both the numerator *and* denominator of the product of two fractions, we can cancel the number a.

The same principle applies to rational expressions. Cancellation of a factor that is common to the numerator and denominator does not change the value of a rational expression. Thus,

$$\frac{x^2(x-1)}{2x(x-2)} = \frac{\cancel{x} \cdot x \cdot (x-1)}{2 \cdot \cancel{x} \cdot (x-2)} = \frac{x(x-1)}{2(x-2)}$$

Example 1   Simplifying a Rational Expression

Simplify.

(a) $\dfrac{-4x^2y}{8xy^2}$ (b) $\dfrac{-6(a-1)(b+1)^2}{-21a(b+1)}$

Solution

(a) $\dfrac{-4x^2y}{8xy^2} = \dfrac{-\cancel{4} \cdot \cancel{x} \cdot x \cdot \cancel{y}}{2 \cdot \cancel{4} \cdot \cancel{x} \cdot \cancel{y} \cdot y} = \dfrac{-x}{2y} = -\dfrac{x}{2y}$

(b) $\dfrac{-6(a-1)(b+1)^2}{-21a(b+1)} = \dfrac{-2 \cdot 3 \cdot (a-1)(b+1)(b+\cancel{1})}{-\cancel{3} \cdot 7 \cdot a(b+\cancel{1})} = \dfrac{2(a-1)(b+1)}{7a}$

✔ Progress Check 1

Simplify.

(a) $\dfrac{14ab^3}{-63a^2b}$ (b) $\dfrac{9(x-1)^2(y^2+1)}{3(y^2+1)(x-1)}$

Answers

(a) $-\dfrac{2b^2}{9a}$ (b) $3(x-1)$

Note in Example 1b that we wrote the integers 6 and 21 as a product of their prime factors. This technique makes it easy to discover common integer factors that can be canceled.

- -

Warning

Although the numbers

$$-\frac{1}{2} \qquad \frac{-1}{2} \qquad \frac{1}{-2}$$

are all equivalent, mathematicians prefer the format $-\frac{1}{2}$. Get in the habit of writing your answers so that the negative sign precedes the rational expression rather than appearing in either the numerator or the denominator.

- -

We summarize a systematic procedure for the simplification of rational expressions.

Step 1. Factor the numerator completely.

Step 2. Factor the denominator completely.

Step 3. Cancel factors that are common to both the numerator and denominator.

Simplifying Rational Expressions

Example 2 Simplifying a Rational Expression

Simplify $\dfrac{x^2 - 4}{x^2 + 5x + 6}$.

Solution

Simplifying	Example
Step 1. Factor the numerator completely.	Step 1. $x^2 - 4 = (x + 2)(x - 2)$
Step 2. Factor the denominator completely.	Step 2. $x^2 + 5x + 6 = (x + 3)(x + 2)$
Step 3. Cancel factors that are common to both the numerator and the denominator.	Step 3. $\dfrac{x^2 - 4}{x^2 + 5x + 6} = \dfrac{\cancel{(x + 2)}(x - 2)}{(x + 3)\cancel{(x + 2)}} = \dfrac{x - 2}{x + 3}$

✔ Progress Check 2

Simplify.

(a) $\dfrac{4 - x^2}{x^2 - x - 6}$ (b) $\dfrac{x^3 - x}{2x^2 - x - 3}$

Answers

(a) $\dfrac{2 - x}{x - 3}$ (b) $\dfrac{x(x - 1)}{2x - 3}$

- -

Warning

(a) Only multiplicative factors of the entire numerator and denominator can be canceled. *Don't* write

$$\frac{2x - y}{x} = 2 - y$$

Since x is *not* a multiplicative factor of the *whole* numerator, we may *not* cancel it.

(b) *Don't write*

$$\frac{y^2 - x^2}{y - x} = y - x$$

To simplify correctly, write

$$\frac{y^2 - x^2}{y - x} = \frac{(y + x)(y - x)}{y - x} = y + x$$

We finish our discussion of cancellation with a somewhat subtle technique. Can you do anything with this rational expression?

$$\frac{x - 5}{5 - x}$$

At first glance you might say, "No, there are no common factors." But if you recognize that $5 - x = -(x - 5)$, then you can see that

$$\frac{x - 5}{5 - x} = \frac{x - 5}{-(x - 5)} = \frac{1(x - 5)}{-1(x - 5)} = \frac{1}{-1} = -1$$

Example 3 Simplifying Rational Expressions
Simplify.

(a) $\dfrac{x^2 - x - 6}{3x - x^2}$

(b) $\dfrac{16 - x^2}{x^2 - 3x - 4}$

Solution

(a) $\dfrac{x^2 - x - 6}{3x - x^2} = \dfrac{(x - 3)(x + 2)}{x(3 - x)} = \dfrac{(x - 3)(x + 2)}{-x(x - 3)} = \dfrac{x + 2}{-x} = -\dfrac{x + 2}{x}$

(b) $\dfrac{16 - x^2}{x^2 - 3x - 4} = \dfrac{(4 + x)(4 - x)}{(x + 1)(x - 4)} = \dfrac{-(4 + x)(x - 4)}{(x + 1)(x - 4)} = -\dfrac{x + 4}{x + 1}$

✔ Progress Check 3

Simplify.

(a) $\dfrac{x^2 + 7x - 8}{x - x^2}$

(b) $\dfrac{9y^2 - x^2}{x - 3y}$

(c) $\dfrac{8 - 2x}{x^2 - 16}$

Answers

(a) $-\dfrac{x + 8}{x}$

(b) $-(3y + x)$

(c) $-\dfrac{2}{x + 4}$

Exercise Set 5.1

In Exercises 1−50 simplify the rational number or rational expression.

1. $\dfrac{3}{24}$

2. $\dfrac{-5}{15}$

3. $\dfrac{63}{-9}$

4. $\dfrac{17}{68}$

5. $-\dfrac{6}{21}$

6. $-\dfrac{18}{8}$

7. $\dfrac{12}{52}$

8. $\dfrac{72}{-30}$

9. $\dfrac{-75}{25}$

10. $\dfrac{19}{21}$

11. $\dfrac{9ab^3}{3ab}$

12. $\dfrac{-7xy^2}{49y^3}$

13. $\dfrac{-16x(z+3)^2}{24x^2(z+3)}$

14. $\dfrac{14(m^2+1)^2(n-2)}{-42(n-2)^2(m^2+1)}$

15. $\dfrac{-16(r+4)^3s}{6(s-1)(r+4)^2}$

16. $\dfrac{8a^2b(c+1)}{18ab^2(c+1)^2}$

17. $\dfrac{3(y^2+z^2)^2}{-12(y^2+z^2)}$

18. $\dfrac{63(a-1)(b-1)(c-1)}{-9(b-1)(a-1)^2}$

19. $\dfrac{4(z^2+z+1)^2}{34(z^2+z+1)}$

20. $\dfrac{63(r-3)^3s^3(t+2)}{9s^4(t+2)^2(r-3)^2}$

21. $\dfrac{3x^2-6x}{-9x+18}$

22. $\dfrac{9xy^2-9x}{-21xy}$

23. $\dfrac{2x^4+x^2}{6x^2+3}$

24. $\dfrac{x^2+2x+4}{xy+2y}$

25. $\dfrac{2x^3+2x^2}{x+1}$

26. $\dfrac{24m^2n^2+48m^2n}{10mn+20}$

27. $\dfrac{3abc+12bc}{15ac+60c}$

28. $\dfrac{2t^2+4t-16}{t^2-4t+4}$

29. $\dfrac{x^3+5x^2+-6x}{2x^2+12x}$

30. $\dfrac{3xy-6x+3y-6}{x^2+2x+1}$

31. $\dfrac{t^3+1}{t^2+t}$

32. $\dfrac{27x^3-y^3}{9x^2-3xy}$

33. $\dfrac{4a^2-9}{2a^2-3a-9}$

34. $\dfrac{9s^2t-4t}{3st^2+2t^2}$

35. $\dfrac{4(xy+2x+y+2)-8(x+1)}{(x+1)y}$

36. $\dfrac{16r^2-25t^2}{16r^2-40t+25t^2}$

37. $\dfrac{3t^4-27t^2}{2t^2-6t}$

38. $\dfrac{8r^3-27}{4r^2-9}$

39. $\dfrac{9a^2b^3-a^2b}{3ab^2-ab}$

40. $\dfrac{4x^2+6x-4}{3x^2+12x+4}$

41. $\dfrac{2x^2+9x+9}{9-x^2}$

42. $\dfrac{3x^2-2x^3}{2x^2-3x}$

43. $\dfrac{a^3-5a^2+6a}{2a-a^2}$

44. $\dfrac{16-n^2}{2n^2-7n-4}$

45. $\dfrac{12r^2b^2-4rb}{rb-3r^2b^2}$

46. $\dfrac{9x^2-36y^2}{36y-18x}$

47. $\dfrac{6t-4t^2}{6t^3-7t^2-3t}$

48. $\dfrac{9r^3s-16rs}{4s^2-3rs}$

49. $\dfrac{-2x^2-5x+3}{x-2x^2}$

50. $\dfrac{2a^2-a+2ab-b}{ab-2a^2b}$

51. Check the following simplification with your graphing calculator, by first storing values for x and y. (See the figure below.)

$$\dfrac{x^2-3xy+2y^2}{x-2y}=x-y$$

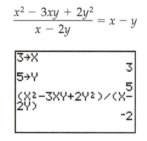

Use the same method to verify your answer to Exercise 50.

5.2 Multiplication and Division of Rational Expressions

If we think of a rational expression as a fraction, then we see that the rule for multiplication is already familiar to us from arithmetic.

Multiplication of Fractions

$$\frac{a}{b} \cdot \frac{c}{d} = \frac{ac}{bd}, \quad b \neq 0, d \neq 0$$

That is, when multiplying two given fractions we obtain a new fraction whose numerator is the product of the numerators of the given fractions and whose denominator is the product of the denominators of the given fractions. The same rule holds for both rational numbers and rational expressions.

Example 1   Multiplication of Rational Numbers and Rational Expressions
Multiply.

(a) $\dfrac{5}{2} \cdot \dfrac{3}{4}$ (b) $\dfrac{3}{4} \cdot \dfrac{x-1}{2}$ (c) $\dfrac{x-1}{2} \cdot \dfrac{x+1}{x}$ (d) $\dfrac{3}{4x} \cdot \dfrac{x-3}{2y} \cdot \dfrac{x+3}{y-1}$

Solution

(a) $\dfrac{5}{2} \cdot \dfrac{3}{4} = \dfrac{5 \cdot 3}{2 \cdot 4} = \dfrac{15}{8}$

(b) $\dfrac{3}{4} \cdot \dfrac{x-1}{2} = \dfrac{3(x-1)}{4 \cdot 2} = \dfrac{3(x-1)}{8}$

(c) $\dfrac{x-1}{2} \cdot \dfrac{x+1}{x} = \dfrac{(x-1)(x+1)}{2 \cdot x} = \dfrac{x^2-1}{2x}$

(d) $\dfrac{3}{4x} \cdot \dfrac{x-3}{2y} \cdot \dfrac{x+3}{y-1} = \dfrac{3(x-3)(x+3)}{4x \cdot 2y(y-1)} = \dfrac{3(x^2-9)}{8xy(y-1)}$

✔ Progress Check 1

Multiply.

(a) $\dfrac{2x}{y} \cdot \dfrac{y+1}{y^2+1}$ (b) $\dfrac{3}{a} \cdot \dfrac{b^2}{2a} \cdot \dfrac{c}{d-3}$

Answers

(a) $\dfrac{2x(y+1)}{y(y^2+1)}$ (b) $\dfrac{3b^2c}{2a^2(d-3)}$

To divide two fractions, we multiply the numerator by the reciprocal of the divisor.

**Division
of Fractions**

$$\frac{\dfrac{a}{b}}{\dfrac{c}{d}} = \frac{a}{b} \cdot \frac{d}{c} = \frac{ac}{bd}, \quad b, c, d \neq 0$$

This rule "works" because we are really multiplying by a cleverly disguised form of 1, namely

$$\frac{\dfrac{d}{c}}{\dfrac{d}{c}} = 1$$

Observe that

$$\frac{\dfrac{a}{b}}{\dfrac{c}{d}} \cdot \frac{\dfrac{d}{c}}{\dfrac{d}{c}} = \frac{\dfrac{ad}{bc}}{\dfrac{cd}{cd}} = \frac{\dfrac{ad}{bc}}{1} = \frac{ad}{bc}$$

Example 2   Division of Rational Numbers and Rational Expressions
Divide.

(a) $\dfrac{\dfrac{2}{5}}{\dfrac{3}{4}}$ (b) $\dfrac{\dfrac{2x}{x-1}}{\dfrac{x-2}{x}}$ (c) $\dfrac{\dfrac{3a^3b^2}{2cd}}{\dfrac{c-1}{2a^2b}}$ (d) $\dfrac{2x}{y} \div \dfrac{3y^3}{x-3}$ (e) $\dfrac{\dfrac{x}{2x+1}}{x-2}$

Solution

(a) $\dfrac{\dfrac{2}{5}}{\dfrac{3}{4}} = \dfrac{2}{5} \cdot \dfrac{4}{3} = \dfrac{2 \cdot 4}{5 \cdot 3} = \dfrac{8}{15}$

(b) $\dfrac{\dfrac{2x}{x-1}}{\dfrac{x-2}{x}} = \dfrac{2x}{x-1} \cdot \dfrac{x}{x-2} = \dfrac{2x^2}{(x-1)(x-2)}$

(c) $\dfrac{\dfrac{3a^3b^2}{2cd}}{\dfrac{c-1}{2a^2b}} = \dfrac{3a^3b^2}{2cd} \cdot \dfrac{2a^2b}{c-1} = \dfrac{6a^5b^3}{2c(c-1)d}$

(d) $\dfrac{2x}{y} \div \dfrac{3y^3}{x-3}$

To solve this problem, we write the expression as a fraction and simplify:

$$\dfrac{\dfrac{2x}{y}}{\dfrac{3y^3}{x-3}} = \dfrac{2x}{y} \cdot \dfrac{x-3}{3y^3} = \dfrac{2x(x-3)}{3y^4}$$

(e) $\dfrac{\dfrac{x}{2x+1}}{x-2} = \dfrac{\dfrac{x}{2x+1}}{\dfrac{x-2}{1}} = \dfrac{x}{2x+1} \cdot \dfrac{1}{x-2} = \dfrac{x}{(2x+1)(x-2)}$

✔ Progress Check 2

Divide.

(a) $\dfrac{\dfrac{5(y-1)^2}{x}}{\dfrac{2(x-1)^2}{y}}$

(b) $\dfrac{3a^2b}{a+1} \div \dfrac{2(b-1)}{a-1}$

Answers

(a) $\dfrac{5y(y-1)^2}{2x(x-1)^2}$

(b) $\dfrac{3a^2(a-1)b}{2(a+1)(b-1)}$

Example 3 Operations on and Simplification of Rational Expressions

Perform the indicated operations and simplify.

(a) $\dfrac{3x^2-27}{12-6x} \cdot \dfrac{2x^2-2x}{x+3}$

(b) $\dfrac{2x^3+3x^2}{10-20x} \div \dfrac{2x^2+3x}{10x-5}$

Solution

(a) $\dfrac{3x^2-27}{12-6x} \cdot \dfrac{2x^2-4x}{x+3} = \dfrac{3(x^2-9)}{6(2-x)} \cdot \dfrac{2x(x-2)}{x+3}$ Remove common factors.

$= \dfrac{3(x+3)(x-3)2x(x-2)}{6(2-x)(x+3)}$ Complete factoring and multiply.

$= -x(x-3)$ Cancel common factors.

(b) $\dfrac{2x^3 + 3x^2}{10 - 20x} \div \dfrac{2x^2 + 3x}{10x - 5} = \dfrac{x^2(2x + 3)}{10(1 - 2x)} \cdot \dfrac{5(2x - 1)}{x(2x + 3)}$ Invert denominator and factor.

$$= -\dfrac{x}{2}$$ Cancel common factors.

✔ **Progress Check 3**

Perform the indicated operations and simplify.

(a) $\dfrac{-2}{3x^2 + 4x + 1} \cdot \dfrac{6x^2 - 4x - 2}{x^2 - 1}$ (b) $\dfrac{10x - 2x^2}{-x^2 + 5x - 6} \div \dfrac{x^2 - 25}{-x^2 + 2x}$

Answers

(a) $\dfrac{-4}{(x + 1)^2}$ (b) $-\dfrac{2x^2}{(x - 3)(x + 5)}$

Exercise Set 5.2

In Exercises 1–8 determine whether each statement is true
(T) or false (F).

1. $\dfrac{3}{8} \cdot \dfrac{x + 5}{4} = \dfrac{3(x + 5)}{32}$ 2. $\dfrac{2}{3} \cdot \dfrac{x + 4}{7} = \dfrac{2x + 4}{21}$

3. $\dfrac{5}{2} \cdot \dfrac{4x + 7}{15} = \dfrac{2x + 7}{3}$ 4. $\dfrac{2x}{5y} \cdot \dfrac{5x + 15}{4} = \dfrac{x(x + 5)}{2y}$

5. $\dfrac{\dfrac{1}{3}}{2x} = \dfrac{x - 1}{6x}$ 6. $\dfrac{\dfrac{x}{2x+1}}{\dfrac{2}{x-1}} = \dfrac{2}{2x + 1}$

7. $\dfrac{\dfrac{2}{3}}{\dfrac{4x}{3x+6}} = \dfrac{x + 6}{2x}$ 8. $\dfrac{\dfrac{x}{x^2-y^2}}{\dfrac{xy}{x+y}} = \dfrac{x(x - y)}{y}$

In Exercises 9–22 simplify, if possible.

9. $\dfrac{6x + 3}{3}$ 10. $\dfrac{8x - 4}{2}$

11. $\dfrac{3x + 2}{3}$ 12. $\dfrac{6x - 3}{5}$

13. $\dfrac{5}{10x^2 - 15}$ 14. $\dfrac{3}{6x - 12y^2}$

15. $\dfrac{5a^4}{25a^2}$ 16. $\dfrac{18}{27} \cdot \dfrac{a^2b^4}{a^3b^2}$

17. $\dfrac{x + 4}{x^2 - 16}$ 18. $\dfrac{y^2 - 25}{y + 5}$

19. $\dfrac{x^2 - 8x + 16}{x - 4}$ 20. $\dfrac{5x^2 - 45}{2x - 6}$

21. $\dfrac{6x^2 - x - 1}{2x^2 + 3x - 2}$ 22. $\dfrac{2x^3 + x^2 - 3x}{3x^2 + x + 2}$

In Exercises 23–56 compute and simplify your answer.

23. $\dfrac{x + 1}{3} \cdot \dfrac{2x + 3}{4}$ 24. $\dfrac{3x - 1}{2y} \cdot \dfrac{2x + 3}{3x + 1}$

25. $\dfrac{a - 4}{3} \cdot \dfrac{9(a + 4)}{b}$ 26. $\dfrac{x + 1}{3x + 6} \cdot \dfrac{6}{x + 1}$

27. $\dfrac{a^2}{4} \div \dfrac{a}{2}$ 28. $\dfrac{2a^2b^4}{3c^3} \div \dfrac{a^3b^2}{6c^5}$

29. $\dfrac{2}{3x - 6} \div \dfrac{3}{2x - 4}$ 30. $\dfrac{5x + 15}{8} \div \dfrac{3x + 9}{4}$

31. $\dfrac{3x^2 + x}{2x + 4} \cdot \dfrac{4}{x^2 + 2x}$ 32. $\dfrac{a^2 - a}{b + 1} \cdot \dfrac{2b}{a^3 - a^2}$

33. $\dfrac{25 - a^2}{b + 3} \cdot \dfrac{2b^2 + 6b}{a - 5}$ 34. $\dfrac{2xy^2}{x + y} \cdot \dfrac{x + y}{4xy}$

35. $\dfrac{2x}{x - 3} \div \dfrac{6x^2}{x + 3}$ 36. $\dfrac{a - a^2}{b - 1} \div \dfrac{a^2 - a}{b}$

37. $\dfrac{4y^2 - 9}{x^2 - 1} \cdot \dfrac{x^2 - x}{3 - 2y}$ 38. $\dfrac{9 - 25b^2}{a^3 + a^2} \div \dfrac{5b - 3}{a + 1}$

39. $\dfrac{x^2 - 4}{x + 1} \div \dfrac{2x + 3}{2x - 4}$ 40. $\dfrac{9}{a^2 - 16} \div \dfrac{3}{a + 4}$

41. $\dfrac{x + 2}{3y} \div \dfrac{x^2 - 2x - 8}{15y^2}$ 42. $\dfrac{3x}{x + 2} \div \dfrac{6x^2}{x^2 - x - 6}$

43. $\dfrac{6x^2 - x - 2}{2x^2 - 5x + 3} \cdot \dfrac{2x^2 - 7x + 6}{3x^2 + x - 2}$

44. $\dfrac{3x^2 - 5x - 2}{4x^2 - 3x - 1} \cdot \dfrac{5x^2 - 3x - 2}{3x^2 + 7x + 2}$

45. $\dfrac{x^2 + 3x - 10}{x^2 + 4x + 3} \div \dfrac{x^2 + 2x - 15}{x^2 - x - 2}$

46. $\dfrac{25 - 15x}{x^2 - 4} \div \dfrac{3x^2 - 8x + 5}{x + 2}$

47. $(x^2 - 4) \cdot \dfrac{2x + 3}{x^2 + 2x - 8}$ 48. $(a^2 - 2a) \cdot \dfrac{a + 1}{6 - a - a^2}$

49. $\dfrac{b^2 - 1}{3 - 2b - b^2} \cdot (-b^2 - 3b)$ 50. $\dfrac{25 - x^2}{10 - 3x - x^2} \div \dfrac{x}{2 - x}$

51. $(x^2 - 2x - 15) \div \dfrac{x^2 - 7x + 10}{x^2 + 1}$

52. $\dfrac{2y^2 - 5y - 3}{y - 4} \div (y^2 + y - 12)$

*53. $\dfrac{x^2 - 4}{x^2 + 2x - 3} \cdot \dfrac{x^2 + 3x - 4}{x^2 - 7x + 10} \cdot \dfrac{x + 3}{x^2 + 3x + 2}$

*54. $\dfrac{x^2 - 9}{6x^2 + x - 1} \cdot \dfrac{2x^2 + 5x + 2}{x^2 + 4x + 3} \cdot \dfrac{x^2 - x - 2}{x^2 - 3x}$

*55. $\left(\dfrac{x + 4}{x + 1} \cdot \dfrac{x - 3}{x - 2} \right) \div \dfrac{x + 4}{x^3 - x^2 - 2x}$

*56. $\dfrac{x - 2}{2x^2 + 5x - 3} \div \left(\dfrac{2x - 1}{x - 2} \cdot \dfrac{x + 4}{x + 3} \right)$

5.3   Addition and Subtraction of Rational Expressions

Here is a basic principle of addition and subtraction that must be remembered:

Addition and Subtraction Principle

> We can add or subtract fractions directly only if they have the same denominator.

The process is already familiar to you.

Addition and Subtraction Rule

$$\frac{a}{c} + \frac{b}{c} = \frac{a + b}{c}$$

$$\frac{a}{c} - \frac{b}{c} = \frac{a - b}{c}$$

Here c is the common denominator. We add the numerators $(a + b)$ to find the numerator of the sum and retain the common denominator. Similarly, we subtract b from a to find the numerator of the difference and retain the common denominator. For example,

$$\frac{2}{x} - \frac{4}{x} + \frac{5}{x} = \frac{2 - 4 + 5}{x} = \frac{3}{x}$$

How do we handle the addition of fractions if the denominators are not the same? We must rewrite each fraction as an equivalent fraction so that they all have the same denominator. Although any common denominator will do, we will concentrate on finding the **least common denominator**, or **LCD**. Here is the procedure:

Least Common Denominator	Example

Example:

$$\frac{1}{x^3 - x^2} \qquad \frac{-2}{x^3 - x} \qquad \frac{3x}{x^2 + 2x + 1}$$

Step 1. Factor the denominator of each fraction completely.

Step 1.

$$\frac{1}{x^2(x - 1)} \qquad \frac{-2}{x(x - 1)(x + 1)} \qquad \frac{3x}{(x + 1)^2}$$

Step 2. Determine the different factors in the denominators of the fractions, and the highest power to which each factor occurs in any denominator.

Step 2.

Factor	Highest power	Final factor
x	2	x^2
$x - 1$	1	$x - 1$
$x + 1$	2	$(x + 1)^2$

Step 3. The product of the factors to their highest power, as determined in Step 2, is the LCD.

Step 3. The LCD is

$$x^2(x - 1)(x + 1)^2$$

Example 1   Finding the Least Common Denominator

Find the LCD of the fractions.

$$\frac{y + 2}{2x^2 - 18} \qquad \frac{4y}{3x^3 + 9x^2} \qquad \frac{y + 1}{(x - 3)^2(y - 1)^2}$$

Solution

Factoring each denominator completely, we have

$$\frac{y + 2}{2(x + 3)(x - 3)} \qquad \frac{4y}{3x^2(x + 3)} \qquad \frac{y + 1}{(x - 3)^2(y - 1)^2}$$

The different factors and the highest power of each factor in any denominator are

Factor	Highest Power	Final Factor
2	1	2
3	1	3
x	2	x^2
$x + 3$	1	$x + 3$
$x - 3$	2	$(x - 3)^2$
$y - 1$	2	$(y - 1)^2$

The LCD is then the product

$$6x^2(x + 3)(x - 3)^2(y - 1)^2$$

✔ **Progress Check 1**

Find the LCD of the fractions.

$$\frac{2a}{(3a^2 + 12a + 12)b} \qquad \frac{-7b}{a(4b^2 - 8b + 4)} \qquad \frac{3}{ab^3 + 2b^3}$$

Answer

$$12ab^3(a + 2)^2(b - 1)^2$$

Having determined the LCD, we must convert each fraction to an equivalent fraction with the LCD as its denominator. We have already seen that multiplying a fraction by 1 yields an equivalent fraction. We can accomplish this conversion by multiplying the fraction by the appropriate equivalent of 1. Here is the process.

Addition of Fractions	**Example**
	$$\dfrac{4}{3x(x + 3)} + \dfrac{x - 1}{x^2(x - 2)}$$
Step 1. Find the LCD.	*Step 1.* LCD is $3x^2(x + 3)(x - 2)$.
Step 2. Examine the first fraction. Multiply it by a fraction whose numerator and denominator are the same and consist of all factors of the LCD that are missing in the denominator of the first fraction.	*Step 2.*

$$\underbrace{\left[\frac{4}{3x(x + 3)}\right]}_{\substack{\text{first} \\ \text{fraction}}} \cdot \underbrace{\frac{x(x - 2)}{x(x - 2)}}_{\substack{\text{factors of LCD missing} \\ \text{in denominator } 3x(x + 3)}}$$

$$= \frac{4x(x - 2)}{3x^2(x + 3)(x - 2)}$$

$$= \frac{4x^2 - 8x}{3x^2(x + 3)(x - 2)}$$

(continues)

Addition of Fractions	Example

Step 3. Repeat Step 2 for each fraction.

Step 3.

second
fraction

$$\left[\dfrac{x-1}{x^2(x-2)}\right] \cdot \dfrac{3(x+3)}{(3(x+3))}$$

factors of LCD missing
in denominator $x^2(x-2)$

$$= \dfrac{3(x-1)(x+3)}{3x^2(x-2)(x+3)}$$

$$= \dfrac{3(x^2+2x-3)}{3x^2(x+3)(x-2)}$$

$$= \dfrac{3x^2+6x-9}{3x^2(x+3)(x-2)}$$

Step 4. The fractions now all have the same denominator. Apply the addition principle. (Do not multiply out the denominators; it may be possible to perform cancellation.)

Step 4. $\dfrac{4}{3x(x+3)} + \dfrac{x-1}{x^2(x-2)}$ Original example

$$= \dfrac{4x^2-8x}{3x^2(x+3)(x-2)} + \dfrac{3x^2+6x-9}{3x^2(x+3)(x-2)}$$

$$= \dfrac{4x^2-8x+3x^2+6x-9}{3x^2(x+3)(x-2)}$$

$$= \dfrac{7x^2-2x-9}{3x^2(x+3)(x-2)}$$

Example 2   Finding the Sum of Rational Expressions

Find the sum:

(a) $\dfrac{3}{2xy} - \dfrac{4}{x^2} + \dfrac{2}{y^2}$ (b) $\dfrac{2x}{x^2-4} + \dfrac{1}{x(x+2)} - \dfrac{1}{x-2}$

Solution

(a) The LCD is $2x^2y^2$. (Verify.) Then

$$\dfrac{3}{2xy} \cdot \dfrac{xy}{xy} - \dfrac{4}{x^2} \cdot \dfrac{2y^2}{2y^2} + \dfrac{2}{y^2} \cdot \dfrac{2x^2}{2x^2} = \dfrac{3xy}{2x^2y^2} - \dfrac{8y^2}{2x^2y^2} + \dfrac{4x^2}{2x^2y^2}$$

$$= \dfrac{3xy - 8y^2 + 4x^2}{2x^2y^2}$$

(b) Since $x^2 - 4 = (x + 2)(x - 2)$, the LCD is $x(x + 2)(x - 2)$. Then

$$\frac{2x}{(x + 2)(x - 2)} \cdot \frac{x}{x} + \frac{1}{x(x + 2)} \cdot \frac{x - 2}{x - 2} - \frac{1}{x - 2} \cdot \frac{x(x + 2)}{x(x + 2)}$$

$$= \frac{2x^2}{x(x + 2)(x - 2)} + \frac{x - 2}{x(x + 2)(x - 2)} - \frac{x(x + 2)}{x(x + 2)(x - 2)}$$

$$= \frac{2x^2 + x - 2 - (x^2 + 2x)}{x(x + 2)(x - 2)} = \frac{2x^2 + x - 2 - x^2 - 2x}{x(x + 2)(x - 2)}$$

$$= \frac{x^2 - x - 2}{x(x + 2)(x - 2)} = \frac{(x - 2)(x + 1)}{x(x + 2)(x - 2)} = \frac{x + 1}{x(x + 2)}$$

✔ Progress Check 2

Find the sum.

(a) $\dfrac{4r - 3}{9r^3} - \dfrac{2r + 1}{4r^2} + \dfrac{2}{3r}$ (b) $\dfrac{2}{n} + \dfrac{3}{n + 1} - \dfrac{5}{n + 2}$

Answers

(a) $\dfrac{6r^2 + 7r - 12}{36r^3}$ (b) $\dfrac{7n + 4}{n(n + 1)(n + 2)}$

Exercise Set 5.3

In Exercises 1–10 find the LCD.

1. $\dfrac{4}{x}, \dfrac{x - 2}{y}$

2. $\dfrac{x}{x - 1}, \dfrac{x + 4}{x + 2}$

3. $\dfrac{5 - a}{a}, \dfrac{7}{2a}$

4. $\dfrac{x + 2}{x}, \dfrac{x - 2}{x^2}$

5. $\dfrac{2b}{b - 1}, \dfrac{3}{(b - 1)^2}$

6. $\dfrac{2 + x}{x^2 - 4}, \dfrac{3}{x - 2}$

7. $\dfrac{4x}{x - 2}, \dfrac{5}{x^2 + x - 6}$

8. $\dfrac{3}{y^2 - 3y - 4}, \dfrac{2y}{y + 1}$

9. $\dfrac{3}{x + 1}, \dfrac{2}{x}, \dfrac{x}{x - 1}$

10. $\dfrac{4}{x}, \dfrac{3}{x - 1}, \dfrac{x}{x^2 - 2x + 1}$

In Exercises 11–58 perform the indicated operations and simplify.

11. $\dfrac{2}{x} + \dfrac{5}{x}$

12. $\dfrac{12}{b + 1} + \dfrac{3}{b + 1}$

13. $\dfrac{x}{y} + \dfrac{2x}{y}$

14. $\dfrac{x^2 + 5}{x + 1} - \dfrac{x^2 + 3}{x + 1}$

15. $\dfrac{2a - 3}{a - 2} + \dfrac{1 - a}{a - 2}$

16. $\dfrac{x + 2}{x - 1} - \dfrac{2x - 3}{x - 1}$

17. $\dfrac{x^2 + 4x}{x + 3} - \dfrac{9 + 4x}{x + 3}$

18. $\dfrac{x^2 + x}{x + 2} + \dfrac{2x + 2}{x + 2}$

19. $\dfrac{2y - 16}{y^2 - 16} + \dfrac{2 - y}{y^2 - 16}$

20. $\dfrac{3x - 5}{x - 4} - \dfrac{x + 3}{x - 4}$

21. $\dfrac{8}{a - 2} + \dfrac{4}{2 - a}$

22. $\dfrac{x}{x^2 - 4} + \dfrac{2}{4 - x^2}$

23. $\dfrac{3y}{2 - y} - \dfrac{5y}{3y - 6}$

24. $\dfrac{a - 1}{a - 3} - \dfrac{a}{12 - 4a}$

25. $\dfrac{3}{x - 1} - \dfrac{x}{x - 1} + \dfrac{3x - 5}{x - 1}$

26. $\dfrac{y^2}{y^2 - 9} + \dfrac{9}{y^2 - 9} - \dfrac{6y}{y^2 - 9}$

27. $\dfrac{2}{x} + \dfrac{1}{5}$

28. $\dfrac{x}{4} - \dfrac{y}{3}$

29. $5 - \dfrac{2}{x}$

30. $\dfrac{x - 1}{3} + 2$

31. $\dfrac{1}{x - 1} + \dfrac{2}{x - 2}$

32. $\dfrac{1}{a + 2} + \dfrac{3}{a - 2}$

33. $\dfrac{a}{8b} - \dfrac{b}{12a}$

34. $\dfrac{4}{3x} - \dfrac{5}{xy}$

35. $\dfrac{4x - 1}{6x^3} + \dfrac{2}{3x^2}$

36. $\dfrac{5}{2x + 6} - \dfrac{x}{x + 3}$

37. $\dfrac{2x}{x - 3} + \dfrac{4x - 2}{9 - 3x}$

38. $\dfrac{3}{a^2 - 16} - \dfrac{2}{a - 4}$

39. $\dfrac{x}{x - y} - \dfrac{y}{x + y}$

40. $\dfrac{5x}{2x^2 - 18} + \dfrac{4}{3x - 9}$

41. $\dfrac{x}{x - y} + \dfrac{y}{x + y}$

42. $\dfrac{2x}{x^2 - 9} + \dfrac{5}{3x + 9}$

43. $\dfrac{4}{r} - \dfrac{3}{r + 2}$

44. $2 + \dfrac{4}{a^2 - 4}$

45. $\dfrac{1}{x - 1} + \dfrac{2x - 1}{(x - 2)(x + 1)}$

46. $\dfrac{2x}{2x + 1} - \dfrac{x - 1}{(2x + 1)(x - 2)}$

47. $\dfrac{a + 2}{a^2 - a} - \dfrac{2a}{a + 1}$

48. $\dfrac{2x}{x^2 + x - 2} + \dfrac{3}{x + 2}$

49. $\dfrac{2}{x - 2} + \dfrac{x}{x^2 - x - 6}$

50. $\dfrac{2x - 1}{x^2 + 5x + 6} - \dfrac{x - 2}{x^2 + 4x + 3}$

51. $\dfrac{2x - 1}{x^3 - 4x} - \dfrac{x}{x^2 + x - 2}$

52. $\dfrac{2x}{x^2 - 1} + \dfrac{x + 1}{x^2 + 3x - 4}$

53. $\dfrac{2}{x + 2} + \dfrac{3}{x - 2} - \dfrac{5}{x + 3}$

54. $\dfrac{2x}{x + 2} + \dfrac{x}{x - 2} - \dfrac{1}{x^2 - 4}$

55. $\dfrac{2}{y^2 - y} - \dfrac{y}{y + 1} + \dfrac{y + 1}{y}$

56. $\dfrac{3}{x^2 + 5x + 6} - \dfrac{2}{x^2 + 4x + 3} + \dfrac{4}{x^2 + x - 2}$

*57. $\left(\dfrac{2}{x - 1} + \dfrac{3}{x - 2} \right) \cdot \left(\dfrac{x^2 + x - 6}{5x - 7} \right)$

*58. $\left[\dfrac{3}{y + 3} - \dfrac{2y}{(y + 3)(y - 1)} \right] \div \left(\dfrac{y^2 - y - 6}{y^2 + 2y - 3} \right)$

59. Look at the chapter opener. Suppose you are playing a game in which there are two possible actions you may perform each turn. Let's say you decide to perform these actions in a ratio of $x : y$ This would mean that you perform the first action $\frac{x}{x + y}$ of the time and the second action $\frac{y}{x + y}$ of the time. (Here's an example. Your opponent flips a coin and you call out heads or tails. If you performed these actions in a ratio of 3:2 then you would call out heads 3/5 of the time and tails 2/5 of the time.)

   Add the two expressions.

$$\dfrac{x}{x + y} + \dfrac{y}{x + y}$$

   Why does the value of the sum make sense in the given context?

60. A *strategy* for a player with two possible "moves" or choices each time a game is played can be expressed as the ratio $x : y$ described in Exercise 59. Suppose a player receives $5 each time she makes the first choice, and $3 each time she makes the second choice. Then the average amount earned per turn would be given by the expression

$$V = \dfrac{5x + 3y}{x + y}$$

   If a player uses the strategy 3:2, what would be the average amount earned per turn?

5.4   Complex Fractions

At the beginning of this chapter, we said that we would like to simplify fractions such as

$$\frac{1 - \dfrac{1}{x}}{\dfrac{1}{x^2} + \dfrac{1}{x}}$$

This is an example of a **complex fraction**, which is an algebraic expression with a fraction or fractions in the numerator or denominator, or both.

There are two methods commonly used to simplify complex fractions. Fortunately, we already have all the tools needed and will apply both methods to the problem.

Example 1   Simplifying a Complex Fraction

Simplify.

$$\frac{1 - \dfrac{1}{x}}{\dfrac{1}{x^2} + \dfrac{1}{x}}$$

Solution

Method 1

Step 1. Find the LCD of all fractions appearing in the numerator and denominator.

Step 1. The LCD of

$$\frac{1}{1}, \frac{1}{x}, \text{ and } \frac{1}{x^2} \text{ is } x^2$$

Step 2. Multiply the numerator and denominator by the LCD. Since this is multiplication by 1, the result is an equivalent fraction. Then simplify.

Step 2.

$$\frac{x^2\left(1 - \dfrac{1}{x}\right)}{x^2\left(\dfrac{1}{x^2} + \dfrac{1}{x}\right)} = \frac{x^2 - x}{1 + x} = \frac{x(x-1)}{x+1}$$

Method 2

Step 1. Combine the terms in the numerator into a single fraction.

Step 1.

$$1 - \frac{1}{x} = \frac{x}{x} - \frac{1}{x} = \frac{x-1}{x} \qquad \text{(numerator)}$$

Step 2. Combine the terms in the denominator into a single fraction.

Step 2.

$$\frac{1}{x^2} + \frac{1}{x} = \frac{1}{x^2} + \frac{x}{x^2} = \frac{1+x}{x^2} \qquad \text{(denominator)}$$

Step 3. Apply the rule for division of fractions, that is, multiply the numerator by the reciprocal of the denominator.

Step 3.

$$\frac{\dfrac{x-1}{x}}{\dfrac{1+x}{x^2}} = \frac{x-1}{\cancel{x}} \cdot \frac{x^{\cancel{2}}}{1+x} = \frac{x(x-1)}{x+1}$$

✔ **Progress Check 1**

Simplify.

(a) $\dfrac{2+\dfrac{1}{x}}{1-\dfrac{2}{x}}$ (b) $\dfrac{a-1}{1-\dfrac{1}{a}}$

Answers

(a) $\dfrac{2x+1}{x-2}$ (b) a

Example 2   Simplifying a Complex Fraction

Simplify.

$$\frac{\dfrac{a}{b}+\dfrac{b}{a}}{\dfrac{1}{a}-\dfrac{1}{b}}$$

Solution

The LCD of all the fractions is ab. Then, using Method 1, we have

$$\frac{\dfrac{a}{b}+\dfrac{b}{a}}{\dfrac{1}{a}-\dfrac{1}{b}}=\frac{ab\left(\dfrac{a}{b}+\dfrac{b}{a}\right)}{ab\left(\dfrac{1}{a}-\dfrac{1}{b}\right)}=\frac{\dfrac{a^2b}{b}+\dfrac{ab^2}{a}}{\dfrac{ab}{a}-\dfrac{ab}{b}}$$

$$=\frac{a^2+b^2}{b-a}=-\frac{a^2+b^2}{a-b}$$

Using Method 2, we first compute the numerator. Since the LCD is ab, we have

$$\frac{a}{b}+\frac{b}{a}=\frac{a}{b}\cdot\frac{a}{a}+\frac{b}{a}\cdot\frac{b}{b}=\frac{a^2+b^2}{ab}$$

We next compute the denominator. Again, since the LCD is ab, we have

$$\frac{1}{a}-\frac{1}{b}=\frac{1}{a}\cdot\frac{b}{b}-\frac{1}{b}\cdot\frac{a}{a}=\frac{b-a}{ab}$$

Then

$$\frac{\dfrac{a}{b}+\dfrac{b}{a}}{\dfrac{1}{a}-\dfrac{1}{b}}=\frac{\dfrac{a^2+b^2}{ab}}{\dfrac{b-a}{ab}}=\frac{a^2+b^2}{ab}\cdot\frac{ab}{b-a}=\frac{a^2+b^2}{b-a}$$

which is equivalent to the answer obtained by Method 1.

✔ **Progress Check 2**

Simplify.

(a) $\dfrac{\dfrac{y}{x}+\dfrac{1}{y}}{\dfrac{x}{y}-\dfrac{1}{x}}$ (b) $\dfrac{\dfrac{1}{x}-y}{\dfrac{1}{y}-x}$

Answers

(a) $\dfrac{x+y^2}{x^2-y}$ (b) $\dfrac{y}{x}$

Example 3   Working with Complex Fractions

Write as a simple fraction.

$$1+\frac{1+\dfrac{1}{x}}{\dfrac{2}{x}-\dfrac{1}{x-1}}$$

Solution

We first work on the complex fraction to simplify it. The LCD of all the fractions is $x(x-1)$. We multiply numerator and denominator by the LCD.

$$\frac{x(x-1)\left(1+\dfrac{1}{x}\right)}{x(x-1)\left(\dfrac{2}{x}-\dfrac{1}{x-1}\right)}=\frac{(x^2-x)+(x-1)}{2(x-1)-x}=\frac{x^2-1}{x-2}$$

We now substitute this equivalent fraction in the original problem, and carry out the addition.

$$1+\frac{1+\dfrac{1}{x}}{\dfrac{2}{x}-\dfrac{1}{x-1}}=1+\frac{x^2-1}{x-2}=\frac{x-2}{x-2}=\frac{x^2-1}{x-2}=\frac{x^2+x-3}{x-2}$$

✔ **Progress Check 3**

Write as a simple fraction.

(a) $\dfrac{1}{\dfrac{1}{x}+1}-1$ (b) $2+\dfrac{x}{1-\dfrac{1}{x}}$

Answers

(a) $-\dfrac{1}{x+1}$ (b) $\dfrac{x^2+2x-2}{x-1}$

Exercise Set 5.4

In Exercises 1–24 simplify.

1. $\dfrac{1+\dfrac{2}{x}}{1-\dfrac{3}{x}}$

2. $\dfrac{x-\dfrac{1}{x}}{2+\dfrac{1}{x}}$

3. $\dfrac{3-\dfrac{4}{x}}{5x}$

4. $\dfrac{2-\dfrac{1}{x+1}}{x-1}$

5. $\dfrac{x+1}{1-\dfrac{1}{x}}$

6. $\dfrac{1-\dfrac{r^2}{s^2}}{1+\dfrac{r}{s}}$

7. $\dfrac{x^2-16}{\dfrac{1}{4}-\dfrac{1}{x}}$

8. $\dfrac{\dfrac{a}{a-b}-\dfrac{b}{a+b}}{a^2-b^2}$

9. $2-\dfrac{1}{1+\dfrac{1}{a}}$

10. $\dfrac{\dfrac{4}{x^2-4}+1}{\dfrac{x}{x^2+x-6}}$

11. $\dfrac{\dfrac{1}{x^2-4}+\dfrac{1}{x-2}}{3-\dfrac{1}{x-2}}$

12. $\dfrac{\dfrac{3}{x+2}-\dfrac{2}{x-1}}{x-1}$

13. $\dfrac{\dfrac{a}{b}-\dfrac{b}{a}}{\dfrac{1}{a}+\dfrac{1}{b}}$

14. $\dfrac{\dfrac{x}{x-2}-\dfrac{x}{x+2}}{\dfrac{2x}{x-2}+\dfrac{x^2}{x-2}}$

15. $3-\dfrac{2}{1-\dfrac{1}{1+x}}$

16. $2+\dfrac{3}{1+\dfrac{2}{1-x}}$

17. $1-\dfrac{1}{1-\dfrac{x-1}{x+1}}$

18. $x^2+\dfrac{2}{x+\dfrac{x}{x-1}}$

19. $a^2+\dfrac{\dfrac{1}{a}+1}{a-\dfrac{1}{a}}$

20. $\dfrac{\dfrac{1}{x-1}-\dfrac{1}{x+1}+1}{\dfrac{1}{x-3}+\dfrac{1}{x+2}}$

21. $\dfrac{y-\dfrac{1}{1-\dfrac{1}{y}}}{y+\dfrac{1}{1+\dfrac{1}{y}}}$

22. $1-\dfrac{1-\dfrac{1}{y}}{y-\dfrac{1}{y}}$

*23. $1-\dfrac{1}{1+\dfrac{1}{1-\dfrac{1}{1+x}}}$

*24. $1+\dfrac{1}{1-\dfrac{1}{1+\dfrac{1}{1+x}}}$

5.5   Equations and Inequalities with Fractions

Suppose we are interested in solving the equation

$$\frac{2}{x-1}+\frac{1}{3}=\frac{1}{x-1}$$

for x. We must first try to clear the equation of all fractions. Once again, the least common denominator (LCD) is exactly what we need. We will explain the method and illustrate it with this equation.

Solving Equations with Fractions	Example
	$$\dfrac{2}{x-1} + \dfrac{1}{3} = \dfrac{1}{x-1}$$
Step 1. Find the LCD.	*Step 1.* LCD is $3(x-1)$.
Step 2. Multiply both sides of the equation by the LCD. Then carry out all possible cancellations. This will leave an equation without fractions.	*Step 2.*

$$3(x-1)\left(\frac{2}{x-1} + \frac{1}{3}\right) = 3(x-1)\left(\frac{1}{x-1}\right)$$

$$3\cancel{(x-1)}\,\frac{2}{\cancel{x-1}} + 3(x-1)\frac{1}{\cancel{3}} = 3\cancel{(x-1)} \cdot \frac{1}{\cancel{x-1}}$$

$$6 + (x-1) = 3$$

| *Step 3.* Solve the resulting equation. | *Step 3.* |

$$5 + x = 3$$
$$x = -2$$

| *Step 4.* Check the answer(s) obtained in Step 3 by substituting in the original equation. Reject any answers that do not satisfy the equation. | *Step 4.* |

$$\frac{2}{-2-1} + \frac{1}{3} \overset{?}{=} \frac{1}{-2-1}$$

$$-\frac{2}{3} + \frac{1}{3} \overset{?}{=} -\frac{1}{3}$$

$$-\frac{1}{3} \overset{\checkmark}{=} -\frac{1}{3}$$

Warning

When we multiply an expression by a factor, we must multiply *each term* in the expression by that factor.

If you are multiplying an expression by the factor $2x$, *don't* write

$$2x\left(\frac{1}{2x} + 5x\right) = 1 + 5x$$

The correct procedure is

$$2x\left(\frac{1}{2x} + 5x\right) = 1 + 10x^2$$

Note that it is not enough to clear the given equation of all fractions and proceed to find an answer. *The answer may not be a solution of the original equation.* Substituting the answer in the original equation may produce a denominator of 0, and division by 0 is not permitted. Thus, when dealing with equations that involve fractions, *you must always check that the answer is a solution* by substituting in the original equation The following example illustrates this point.

Example 1   Solving an Equation

Solve and check.

$$\frac{8x + 1}{x - 2} + 4 = \frac{7x + 3}{x - 2}$$

Solution

Step 1. The LCD is $x - 2$.

Step 2.

$$(x - 2)\left(\frac{8x + 1}{x - 2} + 4\right) = (x - 2)\left(\frac{7x + 3}{x - 2}\right)$$

$$(x - 2)\frac{8x + 1}{x - 2} + (x - 2) \cdot 4 = (x - 2)\frac{7x + 3}{x - 2}$$

$$8x + 1 + 4x - 8 = 7x + 3$$

$$5x = 10$$

Step 3. $x = 2$.

Step 4. Check: 2 is not a solution since substituting 2 in the original equation yields a denominator of 0, and we cannot divide by 0. Thus, the given equation has no solution.

✔ Progress Check 1

Solve and check.

(a) $\dfrac{3}{x} - 1 = \dfrac{1}{2} - \dfrac{6}{x}$ (b) $-\dfrac{2x}{x + 1} = 1 + \dfrac{2}{x + 1}$

Answers

(a) $x = 6$ (b) no solution

Solving Inequalities with Fractions

In this chapter we will limit ourselves to inequalities with fractions that only have constants in the denominators. When the LCD is a positive number, we may proceed to clear fractions in exactly the same manner as with equations.

Example 2   Solving an Inequality

Solve for x.

$$\frac{x}{2} - 9 < \frac{1 - 2x}{3}$$

Solution

Step 1. The LCD is $2 \cdot 3 = 6$.

Step 2. Multiply both sides by the LCD.

$$6\left(\frac{x}{2} - 9\right) < 6\left(\frac{1 - 2x}{3}\right)$$

$$\frac{6x}{2} - 54 < \frac{\overset{2}{\cancel{6}}(1 - 2x)}{\cancel{3}}$$

$$3x - 54 < 2(1 - 2x) = 2 - 4x$$

Step 3.

$$3x - 54 < 2 - 4x$$

$$3x + 4x < 2 + 54$$

$$7x < 56$$

$$x < 8$$

✔ **Progress Check 2**

Solve.

(a) $\dfrac{3x - 1}{4} + 1 > 2 + \dfrac{x}{3}$ (b) $\dfrac{2 + 3x}{5} - 1 \leq \dfrac{x + 1}{3}$

Answers

(a) $x > 3$ (b) $x \leq \dfrac{7}{2}$

In Chapter 2 we provided examples of equations that have no solutions. The same situation applies for inequalities. Here is an example.

Example 3   Solving an Inequality

Solve.

$$\frac{2(x + 1)}{3} < \frac{2x}{3} - \frac{1}{6}$$

Solution

The LCD is 6. Then

$$6\left[\frac{2(x + 1)}{3}\right] < 6\left(\frac{2x}{3} - \frac{1}{6}\right) \qquad \text{Multiply both sides by 6.}$$

$$4(x + 1) < 6\left(\frac{2x}{3}\right) - 6 \cdot \frac{1}{6}$$

$$4x + 4 < 4x - 1$$

$$4 < -1$$

Our procedure has led to a contradiction, indicating that there is no solution to the inequality.

✔ **Progress Check 3**

Solve.

$$\frac{2x-3}{2} \geq x + \frac{2}{5}$$

Answer

no solution

Exercise Set 5.5

In Exercises 1–30 solve and check.

1. $\frac{x}{2} = \frac{5}{3}$

2. $\frac{3x}{4} - 5 = \frac{1}{4}$

3. $\frac{2}{x} + 1 = \frac{3}{x}$

4. $\frac{5}{a} - \frac{3}{2} = \frac{1}{4}$

5. $\frac{x}{x+3} = \frac{3}{5}$

6. $\frac{a}{a-2} = \frac{3}{5}$

7. $\frac{2y-3}{y+3} = \frac{5}{7}$

8. $\frac{1-4x}{1-2x} = \frac{9}{8}$

9. $\frac{1}{x-2} + \frac{1}{2} = \frac{2}{x-2}$

10. $\frac{4}{x-4} - 2 = \frac{1}{x-4}$

11. $\frac{3r+1}{r+3} + 2 = \frac{5r-2}{r+3}$

12. $\frac{2x-1}{x-5} + 3 = \frac{3x-2}{5-x}$

13. $\frac{2x-3}{2x+1} + 3 = \frac{2}{2x+1}$

14. $\frac{4t+3}{2t-1} - 2 = \frac{5}{2t-1}$

15. $\frac{2}{x-2} + \frac{2}{x^2-4} = \frac{3}{x+2}$

16. $\frac{3}{x-1} + \frac{2}{x+1} = \frac{5}{x^2-1}$

17. $\frac{4-3x}{3x-1} = \frac{3}{2} - \frac{2x+3}{1-3x}$

18. $\frac{3a+2}{a-3} + 1 = \frac{a+8}{a-3}$

19. $\frac{x}{x-1} - 1 = \frac{3}{x+1}$

20. $\frac{2}{x-2} + 1 = \frac{x+2}{x-2}$

21. $\frac{4}{b} - \frac{1}{b+3} = \frac{3b+2}{b^2+2b-3}$

22. $\frac{3}{x^2-2x} + \frac{2x-1}{x^2+2x-8} = \frac{2}{x+4}$

23. $\frac{x}{2} - 3 < \frac{1}{2}$

24. $\frac{a}{3} - 2 > \frac{2}{3}$

25. $\frac{x}{2} - 2 \geq x - \frac{3}{2}$

26. $\frac{t}{3} - 1 \leq t + \frac{2}{3}$

27. $\frac{4-x}{3} \geq 2 - x$

28. $\frac{x}{3} - 5 < \frac{2-3x}{4}$

29. $\frac{3x-2}{3} \geq x + \frac{1}{2}$

30. $\frac{2x-1}{3} \geq x + 2$

*31. Solve for y:

$$a + \frac{4}{y-1} = \frac{2}{3}$$

*32. Solve for t:

$$b + \frac{2}{t-1} = \frac{3}{1-t}$$

*33. Solve the inequality for r.

$$\frac{r-1}{2} \leq \frac{r+1}{a} \qquad a > 2$$

*34. Solve the inequality for s.

$$\frac{3s}{a} \leq \frac{a+1}{a^2} \qquad a > 0$$

35. Refer to Section 5.3, Exercise 60. In Game Theory the word "oddment" is sometimes used to express the value of one part of a ratio. So 3 and 2 would be the oddments of the ratio 3:2.

Using the rational expression

$$V = \frac{5x+3y}{x+y}$$

what value of the x oddment would result in a game with value $V = 4.5$, if the y oddment is equal to 1?

5.6 Applications; Work Problems

Many applications involve equations or inequalities with rational expressions. To handle these, you will have to use everything you have learned about "setting up" word problems and then follow the techniques given in the prior section to solve the equation or inequality.

Example 1   Solving a Word Problem

A certain number is 3 times another number. If the sum of their reciprocals is $\frac{20}{3}$, find the numbers.

Solution

Let

$$x = \text{the smaller number}$$

Then

$$3x = \text{the larger number}$$

The reciprocals of these numbers are $\dfrac{1}{x}$ and $\dfrac{1}{3x}$, so that

$$\frac{1}{x} + \frac{1}{3x} = \frac{20}{3}$$

We multiply both sides by the LCD, which is $3x$.

$$3x\left(\frac{1}{x} + \frac{1}{3x}\right) = 3x\left(\frac{20}{3}\right)$$

$$3 + 1 = 20x$$

$$4 = 20x$$

$$x = \frac{4}{20} = \frac{1}{5}$$

The numbers are then $\frac{1}{5}$ and $\frac{3}{5}$.

Check: We add the reciprocals.

$$\frac{5}{1} + \frac{5}{3} = \frac{15}{3} + \frac{5}{3} = \frac{20}{3}$$

and verify that $\frac{1}{5}$ and $\frac{3}{5}$ constitute a solution.

✔ Progress Check 1

One number is twice another. If the difference of their reciprocals is $\frac{8}{3}$, find the numbers.

Answers

$\dfrac{3}{8}$ and $\dfrac{3}{16}$; $-\dfrac{3}{8}$ and $-\dfrac{3}{16}$

Example 2   Solving a Word Problem

The denominator of a fraction is 2 more than its numerator. If $\frac{5}{2}$ is added to the fraction, the result is $\frac{17}{6}$. Find the fraction.

Solution

Let

$$x = \text{the numerator of the fraction}$$

Then

$$x + 2 = \text{the denominator of the fraction}$$

The fraction is then $\dfrac{x}{x + 2}$, and we have

$$\frac{x}{x + 2} + \frac{5}{2} = \frac{17}{6}$$

We multiply both sides by the LCD, which is $6(x + 2)$.

$$6(x + 2)\left(\frac{x}{x + 2} + \frac{5}{2}\right) = 6(x + 2)\left(\frac{17}{6}\right)$$

$$6x + 15(x + 2) = 17(x + 2)$$

$$21x + 30 = 17x + 34$$

$$4x = 4$$

$$x = 1$$

Then

$$\frac{x}{x + 2} = \frac{1}{3}$$

is the fraction. (Verify that the fraction $\frac{1}{3}$ does satisfy the given conditions.)

✔ Progress Check 2

The numerator of a fraction is 3 more than its denominator. If the fraction is subtracted from $\frac{11}{4}$, the result is 1. Find the fraction.

Answer

$$\frac{7}{4}$$

Example 3   Solving a Distance Problem

An airplane flying against the wind travels 150 miles in the same time that it can travel 180 miles with the wind. If the wind speed is 10 miles per hour, what is the speed of the airplane in still air?

Solution

Let r = the rate (or speed) of the airplane in still air. Let's display the information that we have.

	Rate	×	Time	=	Distance
With wind	$r + 10$		t		180
Against wind	$r - 10$		t		150

From the equation rate × time = distance, we know

$$\text{time} = \frac{\text{distance}}{\text{rate}}$$

Since we are told that the time of travel with the wind is the same as that against the wind, we have

$$\text{time with wind} = \text{time against wind}$$

$$\frac{180}{r + 10} = \frac{150}{r - 10}$$

Multiplying both sides of the equation by the LCD, which is $(r + 10)(r - 10)$, we have

$$(r + 10)(r - 10)\left(\frac{180}{r + 10}\right) = (r + 10)(r - 10)\left(\frac{150}{r - 10}\right)$$

$$180(r - 10) = 150(r + 10)$$

$$180r - 1800 = 150r + 1500$$

$$30r = 3300$$

$$r = 110$$

The rate of the plane in still air is 110 miles per hour.

✔ Progress Check 3

An express train travels 200 miles in the same time that a local train travels 150 miles. If the express train travels 20 miles per hour faster than the local train, find the rate of each train.

Answer

local: 60 miles per hour; express: 80 miles per hour

Work Problems

There is a class of problems called **work problems** that lead to equations with fractions. Work problems typically involve two or more people or machines working on the same task. The key to these problems is to express the rate of work per unit of time, whether an hour, a day, a week, or some other unit. For example, if a machine can do a job in 5 days, then

$$\text{rate of machine} = \frac{1}{5} \text{ job per day}$$

If this machine were used for two days, it would perform $\frac{2}{5}$ of the job. In summary:

If a machine (or person) can complete a job in n days, then

$$\text{rate of machine (or person)} = \frac{1}{n} \text{ job per day}$$

$$\text{work done} = \text{rate} \times \text{time}$$

The assumption made in these problems is that the people or machines involved work at the same rate at all times, whether working alone or together.

Example 4   Solving a Work Problem

A firm with two factories receives an order for the manufacture of circuit boards. Factory A can complete the order in 20 days and factory B can complete the order in 30 days. How long will it take to complete the order if both factories are assigned to the task?

Solution

Let x = number of days for completing the job when both factories are assigned. We can display the information in a table.

	Time alone	Rate	×	Time	=	Work done
Factory A	20	$\frac{1}{20}$		x		$\frac{x}{20}$
Factory B	30	$\frac{1}{30}$		x		$\frac{x}{30}$

Since

$$\begin{array}{c}\text{work done by}\\\text{factory A}\end{array} \quad + \quad \begin{array}{c}\text{work done by}\\\text{factory B}\end{array} \quad = \quad 1 \text{ whole job}$$

we have

$$\frac{x}{20} + \frac{x}{30} = 1$$

Multiplying both sides by the LCD, which is 60, we have

$$60\left(\frac{x}{20} + \frac{x}{30}\right) = 60 \cdot 1$$

$$3x + 2x = 60$$

$$5x = 60$$

$$x = 12$$

Thus, it takes 12 days to complete the job if both factories are assigned to the task.

Example 5   Solving a Work Problem

Using a small mower, a student begins to mow a lawn at 12 noon, a job that would take him 9 hours. At 1 P.M. another student, using a tractor, joins him, and they complete the job together at 3 P.M. How many hours would it take to do the job by tractor only?

Solution

Let x = number of hours to do the job by tractor alone. The small mower worked from 12 noon to 3 P.M., or 3 hours; the tractor was used from 1 P.M. to 3 P.M., or 2 hours. All of the information can be displayed in a table.

	Time alone	Rate	×	Time	=	Work done
Small mower	9	$\dfrac{1}{9}$		3		$\dfrac{3}{9}$
Tractor	x	$\dfrac{1}{x}$		2		$\dfrac{2}{x}$

since

$$\begin{array}{c}\text{work done by} \\ \text{small mower}\end{array} + \begin{array}{c}\text{work done by} \\ \text{tractor}\end{array} = 1 \text{ whole job}$$

we have

$$\frac{3}{9} + \frac{2}{x} = 1$$

To solve, multiply both sides by the LCD, which is $9x$.

$$9x\left(\frac{3}{9} + \frac{2}{x}\right) = 9x \cdot 1$$
$$3x + 18 = 9x$$
$$18 = 6x$$
$$x = 3$$

Thus, by tractor alone, the job can be done in 3 hours.

✔ **Progress Check 5**

A printing press can print the morning newspaper in 6 hours. After the press has been in operation for 2 hours, a second press joins in printing the paper, and both presses finish the job in 2 more hours. How long would it take the second press to print the morning newspaper if it had to do the entire job alone?

Answer

6 hours

Exercise Set 5.6

1. If two thirds of a certain number is added to one half of the number, the result is 21. Find the number.

2. If one fourth of a certain number is added to one third of the number, the result is 14. Find the number.

3. A certain number is twice another. If the sum of their reciprocals is 4, find the numbers.

4. A certain number is 3 times another. If the difference of their reciprocals is 8, find the numbers. (There are two solutions.)

5. The denominator of a fraction is one more than its numerator. If $\frac{1}{2}$ is added to the fraction, the result is $\frac{5}{4}$. Find the fraction.

6. The numerator of a certain fraction is 3 less than its denominator. If $\frac{1}{10}$ is added to the fraction, the result is $\frac{1}{2}$. Find the fraction.

7. If $\frac{3}{2}$ is added to twice the reciprocal of a certain number, the result is 2. Find the number.

8. If $\frac{1}{3}$ is subtracted from 3 times the reciprocal of a certain number, the result is $\frac{25}{6}$. Find the number.

9. John can mow a lawn in 2 hours, and Peter can mow the same lawn in 3 hours. How long would it take to mow the lawn if they worked together?

10. Computer A can carry out an engineering analysis in 4 hours, and computer B can do the same job in 6 hours. How long would it take to complete the job if both computers worked together?

11. Jackie can paint a certain room in 3 hours, Lisa in 4 hours, and Susan in 2 hours. How long will it take to paint the room if they all work together?

12. A mechanic and assistant, working together, can repair an engine in 3 hours. Working alone, the mechanic can complete the job in 5 hours. How long would it take the assistant to do the job alone?

13. Copying machine A and B, working together, can prepare enough copies of the annual report for the board of directors meeting in 2 hours. Machine A, working alone, requires 3 hours to do the job. How long would it take machine B to do the job by itself?

14. A 5-horsepower snowblower together with an 8-horsepower snowblower can clear a parking lot in 1 hour. The 5-horsepower blower, working alone, can do the job in 3 hours. How long would it take the 8-horsepower blower to do the job by itself?

15. Hoses A and B together can fill a swimming pool in 5 hours. If hose A alone takes 12 hours to fill the pool, how long would it take hose B to fill the pool?

16. A senior copy editor together with a junior copy editor can edit a book in 3 days. The junior editor, working alone, would take twice as long to complete the job as the senior editor would require if working alone. How long would it take each editor to complete the job by herself?

17. Hose A can fill a certain vat in 3 hours. After 2 hours of pumping, hose A is turned off. Hose B is then turned on and completes filling the vat in 3 hours. How long would it take hose B alone to fill the vat?

18. A shovel dozer together with a large backhoe can complete a certain excavation project in 4 hours. The shovel dozer is half as fast as the large backhoe. How long would it take each piece of equipment to complete the job by itself?

19. A printing shop starts a job at 10 A.M. using press A. Using this press alone, it would take 8 hours to complete the job. At 2 P.M. press B is also turned on, and both presses together finish the job at 4 P.M. How long would it take press B to do the job by itself?

20. A moped covers 40 miles in the same time that a bicycle covers 24 miles. If the rate of the moped is 8 miles per hour faster than the bicycle, find the rate of each vehicle.

21. A boat travels 20 kilometers upstream in the same time that it would take the same boat to travel 30 kilometers downstream. If the rate of the stream is 5 kilometers per hour, find the speed of the boat in still water.

22. An airplane flying against the wind travels 300 miles in the same time that it would take the same plane to travel 400 miles with the wind. If the wind speed is 20 miles per hour, find the speed of the airplane in still air.

23. Car A can travel 20 kilometers per hour faster than car B. If car B covers 240 kilometers in the same time that car B covers 200 kilometers, what is the speed of each car?

24. A sedan is 20 miles per hour slower than a sports car. If the sedan can travel 160 miles in the same time that the sports car travels 240 miles, find the speed of each car.

5.7   Ratio and Proportion

Suppose that in looking about your mathematics classroom you find there are 10 male and 14 female students. If we understand **ratio** to be the quotient of two quantities, we see that the ratio of male students to female students is $\frac{10}{14}$ or $\frac{5}{7}$, which we can also write as 10:14 (read "10 to 14").

Ratio

Example 1   Simple Ratios
The entire stock of a small photography store consists of 75 Kodak and 60 Polaroid cameras.

(a) What is the ratio of Kodak to Polaroid cameras?

(b) What is the ratio of Polaroid cameras to the entire stock?

Solution

(a) $\dfrac{\text{Kodak}}{\text{Polaroid}} = \dfrac{75}{60} = \dfrac{5}{4}$ (or Kodak:Polaroid = 5:4)

(b) $\dfrac{\text{Polaroid}}{\text{entire stock}} = \dfrac{60}{135} = \dfrac{4}{9}$ (or Polaroid:entire stock = 4:9)

✔ Progress Check 1

The American alligator is an endangered species. On an American alligator reserve, there are 600 females and 900 males. Find the ratio of

(a) males to females.

(b) females to males.

(c) females to total number of alligators.

Answers

(a) 9:6 or $\dfrac{3}{2}$ (b) 6:9 or $\dfrac{2}{3}$ (c) 6:15 or $\dfrac{2}{5}$

Ratios can often be used to solve word problems. They enable us to set up equations that can then be solved.

Example 2   Using Ratios in a Word Problem

The length and width of a rectangular room are in the ratio 3:4. If the perimeter of the room is 70 feet, what are the dimensions of the room?

Solution

Let $3x$ denote the length of the room. Then the width must be $4x$, since

$$\frac{\text{length}}{\text{width}} = \frac{3}{4} = \frac{3x}{4x}$$

The perimeter P of the rectangle is given by

$$P = \text{length} + \text{length} + \text{width} + \text{width}$$
$$70 = 2(\text{length} + \text{width})$$
$$70 = 2(3x + 4x)$$
$$70 = 14x$$
$$x = 5 \text{ feet}$$

Thus,

$$\text{length} = 3x = 3(5) = 15 \text{ feet}$$
$$\text{width} = 4x = 4(5) = 20 \text{ feet}$$

✔ **Progress Check 2**

The ratios of two angles of a triangle to the smallest angle are 1:2 and 1:3, respectively. Find the measure of each angle. (*Hint:* The sum of the angles of a triangle is 180°.)

Answer

30°, 60°, 90°

Proportion

When two ratios are set equal to each other we have what is called a **proportion**. We shall soon see that proportions will be useful in solving many word problems. First we practice the mechanics of operating with proportions.

Example 3   Proportions

Solve for x.

$$\frac{x}{12} = \frac{4}{9}$$

Solution

Multiplying both sides of the equation by 12, we have

$$\frac{x}{12} \cdot \frac{12}{1} = \frac{4}{9} \cdot \frac{12}{1} = \frac{48}{9} = \frac{16}{3}$$

Thus,

$$x = \frac{16}{3}$$

✔ **Progress Check 3**

Solve for r.

(a) $\dfrac{3}{r-1} = \dfrac{1}{4}$ (b) $\dfrac{4}{2} = \dfrac{2r}{5}$

Answers

(a) $r = 13$ (b) $r = 5$

The Most Pleasing Rectangle

From the time of the ancient Greeks, certain ratios have played a surprising role in aesthetics and, in particular, in architecture.

Suppose that a line segment of length L is divided into two parts of lengths a and b, as in Figure 1. If

Figure 1 Golden Ratio

$$\frac{L}{a} = \frac{a}{b}$$

then the ratio $a{:}b$, denoted by ϕ (the Greek letter phi) is called the **golden ratio**. The great German astronomer Kepler called it the "divine proportion," and many extraordinary properties of this number have been developed since the Middle Ages. We will show in Section 9.2 that the numerical value of ϕ is approximately 1.61803.

The ancient Greek architects observed that a rectangle the lengths of whose adjacent sides are in the ratio $\phi{:}1$ appears to be the most pleasing rectangle to a majority of viewers. This rectangle, shown in Figure 2, is called the **golden rectangle**, and psychological experiments in the late 1800s backed up the findings of the early Greeks, whose architects put great faith in the golden rectangle. The proportions of the Parthenon in Athens, built in the fifth century B.C., are those of the golden rectangle.

Figure 2 Golden Rectangle

Golden Rectangle			
L	a	b	ϕ
1	.618033989	.381966011	1.61803399
2	1.23606798	.763932023	1.61803399
3	1.85410197	1.14589803	1.61803399
4	2.47213596	1.52786405	1.61803399
5	3.09016994	1.90983006	1.61803399
6	3.70820393	2.29179607	1.61803399
7	4.32623792	2.267376208	1.61803399
8	4.94427191	3.05572809	1.61803399
9	5.56230590	3.43769410	1.61803399
10	6.18033989	3.81966011	1.61803399

Applications

We now turn to the use of proportions in the solution of applied problems.

Example 4   Proportions in a Word Problem

ABC University has determined that a student-teacher ratio of 19:2 is ideal. If there will be 855 students next fall, how large a teaching staff will be required, assuming that the ideal student-faculty ratio will be maintained?

Solution

Let x denote the number of teachers. Then

$$\frac{\text{students}}{\text{teachers}} = \frac{19}{2} = \frac{855}{x}$$

Then, multiplying by $2x$ to clear fractions, we have

$$19x = 2(855) = 1710$$

$$x = \frac{1710}{19} = 90$$

Thus, 90 teachers are required.

✔ Progress Check 4

Four out of every five homes in suburban Philadelphia have two telephones. If 25,000 new homes are to be built, how many of these will have two telephones?

Answer

20,000

Example 5   Proportions in a Word Problem

A landscaping service advertises that the cost of sodding a 1500-square-foot area is $240. What would be the proportional cost of sodding an area of 3500 square feet?

Solution

Let x be the cost of sodding the larger area. Then

$$\frac{\text{area}}{\text{cost}} = \frac{1500}{240} = \frac{3500}{x}$$

or, after clearing fractions,

$$1500x = 840,000$$

$$x = 560$$

Thus, the proportional cost is $560.

✔ Progress Check 5

The cost of an airplane flight of 600 miles is $75. What is the proportional cost of a flight of 1600 miles?

Answer

$200

Exercise Set 5.7

In Exercises 1−6 write as a ratio.

1. 5.08 centimeters to 2 inches

2. 2 inches to 5.08 centimeters

3. 8 feet to 2.5 feet

4. 1.3 inches to 12 inches

5. 12 cubic feet to 16 cubic feet

6. 2.12 quarts to 2 liters

7. One side of a triangle is 8 centimeters. The other two sides are in the ratio 5:4. If the perimeter of the triangle is 44 centimeters, find the dimension of the other two sides.

8. An artist wants to make a rectangular frame whose length and width are in the ratio 2:3. If the amount of framing material that is available is 25 inches, find the dimensions of the frame.

In Exercises 9−14 solve for the unknown in each proportion.

9. $\dfrac{x}{3} = \dfrac{6}{5}$

10. $\dfrac{y}{4} = \dfrac{2}{3}$

11. $\dfrac{5}{2} = \dfrac{3}{4r}$

12. $\dfrac{6}{5r} = \dfrac{2}{3}$

13. $\dfrac{2}{r+1} = \dfrac{1}{3}$

14. $\dfrac{5}{s-1} = \dfrac{3}{2}$

15. Two numbers whose sum is 30 are in the ratio of 3:7. Find the numbers.

16. A stockbroker charges a commission of $42 on the purchase or sale of 500 shares of stock. What would be the proportional commission on the purchase or sale of 800 shares of stock?

17. A taxpayer pays a state tax of $400 on an income of $12,000. What is the proportional tax on an income of $15,000?

18. In a certain county of Ohio, the ratio of Republicans to Democrats is 3:2.

 (a) If there are 1800 Republicans, how many Democrats are there?

 (b) If there are 1800 Democrats, how many Republicans are there?

19. A toy train manufacturer makes a $\frac{1}{2}$-foot-long locomotive model of a 40-foot-long actual locomotive. If the same scale is maintained, how long is a sleeping car whose scale model is 0.75 foot long?

20. On a certain map, 2 centimeters represents 25 kilometers. How many kilometers does 8 centimeters represent?

21. If 5 out of 6 people in Philadelphia read *The Inquirer*, how many readers of this paper are there in an area with a population of 66,000 people?

22. A car uses 12 gallons of gasoline to travel 216 miles. Assuming the same type of driving, how many gallons of gasoline will be used on a 441-mile trip?

23. If a photocopying machine can produce 740 copies in 40 minutes, how many copies can it produce in 52 minutes?

24. A chemical plant that makes 120 tons daily of a certain product discharges 500 gallons of waste products into a nearby stream. If production is increased to 200 tons daily, how many gallons of waste products will be dumped into the stream?

25. A 150-pound person is given 18 cubic centimeters of a certain drug for a metabolic disorder. How much of the drug will be required by a 200-pound person, assuming the same dose-to-weight ratio?

26. A marketing research firm has determined that two out of five suburban car owners have a station wagon. How many station wagon owners are there among 40,000 suburban car owners?

*27. Solve the following proportion for r:

$$\frac{3}{r-1} = \frac{4}{a}$$

*28. Solve the following proportion for s:

$$\frac{2s}{a} = \frac{s-1}{2}$$

5.8   Critical Thinking Problems

In previous sections, we learned how to solve a variety of word problems. We will now review some of these methods.

Example 1   Making Equal Amounts of Money
Bob and Jamie work at Denny's restaurant. Bob received $48 as tips. When Jamie counted her tips, she had $26. How much money should Bob give to Jamie so that they will both have the same amount of tips?

Solution
After you read the problem, ask yourself, What we are looking for? How much money should Bob give to Jamie?

We don't know. So, let's say that

$$x = \text{the amount of money that Bob should give to Jamie}$$

If Bob gives x amount of money to Jamie, then Bob has $48 - x$ and Jamie has $26 + x$. Since they now have equal amounts, we can set these expressions so that they are equal to each other.

$$\$48 - x = \$26 + x$$
$$48 - x - x = 26 + x - x \qquad \text{Subtracting } x \text{ from both sides}$$
$$48 - 2x = 26$$
$$48 - 2x - 48 = 26 - 48 \qquad \text{Subtracting 48 from both sides}$$
$$-2x = -22$$
$$\frac{-2x}{-2} = \frac{-22}{-2} \qquad \text{Dividing both sides by } -2$$
$$x = \$11$$

Check:
$$\text{Bob will have } \$48 - \$11 = \$37.$$
$$\text{Jamie will have } \$26 + \$11 = \$37.$$

Therefore, Bob must give $11 to Jamie.

✔ **Progress Check 1**

(a) Mrs. Johns has $5,800 in her savings account and Mr. Johns has $3,600 in his. In order for them to have the same amount in each account, how much should Mrs. Johns give to Mr. Johns?

(b) David has $45 and Paul has $15. How much money should David give to Paul so that Paul's new amount is twice David's new amount?

Answers
(a) $1,100   (b) $25

Let's practice more motion problems. Once again, we will use the distance formula.

$$\text{distance} = \text{rate} \cdot \text{time}$$

Example 2 Finding the Speed of a Car

I drive a car 220 miles from Cerritos to Santa Maria, taking three different freeways—605 North, 5 North, and 101 North. I drive at a rate of r mph for 30 minutes on 605 North, at a rate that is 10 mph faster for the next 45 minutes on 5 North, and at a rate that is two times faster than the rate on 605 North for the next 2.5 hours on 101 North. Find the speed of my car on each freeway.

Solution

We need to find rates of travel on each different freeway. Once we find one of the rates, then we can figure out the remaining two rates.

First, what is the rate on 605 North? We don't know, so we let

$$r = \text{the rate of the car on 605 North}$$

Then what is the rate on 5 North?

rate on 5 North = rate that is 10 mph faster than the rate on 605 North
rate on 5 North = $10 + r$

What is the rate on 101 North?

rate on 101 North = rate that is twice the rate on 605 North
rate on 101 North = $2r$

Be careful to convert units for time. Since the rate is miles per hour (we simply write *mph*), we need to convert 30 minutes and 45 minutes to hours.

	rate	time	distance
605 North	r	$\frac{30}{60} = \frac{1}{2}$ hr	$\frac{1}{2}r$
5 North	$r + 10$	$\frac{45}{60} = \frac{3}{4}$ hr	$\frac{3}{4}(r + 10)$
101 North	$2r$	2.5 hr	$2.5(2r)$

The sum of the distances traveled on the three different freeways is 200 miles. We write the equation as follows:

$$\frac{1}{2}r + \frac{3}{4}(r + 10) + 2.5(2r) = 220$$

Let's solve this equation.

To eliminate fractions, we will multiply both sides by the least common denominator (LCD), which is 4.

$$4 \cdot \left[\frac{1}{2}r + \frac{3}{4}(r + 10) + 2.5(2r)\right] = 220 \cdot 4$$

$$4 \cdot \frac{1}{2}r + 4 \cdot \frac{3}{4}(r + 10) + 4 \cdot 2.5 \cdot (2r) = 880$$

$$2r + 3(r + 10) + 10(2r) = 880$$

$$2r + 3r + 30 + 20r = 880 \qquad \text{Distributive Property}$$

$$25r + 30 = 880 \qquad \text{Combining like terms}$$

$$25r + 30 - 30 = 880 - 30 \qquad \text{Subtracting 30 from both sides}$$

$$25r = 850$$

$$\frac{25r}{25} = \frac{850}{25} \qquad \text{Dividing both sides by 25}$$

$$r = 34 \text{ mph}$$

Since $r = 34$, the rate on 605 North is 34 mph.

The rate on 5 North is

$$= r + 10$$
$$= 34 + 10$$
$$= 44 \text{ mph}$$

The rate on 101 North is

$$= 2r$$
$$= 2(34)$$
$$= 68 \text{ mph}$$

Check: We can check the solution by substituting $r = 34$ into the original equation.

$$\frac{1}{2}(34) + \frac{3}{4}(34 + 10) + 2.5(2 \cdot 34) = 220$$

$$17 + \frac{3}{4}(44) + 2.5(68) = 220$$

$$17 + 3(11) + 170 = 220$$
$$17 + 33 + 170 = 220$$
$$50 + 170 = 220$$
$$220 = 220$$

Therefore, the three rates are 34 mph on 605 North, 44 mph on 5 North, and 68 mph on 101 North.

✔ Progress Check 2

(a) On a trip Mr. Brown drives at r mph for the first 2 hours and then at 65 miles per hour for the next 3 hours. The total distance Mr. Brown travels is 265 miles. Find the rate r.

(b) Paul drives at 55 mph for t hours on the freeway and then drives at 40 mph on the road. His total driving time is 5 hours. Find the number of hours he drives at each rate if the total distance he travels is 245 miles.

Answers

(a) 35 mph　　(b) 3 hours at 55 mph and 2 hours at 40 mph

■ ■ ■

Terms and Symbols

algebraic fraction	proportion	rational number
cancellation principle	ratio $a{:}b$	work problems
complex fraction	rational expression	
LCD		

Key Ideas for Review

Topic	Key Idea
Cancellation principle	Nonzero *factors* appearing in both the numerator and denominator of a fraction may be canceled, provided they are factors of the entire numerator and the entire denominator.
Simplifying a rational expression	To simplify a rational expression, follow these steps: *Step 1.* Factor the numerator completely. *Step 2.* Factor the denominator completely. *Step 3.* Use the cancellation principle to cancel factors that are common to both the numerator and the denominator.
Multiplication and division of rational expressions	$$\frac{a}{b} \cdot \frac{c}{d} = \frac{ac}{bd} \qquad \frac{\dfrac{a}{b}}{\dfrac{c}{d}} = \frac{a}{b} \cdot \frac{d}{c} = \frac{ad}{bc}$$
Addition and subtraction of rational expressions	To add or subtract rational expressions with the same denominator, follow these rules: $$\frac{a}{c} + \frac{b}{c} = \frac{a+b}{c}$$ $$\frac{a}{c} - \frac{b}{c} = \frac{a-b}{c}$$
Least Common Denominator (LCD)	The LCD of two or more algebraic fractions is found by forming the product of all the different factors in the denominators, each factor raised to the highest power that it has in any denominator.

(continues)

Key Ideas for Review, continued

Topic	Key Idea
Complex fractions	Complex fractions can be simplified by two methods:
	Method 1. Multiply the numerator and denominator by the LCD of all the fractions appearing in the complex fraction.
	Method 2. Reduce the numerator and denominator, independently, into simple fractions, and then perform the division.
Equations and inequalities with fractions	To solve an equation involving fractions, find the LCD and multiply both sides of the equation by the LCD. This will produce an equation without fractions. If the LCD involved the unknown, then the answer *must be checked.*
	Inequalities with only constants in the denominator can be handled in the same manner as equations, if we choose the LCD to be a positive number.

Common Errors

1. It is essential to factor completely before attempting cancellation. This will allow you to see which factors are common to the entire numerator and the entire denominator.

2. *Don't* write

$$\frac{xy - 2y}{x} = y - 2y$$

Since x is not a factor of the entire numerator, we may not cancel.

3. *Don't* write

$$\frac{x^2 - y^2}{x - y} = x - y$$

After factoring completely, we see that

$$\frac{x^2 - y^2}{x - y} = \frac{(x + y)(x - y)}{x - y} = x + y$$

4. If an equation is multiplied by an LCD involving a variable, you must check that the answer is a solution of the original equation. The answer may result in a zero in a denominator, in which case it is not a solution.

Review Exercises

Solutions to exercises whose numbers are in bold are in the Solutions section in the back of the book.

5.1 In Exercises 1–4 simplify the given expression, if possible.

1. $\dfrac{5x + 10}{5}$

2. $\dfrac{2x - 3}{2}$

3. $\dfrac{x^2 - 2x - 8}{x + 2}$

4. $\dfrac{4x^3 - 2x^2 + 6x}{2x}$

5.2 In Exercises 5–10 compute and simplify.

5. $\dfrac{x - 1}{2} \cdot \dfrac{x - 2}{3}$

6. $\dfrac{2x - 1}{3} \cdot \dfrac{2x + 1}{2}$

7. $\dfrac{4x}{x + 1} \div \dfrac{2x^2}{x - 1}$

8. $\dfrac{2x^3 - 8x}{x^2 - 3x - 4} \div \dfrac{x^2 - 2x}{x^2 - 1}$

9. $\dfrac{2x^2 + 3x - 2}{3x^2 + x - 2} \cdot \dfrac{2x^2 + 5x + 3}{2x^2 + 5x + 2}$

10. $\dfrac{x^2 + x - 6}{x^2 - 9} \div \dfrac{x^2 + 5x + 6}{x^2 - 4x + 3}$

5.3 In Exercises 11–14 find the least common denominator.

11. $\dfrac{5}{x + 2}, \dfrac{2}{x - 2}$

12. $\dfrac{3x}{x - 2}, \dfrac{5 + x}{(x - 2)^2}$

13. $\dfrac{3y}{y^2 - 4}, \dfrac{2}{y + 2}, \dfrac{4y^2}{y^2 - 2y}$

14. $\dfrac{2x}{3y}, \dfrac{x - 1}{y^2}, \dfrac{x^2 + 2x}{y - 1}$

In Exercises 15–20 perform the indicated operations and simplify.

15. $\dfrac{2 - x^2}{x} + \dfrac{4 + 2x^2}{3x}$ **16.** $\dfrac{2a - 1}{a - 1} + \dfrac{2a}{a + 1}$

17. $3 - \dfrac{2a}{a - 2}$

18. $\dfrac{2y}{(2x + 3)(x - 1)} - \dfrac{y - 1}{2x + 3}$

19. $\dfrac{x + 1}{2(x^2 - 9)} + \dfrac{x - 3}{3(x - 3)} - \dfrac{x}{x + 3}$

20. $2 - \dfrac{x}{x^2 - 1} + \dfrac{2x - 3}{2(x + 1)}$

5.4 In Exercises 21–26 simplify the given expression.

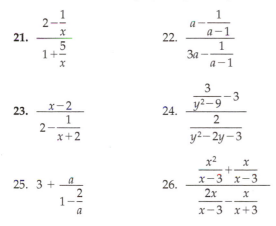

21. $\dfrac{2 - \dfrac{1}{x}}{1 + \dfrac{5}{x}}$ **22.** $\dfrac{a - \dfrac{1}{a - 1}}{3a - \dfrac{1}{a - 1}}$

23. $\dfrac{x - 2}{2 - \dfrac{1}{x + 2}}$ **24.** $\dfrac{\dfrac{3}{y^2 - 9} - 3}{\dfrac{2}{y^2 - 2y - 3}}$

25. $3 + \dfrac{a}{1 - \dfrac{2}{a}}$ **26.** $\dfrac{\dfrac{x^2}{x - 3} + \dfrac{x}{x - 3}}{\dfrac{2x}{x - 3} - \dfrac{x}{x + 3}}$

5.5 In Exercises 27–32 solve and check.

27. $\dfrac{x}{2} = \dfrac{2}{7}$ **28.** $\dfrac{2x - 1}{3} = \dfrac{2}{3}$

29. $\dfrac{2a}{5} + 1 = \dfrac{3}{4}$ **30.** $\dfrac{y}{2y - 1} = \dfrac{2}{5}$

31. $\dfrac{2x + 1}{2x - 1} = -\dfrac{2}{3}$ **32.** $\dfrac{2r - 1}{2r + 3} - 2 = \dfrac{3}{2r + 3}$

5.6 **33.** The denominator of a fraction is 2 less than its numerator. If $\frac{2}{3}$ is added to the fraction, the result is $\frac{7}{3}$. Find the fraction.

34. A certain number is three times another. If the difference of their reciprocals is $\frac{2}{3}$, find the number. (There are two answers.)

35. If $\frac{1}{2}$ is added to three times the reciprocal of a certain number, the result is 2. Find the number.

36. A typing service finds that employee A can type a complete manuscript in 10 days, and employee

B can type it in 15 days. How long will it take to type the manuscript if both employees work on it?

37. Two photographers working together can complete a fashion assignment in 3 hours. Working alone, the senior photographer can complete the job in 5 hours. How long would it take the junior photographer to complete the job?

38. The first author of a mathematics textbook starts to work on the book on January 1, 2005, and can complete the book on December 31, 2005, if he works on it alone. On July 1, 2005, his co-author starts to work on the book, and together they complete the book on October 1, 2005. How long would it take the second author to write the book by himself? Assume that each month has 30 days.

39. John can decorate the gym for the Saturday night dance in 4 hours, Mary in 6 hours, and Stacy in 8 hours. How long will the job take if all three work together?

40. A canoe travels 30 kilometers upstream in the same time that it would take the canoe to travel 50 kilometers downstream. If the rate of the stream is 4 kilometers per hour, what is the speed of the canoe in still water?

41. Computer A does 200 million computations in the same time that computer B does 120 million computations. If computer A is 10 million computations per second faster than computer B, how many operations per second does each computer carry out?

42. A cyclist riding against the wind travels 120 miles in the same time that she can travel 600 miles with the wind. If wind speed is 20 miles per hour, what is the speed of the cyclist in still air?

5.7 In Exercises 43–46 solve for the unknown in each proportion.

43. $\dfrac{3x}{4} = \dfrac{3}{2}$ **44.** $\dfrac{2y - 1}{3} = \dfrac{5}{3}$

45. $\dfrac{2}{2r + 3} = \dfrac{1}{2}$ **46.** $\dfrac{3}{r - 2} = \dfrac{2}{r + 3}$

47. If 2 out of 7 students in your English class smoke, how many smokers are there if the class has 35 students?

48. Suppose that the annual return on a $5000 investment is $12.50. What is the proportional return on a $1250 investment?

49. The cost of a 180-square-foot carpet is $600. What is the cost of a 240-square-foot carpet that is made of the same material?

50. The ratio of nuts to raisins in a health food snack is 2:3. How many ounces of raisins are there in a 2-pound (32-ounce) pack of the snack?

Progress Test 5A

1. Multiply $\dfrac{-8x^2(4-x^2)}{2y^2} \cdot \dfrac{3y}{x-2}$.

2. Divide $\dfrac{2x^2-x-6}{x^2+x-12}$ by $\dfrac{-x^2-2x+8}{3x^2-10x+3}$.

3. Compute $\dfrac{2x^2-5x+2}{5-x} \div \dfrac{3x}{x^2-6x+5}$.

4. Find the LCD of $\dfrac{2}{(x-1)y}, \dfrac{-4}{y^2}$, and $\dfrac{x+2}{5(x-1)^2}$.

5. Find $\dfrac{2}{x-5} - \dfrac{11}{5-x}$.

6. Find $\dfrac{4}{y(y+1)} - \dfrac{3y}{y+1} + \dfrac{y-1}{2y}$.

7. Simplify.
$$\dfrac{6x-3}{2-\dfrac{1}{x}}$$

8. Simplify.
$$\dfrac{1-\dfrac{7}{x^2-9}}{\dfrac{x-4}{x^2+x-6}}$$

9. Solve $\dfrac{-5x-2}{2x+6} - 2 = \dfrac{x+4}{x+3}$.

10. Solve $\dfrac{2x+3}{2} \le \dfrac{x}{6} - 4$.

11. An apprentice plumber can complete a job in 6 hours. After he has been working on the assignment for 2 hours, he is joined by a master plumber, and the two complete the job in 1 more hour. How long would it take the master plumber working alone to do the entire job?

12. Solve $\dfrac{3}{n+2} = \dfrac{1}{2}$.

13. The interest on a $3000 loan is $125. What is the interest on a $7000 loan at the same interest rate for the same length of time?

Progress Test 5B

1. Multiply $\dfrac{14(y-1)}{3(x^2-y^2)} \cdot \dfrac{9(x+y)}{-7y^2}$.

2. Divide $\dfrac{5-x}{3x^2+5x-2}$ by $\dfrac{x^2-4x-5}{2x^2+3x-2}$.

3. Compute $\dfrac{x^4-x^2}{x^2-4} \div \dfrac{x^2-x}{-2x+4}$.

4. Find the LCD of $\dfrac{y-1}{x^2(y+1)}, \dfrac{x-2}{2x(y-1)}$, and $\dfrac{3x}{4(y+1)^2}$.

5. Find $\dfrac{x+1}{3-x} + \dfrac{x-1}{x-3}$.

6. Find $\dfrac{3}{4(v-1)} + \dfrac{v+2}{v^2(v-1)} - \dfrac{v+1}{2v}$.

7. Simplify.
$$\dfrac{2x-4}{\dfrac{2}{x}-1}$$

8. Simplify.
$$\dfrac{\dfrac{x^2-x-6}{2x+2}}{\dfrac{3}{x^2-1}-1}$$

9. Solve $\dfrac{1-4x}{2x-2} + 6 = \dfrac{2x}{1-x}$.

10. Solve $\dfrac{3-x}{3} + 3 \ge \dfrac{x}{2}$.

11. A fast collator can do a job in 4 hours while a slower-model collator requires 6 hours. They are both assigned

to a job, but after one hour the slower collator is reassigned. How long will it take the faster collator to finish the job?

12. Solve $\dfrac{4}{t-1} = \dfrac{2}{3}$.

13. A golfer cards a 36 for the first 8 holes. What is her proportional score for 18 holes?

Chapter 5 Project

To get more out of this chapter project, try reading a little of the classic book *The Compleat Strategyst* by J. D. Williams, McGraw-Hill, © 1954. The subject of game theory is complex but rewarding. Rational expressions may be used to represent the *value* of a game. The value of a game is the average payoff you may expect to receive each time you play, if you play using the appropriate strategy! A payoff may be measured in points, dollars, or any countable units.

Look at Exercises 59 and 60 in Section 5.3, and Exercise 35 in Section 5.5. Now invent a simple game, perhaps using coins or dice. It should involve two players, and have a set number of options for each player on each turn. Include a description of payoffs to each player; i.e., what is the reward if you win on any given turn? Look for a description of the classic finger game Morra for a good example.

What strategies (plans of action) would improve the payoffs for either player in your game? Or is it completely random?

CHAPTER 6

Functions

The concept of function is of the greatest impor-tance, not only in pure mathematics but also in practical applications.

—Richard Courant and Herbert Robbins

Try this experiment. Listen to a cricket chirping, and count the number of times it chirps in one minute. Divide that number by 4, then add 40. Now compare that result to the temperature in degrees Fahrenheit. Is your result close? It probably is.

This is one example of a *function*. For this experiment, the outside tempera-ture in degrees Fahrenheit is treated as a function of the number of times a cricket chirps in fifteen seconds. This rule of thumb has actually been shown to have validity. Find out how by looking up Svante Arrhenius at http://scienceworld.wolfram.com/biography/.

We will look at this function more closely in several sections of this chapter. By looking at its graph, determining the slope, finding its inverse, etc., you will see how functions help us to predict events in the world around us. (See the chapter project.)

■ ■ ■

http://scienceworld.wolfram.com/biography/

What is the result of increased fertilization on the growth of an azalea in a garden? If the minimum wage is increased, what will be the effect on the number of unemployed workers? When a submarine dives, can we calculate the water pressure against the hull at a given depth?

Each of the questions posed above seeks a relationship between phenomena. The search for relationships, or correspondence, is a central activity in our attempts to understand the universe; it is used in mathematics, engineering, the physical and biological sciences, the social sciences, business and economics.

The concept of a function has been developed as a means of organizing and assisting the study of relationships. Since graphs are powerful means of exhibiting relationships, we begin with a study of the Cartesian, or rectangular, coordinate system. We then formally define a function and offer a number of ways of viewing the concept of a function. Function notation will be introduced to provide a convenient means of writing functions.

We will also explore some special types of functional relationships (increasing and decreasing functions), the effect of combining functions in various ways and how functions can be used to describe certain processes.

6.1   Rectangular Coordinate Systems

In Chapter 1 we associated the system of real numbers with points on the real number line. That is, we saw that there is a one-to-one correspondence between the system of real numbers and points on the real number line.

We will now develop an analogous way to handle points in a plane. We begin by drawing a pair of perpendicular lines intersecting at a point O called the **origin**. One of the lines, called the **x-axis**, is usually drawn in a horizontal position. The other line, called the **y-axis**, is usually drawn vertically.

If we think of the x-axis as a real number line, we may mark off some convenient unit of length, with positive numbers to the right of the origin and negative numbers to the left of the origin. Similarly, we may think of the y-axis as a real number line. Again, we may mark off a convenient unit of length (usually the same as the unit of length on the x-axis), with the upward direction representing positive numbers and the downward direction negative numbers. The x- and y-axes are called **coordinate axes**, and together they constitute a **rectangular coordinate system**, also called a **Cartesian coordinate system** (Figure 1).

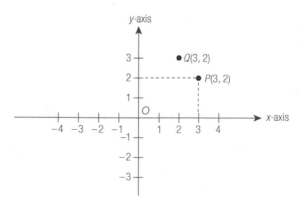

Figure 1   Coordinates of a Point

By using coordinate axes, we can outline a procedure for labeling a point P in the plane (see Figure 1). From P, draw a perpendicular line to the x-axis and note that it meets the x-axis at $x = 3$. Now draw a perpendicular line from P to the y-axis and note that it meets the y-axis at $y = 2$. We say that the **coordinates** of P are given by the **ordered pair** (3, 2). The term "ordered pair" means that the order is significant, that is, the ordered pair (3, 2) is different from the ordered pair (2, 3). In fact, the ordered pair (2, 3) gives the coordinates of the point Q shown in Figure 1.

The first number of the ordered pair (a, b) is sometimes called the **abscissa** of P and the second number is called the **ordinate** of P. We will use a simpler terminology. We call a the **x-coordinate** (since we measure it along the x-axis) and b the **y-coordinate** (since we measure it along the y-axis).

Let's recap what we have done. We now have a procedure by which each point P in the plane determines a unique ordered pair of real numbers (a, b). It is customary to write the point P as $P(a, b)$. It is also true that every ordered pair of real numbers (a, b) determines a unique point P in the plane that is a units from the y-axis and b units from the x-axis.

We can note a few additional facts, using Figure 2:

- The coordinate axes divide the plane into four **quadrants**, which we label I, II, III, and IV, as shown in Figure 2. The point $(-3, 2)$ is in Quadrant II; the point $(2, -4)$ is in Quadrant IV.

- All points on the x-axis have a y-coordinate of 0. For example, point A has coordinates $(-1, 0)$; point E has coordinates $(3, 0)$.

- All points on the y-axis have an x-coordinate of 0. For example, point C has coordinates $(0, 3)$ and point F has coordinates $(0, -3)$.

- The x-coordinate of a point is the distance of the point from the x-axis; the y-coordinate is the distance from the x-axis. Point $D(2, 3)$ is 2 units from the y-axis and 3 units from the x-axis.

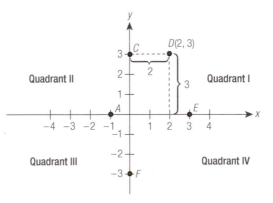

Figure 2   The Four Quadrants

Example 1   Finding the Coordinates of a Point

Find the coordinates of the points A, B, C, D, and E in Figure 3.

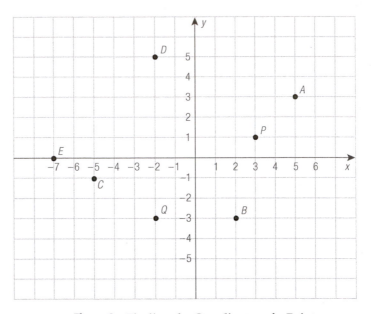

Figure 3   Finding the Coordinates of a Point

Solution

$A(5, 3)$ $B(2, -3)$ $C(-5, -1)$ $D(-2, 5)$ $E(-7, 0)$

✔ Progress Check 1

Using Figure 3 in Example 1, find the coordinates of

(a) P and Q.

(b) the point 1 unit to the right and 2 units below A.

(c) the point 3 units to the left and 4 units up from C.

Answers

(a) $P(3, 1)$, $Q(-2, -3)$ (b) $(6, 1)$ (c) $(-8, 3)$

Example 2   Plotting Points

Plot the following points and state the quadrant in which each point lies.

$A(1, 6)$ $B(-3, -3)$ $C(-3, 2)$ $D(2, -5)$

$E(4, 0)$ $F(0, -1)$

Solution

See Figure 4.

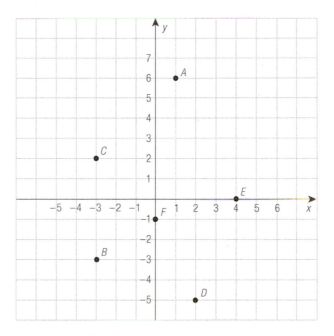

Figure 4   **Plotting Points**

A: Quadrant I   B: Quadrant III   C: Quadrant II
D: Quadrant IV   E: Not in a quadrant   F: Not in a quadrant

✔ **Progress Check 2**

Plot each of the following points and state the quadrant in which it lies.

$L(-4, -1)$ $R(2, 5)$ $M(0, 3)$
$S(-1, 0)$ $T(-2, 3)$ $U(3, -1.5)$

Answers

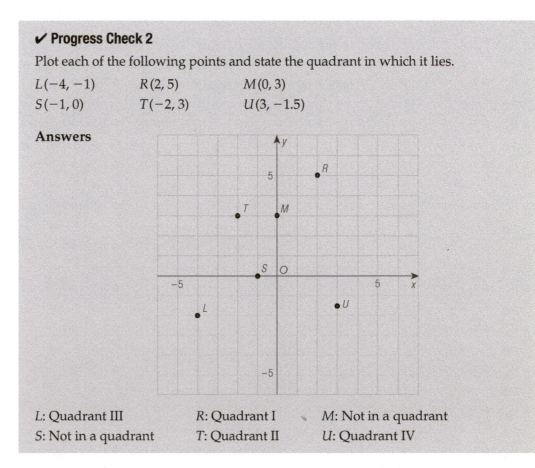

L: Quadrant III   R: Quadrant I   M: Not in a quadrant
S: Not in a quadrant   T: Quadrant II   U: Quadrant IV

Graphs of Equations

The Cartesian coordinate system provides a means of drawing a "picture" or **graph of an equation in two variables**. In general, when we refer to the graph of an equation in two variables x and y, we shall mean the set in the plane of all points $P(x, y)$ whose coordinates (x, y) satisfy the given equation.

Let's graph $y = x^2 - 4$, an equation in the variables x and y. A solution to this equation is any pair of values that when substituted in the equation in place of x and y yields a true statement. If we choose a value for x, say, $x = 3$, and substitute this value of x in the equation, we will obtain the corresponding value of y.

$$y = x^2 - 4$$
$$y = (3)^2 - 4 = 5$$

Thus, $x = 3$, $y = 5$ is a solution. Table 1 shows a number of solutions. (Verify that these are solutions.)

Table 1 Points on the Graph of $y = x^2 - 4$

x	-3	-2	-1	0	1	2	$\dfrac{5}{2}$
$y = x^2 - 4$	5	0	-3	-4	-3	0	$\dfrac{9}{4}$

We can treat the numbers in Table 1 as ordered pairs (x, y) and plot the points that they represent. Figure 5a shows the points; in Figure 5b we have joined the points to form a smooth curve, which is the graph of the equation.

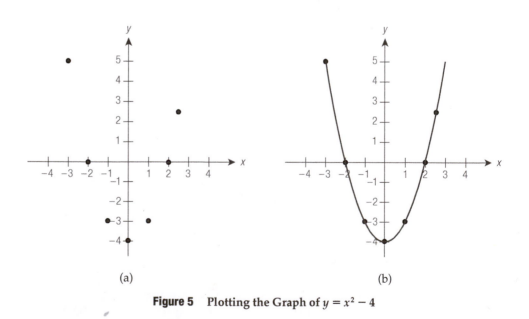

(a)   (b)

Figure 5   Plotting the Graph of $y = x^2 - 4$

Example 3   Absolute Value in Graphing

Graph the equation $y = |x + 1|$.

Solution

Form a table by assigning values to x and then calculating the corresponding values of y.

x	-3	-2	-1	0	1	2	3	4
$y = |x + 1|$	2	1	0	1	2	3	4	5

(Verify that the table entries are correct. Remember—we are dealing with absolute value.) Now we plot the points and join the points in a "smooth" curve (Figure 6). The curve of $y = |x + 1|$ appears to be two rays intersecting at the point $(-1, 0)$. (A ray is a line segment of indefinite length starting from a fixed point.)

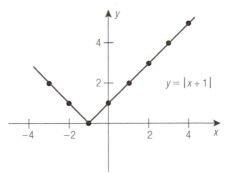

Figure 6   Graph of the Equation $y = |x + 1|$

✔ Progress Check 3

Graph the equations.

(a) $y = 4 - x^2$ (b) $y = |x - 2|$

Answers

(a)   (b)

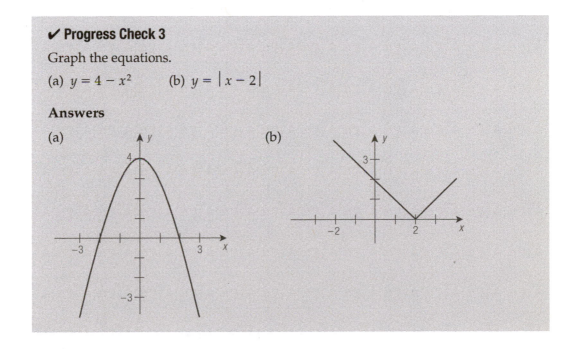

Example 4   Finding the Ordered Pairs (x, y)

Graph the equation $x = y^2 + 1$.

Solution

We need to find ordered pairs (x, y) that will satisfy the given equation. In this case it is easiest to pick a value of y and find the corresponding value of x from the given equation. Thus, if $y = 0$, then $x = 1$, and if $y = 1$, then $x = 2$. In this manner we obtain the following table.

y	-3	-2	-1	0	1	2	3
x	10	5	2	1	2	5	10
(x, y)	$(10, -3)$	$(5, -2)$	$(2, -1)$	$(1, 0)$	$(2, 1)$	$(5, 2)$	$(10, 3)$

The graph is shown in Figure 7.

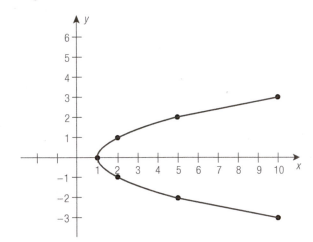

Figure 7   Graph of the Equation $x = y^2 + 1$

✔ **Progress Check 4**

Graph the equation $x = 4 - y^2$.

Answer

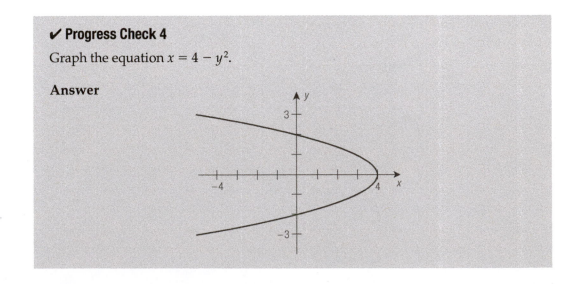

Exercise Set 6.1

In Exercises 1 and 2 find the coordinates of the points A, B, C, D, E, F, G, and H from the graphs.

1.

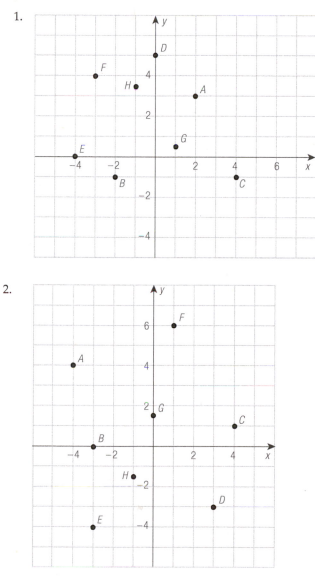

2.

In Exercises 3−8 plot the given points.

3. $(2, 3)$, $(-3, -2)$, $(-1, 0)$, $(4, -4)$, $(-1, 1)$, $(0, -2)$

4. $(-3, 4)$, $(3, 0)$, $(3, 2)$, $(3, -3)$, $(0, 4)$, $(-1, -2)$

5. $(4, -3)$, $(1, 4)$, $(-5, 2)$, $(0, 0)$, $(-4, 0)$, $(-4, -5)$

6. $(-4, -2)$, $(2, 1)$, $(-3, 1)$, $(-2, 0)$, $(0, 2)$, $(1, -3)$

7. $\left(-\frac{1}{2}, \frac{1}{2}\right)$, $(2.5, 1.5)$, $(-7.5, -2.5)$, $\left(1, -\frac{1}{2}\right)$, $\left(-\frac{1}{2}, 0\right)$, $\left(0, \frac{1}{4}\right)$

8. $\left(-\frac{5}{2}, -\frac{3}{2}\right)$, $\left(0, -\frac{1}{2}\right)$, $\left(\frac{1}{4}, 1\right)$, $\left(-1, \frac{3}{2}\right)$, $\left(0, \frac{3}{2}\right)$, $\left(\frac{1}{2}, 0\right)$

9. Using the figure in Exercise 1, find the coordinates of
    (a) the point 2 units to the left and 1 unit above B.
    (b) the point 4 units to the right and 5 units below A.

10. Using the figure in Exercise 2, find the coordinates of
    (a) the point 3 units to the right and 2 units above A.
    (b) the point 2 units to the left and 1 unit below H.

In Exercises 11−22, without plotting, name the quadrant in which the given point is located.

11. $(2, 4)$

12. $(-3, 80)$

13. $(200, -80)$

14. $(-5, 20)$

15. $(-8, -26)$

16. $(40, -20.1)$

17. $(\pi, 8)$

18. $(-2, 0.3)$

19. $(-84.7, -12.8)$

20. $(2.84, -80)$

21. $\left(\frac{17}{4}, \frac{4}{5}\right)$

22. $(-0.5, 0.3)$

23. Which of the following are solutions to $2x - 3y = 12$?
    (a) $(0, -4)$ (b) $(1, 3)$ (c) $(3, 1)$ (d) $(3, -2)$

24. Which of the following are solutions to $3x + 2y = 18$?
    (a) $(-4, 15)$ (b) $\left(0, -\frac{3}{2}\right)$ (c) $(-9, 0)$ (d) $(4, 3)$

25. Which of the following are solutions to $2x + 3y^2 = 18$?
    (a) $(3, -2)$ (b) $(2, 1)$ (c) $(9, 0)$ (d) $(15, 4)$

26. Which of the following are solutions to $3x^2 - 2y = 12$?
    (a) $(0, -6)$ (b) $(4, 30)$ (c) $(2, 0)$ (d) $(-2, 12)$

27. Consider the equation $4x + 3y = 12$. Complete the following table so that each ordered pair (x, y) is a solution of the given equation.

x	1		0		-3	
y		-2		0		2

28. Consider the equation $2x - 3y = 6$. Complete the following table so that each ordered pair (x, y) is a solution of the given equation.

x	6		0		-3	
y		-6		0		2

In Exercises 29−59 graph the given equation. (Use a calculator for Exercises 54−59.)

29. $y = 2x$

30. $y = 3x$

31. $y = 2x + 4$

32. $y = -3x + 5$

33. $3x - 2y = 6$

34. $x = 2y + 3$

35. $3x + 5y = 15$

36. $x = 2$

37. $y = -3$

38. $y = x^2 + 3$

39. $y = 3 - x^2$

40. $y = 3x - x^2$

41. $x = y^2 - 1$

42. $x = 2 - y^2$

43. $y = x^3 + 1$

44. $y = x^3 - 2$

45. $x = y^3 - 1$

46. $x = 2 - y^3$

47. $y = |x - 2|$

48. $y = |x + 3|$

49. $y = |x| + 1$

50. $y = \dfrac{1}{2x + 1}$

51. $xy = 2$

52. $2x^2 + y = 4$

53. $x^2 - y + 8 = 0$

54. $2.23y - 6.47x + 3.41 = 0$

55. $7.37y + 2.75x = 9.46$

56. $3.17x^2 - 2.02y - 3.73 = 0$

57. $6.59x^2 + 3.72y = -9.82$

58. $4.81y^2 - 3.07x + 4.21 = 0$

59. $8.07y^2 + 0.11x = 3.46$

60. Graph the set of all points whose y-coordinate is 3.

61. What is the equation whose graph is shown below?

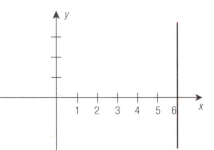

*62. The points $A(2, 7)$, $B(4, 3)$, and $C(x, 3)$ determine a right triangle whose hypotenuse is AB. Find x.

*63. The points $A(2, 6)$, $B(4, 6)$, $C(4, 8)$, and $D(x, y)$ form a rectangle. Find x and y.

*64. The points $A(2, 7)$, $B(4, 3)$, and $C(x, y)$ determine a right triangle with one side parallel to the x-axis and one side parallel to the y-axis and whose hypotenuse is AB. Find x and y. (*Hint:* There is more than one answer.)

6.2   Functions and Function Notation

Functions

The equation

$$y = 2x + 3$$

can be thought of as a rule that assigns a value to y for every value of x. If we let X denote the set of values that we can assign to x and let Y denote the set of values that the equation assigns to y, we can show the correspondence schematically (Figure 8).

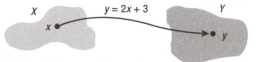

Figure 8   Correspondence Determined by an Equation

We are particularly interested in those rules that assign exactly one y in Y for a given x in X. This type of correspondence plays a fundamental role in many mathematical applications and is given a special name.

A **function** is a rule that, for each x in a set X, assigns exactly one y in a set Y. The element y is called the **image** of x. The set X is called the **domain** of the function, and the set of all images is called the **range** of the function.

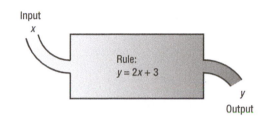

Figure 9   The Function Machine for the Rule $y = 2x + 3$

We can think of the rule defined by the equation $y = 2x + 3$ as a function machine (see Figure 9). Each time we drop a value of x into the input hopper, exactly one value of y falls out of the output hopper. If we drop in $x = 5$, the function machine follows the rule and produces $y = 13$. If the rule in the machine drops out more than one value of y for a given x, then it is not a function. Since we are free to choose those values of x that we drop into the machine, we call x the **independent variable**; the value of y that drops out depends upon the choice of x, and y is called the **dependent variable**. We say the dependent variable is a function of the independent variable; that is, *the output is a function of the input.*

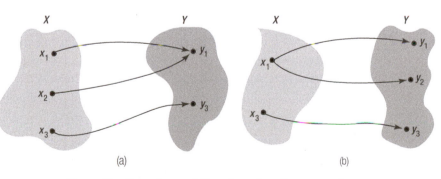

Figure 10   Function and Non-function Correspondence

Let's look at a few schematic presentations. The correspondence in Figure 10a is a function; for each x in X there is exactly one corresponding value of y in Y. True, y_1 is the image of both x_1 and x_2, but this does not violate the definition of a function! However, the correspondence in Figure 10b is not a function, since x_1 is assigned to both y_1 and y_2, which does violate the definition of a function.

Vertical Line Test

There is a graphic way to test if an equation determines a function. Let's graph the equations $y = x^2$ and $y^2 = x$ in which x is the independent variable. Now draw vertical lines on both graphs in Figure 11. No vertical line intersects the graph of $y = x^2$ in more than one point; however, some vertical lines intersect the graph of $y^2 = x$ in two points. This is another way of saying that the equation $y = x^2$ assigns exactly one y for each x and therefore determines y as a function of x. On the other hand, the equation $y^2 = x$ assigns *two* values of y to some values of x, so the correspondence does not determine y as a function of x. Thus, *not every equation in two variables determines one variable as a function of the other.*

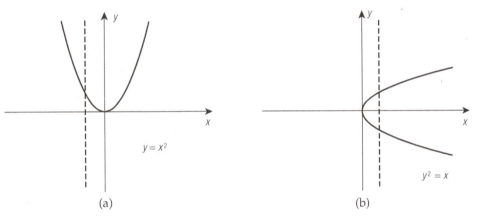

(a)   (b)

Figure 11 The Vertical Line Test

Vertical Line Test

> If any vertical line meets the graph of an equation in more than one point, then the equation does not determine a function.

In general, we will consider the domain of a function to be the set of all real numbers for which the function is defined, that is, for which the dependent variable assumes a real value. For example, the domain of the function determined by the equation

$$y = \frac{2}{x - 1}$$

is the set of real numbers other than $x = 1$, since division by 0 is not defined.

The range of a function is, in general, not as easily determined as is the domain. The range is the set of all y values that occur in the correspondence; that is, it is the set of all outputs of the function. For our purposes it will be adequate to determine the range by examining the graph of the function.

Example 1 Graphs and Functions

Graph the equation. If the correspondence determines a function, find the domain and range.

$$y = 4 + x, \quad 0 \le x \le 5$$

Solution

See Figure 12. The graph is a line segment and it is clear that no vertical line meets the graph in more than one point. The equation therefore determines a function.

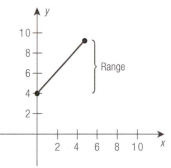

Figure 12   Graph of $y = 4 + x$, $0 \leq x \leq 5$

We are given that $0 \leq x \leq 5$, and since the function is defined for all such x, the domain is $\{x \mid 0 \leq x \leq 5\}$. We see from the graph that the range is $\{y \mid 4 \leq y \leq 9\}$.

✔ Progress Check 1

Graph the equation $y = x^2 - 4$, $-3 \leq x \leq 3$. If the correspondence determines a 226function, find the domain and range.

Answer

The desired graph is the portion of the curve shown in Figure 5b of Section 6.1 for the values of x between -3 and 3. The domain is $\{x \mid -3 \leq x \leq 3\}$; the range is $\{y \mid -4 \leq y \leq 5\}$.

Example 2   Graphs and Functions

Which of the equations whose graphs are shown in Figure 13 determine functions?

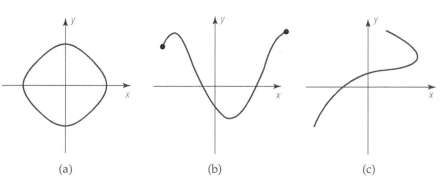

(a)   (b)   (c)

Figure 13   Which Graphs Determine a Function?

Solution

(a) Not a function. Some vertical lines meet the graph in more than one point.

(b) A function. Passes the vertical line test.

(c) Not a function. Fails the vertical line test.

✔ **Progress Check 2**

Which of the equations whose graphs are shown in Figure 14 determine functions?

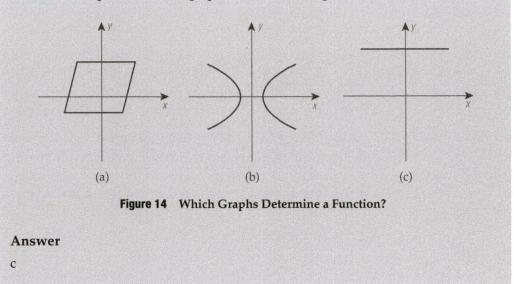

Figure 14   Which Graphs Determine a Function?

Answer

c

Function Notation

There is a special notation used for functions. We express the functional relation

$$y = 2x + 3$$

by writing

$$f(x) = 2x + 3$$

The symbol "$f(x)$" is read "f of x" and denotes the *output* corresponding to the *input x*. The statement "find the value of y corresponding to $x = 5$" becomes "find $f(5)$"; that is, $f(5)$ designates the value of $y = f(x)$ when $x = 5$. To find this output, we merely substitute 5 into the expression in place of x. We then obtain

$$y = f(5) = 2(5) + 3 = 13$$

Thus, the output is 13 when the input is 5.

> To **evaluate** a function f for a given value of the independent variable x is to find the output $f(x)$ corresponding to the input x.

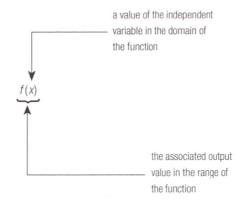

a value of the independent variable in the domain of the function

$f(x)$

the associated output value in the range of the function

A function may be denoted by a letter other than f. Thus, F, g, h, and C may all denote a function.

Example 3   Using Function Notation

(a) If $f(x) = 2x^2 - 2x + 1$, find $f(-1)$.

(b) If $f(t) = 3t - 1$, find $f(a^2)$.

Solution

(a) We substitute -1 in place of x.

$$f(-1) = 2(-1)^2 - 2(-1) + 1 = 5$$

(b) We substitute a^2 in place of t.

$$f(a^2) = 3(a^2) - 1 = 3a^2 - 1$$

✔ Progress Check 3

(a) If $f(u) = u^3 + 3u - 4$, find $f(-2)$.

(b) If $f(t) = t^2 + 1$, find $f(t - 1)$.

Answers

(a) -18 (b) $t^2 - 2t + 2$

Example 4   Using Function Notation

Let the function f be defined by $f(x) = x^2 - 1$. Find the following:

(a) $f(-2)$ (b) $f(a + h)$ (c) $f(a + h) - f(a)$ (d) $2f(x)$ (e) $f\left(\dfrac{1}{x}\right)$

Solution

(a) $f(-2) = (-2)^2 - 1 = 4 - 1 = 3$

(b) $f(a + h) = (a + h)^2 - 1 = a^2 + 2ah + h^2 - 1$

(c) $f(a + h) - f(a) = (a + h)^2 - 1 - (a^2 - 1)$
$$= a^2 + 2ah + h^2 - 1 - a^2 + 1$$
$$= 2ah + h^2$$

(d) $2f(x) = 2(x^2 - 1) = 2x^2 - 2$

(e) $f\left(\dfrac{1}{x}\right) = \left(\dfrac{1}{x}\right)^2 - 1 = \dfrac{1}{x^2} - 1 = \dfrac{1 - x^2}{x^2}$

✔ Progress Check 4

Let the function f be defined by $f(t) = t^2 + t - 1$. Find the following:

(a) $f(0)$ (b) $f(a + h)$ (c) $f(a + h) - f(a)$

Answers

(a) -1 (b) $a^2 + 2ah + h^2 + a + h - 1$ (c) $2ah + h^2 + h$

Warning

(a) *Don't* write

$$f(a + 3) = f(a) + f(3)$$

Function notation is not to be confused with the distributive law.

(b) *Don't* write

$$f(a + 3) = f(a) + 3$$

To evaluate $f(a + 3)$, substitute $a + 3$ for each occurrence of the independent variable.

(c) *Don't* write

$$f(x^2) = f \cdot x^2$$

The use of parentheses in function notation does not imply muliplication.

(d) *Don't* write

$$f(x^2) = [f(x)]^2$$

Squaring x is not the same as squaring $f(x)$.

(e) *Don't* write

$$f(3x) = 3f(x)$$

Example 5 A Formula in Function Notation

The correspondence between Fahrenheit temperature F and Celsius temperature C is given by

$$F(C) = \frac{9}{5}C + 32$$

which is often simply written as $F = \frac{9}{5}C + 32$.

(a) Find the Fahrenheit temperature corresponding to a Celsius reading of 37° (normal body temperature).

(b) Write C as a function of F.

(c) Find the Celsius temperature corresponding to a Fahrenheit reading of 212° (the boiling point of water).

Solution

(a) We substitute $C = 37$ to find $F(37)$.

$$F(37) = \frac{9}{5}(37) + 32 = 98.6$$

Normal body temperature is 98.6° Fahrenheit.

(b) We solve the equation for C.

$$F(C) = \frac{9}{5}C + 32$$

$$F - 32 = \frac{9}{5}C$$

$$C = \frac{5}{9}(F - 32)$$

or

$$C(F) = \frac{5}{9}(F - 32)$$

(c) We substitute $F = 212$ to find $C(212)$.

$$C = \frac{5}{9}(F - 32)$$

$$C(212) = \frac{5}{9}(212 - 32) = \frac{5}{9}(180) = 100$$

Water boils at 100° Celsius.

✔ **Progress Check 5**

Suppose that an object is dropped from a fixed height. If we neglect air resistance, the distance s (in feet) that the object has fallen after t seconds is a function of t given by

$$s(t) = 16t^2$$

(Note that the function does *not* depend upon the mass of the object.) Find the distance traveled by an object when t is

(a) 2 seconds.

(b) 4 seconds.

(c) How long does it take an object to fall 400 feet?

Answers

(a) 64 feet   (b) 256 feet   (c) 5 seconds

Exercise Set 6.2

In Exercises 1–10 graph the given equation. If the correspondence is a function, determine the domain and range.

1. $y = 3 + x$, $0 \le x \le 4$

2. $y = 2 - x$, $-2 \le x \le 5$

3. $y = x^2 + 1$

4. $y = 9 - x^2$

5. $y = x^2 - 4$

6. $y = -4 - x^2$

7. $y = |x|$, $-2 \le x \le 3$

8. $y = |x + 1|$, $-3 \le x \le 1$

9. $y = |2x - 1|$, $-1 \le x \le 2$

10. $y = |x| - 1$, $-2 \le x \le 2$

In Exercises 11–18 determine the domain of the given function.

11. $f(x) = 2x^2 + x - 3$

12. $g(t) = \dfrac{1}{t - 2}$

13. $f(v) = \dfrac{1}{(v - 3)(v + 1)}$

14. $g(x) = \dfrac{x - 3}{(x + 2)(x - 4)}$

15. $f(x) = \dfrac{x - 2}{x + 1}$

16. $h(t) = \dfrac{t}{(t - 3)(t + 5)}$

17. $f(x) = \dfrac{5}{x}$

18. $g(s) = \dfrac{5s}{s - 2}$

In Exercises 19–30 determine whether or not the given curve is the graph of a function.

19.

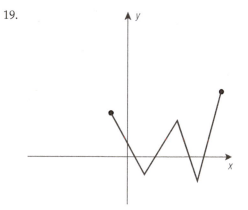

20.

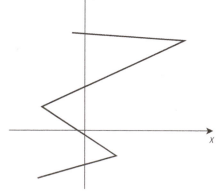

21.

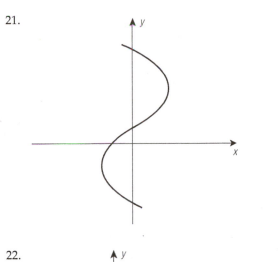

24.

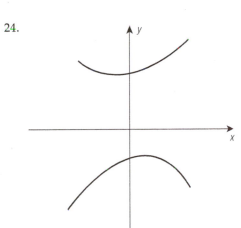

22.

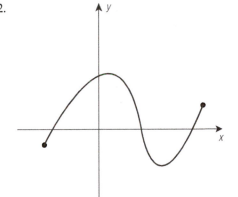

25.

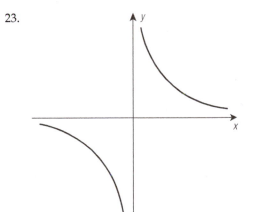

23.

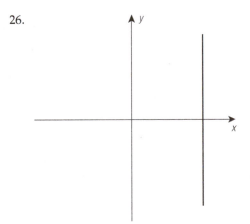

26.

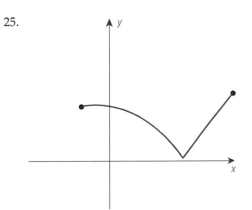

27.

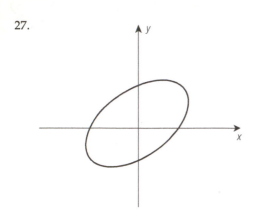

28.

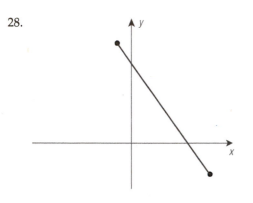

29.

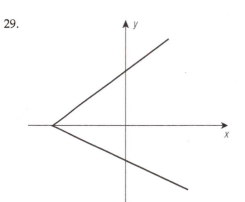

30.

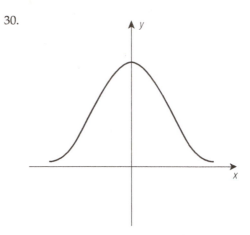

In Exercises 31−36 the function f is defined by $f(x) = 2x^2 + 5$. Compute the given expression.

31. $f(0)$

32. $f(-2)$

33. $f(a)$

34. $f(3x)$

35. $3f(x)$

36. $-f(x)$

In Exercises 37−42 the function g is defined by $g(x) = x^2 + 2x$. Compute the given expression.

37. $g(-3)$

38. $g\left(\dfrac{1}{x}\right)$

39. $\dfrac{1}{g(x)}$

40. $g(-x)$

41. $g(a + h)$

42. $\dfrac{g(a + h) - g(a)}{h}$

In Exercises 43−48 the function F is defined by $F(x) = \dfrac{x^2 + 1}{3x - 1}$. Compute the given expression.

43. $F(-2.73)$

44. $F(16.11)$

45. $\dfrac{1}{F(x)}$

46. $F(-x)$

47. $2F(2x)$

48. $F(x^2)$

In Exercises 49−54 the function r is defined by $r(t) = \dfrac{t - 2}{t^2 + 2t - 3}$. Compute the given expression.

49. $r(-8.27)$

50. $r(2.04)$

51. $r(2a)$

52. $2r(a)$

53. $r(a + 1)$

54. $r(1 + h)$

55. A tour operator who runs charter flights to Rome has established the following pricing schedule. For a group of no more than 100 people, the round trip fare per person is $300. For a group that has more than 100 but fewer than 150 people, the fare will be $250 for each person in excess of 100 people. Write the tour operator's total revenue R as a function of the number of people x in the group.

56. A firm packages and ships 1-pound jars of instant coffee. The cost C of shipping is 40 cents for the first pound and 25 cents for each additional pound.

    (a) Write C as a function of the weight w (in pounds) for $0 < w < 30$.

    (b) What is the cost of shipping a package containing 24 jars of instant coffee?

57. Suppose that x dollars are invested at 7% interest per year compounded annually. Express the amount A in the account at the end of one year as a function of x.

58. The rate of a car rental firm is $19 daily, plus 18¢ per mile that the rented car is driven.

    (a) Express the cost c of renting a car as a function of the number of miles m traveled in one day.

    (b) What is the domain of the function?

    (c) How much would it cost to rent a car for a one-day 100-mile trip?

59. In a wildlife preserve, the population P of eagles depends upon the population x of rodents, its basic food supply. Suppose that P is given by

    $$P(x) = 0.002x + 0.004x^2$$

    What is the eagle population when the rodent population is

    (a) 500?   (b) 2000?

60. A record club offers the following sale. If 3 records are bought at the regular price of $7.98 each, you may purchase up to 7 more records at half price.

    (a) Express the total cost c to a customer as a function of the number r of half-price records bought.

    (b) What is the domain of this function?

    (c) How much will it cost to buy a total of 8 records?

*61. A function f is called **even** if $f(-x) = f(x)$ for every value x in the domain of f; it is called **odd** if $f(-x) = -f(x)$ for all such values x. Determine whether the following functions are even, odd, or neither.

    (a) $f(x) = x^2 + 1$ (b) $f(x) = x^3$

    (c) $f(x) = x^2 + x$ (d) $f(x) = |x|$

*62. Express the area A of an equilateral triangle as a function of the length s of its side.

63. Express the diameter d of a circle as a function of its circumference C.

64. Express the perimeter P of a square as a function of its area A.

65. Read the chapter opening.

    (a) Express the outside temperature T in degrees Fahrenheit as a function of the number of times n that a cricket is heard to chirp in one minute.

    (b) What would the outside temperature be if a cricket was heard to chirp 130 times?

66. (a) Find $f(80)$ for the function

    $$f(t) = \frac{E}{R}\left(\frac{1}{T} - \frac{1}{t}\right)$$

    if E, R, and T are constants equal to 49 thousand, 8.3145, and 296, respectively. (This is a formula from chemistry that is the basis for the cricket rule-of-thumb in Exercise 65).

    (b) Use your graphing calculator to set up a LIST of values for the constant t: {71, 76, 84, 89, 90}, then reevaluate the function using the LIST.

67. MATHEMATICS IN WRITING:

    (a) Explain in your own words the phrase *domain of a function*.

    (b) Give an example of a function whose domain excludes the number 2. Explain in a complete sentence.

    (c) Give an example of a function whose domain excludes all real numbers less than 5. Explain in a complete sentence.

    (d) How can your graphing calculator help you to determine the range of a function? Give an example.

6.3   Graphs of Functions

We have used the graph of an equation to help us find out whether or not the equation determines a function. It is therefore natural that when we speak of the **graph of a function** such as

$$f(x) = -2x + 4$$

we mean the graph of the equation

$$y = -2x + 4$$

We can therefore use the method of plotting points developed in Section 6.1 to plot the graph of a function determined by an equation.

At times, functions are defined other than by equations. In many important applications, a function may be defined by a table, or by several formulas. We illustrate this by several examples.

Example 1   A Function Defined by Several Rules

The commission earned by a door-to-door cosmetics salesperson is determined as shown in the table.

Weekly Sales	Commission
Less than $300	20% of sales
$300 or more but less than $400	$60 + 35% of salves over $300
$400 or more	$95 + 60% of sales over $400

(a) Express the commission C as a function of sales s.

(b) Find the commission if the weekly sales are $425.

(c) Sketch the graph of the function.

Solution

(a) The function C can be described by three equations:

$$C(s) = \begin{cases} 0.2s & \text{if } s < 300 \\ 60 + 0.35(s - 300) & \text{if } 300 \leq s < 400 \\ 95 + 0.60(s - 400) & \text{if } s \geq 400 \end{cases}$$

(b) When $s = 425$, we must use the third equation and substitute to determine $C(425)$.

$$C(425) = 95 + 0.6(425 - 400)$$
$$= 95 + 0.6(25)$$
$$= 110$$

The commission on sales of $425 is $110.

(c) The graph of the function C consists of three line segments (Figure 15).

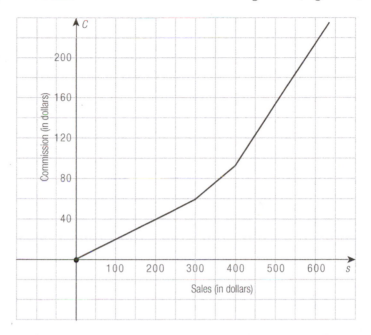

Figure 15   Graph of a Function Defined by Several Rules

✔ **Progress Check 1**

The state tax due is given in the following table:

Annual Income	Tax Due
Under $5000	1% of income
$5000 or more, but less than $15,000	$50 + 2% of income over $5000
$15,000 or more	$250 + 4% of income over $15,000

(a) Express the tax T as a function of income d.

(b) Find the tax due if the income is $7000.

(c) Find the tax due if the income is $18,000.

(d) Sketch the graph of the function T.

Answers

(a)
$$T(d) = \begin{cases} 0.01d & \text{if } d < 5000 \\ 50 + 0.02(d - 5000) & \text{if } 5000 \le d < 15{,}000 \\ 250 + 0.04(d - 15{,}000) & \text{if } d \ge 15{,}000 \end{cases}$$

(b) $T(7000) = 90$

(c) $T(18{,}000) = 370$

(continues)

(d)

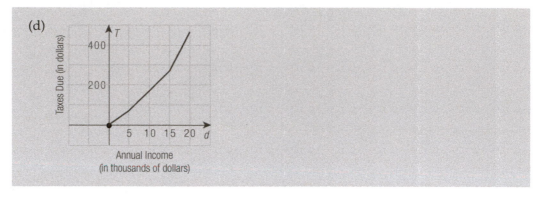

Example 2 A Function Defined by Several Equations

Sketch the graph of the function defined by

$$f(x) = \begin{cases} x^2 & \text{if } -2 \le x \le 2 \\ 2x + 1 & \text{if } 2 < x \le 5 \end{cases}$$

Solution

We form a table of points to be plotted.

x	-2	-1	0	1	2	3	4	5
$f(x)$	4	1	0	1	4	7	9	11

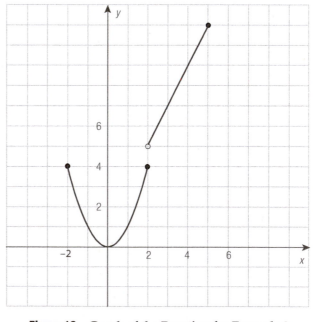

Figure 16 Graph of the Function for Example 2

See Figure 16. Note that the graph has a gap. Also note that the point $(2, 5)$ has been marked with an open circle to indicate that it is not on the graph of the function. Had the point (2, 5) been included, we would have two values of y corresponding to $x = 2$, and we would not have a function.

✔ Progress Check 2

Sketch the graph of the function defined by

$$f(x) = \begin{cases} 2x, & -2 \leq x < 4 \\ 5, & x \geq 4 \end{cases}$$

Answer

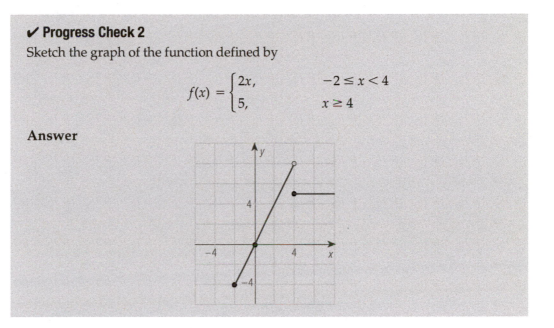

Linear Functions

The function

$$f(x) = ax + b$$

is called a **linear function**. We will study this function in detail in the next chapter and will show that its graph is a straight line. For now, we sketch the graphs of a few linear functions to "convince" ourselves that the graphs appear to be straight lines.

Example 3   Graphing Linear Functions

Sketch the graphs of $f(x) = x$ and $g(x) = -x + 2$ on the same coordinate axes.

Solution

We need to graph $y = x$ and $y = -x + 2$. We form a table of values, plot the corresponding points, and connect these by "smooth" curves. See Figure 17.

x	$y = x$	$y = -x + 2$
-4	-4	6
-2	-2	4
0	0	2
1	1	1
3	3	-1

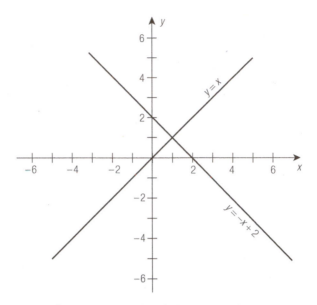

Figure 17   **Graphs of Linear Functions**

✔ **Progress Check 3**

Sketch the graphs of $f(x) = 2x + 1$ and $g(x) = -3x + 1$ on the same coordinate axes.

Answer

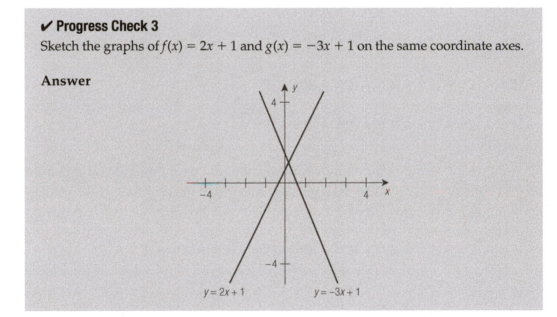

Quadratic Functions

The function

$$f(x) = ax^2 + bx + c, \quad a \neq 0$$

is called a **quadratic function**. The graph of this function is called a **parabola** and will be studied in detail in a later chapter.

Example 4   Graphing a Quadratic Function

Sketch the graph of $f(x) = 2x^2 - 4x + 3$.

Solution

We need to graph $y = 2x^2 - 4x + 3$. We form a table of values, plot the corresponding points, and connect these by a "smooth" curve. See Figure 18.

x	y
−1	9
0	3
1	1
2	3
3	9

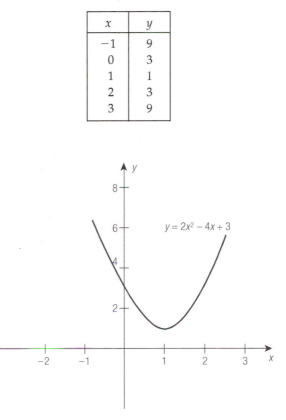

Figure 18   Graph of a Quadratic Equation

✔ **Progress Check 4**

Sketch the graph of $f(x) = -x^2 + 4x - 5$.

Answer

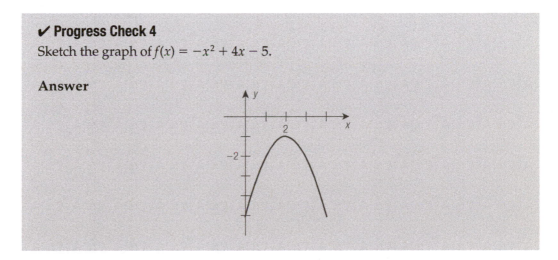

Polynomial Functions

In Chapter 2 we were introduced to polynomials and were shown how to determine the degree of a polynomial. Polynomials in one variable are of particular interest because they always determine a function. Here are some examples.

$$P(x) = x^2 - 3x + 1 \qquad P(x) = -2x^5 + \frac{1}{2}x^3 + 2x - 4$$

Linear and quadratic functions are **polynomial functions** of the first and second degree, respectively. The graph of a linear function is always a straight line; the graph of a quadratic function is always a parabola. The graphs of higher-degree polynomials are more complex, but are always "smooth curves" and are often used in mathematics to illustrate a point or to test an idea. The exercises are intended to help you gain experience with the graphs of polynomial functions.

Exercise Set 6.3

In Exercises 1–30 sketch the graph of each given function.

1. $f(x) = 3x + 4$

2. $f(x) = 2x - 3$

3. $f(x) = 3 - x$

4. $g(x) = -4 - 3x$

5. $f(x) = 2x^2 + 3$

6. $h(x) = 2x^2 - 3$

7. $g(x) = 5 - 2x^2$

8. $f(x) = -4 - 3x^2$

9. $h(x) = x^2 - 4x + 4$

10. $g(x) = 3x - 2x^2$

11. $f(x) = \dfrac{2}{x - 3}$

12. $f(x) = \dfrac{3}{2x + 1}$

13. $g(x) = \dfrac{3x - 4}{2}$

14. $h(x) = \dfrac{4 - x}{3}$

15. $h(x) = |x - 1|$

16. $f(x) = 2|1 - x|$

17. $f(x) = |x| + 1$

18. $g(x) = 2|x| - 1$

19. $f(x) = 3$

20. $f(x) = -5$

21. $f(x) = \begin{cases} -3x, & -4 \le x \le 2 \\ -3, & x > 2 \end{cases}$

22. $f(x) = \begin{cases} 3, & x < -2 \\ -2x, & x \ge -2 \end{cases}$

23. $g(x) = \begin{cases} \dfrac{1}{2}x + 1, & x \le 2 \\ -2x + 6, & x > 2 \end{cases}$

24. $f(x) = \begin{cases} |x + 1|, & x < -1 \\ x, & x \ge -1 \end{cases}$

25. $f(x) = \begin{cases} 2, & x < 3 \\ 1, & x > 3 \end{cases}$

26. $f(x) = \begin{cases} 2, & x < 3 \\ 1, & x = 3 \\ -3, & x > 3 \end{cases}$

27. $f(x) = \begin{cases} -4x - 1, & x \le -1 \\ -x + 2, & x > -1 \end{cases}$

28. $f(x) = \begin{cases} x + 1, & x < -1 \\ -x^2 + 1, & x > -1 \end{cases}$

29. $h(x) = \begin{cases} x^2, & x < 1 \\ 2, & x \ge 1 \end{cases}$

30. $g(x) = \begin{cases} -x^2 + 2, & x \le 2 \\ -3x + 1, & x > 2 \end{cases}$

In Exercises 31–38 sketch the graphs of the given functions on the same coordinate axes.

31. $f(x) = x^2, g(x) = 2x^2, h(x) = \dfrac{1}{2}x^2$

32. $f(x) = \dfrac{1}{2}x^2, g(x) = \dfrac{1}{3}x^2, h(x) = \dfrac{1}{4}x^2$

33. $f(x) = 2x^2, g(x) = -2x^2$

34. $f(x) = x^2 - 2, g(x) = 2 - x^2$

35. $f(x) = x^3, g(x) = 2x^3$

36. $f(x) = \dfrac{1}{2}x^3, g(x) = \dfrac{1}{4}x^3$

37. $f(x) = x^3, g(x) = -x^3$

38. $f(x) = -2x^3, g(x) = -4x^3$

In Exercises 39–42 sketch the graph of each given function.

39. $f(x) = 0.65x^2 - 0.44$

40. $f(x) = 0.84x^2 + 0.17x - 0.55$

41. $f(x) = 0.15x^3 - 2.1x^2 + 4.6$

42. $f(x) = -3.4x^2 - 1.8x + 6.3$

43. Graph the shipping function of Exercise 56, Section 6.2.

44. Graph the temperature function of Example 5, Section 6.2.

*45. The telephone company charges a fee of $6.50 per month for the first 100 message units and an additional fee of 6 cents for each of the next 100 message units. A reduced rate of 5 cents is charged for each message unit after the first 200 units. Express the monthly charge C as a function of the number of message units x. Graph this function.

*46. The annual dues of a union are as shown in the table.

Employee's annual salary	Annual dues
Less than $8000	$60
$8000 or more, but less than $15,000	$60 + 1% of the salary in excess of $8000
$15,000 or more	$130 + 2% of the salary in excess of $15,000

Express the annual dues d as a function of the salary. Graph this function.

47. MATHEMATICS IN WRITING: Store the LIST {3,4,5,6} as L_1, then graph

$$y = 3x + L_1$$

Write a brief paragraph explaining your results.

48. Refer to Exercise 65 in section 6.2.

(a) Graph the function you found in part a.

(b) Find the slope of the line.

(c) What is the y-intercept of the line?

49. The Celsius temperature C is related to Fahrenheit temperature F by the formula

$$C = \frac{5}{9}(F - 32)$$

Refer to exercise 48 above.

(a) Write a linear equation expressing the outside temperature in degrees Celsius in terms of n, the number of times a cricket chirps in one minute.

(b) Graph this linear relationship.

6.4   Increasing and Decreasing Functions

We way that the straight line in Figure 19a is increasing or rising, since the values of y increase as we move from left to right. Since the graph of a function f is obtained by sketching $y = f(x)$, we can give a precise definition of **increasing** and **decreasing functions**.

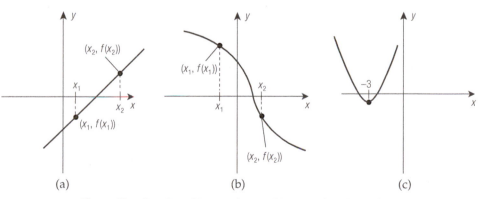

(a)   (b)   (c)

Figure 19   Graphs of Increasing and Decreasing Functions

Increasing and Decreasing Functions

- A function f is increasing if $f(x_2) > f(x_1)$ whenever $x_1 < x_2$.
- A function f is decreasing if $f(x_2) < f(x_1)$ whenever $x_1 < x_2$.

In other words, if a function is increasing, the dependent variable y assumes larger values as we move from left to right (Figure 19a); for a decreasing function (Figure 19b), y takes on smaller values as we move from left to right. The function pictured in Figure 19c is neither increasing nor decreasing, according to this definition. In fact, one portion of the graph is decreasing and another is increasing. We can modify our definition of increasing and decreasing functions so as to apply to *intervals* in the domain. A function may then be increasing in some intervals and decreasing in others.

Returning to Figure 19c, we see that the function whose graph is shown is decreasing when $x \le -3$ and increasing when $x \ge -3$. This is the "usual" situation for a function—there are intervals in which the function is increasing and intervals in which it is decreasing. Of course, there is another possibility. The function may have the same value over an interval, in which case we call it a **constant function** over that interval.

Example 1 Determining Where a Function Is Increasing and Decreasing

Given the function $f(x) = 1 - x^2$, determine where the function is increasing and where it is decreasing.

Solution

We obtain the graph of $y = 1 - x^2$ by plotting several points. See Figure 20.

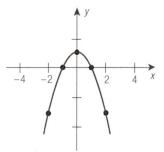

Figure 20 Graph of $f(x) = 1 - x^2$

From the graph we see that

$$f \text{ is increasing when } x \le 0$$
$$f \text{ is decreasing when } x \ge 0$$

✔ **Progress Check 1**

Given $f(x) = x^2 + 2x$, determine where the function is increasing and where the function is decreasing.

Answer

increasing when $x \geq -1$; decreasing when $x \leq -1$

Example 2   Determining Where a Function Is Increasing and Decreasing

The function f is defined by

$$f(x) = \begin{cases} |x| & \text{if } x \leq 2 \\ -3 & \text{if } x > 2 \end{cases}$$

Find the values of x for which the function is increasing, decreasing, and constant.

Solution

We sketch the graph of f by plotting a number of points. See Figure 21. From the graph we determine that

f is increasing if $0 \leq x \leq 2$

f is decreasing if $x \leq 0$

f is constant and has value -3 if $x > 2$

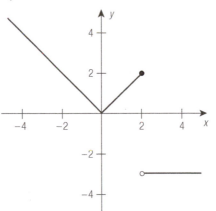

Figure 21   Graph for Example 2

✔ **Progress Check 2**

The function f is defined by

$$f(x) = \begin{cases} 2x + 1 & \text{if } x < -1 \\ 0 & \text{if } -1 \leq x \leq 3 \\ -2x + 1 & \text{if } x > 3 \end{cases}$$

Find the values of x for which the function is increasing, decreasing, and constant.

Answer

increasing if $x < -1$; decreasing if $x > 3$; constant if $-1 \leq x \leq 3$

Example 3   Determining Where a Function Is Increasing and Decreasing

The function f is defined by

$$f(x) = \frac{1}{x}$$

Find the values of x for which the function is increasing, decreasing, and constant.

Solution

We obtain the graph of f by plotting several points. See Figure 22. Since the graph is made up of two parts, we must treat the question of increasing and decreasing separately for each part. From the graph we see that

f is decreasing if $x > 0$

f is decreasing if $x < 0$

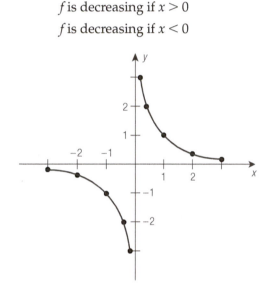

Figure 22   Graph for Example 3

✔ **Progress Check 3**

The function f is defined by

$$f(x) = \frac{1}{x + 4}$$

Find the values of x for which the function is increasing, decreasing, and constant.

Answer

decreasing if $x > -4$; decreasing if $x < -4$

Exercise Set 6.4

In Exercises 1−24 determine the values of x where the function is increasing, decreasing, and constant.

1. $f(x) = \frac{1}{3}x + 2$

2. $f(x) = 3 - \frac{1}{2}x$

3. $f(x) = x^2 + 1$

4. $f(x) = x^2 - 4$

5. $f(x) = 9 - x^2$

6. $f(x) = x^2 - 3x$

7. $f(x) = 4x - x^2$

8. $f(x) = x^2 - 2x + 4$

9. $f(x) = \frac{1}{2}x^2 + 3$

10. $f(x) = 4 - \frac{1}{2}x^2$

11. $f(x) = (x - 2)^2$

12. $f(x) = |x - 1|$

13. $f(x) = |2x + 1|$

14. $f(x) = \begin{cases} x, & x < 2 \\ 2, & x \geq 2 \end{cases}$

15. $f(x) = \begin{cases} 2x, & x > -1 \\ -x - 1, & x \leq -1 \end{cases}$

16. $f(x) = \begin{cases} x + 1, & x > 2 \\ 1, & -1 \leq x \leq 2 \\ -x + 1, & x < -1 \end{cases}$

17. $f(x) = (x + 1)^3$

18. $f(x) = \frac{1}{2}(x - 1)^3$

19. $f(x) = (x - 2)^3$

20. $f(x) = x^3 + 1$

21. $f(x) = (x - 1)^4$

22. $f(x) = x^4 + 1$

*23. $f(x) = \frac{1}{x - 1}$

*24. $f(x) = x + \frac{1}{x}$

*25. A manufacturer of skis finds that the profit made from selling x pairs of skis per week is given by
$$P(x) = 80x - x^2 - 60$$
For what values of x is $P(x)$ increasing? For what values is it decreasing?

*26. A psychologist who is training chimpanzees to understand human speech finds that the number $N(t)$ of words learned after t weeks of training is given by
$$N(t) = 80t - t^2, \quad 0 \leq t \leq 80$$
For what values of t does $N(t)$ increase? For what values does it decrease?

*27. It has been found that x hours after a dosage of a standard drug has been given to a person, the change in blood pressure is given by
$$P(x) = \frac{x^3}{3} - \frac{7}{2}x^2 + 10x, \quad 0 \leq x \leq 6$$
During the 6-hour period of observation, when will the blood pressure be increasing? When will it be decreasing?

*28. Suppose that the profit made by a moped manufacturer from selling x mopeds per week is given by
$$P(x) = x^2 - 1000x + 500$$
For what values of x is $P(x)$ increasing? For what values is it decreasing?

29. MATHEMATICS IN WRITING: Explain in your own words how the slope of a line can help you to predict how the function outputs are changing with changes in the inputs. Are the graphs in Exercises 1 and 2 *rising* or *falling*? How can you tell? What is the importance of knowing whether a graph is rising or falling?

30. Graph the function $f(x) = x^3 - 12x$ in your calculator. Select an appropriate viewing window. Use the TRACE feature to determine the intervals where the function is increasing or decreasing.

6.5 Direct and Inverse Variation

Direct Variation

Two functional relationships occur so frequently that they are given distinct names. They are direct variation and inverse variation. Two quantities are said to **vary directly** if an increase in one causes a proportional increase in the other. In the table

x	1	2	3	4
y	3	6	9	12

we see that an increase in x causes a proportional increase in y. If we look at the ratios y/x we have

$$\frac{y}{x} = \frac{3}{1} = \frac{6}{2} = \frac{9}{3} = \frac{12}{4} = 3$$

or $y = 3x$. The ratio y/x remains constant for all values of y and $x \neq 0$. This is an example of the

Principle of Direct Variation

y varies directly as x means $y = kx$ for some constant k.

As another example, y varies directly as the square of x means $y = kx^2$ for some constant k. Direct variation, then, involves a constant k, which is called the **constant of variation**.

Example 1   Direct Variation

Write the appropriate equation, solve for the constant of variation k, and use this k to relate the variables.

(a) d varies directly as t, and $d = 15$ when $t = 2$.

(b) y varies directly as the cube of x, and $y = 24$ when $x = -2$.

Solution

(a) Using the principle of direct variation, the functional relationship is

$$d = kt \quad \text{for some constant } k$$

Substituting the values $d = 15$ and $t = 2$, we have

$$15 = k \cdot 2$$
$$k = \frac{15}{2}$$

Therefore,

$$d = \frac{15}{2}t$$

(b) Using the principle of direct variation, the functional relationship is

$$y = kx^3 \quad \text{for some constant } k$$

Substituting the values $y = 24$, $x = -2$, we have

$$24 = k \cdot (-2)^3 = -8k$$
$$k = -3$$

Thus,

$$y = -3x^3$$

Inverse Variation

Two quantities are said to **vary inversely** if an increase in one causes a proportional decrease in the other. In the table

x	1	2	3	4
y	24	12	8	6

we see that an increase in x causes a proportional decrease in y. If we look at the product xy we have

$$xy = 1 \cdot 24 = 2 \cdot 12 = 3 \cdot 8 = 4 \cdot 6 = 24$$

or $y = 24/x$. In general, we have the

Principle of Inverse Variation

> y varies inversely as x means $y = \dfrac{k}{x}$ for some constant k.

Once again, k is called the constant of variation.

Example 2　Inverse Variation

Write the appropriate equation, solve for the constant of variation k, and use k to relate the variables.

(a) m varies inversely as d, and $m = 9$ when $d = -3$.

(b) y varies inversely as the square of x, and $y = 10$ when $x = 10$.

Solution

(a) The principle of inverse variation tells us that

$$m = \frac{k}{d}$$

for some constant k. Substituting $m = 9$ and $d = -3$ yields $k = -27$. Thus,

$$m = \frac{-27}{d}$$

(b) The functional relationship is

$$y = \frac{k}{x^2} \quad \text{for some constant } k$$

Substituting $y = 10$ and $x = 10$, we have

$$10 = \frac{k}{(10)^2} = \frac{k}{100}$$
$$k = 1000$$

Thus,

$$y = \frac{1000}{x^2}$$

✔ **Progress Check 2**

If v varies inversely as the cube of w, and $v = 2$ when $w = -2$, find the constant of variation.

Answer

-16

Joint Variation

An equation of variation can involve more than two variables. We say that a quantity **varies jointly** as two or more other quantities if it varies directly as their product.

Example 3   Joint Variation
Express as an equation: P varies jointly as R, S, and the square of T.

Solution
Since P must vary directly as $R \cdot S \cdot T^2$, we have $P = k \cdot R \cdot S \cdot T^2$ for some constant k.

✔ **Progress Check 3**

Express as an equation: m varies jointly as p and q, and inversely as d.

Answer

$$m = \frac{kpq}{d}$$

Example 4   Joint Variation

Find the constant of variation if x varies jointly as y and z, and $x = 30$ when $y = 2$ and $z = 3$.

Solution

We have

$$x = k \cdot y \cdot z \quad \text{for some constant } k$$

and substitute for x, y, and z.

$$30 = k \cdot 2 \cdot 3$$
$$30 = 6k$$
$$k = 5$$

Thus,

$$x = 5yz$$

✔ **Progress Check 4**

Find the constant of variation if x varies jointly as y and the cube of z, and inversely as t, and $x = -\frac{1}{4}$ when $y = -1$, $z = -2$, and $t = 4$.

Answer

$-\dfrac{1}{8}$

Exercise Set 6.5

1. In the following table, y varies directly as x.

x	2	3	4	6	8	12		
y	8	12	16	24			80	120

   (a) Find the constant of variation.

   (b) Write an equation showing that y varies directly as x.

   (c) Complete the blanks in the table.

2. In the following table, y varies inversely as x.

x	1	2	3	6	9	12	15	18		
y	6	3	2	1	$\frac{2}{3}$	$\frac{1}{2}$			$\frac{1}{4}$	$\frac{1}{10}$

   (a) Find the constant of variation.

   (b) Write an equation showing that y varies inversely as x.

   (c) Complete the blanks in the table.

3. If y varies directly as x, and $y = -\frac{1}{4}$ when $x = 8$,

   (a) find the constant of variation.

   (b) find y when $x = 12$.

4. If C varies directly as the square of s, and $C = 12$ when $s = 6$,

   (a) find the constant of variation.

   (b) find C when $s = 9$.

5. If s varies directly as the square of t and $s = 10$ when $t = 10$,

   (a) find the constant of variation.

   (b) find s when $t = 5$.

6. If V varies directly as the cube of T, and $V = 16$ when $T = 4$,

   (a) find the constant of variation.

   (b) find V when $T = 6$.

7. If y varies inversely as x, and $y = -\frac{1}{2}$ when $x = 6$,

   (a) find the constant of variation.

   (b) find y when $x = 12$.

8. If V varies inversely as the square of p, and $V = \frac{2}{3}$ when $p = 6$,

   (a) find the constant of variation.

   (b) find V when $p = 8$.

9. If K varies inversely as the cube of r, and $K = 8$ when $r = 4$,

   (a) find the constant of variation.

   (b) find K when $r = 5$.

10. If T varies inversely as the cube of u, and $T = 2$ when $u = 2$,

    (a) find the constant of variation.

    (b) find T when $u = 5$.

11. If M varies directly as the square of r and inversely as the square of s, and if $M = 4$ when $r = 4$ and $s = 2$,

    (a) write the appropriate equation relating M, r, and s.

    (b) find M when $r = 6$ and $s = 5$.

12. If f varies jointly as u and v, and $f = 36$ when $u = 3$ and $v = 4$,

    (a) write the appropriate equation connecting f, u, and v.

    (b) find f when $u = 5$ and $v = 2$.

13. If T varies jointly as p and the cube of v and inversely as the square of u, and if $T = 24$ when $p = 3$, $v = 2$, and $u = 4$,

    (a) write the appropriate equation connecting T, p, v, and u.

    (b) find T when $p = 2$, $v = 3$, and $u = 36$.

14. If A varies jointly as the square of b and the square of c, and inversely as the cube of d, and if $A = 18$ when $b = 4$, $c = 3$, and $d = 2$,

    (a) write the appropriate equation relating A, b, c, and d.

    (b) find A when $b = 9$, $c = 4$, and $d = 3$.

15. The distance s an object falls from rest in t seconds varies directly as the square of t. If an object falls 144 feet in 3 seconds,

    (a) how far does it fall in 4 seconds?

    (b) how long does it take to fall 400 feet?

16. In a certain state the income tax paid by a person varies directly as the income. If the tax is $20 per month when the monthly income is $1600, find the tax due when the monthly income is $900.

17. The resistance R of a conductor varies inversely as the area A of its cross section. If $R = 20$ ohms when

$A = 8$ square centimeters, find R when $A = 12$ square centimeters.

18. The pressure P of a certain enclosed gas varies directly as the temperature T and inversely as the volume V. Suppose that 300 cubic feet of gas exert a pressure of 20 pounds per square foot when the temperature is 500°K (absolute temperature measured in the Kelvin scale). What is the pressure of this gas when the temperature is lowered to 400°K and the volume is increased to 500 cubic feet?

19. The intensity of illumination I from a source of light varies inversely as the square of the distance d from the source. If the intensity is 200 candlepower when the source is 4 feet away,

    (a) what is the intensity when the source is 6 feet away?

    (b) how close should the source be to provide an intensity of 50 candlepower?

20. The weight of a body in space varies inversely as the square of its distance from the center of the earth. If a body weighs 400 pounds on the surface of the earth, how much does it weigh 100 miles above the surface of the earth? (Assume that the radius of the earth is 4000 miles.)

21. The equipment cost of a printing job varies jointly as the number of presses and the number of hours that the presses are run. When 4 presses are run for 6 hours, the equipment cost is $1200. If the equipment cost for 12 hours of running is $3600, how many presses are being used?

22. The current I in a wire varies directly as the electromotive force E, and inversely as the resistance R. If the current of 36 amperes is obtained with a wire that has resistance of 10 ohms, and the electromotive force is 120 volts, find the current produced when $E = 220$ volts and $R = 30$ ohms.

23. The illumination from a light source varies directly as the intensity of the source, and inversely as the square of the distance from the source. If the illumination is 50 candlepower per square foot when 2 feet away from a light source whose intensity is 400 candlepower, what is the illumination when 4 feet away from a source whose intensity is 3840 candlepower?

24. If f varies directly as u and inversely as the square of v, what happens to f if both u and v are doubled?

6.6   Critical Thinking Problems

We learned that $y = ax + b$ is a linear function and its graph is a straight line. We call $y = ax^2 + bx + c$, $(a \neq 0)$ a quadratic function. The graph of a quadratic function is a parabola.

We may use these tools to model functions in our real life.

Example 1   Predicting Weight

Suppose that you are on a diet. To lose weight, you avoid foods with too much sugar or fat. Below is your weight chart. Define a linear function representing this chart. Determine your weight after 3 months if you stay on the diet.

Weeks after diet	0	1	2	3	4	5
Weight	147	145	143	141	139	137

Solution

Notice that each week you lose the same number of pounds. This function, then, is a linear function. We will find the function in the form $y = mx + b$.

Let's find the slope and y-intercept. By looking at the chart, you can see that you would write the slope as losing 2 pounds per week ($m = -2$). Alternatively, you can find the slope algebraically by choosing any two points.

$$\text{Slope} = m = \frac{\text{change in } y\text{–values}}{\text{change in } x\text{–values}}$$

$$m = \frac{145 - 147}{1 - 0} = \frac{141 - 143}{3 - 2} = \frac{-2}{1} = -2$$

Let's use the point $(0, 147)$. By definition, this point defines the y-intercept since $x = 0$. Thus, the y-intercept is 147 ($b = 147$). Using the slope and y-intercept form $y = mx + b$, we write a linear function describing the chart. By substituting $m = -2$ and $b = 147$, the linear function describing the chart is $f(x) = y = -2x + 147$.

To find your weight after 3 months, let's convert 3 months to weeks. Since 3 months = 12 weeks,

$$y = f(12) = -2(12) + 147$$
$$y = -24 + 147$$
$$y = 123 \text{ pounds}$$

If you stay on the diet, then you will weigh 123 pounds after 3 months or 12 weeks.

✔ Progress Check 1

Mr. Jones bought a computer costing $1,800 for his school. He expects to use it for 6 years. The value y (in dollars) of the computer in x years is given by $y = -250x + 1,800$. Complete the table.

x	0	1	2	3	4	5	6
y							

Answer

x	0	1	2	3	4	5	6
y	1,800	1,550	1,300	1,050	800	550	300

Example 2   How Many Animals?

Mr. and Mrs. Smith own a farm. They have a total of 52 cows and chickens. They decide to count the number of feet on all the animals. There are a total of 134 feet. Find the number of cows and chickens.

Solution

Cows have four feet and chickens have two feet.

If there are two cows, then there will be $4 \cdot 2 = 8$ feet.

If there are ten cows, then there will be $4 \cdot 10 = 40$ feet.

Now we write

$$\text{the number of cow's feet} = 4 \cdot (\text{number of cows})$$

Chickens have two feet, so we write

$$\text{the number of chicken's feet} = 2 \cdot (\text{number of chickens})$$

How many cows are there? We don't know. We will let x represent the unknown value.
Let

$$x = \text{the number of cows}$$

Then

$$52 - x = \text{the number of chickens}$$

We write,

$$\text{number of cow's feet} + \text{number of chicken's feet} = 134$$

So

$$4x + 2(52 - x) = 134$$

Solve the equation for x.

$4x + 2(52 - x) = 134$	Distributive Property
$4x + 104 - 2x = 134$	
$2x + 104 = 134$	Combine like terms
$2x = 30$	Subtract 104 from both sides
$x = 15 \text{ cows}$	Divide both sides by 2

The number of chickens is $52 - x$ or

$$52 - 15$$
$$= 37 \text{ chickens}$$

There are 15 cows and 37 chickens.

✔ Progress Check 2

(a) You go to the Strawberry Festival in Arroyo Grande. The parking lot is filled with cars and motorcycles. There are a total of 308 wheels. You count a total of 63 cars. How many motorcycles are there?

(b) You took a Statistics test. There were 50 questions. Each correct answer was 5 points, but each incorrect answer was −3 points. If you earned 98 points, how many correct and incorrect answers did you get?

Answers

(a) 28 motorcycles   (b) 31 correct answers and 19 incorrect answers

The Pythagorean Theorem

A triangle has three sides, each of which is a straight line. The sum of the three interior angles is 180°. If one of the interior angles of a triangle is 90° then this triangle is called a **right triangle**. The longest side of a right triangle lies directly opposite the 90° angle and is called the **hypotenuse**. The two other sides are called **legs**. One of the most important theorems in mathematics is called the **Pythagorean Theorem**, named after the mathematician Pythagorus.

The Pythagorean Theorem states that in a right triangle the sum of the squares of the two sides is equal to the square of the hypotenuse. The converse of this statement is also true. If the sum of the squares of two sides is equal to the square of the third side, then it is a right triangle.

$$a^2 + b^2 = c^2$$
$$(\text{side})^2 + (\text{side})^2 = (\text{hypotenuse})^2$$

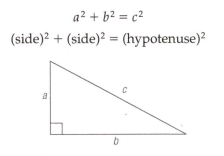

Example 3   Determining a Right Triangle

(a) Determine whether the following is a right triangle: A triangle with sides of 3 ft, 4 ft, and 5 ft.

(b) Find the missing side given a right triangle with one side that is 8 inches and a hypotenuse that is 10 inches.

Solution

(a) The longest side is 5 ft. The other sides are 3 ft and 4 ft. Let's use the Pythagorean Theorem.

$$(\text{side})^2 + (\text{side})^2 \overset{?}{=} (\text{hypotenuse})^2$$
$$(3)^2 + (4)^2 \overset{?}{=} ((5)^2$$
$$9 + 16 = 25$$

Yes, it is a right triangle.

(b) The hypotenuse of the triangle is 10 inches and one of the sides is 8 inches. Let's find the unknown leg. Once again using $(\text{side})^2 + (\text{side})^2 = (\text{hypotenuse})^2$,

$$(8)^2 + (\text{side})^2 = (10)^2$$
$$64 + (\text{side})^2 = 100$$
$$(\text{side})^2 = 36 \qquad \text{Subtracting 64 from both sides}$$
$$\text{side} = 6$$

The missing side is 6 inches.

We will learn later how we find the square root of a number. (Instead of finding the number whose square is 36, we may write it as leg $= \sqrt{36} = \sqrt{6^2} = 6$.)

✔ Progress Check 3

A ladder is leaning against a building. The ladder is 13 feet long and the bottom of the ladder is 5 feet from the building. How high up the side of the building does the ladder reach?

Answer

12 feet

■ ■ ■

Terms and Symbols

abscissa	function notation, $f(x)$	origin
Cartesian coordinate system	graph of a function	parabola
constant function	graph of an equation in two	polynomial function
constant of variation	variables	quadrant
coordinate axes	image	quadratic functions
coordinates of a point	increasing function	range
decreasing function	independent variable	rectangular coordinate system
dependent variable	inverse variation	vertical line test
direct variation	joint variation	x-axis
domain	linear function	x-coordinate
"evaluate" a function	ordered pair	y-axis
function	ordinate	y-coordinate

Key Ideas for Review

Topic	Key Idea
Rectangular coordinate system	In a rectangular coordinate system, every ordered pair of real numbers (a, b) corresponds to a point in the plane, and every point in the plane corresponds to an ordered pair of real numbers.
Graph of an equation	An equation in two variables can be graphed by plotting points that satisfy the equation and then joining the points to form a smooth curve.
Function	A function is a rule that assigns exactly one element y of a set Y to each element x of a set X. The domain is the set of inputs and the range is the set of outputs.
notation	Function notation gives both the definition of the function and the value or expression at which to evaluate the function. Thus, if f is defined by $f(x) = x^2 + 2x$, then the notation $f(3)$ denotes the result of replacing the independent variable x by 3 wherever it appears: $f(3) = 3^2 + 2(3) = 15$.

(continues)

Key Ideas for Review, continued

Topic	Key Idea
defining a function	An equation is not the only way to define a function. Sometimes a function is defined by a table or chart, or by several equations. Moreover, not every equation determines a function.
graph	To graph $f(x)$, simply graph the equation $y = f(x)$. The graph of a function can have holes or gaps, and can be defined in "pieces."
vertical line test	A graph represents a function $y = f(x)$ if no vertical line meets the graph in more than one point.
polynomials	Polynomials in one variable determine functions and have "smooth" curves as their graphs.
increasing and decreasing	As we move from left to right, the graph of an increasing function rises and the graph of a decreasing function falls.
constant	The graph of a constant function neither rises nor falls; it is horizontal.
Direct and inverse variation	Direct and inverse variation are functional relationships. We say that y varies directly as x if $y = kx$ for some constant k. We say that y varies inversely as x if $y = k/x$ for some constant k.
Joint variation	We say that y varies jointly as two or more other quantities if it varies directly as their product.

Common Errors

1. Function notation is not distributive. *Don't* write

$$f(a + 3) = f(a) + f(3)$$

or

$$f(a + 3) = f(a) + 3$$

Instead, substitute $a + 3$ for the independent variable.

2. *Don't* write

$$f(x^2) = [f(x)]^2$$

or

$$f(x^2) = f \cdot x^2$$

Again, the notation $f(x^2)$ denotes the output when we replace the independent variable by x^2.

3. It is legitimate for the graph of a function to have holes or gaps. Don't force the graph of every function to be "continuous."

Review Exercises

Solutions to exercises whose numbers are in bold are in the Solutions section in the back of the book.

6.1

1. If A is the point with coordinates $(2, -3)$, find the coordinates of the point B that is 4 units to the left and 1 unit below A.

2. If A is the point with coordinates $(-3, -2)$, find the coordinates of the point B that is 3 units above A.

3. Without plotting, name the quadrant in which the point $(-3, 2)$ is located.

4. Which of the following are solutions to

$$2x^2 - 5y = -7?$$

   (a) $(2, 3)$ (b) $(2, -3)$ (c) $(-2, -3)$ (d) $(-2, 3)$

5. Which of the following are solutions to

$$x - y^2 = 3?$$

   (a) $(-1, 2)$ (b) $(1, 4)$ (c) $(-2, -7)$ (d) $(3, 0)$

6. Complete the following table for the equation $2x + 5y = 20$.

x	2		0		3	
y		-1		0		4

In Exercises 7–9 graph the given equation.

7. $y = -3x$

8. $x = -2y + 1$

9. $y = 3x - x^2$

10. Graph the set of all points whose x- and y-coordinates are equal.

6.2 In Exercises 11 and 12 graph the given equation. If the correspondence is a function, determine the domain and range.

11. $y = 2x - x^2$

12. $x = y^2 - 1$

In Exercises 13 and 14 determine the domain of the given function.

13. $f(x) = \dfrac{x - 3}{x + 4}$

14. $g(t) = \dfrac{3}{t^2 + t - 12}$

In Exercises 15 and 16 determine whether or not the given curve is the graph of a function.

15.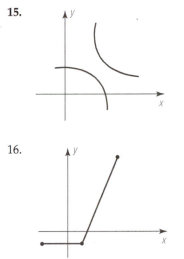

16.

17. The function f is defined by $f(x) = x^2 - x + 2$. Compute the following:

   (a) $f(2)$ (b) $f(0)$ (c) $f(-3)$

18. The function g is defined by

$$g(t) = \frac{t - 3}{t + 1}$$

   Compute the following:

   (a) $g(-5)$ (b) $g(0)$ (c) $g(3)$

19. Suppose that an object drops from a fixed height. If we neglect air resistance, the force of the earth's gravity causes the object to hit the ground after t seconds. The relationship of t to the distance s (in feet) the object falls is given by

$$s = 16t^2$$

   (Note that the function does not depend upon the mass of the body.)

   (a) What is the distance traveled by an object when t is 2 seconds? What is the distance traveled in 4 seconds?

   (b) How long does it take the object to fall 144 feet?

20. Express the area A of a circle as a function of its diameter d.

6.3 In Exercises 21−26 sketch the graph of the given function.

21. $f(x) = 2x - 1$

22. $g(x) = -3x + 2$

23. $h(x) = 2x + x^2$

24. $f(x) = x - x^3$

25. $g(x) = \begin{cases} x - 1, & x \le -1 \\ x^2, & -1 < x \le 2 \\ -2, & x > 2 \end{cases}$

26. $h(x) = \begin{cases} x + 2, & x < 2 \\ x^2, & x \ge 2 \end{cases}$

In Exercises 27 and 28 sketch the graphs of the given functions on the same coordinate axes.

27. $f(x) = x^2 + 1, g(x) = 2x^2 + 1$

28. $f(x) = x^3 + 2, g(x) = -x^3 + 2$

29. A photography shop sells powdered developer. The cost C of shipping an order is 15 cents for each of the first 5 pounds, and 10 cents for each additional pound.

   (a) Write C as a function of the number n of pounds in an order, for $0 < n \le 20$.

   (b) Sketch the graph of the function C for $0 < n \le 20$.

   (c) What is the cost of shipping an order that consists of 16 pounds of developer?

30. A stereo shop runs the following advertisement: "Big sale on 90-minute tape cassettes! Pay $2.20 each for the first 10 cassettes, $2.15 each for the next 15 cassettes, and $2.05 for each cassette beyond 25."

   (a) Express the cost C as a function of the number x of cassettes purchased.

   (b) What is the cost of buying 32 cassettes?

6.4 In Exercises 31−38 determine the values of x where the function is increasing, decreasing, and constant.

31. $f(x) = 2 - x$

32. $f(x) = x^2 - x$

33. $f(x) = x^2 + 1$

34. $f(x) = x^2 - x - 6$

35. $f(x) = (x - 1)^2$

36. $f(x) = (x + 2)^2 - 4$

37. $f(x) = \begin{cases} x - 3, & x < 1 \\ 2, & 1 < x \le 3 \\ -x + 5, & x > 3 \end{cases}$

38. $f(x) = \begin{cases} x + 2, & x < -2 \\ x^2, & -2 \le x < 4 \\ 3, & x \ge 4 \end{cases}$

39. The cost C of manufacturing x quarts of a certain pharmaceutical is given (in dollars) by

$$C(x) = x^2 - 20x + 800$$

   For what values of x is $C(x)$ increasing? For what values is it decreasing?

40. After x hours of weightlessness, it is found that a subject requires $T(x)$ minutes to solve a certain puzzle. If

$$T(x) = 20 + 4x - x^2$$

   for what values of x is $T(x)$ increasing? For what values is it decreasing?

6.5 41. In the following table y varies directly as the square of t.

t	1	2	3	4	
y	$\frac{1}{2}$	2	$\frac{9}{2}$		$\frac{25}{2}$

   (a) Write the appropriate equation relating y and t.

   (b) Find the constant of variation.

   (c) Complete the blanks in the table.

42. In the following table M varies inversely as the cube of n.

n	2	3	4	
M	$\frac{1}{12}$	$\frac{2}{81}$		$\frac{2}{375}$

   (a) Write the appropriate equation relating M and n.

   (b) Find the constant of variation.

   (c) Complete the blanks in the table.

43. If F varies directly as the square of r, and $F = 6$ when $r = 3$,

   (a) find the constant of variation.

   (b) find F when $r = 6$.

44. If A varies inversely as the cube of b, and $A = \frac{3}{16}$ when $b = 2$,

    (a) find the constant of variation.

    (b) find A when $b = 4$.

45. If S varies jointly as t and the square of u, and $S = 18$ when $t = 4$ and $u = 9$, find S when $t = 6$ and $u = 3$.

46. If K varies jointly as b and c and inversely as the square of d, and if $K = \frac{3}{4}$ when $b = 6$, $c = 2$, and $d = 2$, find K when $b = 4$, $c = 3$, and $d = 4$.

47. In the following table z varies jointly as x and y.

x	2	3	4	2	
y	3	5	2		3
z	9	$\frac{45}{2}$	12	15	18

Complete the blanks in the table.

48. In the following table T varies directly as r and inversely as the square of s.

r	2	3	4	5	
s	3	2	5		3
T	$\frac{8}{27}$	1	$\frac{16}{75}$	$\frac{5}{3}$	$\frac{4}{9}$

Complete the blanks in the table.

49. The output of an employee on an assembly line varies directly as the number of hours on a training course. If the employee can turn out 18 items per hour after a 6-hour training course, how many items can she turn out per hour after a 10-hour course?

50. The time required by a subject to solve a certain puzzle varies jointly as the temperature of the room and the number of hours without sleep. If it takes a certain subject 10 minutes to solve the puzzle in a 60°F room after 10 hours without sleep, how long will it take the same subject to solve the puzzle in a 90° room after 20 hours without sleep?

51. A software firm finds that the revenue R received from the sale of one of its products varies directly as the amount spent on advertising and inversely as the length of the training manual. If the firm received $1,000,000 of revenue on a product with a 100-page training manual after spending $50,000 on advertising, how much revenue would it have received if the manual had been 120 pages long and $75,000 had been spent on advertising?

Progress Test 6A

1. Sketch the graph of $y = -2x^3 + 1$.

2. Find the domain of the function $f(x) = \dfrac{2x}{x + 3}$.

3. Find the domain of the function $g(y) = \dfrac{2}{y^2 - 4}$.

4. Use the vertical line test to determine if the equations
$$y = \begin{cases} |x|, & -3 \le x \le 3 \\ x^2, & x > 0 \end{cases}$$
define a function.

5. Is the following the graph of a function?

6. Evaluate $f(-\frac{1}{2})$ for $f(x) = x^2 - 3x + 1$.

7. Evaluate $f(2t)$ for $f(x) = \dfrac{1 - x^2}{1 + x^2}$.

8. Evaluate $\dfrac{f(a + h) - f(a)}{h}$ for $f(x) = 2x^2 + 3$.

9. Sketch the graph of the function
$$f(x) = \begin{cases} x - 1, & -5 \le x \le -1 \\ x^2, & -1 < x \le 2 \\ -2, & 2 < x \le 5 \end{cases}$$

10. Sketch the graph of $f(x) = x^2 - 4x + 2$.

11. If R varies directly as q, and $R = 20$ when $q = 5$, find R when $q = 40$.

12. If S varies inversely as the cube of t, and $S = 8$ when $t = -1$, find S when $t = -2$.

13. If P varies jointly as q and r, and inversely as the square of t, and if $P = -3$ when $q = 2$, $r = -3$, and $t = 4$, find P when $q = -1$, $r = \frac{1}{2}$, and $t = 4$.

14. Determine the intervals where the function $f(x) = x^2 - 2x + 1$ is increasing, decreasing, and constant.

15. Determine the intervals where the function
$$f(x) = \begin{cases} |x - 1|, & x < 3 \\ -1, & x \geq 3 \end{cases}$$
is increasing, decreasing, and constant.

Progress Test 6B

1. Sketch the graph of $y = \frac{1}{2}x^3 - 1$.

2. Find the domain of the function $f(t) = \dfrac{t}{2t - 1}$.

3. Find the domain of the function $g(x) = \dfrac{4x}{1 - x^2}$.

4. Use the vertical line test to determine if the equations
$$y = \begin{cases} |x - 1|, & x \leq 5 \\ 4, & x \geq 5 \end{cases}$$
define a function.

5. Is the following the graph of a function?

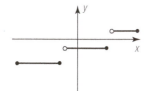

6. Evaluate $f(-1)$ for $f(x) = \dfrac{x^2 + 2}{x}$.

7. Evaluate $f\left(\dfrac{a}{2}\right)$ for $f(x) = (1 + x)^2$.

8. Evaluate $\dfrac{f(a + h) - f(a)}{h}$ for $f(x) = -x^2 + 2$.

9. Sketch the graph of the function
$$f(x) = \begin{cases} |x| + 1, & -4 \leq x < 1 \\ 2x, & 1 \leq x \leq 4 \\ 4, & x > 4 \end{cases}$$

10. Sketch the graph of $f(x) = -x^2 + 2x$.

11. If L varies directly as the cube of r, and $L = 2$ when $r = -\frac{1}{2}$, find L when $r = 4$.

12. If A varies inversely as the square of b, and $A = -2$ when $b = 4$, find A when $b = 3$.

13. If T varies jointly as a and the square of b, and inversely as the cube of c, and if $T = 64$ when $a = -1$, $b = \frac{1}{2}$, and $c = 2$, find T when $a = 2$, $b = 4$, and $c = -1$.

14. Determine the intervals where the function $f(x) = |x - 2|$ is increasing, decreasing, and constant.

15. Determine the intervals where the function
$$f(x) = \begin{cases} 5, & x < -1 \\ |x|, & -1 \leq x \leq 3 \\ -1, & x > 3 \end{cases}$$
is increasing, decreasing, and constant.

Chapter 6 Project

At the beginning of this chapter, we mentioned a function that relates the number of times n a cricket chirps in one minute to the outside temperature in degrees Fahrenheit. Here is that function (you have seen it several times!)

$$f(n) = \frac{n}{4} + 40$$

What would the temperature be if you heard 36 chirps in one minute? in 52 minutes? Use your graphing calculator to set up a TABLE, pairing the inputs (number of chirps) with the outputs (temperature) for ten values of n.

For this chapter's project, look back at Section 6.2, Exercise 65, and Section 6.3, Exercises 48 and 49.

Put these results together with your table, and answer the following question.

MATHEMATICS IN WRITING: In your own words, explain how the concepts of *function*, *line*, and *slope* can be used to describe and predict phenomenon in the world around us.

Mathematics and biology go well together! The same could be said for physics, chemistry, or just about any branch of science. The concept of function is crucial to understanding how scientists model the real world with mathematics.

Explore the connections between mathematics and biology further at http://archives.math.utk.edu/mathbio/.

http://archives.math
.utk.edu/mathbio/

CHAPTER 7

The Straight Line

*For as long as we can reliably reach into the past we find
the development of mathematics intimately connected
with the development of the whole of our civilization.*

—Marc Kac

Architects throughout history have used mathematical principles to design spaces and structures of beauty and utility. From the pyramids of ancient Egypt to the subways of modern American cities, concepts of design have relied upon an understanding of the concepts of algebra.

How is algebra used to put a roof over your head? Probably, the roof you are under right now can be modeled by a straight line. Is it shallow or steep? What does a roofer mean when she says that the pitch of a roof is $\frac{5}{12}$? Expressed another way, this fraction is equal to nearly 42%. This is how the designer of a highway would express this same concept, except that he would call it a grade rather than a pitch. In this chapter's project, we will use linear equations to create a model for a roof with a pitch of $\frac{5}{12}$.

■ ■ ■

In Chapter 6 we said that functions of the form $f(x) = ax + b$ are called linear functions, and we saw that the graphs of such functions appear to be straight lines. In this chapter we will demonstrate that these conjectures are well founded: the graph of a linear function is indeed a straight line.

The concept of slope is introduced and is used to develop two important forms of the equation of the straight line, the point-slope form and the slope-intercept form. Horizontal, vertical, parallel, and perpendicular lines are also explored.

Finally, the graphs of linear inequalities are discussed, and a simple technique for sketching such graphs is developed.

7.1   Slope of the Straight Line

In Figure 1 we have drawn a straight line L that is not vertical. We have indicated the distinct points $P_1(x_1, y_1)$ and $P_2(x_2, y_2)$ on L. The increments or changes $x_2 - x_1$ and $y_2 - y_1$ in the x- and y-coordinates, respectively, from P_1 to P_2 are also indicated. Note that the increment $x_2 - x_1$ cannot be zero, since L is not vertical.

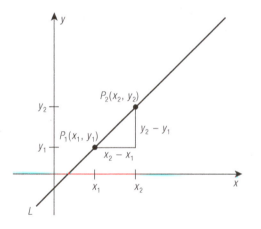

Figure 1   Increments on the Line L

If $P_3(x_3, y_3)$ and $P_4(x_4, y_4)$ are another pair of points on L, as shown in Figure 2, the increments $x_4 - x_3$ and $y_4 - y_3$ will, in general, be different from the increments obtained by using P_1 and P_2. Since triangles P_1AP_2 and P_3BP_4 are similar, however, the corresponding sides are in proportion; that is, the ratios

$$\frac{y_4 - y_3}{x_4 - x_3} \text{ and } \frac{y_2 - y_1}{x_2 - x_1}$$

are the same. This ratio is called the **slope of the line** L and is denoted by m.

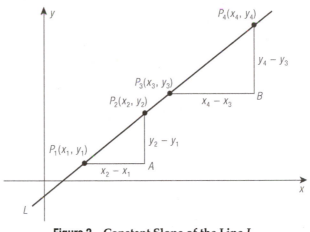

Figure 2   Constant Slope of the Line L

Slope of a Line

The slope of a line that is not vertical is given by

$$m = \frac{y_2 - y_1}{x_2 - x_1}$$

where $P_1(x_1, y_1)$ and $P_2(x_2, y_2)$ are any two distinct points on the line. For a vertical line, $x_1 = x_2$, so $x_2 - x_1 = 0$. Since we cannot divide by 0, we say that a vertical line has no slope.

For a horizontal line, $y_1 = y_2$, so $y_2 - y_1 = 0$, and the slope $m = 0$. Observe that having *no slope* is different from having *zero slope*.

Example 1   Finding the Slope of a Line
Find the slope of the line that passes through the given pair of points.

(a) $(4, 2)$ and $(1, -2)$ (b) $(-5, 2)$ and $(-2, -1)$

Solution
(a) We may choose either point as (x_1, y_1) and the other as (x_2, y_2). Our choice is

$$(x_1, y_1) = (4, 2)$$
$$(x_2, y_2) = (1, -2)$$

Then

$$m = \frac{y_2 - y_1}{x_2 - x_1} = \frac{-2 - 2}{1 - 4} = \frac{-4}{-3} = \frac{4}{3}$$

If we had reversed the choice we would have

$$(x_1, y_1) = (1, -2)$$
$$(x_2, y_2) = (4, 2)$$

and

$$m = \frac{y_2 - y_1}{x_2 - x_1} = \frac{2 - (-2)}{4 - 1} = \frac{4}{3}$$

which is the same result. Reversing the choice does not affect the value of m. (Why?)

(b) Let $(x_1, y_1) = (-5, 2)$ and $(x_2, y_2) = (-2, -1)$. Then

$$m = \frac{y_2 - y_1}{x_2 - x_1} = \frac{-1 - 2}{-2 - (-5)} = \frac{-3}{3} = -1$$

✔ Progress Check 1

Find the slope of the line that passes through the given pair of points.

(a) $(2, -4)$ and $(4, 1)$ (b) $(-1, -3)$ and $(-2, -5)$

Answers

(a) $\frac{5}{2}$ (b) 2

Warning

Once you have chosen a point as (x_1, y_1), you must be consistent. If you have $(x_1, y_1) = (5, 2)$ and $(x_2, y_2) = (1, 6)$, *don't* write

$$m = \frac{6 - 2}{5 - 1} = \frac{4}{4} = 1$$

This answer has the wrong sign, because

$$\frac{y_2 - y_1}{x_1 - x_2} \neq \frac{y_2 - y_1}{x_2 - x_1}$$

Meaning of Slope

Slope is a means of measuring the steepness of a line. That is, slope specifies the number of units we must move up or down to reach the line after moving 1 unit to the right of the line. In Figure 3 we have displayed several lines with positive and negative slopes. We can summarize this way:

Let m be the slope of a line L.

1. When $m > 0$, the line is the graph of an **increasing function.**

2. When $m < 0$, the line is the graph of a **decreasing function.**

3. When $m = 0$, the line is the graph of a **constant function.**

4. Slope does not exist for a vertical line, and a vertical line is not the graph of a function.

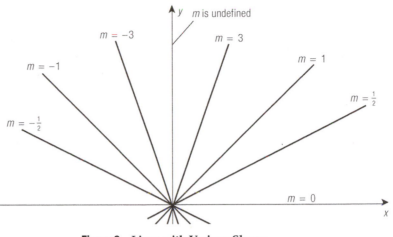

Figure 3 **Lines with Various Slopes**

Example 2 Finding the Slope of a Line

Find the slope of the line through the given points and state whether the line is rising or falling.

(a) $(1, 2)$ and $(-2, -7)$ (b) $(1, 0)$ and $(3, -2)$

Solution

(a) Let

$$(x_1, y_1) = (1, 2)$$
$$(x_2, y_2) = (-2, -7)$$

Then

$$m = \frac{y_2 - y_1}{x_2 - x_1} = \frac{-7 - 2}{-2 - 1} = \frac{-9}{-3} = 3$$

Since m is positive, the line *rises* from left to right (see Figure 4).

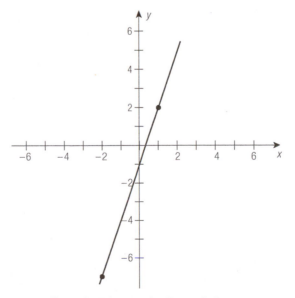

Figure 4 **Diagram for Example 2a**

(b) Let

$$(x_1, y_1) = (1, 0)$$
$$(x_2, y_2) = (3, -2)$$

Then

$$m = \frac{y_2 - y_1}{x_2 - x_1} = \frac{-2 - 0}{3 - 1} = \frac{-2}{2} = -1$$

Since m is negative, the line *falls* from left to right (see Figure 5).

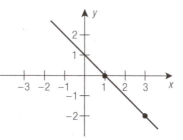

Figure 4   Diagram for Example 2b

✔ Progress Check 2

Find the slope of the line that passes through the given points and state whether the line is rising, falling, or constant.

(a) $(-1, -3)$ and $(0, 1)$ (b) $(-1, -4)$ and $(3, -4)$ (c) $(2, 0)$ and $(4, -1)$

Answers

(a) 4; rising   (b) 0; constant   (c) $-\frac{1}{2}$; falling

---

Exercise Set 7.1

In Exercises 1–8 find the slope of the line passing through the given points and state whether the line is rising or falling.

1. $(2, 3)$ and $(-1, -3)$ 2. $(1, 2)$ and $(-2, 5)$

3. $(1, -4)$ and $(-1, -2)$ 4. $(2, -3)$ and $(3, 2)$

5. $(-2, 3)$ and $(0, 0)$ 6. $\left(\frac{1}{2}, 2\right)$ and $\left(\frac{3}{2}, 1\right)$

7. $(2, 4)$ and $(-3, 4)$ 8. $(-2, 2)$ and $(-2, -4)$

In Exercises 9–12 refer to Figure 6 and indicate whether the slope of the given line is positive (P) or negative (N).

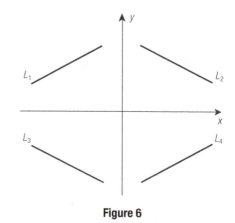

Figure 6

9. L_1

10. L_2

11. L_3

12. L_4

In Exercises 13–16 use Figure 7 to determine whether the given statement is true (T) or false (F).

13. The slope of L_1 is greater than the slope of L_2.

14. The slope of L_3 is less than the slope of L_4.

15. The slope of L_2 is greater than the slope of L_3.

16. The slope of L_4 is less than the slope of L_1.

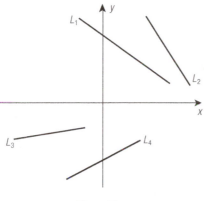

Figure 7

In Exercises 17–20 find the slope of the lines in Figure 8.

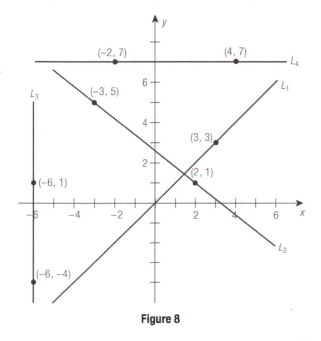

Figure 8

17. L_1

18. L_2

19. L_3

20. L_4

*21. Find a real number c so that the points $(-3, 2)$ and $(c, 4)$ lie on a straight line whose slope is 2.

*22. Find a real number c so that the points $(2, 1)$ and $(c, 2c + 1)$ lie on a straight line whose slope is 3.

23. The slope of a roof is called *pitch*, and it is usually expressed as a fraction with a denominator of 12. (See the chapter opener.) So, a roof with a slope of $\frac{1}{2}$ has a pitch of $\frac{6}{12}$. Suppose I design a roof with triangular cross section, so that the peak of the house is 20 feet above ground level, and the eaves are 14 feet above ground level. How wide would this house be if the pitch of the roof were $\frac{3}{12}$?

24. Refer to Exercise 23. How high would the peak of a house with a triangular roof be, if the house is 72 feet wide, the eaves are 40 feet above ground level, and the pitch of the roof is $\frac{2}{12}$?

25. The grade of a highway is usually expressed as a percent. So, a highway with a grade of 1% has a slope of $\frac{1}{100}$. Suppose one point on a highway is at an elevation of 300 feet above sea level, and a point 100 feet farther along the highway is at an elevation of 304 feet. What is the grade of this highway?

26. Refer to Exercise 25. Suppose the grade of a highway is 8.4%, and one point is 650 feet above sea level. What is the elevation of a point 250 feet farther up the highway?

7.2   Equations of the Straight Line

Point-Slope Form

We can apply the concept of slope to develop important forms of the equations of a straight line. In Figure 9, the point $P_1(x_1, y_1)$ lies on a line L whose slope is m. If $P(x, y)$ is any other point on L, then we may use P and P_1 to compute m, that is,

$$m = \frac{y - y_1}{x - x_1}$$

which can be written in the form

$$y - y_1 = m(x - x_1)$$

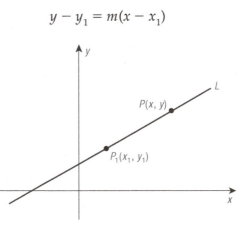

Figure 9   Deriving the Point-Slope Form

Every point on L, including (x_1, y_1) satisfies this equation. Conversely, any point satisfying this equation must lie on the line L, since there is only one line through $P_1(x_1, y_1)$ with slope m. This result is so important that the equation is a given a special name.

Point-Slope Form

$$y - y_1 = m(x - x_1)$$

is an equation of the line with slope m that passes through the point (x_1, y_1).

Example 1   Applying the Point-Slope Form

Find an equation of the line with slope -2 that passes through the point $(4, -1)$. Sketch the line.

Solution

We have $m = -2$ and $(x_1, y_1) = (4, -1)$. Using the point-slope form,

$$y - y_1 = m(x - x_1)$$
$$y - (-1) = -2(x - 4)$$
$$y + 1 = -2x + 8$$
$$y = -2x + 7$$

To sketch the line, we need a second point. We can substitute a value of x, such as $x = 0$, in the equation of the line to obtain another point. See Figure 10.

x	y
4	-1
0	7

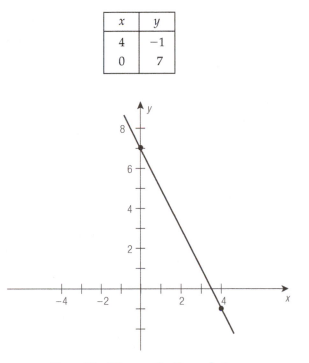

Figure 10   Diagram for Example 1

✔ **Progress Check 1**

Find an equation of the line with slope 3 that passes through the point $(-1, -5)$.

Answer

$y = 3x - 2$

It is also possible to use the point-slope form to find an equation of a line when we know two points on the line.

Example 2   Finding the Equation of a Line through Two Points
Find an equation of the line that passes through the points $(6, -2)$ and $(-4, 3)$.

Solution
First, we find the slope. If we let

$$(x_1, y_1) = (6, -2)$$
$$(x_2, y_2) = (-4, 3)$$

Then

$$m = \frac{y_2 - y_1}{x_2 - x_1} = \frac{3 - (-2)}{-4 - 6} = \frac{5}{-10} = -\frac{1}{2}$$

Next, the point-slope form is used with $m = -\frac{1}{2}$ and $(x_1, y_1) = (6, -2)$.

$$y - y_1 = m(x - x_1)$$

$$y - (-2) = -\frac{1}{2}(x - 6)$$

$$y + 2 = -\frac{1}{2}x + 3$$

$$y = -\frac{1}{2}x + 1$$

✔ Progress Check 2

Find an equation of the line through the points $(3, 0)$ and $(-15, -6)$.

Answer

$$y = \frac{1}{3}x - 1$$

Slope-Intercept Form

There is another form of the equation of the straight line that is very useful. In Figure 11, the line L meets the y-axis at the point $(0, b)$ and is assumed to have slope m. Then we can let $(x_1, y_1) = (0, b)$ and use the point-slope form.

$$y - y_1 = m(x - x_1)$$
$$y - b = m(x - 0)$$
$$y = mx + b$$

The Pirate Treasure (Part I)

Five pirates traveling with a slave found a chest of gold coins. The pirates agreed to divide the coins among themselves the following morning.

During the night Pirate 1 awoke and, not trusting his fellow pirates, decided to remove his share of the coins. After dividing the coins into five equal lots, he found that one coin remained. The pirate took his lot and gave the remaining coin to the slave to ensure his silence.

Later that night Pirate 2 awoke and decided to remove his share of the coins. After dividing the remaining coins into five equal lots, he found one coin left over. The pirate took his lot and gave the extra coin to the slave.

That same night the process was repeated by Pirates 3, 4, and 5. Each time there remained one coin, which was given to the slave.

In the morning these five compatible pirates divided the remaining coins into five equal lots. Once again a single coin remained.

Question: What is the minimum number of coins there could have been in the chest? (For help, see Part II on page 271.)

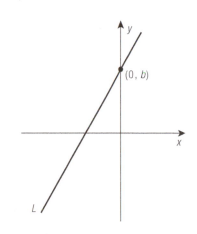

Figure 11   Deriving the Slope-Intercept Form

We call *b* the **y-intercept** and we now have the following result:

Slope-Intercept Form

The graph of the equation

$$y = mx + b$$

is a straight line with slope *m* and y-intercept *b*.

The last result leads to the important conclusion mentioned in the introduction to this section. Since the graph of $y = mx + b$ is the graph of the function $f(x) = mx + b$, we have shown that the *graph of a linear function is a nonvertical straight line.*

Example 3   Applying the Slope-Intercept Form

Find an equation of the line with slope -1 and y-intercept 5.

Solution

We substitute $m = -1$ and $b = 5$ in the equation

$$y = mx + b$$

to obtain

$$y = -x + 5$$

✔ **Progress Check 3**

Find an equation of the line with slope $\frac{1}{2}$ and y-intercept -4.

Answer

$$y = \frac{1}{2}x - 4$$

Example 4   Finding the Slope and y-Intercept

Find the slope and y-intercept of the line $y = -2x - 4$.

Solution

This example illustrates the most important use of the slope-intercept form: to find the slope and y-intercept directly from the equation. We have to align corresponding coefficients of x and the constant terms.

$$
\begin{array}{ccc}
y = & -2x & - 4 \\
 & | & | \\
y = & mx & + b
\end{array}
$$

Then $m = -2$ is the slope and $b = -4$ is the y-intercept.

✔ **Progress Check 4**

Find the slope and y-intercept of the line $y = -\frac{1}{3}x + 14$.

Answer

slope $= m = -\frac{1}{3}$; y-intercept $= b = 14$

Example 5   Finding the Slope and y-Intercept

Find the slope and y-intercept of the line $y - 3x + 1 = 0$.

The Pirate Treasure (Part II)

First, note that any number that is a multiple of 5 can be written in the form $5n$, where n is an integer. Since the number of coins found in the chest by Pirate 1 was one more than a multiple of 5, we can write the original number of coins C in the form $C = 5n + 1$, where n is a positive integer. Now, Pirate 1 removed his lot of n coins and gave one to the slave. The remaining coins can be calculated as

$$5n + 1 - (n + 1) = 4n$$

and since this is also one more than a multiple of 5, we can write $4n = 5p + 1$, where p is a positive integer. Repeating the process, we have the following sequence of equations.

$$
\begin{aligned}
C &= 5n + 1 && \text{found by Pirate 1} \\
4n &= 5p + 1 && \text{found by Pirate 2} \\
4p &= 5q + 1 && \text{found by Pirate 3} \\
4q &= 5r + 1 && \text{found by Pirate 4} \\
4r &= 5s + 1 && \text{found by Pirate 5} \\
4s &= 5t + 1 && \text{found next morning}
\end{aligned}
$$

Solving for s in the last equation and substituting successively in the preceding equations leads to the requirement that

$$1024n - 3125t = 2101 \qquad (1)$$

where n and t are positive integers. Equations such as this that require integer solutions are called Diophantine equations, and there is an established procedure for solving them that is studied in courses in number theory.

You might want to try to solve Equation (1) using a computer program. Since

$$n = \frac{3125t1 - 101}{1024}$$

you can substitute successive integer values for t until you produce an integer result for n. The BASIC program shown at the left does just that.

```
BASIC Program

10    FOR K = 1 TO 3200
20    X = (3125*K + 2101)/1024
30    I = INT(X)
40    IF X = I THEN GO TO 60
50    NEXT K
60    PRINT "MINIMUM NUMBER OF COINS = "; 5*I + 1
70    END
```

Solution

The equation must be written in the form $y = mx + b$. That is, we must solve for y.

$$y = 3x - 1$$

We see that $m = 3$ is the slope, and that $b = -1$ is the y-intercept.

✔ **Progress Check 5**

Find the slope and y-intercept of the line $2y + x - 3 = 0$.

Answer

slope $= m = -\frac{1}{2}$; y-intercept $= b = \frac{3}{2}$

General First-Degree Equation

Throughout this chapter we have been dealing with first-degree equations in two variables. The **general first-degree equation** in x and y can always be written in the form

$$Ax + By + C = 0$$

where A, B, and C are constants and A and B are not both zero. We can rewrite this equation as

$$By = -Ax - C$$

If $B \neq 0$, the equation becomes

$$y = -\frac{A}{B}x - \frac{C}{B}$$

whose graph is a straight line with slope $-A/B$ and y-intercept $-C/B$. If $B = 0$, the equation becomes $Ax + C = 0$, whose graph is a vertical line. If $A = 0$, the equation becomes $By + C = 0$, whose graph is a horizontal line. If $C = 0$, the equation becomes $Ax + By = 0$, whose graph is a straight line passing through the origin. We have therefore proved the following:

The General First-Degree Equation

- The graph of the general first-degree equation

$$Ax + By + C = 0 \quad (A \text{ and } B \text{ not both zero})$$

  is a straight line.

- If $B = 0$, the graph is a vertical line.

- If $A = 0$, the graph is a horizontal line.

- If $C = 0$, the line passes through the origin.

Warning

1. Given the equation $y + 2x - 3 = 0$, *don't* write $m = 2, b = -3$. You must rewrite the equation by solving for y:

$$y = -2x + 3$$

   Then obtain $m = -2, b = 3$.

2. Given the equation $y = 5x - 6$, *don't* write $m = 5, b = 6$. The sign is part of the answer, so the correct answer is $m = 5, b = -6$.

Exercise Set 7.2

1. Which of the following are linear equations in x and y?

   (a) $3x + 2y = 4$

   (b) $xy = 2$

   (c) $2x^2 - y = 5$

   (d) $2\left(x - \dfrac{3}{2}\right) + 5y = 4$

2. Which of the following are linear equations in x and y?

   (a) $2x^2 + y = 7$

   (b) $3x - 2y = 7$

   (c) $\dfrac{1}{2}(2x^2 - 4) + 4y = 2$

   (d) $x = 2y - 3$

In Exercises 3–10 express each equation in the form $Ax + By + C = 0$ and state the values of A, B, and C.

3. $y = 2x - 3$

4. $y - 2 = \dfrac{3}{2}(x - 4)$

5. $y = 3$

6. $x = \dfrac{3}{4}y - 1$

7. $3\left(x - \dfrac{1}{3}\right) - 2y = 6$

8. $2x + 5y + 7 = 0$

9. $x = \dfrac{1}{2}$

10. $y + 1 = -\dfrac{1}{2}(x - 2)$

11. Does the point $(-1, 3)$ lie on the straight line $2x + 3y = 7$?

12. Does the point $(4, 2)$ lie on the straight line $3x - 2y = 2$?

In Exercises 13–24 graph the equation.

13. $y = 2x + 1$

14. $y = 3x - 2$

15. $y = -2x + 3$

16. $y = 3x$

17. $x = 2y + 1$

18. $x = y + 2$

19. $x = -2y + 3$

20. $x = \dfrac{1}{2}y$

21. $y + 2x = 4$

22. $2y - x = 0$

23. $x + 2y + 3 = 0$

24. $x - 3y + 6 = 0$

In Exercises 25–32 find the point-slope form of the line satisfying the given conditions.

25. Its slope is 2 and it passes through the point $(-1, 3)$.

26. Its slope is $-\dfrac{1}{2}$ and it passes through the point $(1, -2)$.

27. Its slope is 3 and it passes through the point $(0, 0)$.

28. Its slope is 0 and it passes through the point $(-1, 3)$.

29. It passes through the points $(2, 4)$ and $(-3, -6)$.

30. It passes through the points $(-3, 5)$ and $(1, 7)$.

31. It passes through the points $(0, 0)$ and $(3, 2)$.

32. It passes through the points $(-2, 4)$ and $(3, 4)$.

In Exercises 33–36 find the slope-intercept form of the line satisfying the given properties.

33. Its slope is 3 and its y-intercept is 2.

34. Its slope is -3 and its y-intercept is -3.

35. Its slope is 0 and its y-intercept is 2.

36. Its slope is $-\dfrac{1}{2}$ and its y-intercept is $\dfrac{1}{2}$.

37. Does the point $(4, 2)$ lie on the line with slope -2 that passes through the point $(3, 4)$?

38. Does the point $(-1, 3)$ lie on the line passing through the points $(1, 3)$ and $(4, -3)$?

In Exercises 39–50 find the slope and y-intercept of the given line.

39. $y = 3x + 2$

40. $y = -\dfrac{2}{3}x - 4$

41. $x = -5$

42. $x = 3$

43. $y = 3$

44. $y = -4$

45. $3x + 4y = 5$

46. $2x + 3y = 6$

47. $2x - 5y + 3 = 0$

48. $3x + 4y + 2 = 0$

49. $x = \dfrac{2}{3}y + 2$

50. $x = -\dfrac{1}{2}y + 3$

In Exercises 51–56 determine whether the given line rises from left to right or falls from left to right.

51. $y = 2x + 3$

52. $y = -\dfrac{3}{2}x + 5$

53. $y = -\dfrac{3}{4}x - 2$

54. $y = \dfrac{4}{5}x - 6$

55. $x = 2y - 5$

56. $x = 3 - 4y$

In Exercises 57–62 find the slope-intercept form of the line determined by the given points.

57. $(-1, 2)$ and $(3, 5)$

58. $(-2, -3)$ and $(3, 4)$

59. $(32.65, -17.47)$ and $(-4.76, 19.24)$

60. $(0, 14.38)$ and $(-7.62, 3.04)$

61. $(-6.45, -12.42)$ and $(8.44, 0)$

62. $(0, 0)$ and $(-4.47, 9.31)$

In Exercises 63 and 64 find the slope-intercept form of the given line.

63.

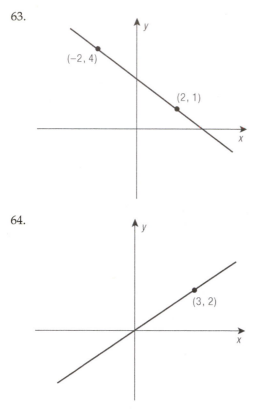

(−2, 4)

(2, 1)

64.

(3, 2)

In Exercises 65−68 identify the variables and write an equation relating them.

65. A rental firm charges $8, plus $1.50 per hour, for use of a power aerator.

66. A taxi charges 60 cents, plus 35 cents per mile.

67. A brokerage firm charges $25, plus 12 cents per share.

68. A theater may be rented for $200, plus $1.25 per person.

69. The Celsius (C) and Fahrenheit (F) temperature scales are related by a linear equation. Water boils at 212°F, or 100°C; it freezes at 32°F, or 0°C.

   (a) Write a linear equation expressing F in terms of C.

   (b) What is the Fahrenheit temperature when the Celsius temperature is 20°?

70. The college bookstore sells a textbook costing $10 for $13.50 and a textbook costing $12 for $15.90. If the markup policy of the bookstore is linear, write an equation that relates sales price S and cost C. What is the cost of a textbook that sells for $22?

71. An appliance manufacturer finds that it had sales of $200,000 five years ago and sales of $600,000 this year. If the growth in sales is assumed to be linear, what will the sales be five years from now?

72. A product that sold for $250 three years ago sells for $325 this year. If price increases are assumed to be linear, how much will the product sell for six years from now?

*73. Find a real number c such that $P(-2, 2)$ is on the line $3x + cy = 4$.

*74. Find a real number c such that the line $cx - 5y + 8 = 0$ has x-intercept 4.

*75. If the points $(-2, -3)$ and $(-1, 5)$ are on the graph of a linear function f, find $f(x)$.

*76. If $f(1) = 4$ and $f(-1) = 3$ and the function f is linear, find $f(x)$.

*77. Prove that the linear function $f(x) = ax + b$ is an increasing function if $a > 0$ and is a decreasing function if $a < 0$.

*78. If x_1 and x_2 are the abscissas of two points on the graph of the function $y = f(x)$, show that the slope m of the line connecting the two points can be written as

$$m = \frac{f(x_2) - f(x_1)}{x_2 - x_1}$$

79. A manufacturing process costs $12,000 to get started, then an additional $350 to produce each unit. Set up a linear cost function and graph it with your graphing calculator. You will need to change the WINDOW to "find" the graph.

   Use your graph to determine the largest number of units that could be produced if costs must be kept under $600,000. (Hint: Graph a horizontal line $y = 600,000$ and look for the point of intersection with your original graph.)

80. Use your graphing calculator to see how changing the values of A and B affect the graph of the line $Ax + By = 0$. What do you get if A and B have the same absolute value but are opposite in sign? (Hint: Choose a SQUARE viewing window from your ZOOM menu.)

81. Investigate the concept of slope further by storing a LIST of various slopes. Let $L_1 = \{1, 2, 3, 4, 5\}$ and enter the equation seen in the graphic below:

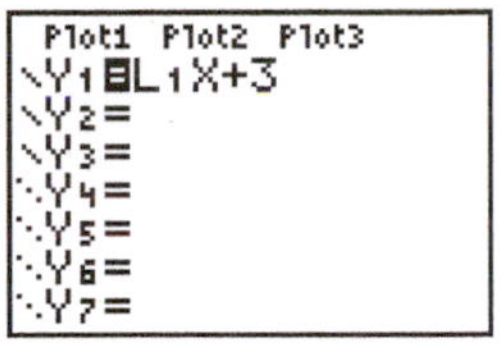

```
Plot1  Plot2  Plot3
\Y1 ▉L1X+3
\Y2=
\Y3=
\Y4=
\Y5=
\Y6=
\Y7=
```

Explain in your own words how the changing values in your list affect the lines.

82. Repeat Exercise 81 with the following list: $\{1, 0.1, 0.01\}$.

83. Suppose a roofer decided to design a roof (with a triangular cross section) by first writing the equation of a straight line. She decides to consider a point at the base of the house as the origin of a coordinate system. So, a point at the base of the roof has coordinates $(0, 25)$, since the edge of the roof is 25 feet above ground level. If the roofer desires a pitch (slope) of $\frac{4}{12}$, what is the equation of the line she needs?

84. Refer back to exercise 83. Graph the equation you found. (You may use your graphing calculator.) Determine the heights of the peak of the roof for various possible values of x (say, 20 feet, 30 feet, and 40 feet.) Draw the house for each value of x.

7.3   Further Properties of the Straight Line

Horizontal and Vertical Lines

Horizontal and vertical lines are special cases that deserve particular attention. In Figure 12a we have a vertical line through the point $(3, 2)$. Choose any other point on the line and answer the question: What is the x-coordinate of the point? You now see that every point on this vertical line has an x-coordinate of 3. The equation of the line is $x = 3$, since x remains constant. If we take a second point on this line, say, $(3, 4)$, we see that the slope is

$$m = \frac{y_2 - y_1}{x_2 - x_1} = \frac{4 - 2}{3 - 3} = \frac{2}{0}$$

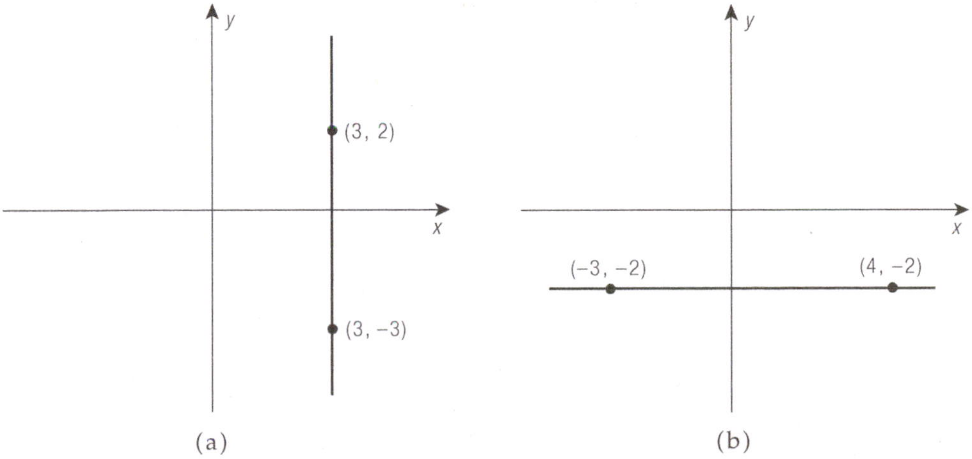

Figure 12   **Deriving the Equations of Horizontal and Vertical Lines**

Since we cannot divide by 0, we say that the slope is undefined.

Vertical Lines

The equation of the vertical line through (a, b) is

$$x = a$$

A vertical line has no slope.

Looking at Figure 12b, we see that the coordinates of all points on the horizontal line through $(4, -2)$ have the form $(x, -2)$. The equation of the line is then $y = -2$, since y remains constant. If we choose a second point on the line, say $(6, -2)$, we find that the slope is

$$m = \frac{y_2 - y_1}{x_2 - x_1} = \frac{-2 - (-2)}{6 - 4} = \frac{0}{2} = 0$$

Horizontal Lines

The equation of the horitontal line throuh (a, b) is

$$y = b$$

The slope of a horizontal line is 0.

Example 1   Finding the Equations of Horizontal and Vertical Lines

Find the equations of the horizontal and vertical lines through the point $(-4, 7)$.

Solution

The horizontal line has the equation $y = 7$. The vertical line has the equation $x = -4$.

✔ **Progress Check 1**

Find the equations of the horizontal and vertical lines through the point $(5, -6)$.

Answer

horizontal line: $y = -6$; vertical line: $x = 5$

Example 2   Line with Zero Slope

Find the equation of the line passing through the points $(4, -1)$ and $(-5, -1)$.

Solution

Let $(x_1, y_1) = (4, -1)$ and $(x_2, y_2) = (-5, -1)$. The slope is

$$m = \frac{y_2 - y_1}{x_2 - x_1} = \frac{-1 - (-1)}{-5 - 4} = \frac{0}{-9} = 0$$

The equation then is

$$y - y_1 = m(x - x_1)$$
$$y - (-1) = 0(x - 4)$$
$$y + 1 = 0$$
$$y = -1$$

There is another way of solving this problem. Since both points have the same y-coordinate, we are dealing with a horizontal line. The equation of a horizontal line through $(a, -1)$ is $y = -1$.

✔ **Progress Check 2**

Find an equation of the line passing through $(6, -1)$ and $(6, 7)$.

Answer

$x = 6$

Parallel and Perpendicular Lines

In Figure 13 we have sketched two lines that are parallel. Clearly, the two lines have the same "steepness," or slope. In general, we can make the following statements:

Parallel Lines

> Parallel lines have the same slope.
>
> Lines that have the same slope are parallel.

Exercises 37 and 38 will guide you through a geometric proof of these results.

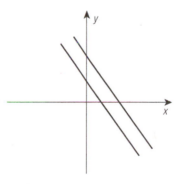

Figure 13   Parallel Lines

Example 3   Slope and Parallel Lines

Find the slope of every line parallel to the line $y = -\frac{2}{3}x + 5$.

Solution

Since $y = -\frac{2}{3}x + 5$ is in the form $y = mx + b$, we see that the slope $m = -\frac{2}{3}$. Every line parallel to $y = -\frac{2}{3}x + 5$ has the same slope, so we conclude that all such lines also have slope $m = -\frac{2}{3}$.

> ✔ **Progress Check 3**
>
> Find the slope of every line parallel to the line $y - 4x + 5 = 0$.
>
> **Answer**
>
> $m = 4$

Example 4   Equations of Parallel Lines

Find an equation of the line passing through the point $(2, -1)$ and parallel to $y = \frac{1}{2}x - 5$.

Solution

The slope of the line $y = \frac{1}{2}x - 5$ and of every line parallel to it is $m = \frac{1}{2}$. Letting $(x_1, y_1) = (2, -1)$ we have

$$y - y_1 = m(x - x_1)$$

$$y - (-1) = \frac{1}{2}(x - 2)$$

$$y + 1 = \frac{1}{2}x - 1$$

$$y = \frac{1}{2}x - 2$$

> ✔ **Progress Check 4**
>
> Find an equation of the line passing through the point $(-8, 4)$ and parallel to $2y - 2x + 17 = 0$.
>
> **Answer**
>
> $y = x + 12$

Slope can also be used to determine if two lines are perpendicular.

If two lines with slopes m_1 and m_2 are perpendicualr, then $m_2 = -1/m_1$.

If the slopes m_1 and m_2 of two lines satisfy $m_2 = -1/m_1$, then the two lines are perpendicular.

Perpendicular Lines

This criterion for perpendicularity, which applies only when neither line is vertical, can be established by a geometric argument. (See Exercises 39 and 40.) The following example illustrates the use of this criterion.

Example 5   Equations of Perpendicular Lines

Find an equation of the line passing through the point $(-3, 4)$ and perpendicular to the line $y = 3x - 2$. Sketch both lines.

Solution

The line $y = 3x - 2$ has slope $m_1 = 3$. The line we seek has slope $m_2 = -1/m_1 = -1/3$ and passes through $(x_1, y_1) = (-3, 4)$. See Figure 14.

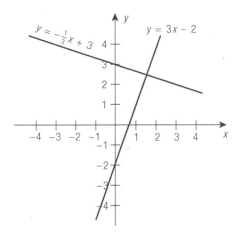

Figure 14   Perpendicular Lines

Thus,

$$y - y_1 = m(x - x_1)$$

$$y - 4 = -\frac{1}{3}[x - (-3)]$$

$$y - 4 = -\frac{1}{3}(x + 3) = -\frac{1}{3}x - 1$$

$$y = -\frac{1}{3}x + 3$$

✔ **Progress Check 5**

Find an equation of the line passing through the point $(2, -3)$ and perpendicular to the line $2y + 4x - 1 = 0$.

Answer

$y = \dfrac{1}{2}x - 4$

Example 6 Determining if Lines Are Parallel or Perpendicular

State whether each pair of lines is parallel, perpendicular, or neither.

(a) $y - 3x + 11 = 0$; $2y = 6x - 4$

(b) $y = -4x + 1$; $2y = -4x + 9$

(c) $3y - x - 7 = 0$; $2y + 6x + 8 = 0$

Solution

In each case, we must determine the slope of each of the lines.

(a) $y - 3x + 11 = 0$ $2y = 6x - 4$

$\qquad\qquad y = 3x - 11 \qquad\qquad\qquad y = 3x - 2$

$\qquad\qquad m_1 = 3 \qquad\qquad\qquad\qquad m_2 = 3$

The lines are parallel, since they have the same slope.

(b) $y = -4x + 1$ $2y = -4x + 9$

$\qquad\qquad\qquad\qquad\qquad\qquad y = -2x + \dfrac{9}{2}$

$m_1 = -4 \qquad\qquad\qquad m_2 = -2$

Since $m_1 \neq m_2$, the lines cannot be parallel. Also, since

$$-\frac{1}{m_1} = -\frac{1}{-4} = \frac{1}{4} \neq m_2$$

the lines are not perpendicular. Therefore, the lines are neither parallel nor perpendicular.

(c) $3y - x - 7 = 0$ $2y + 6x + 8 = 0$

$\qquad\qquad 3y = x + 7 \qquad\qquad\qquad 2y = -6x - 8$

$\qquad\qquad y = \dfrac{1}{3}x + \dfrac{7}{3} \qquad\qquad\qquad y = -3x - 4$

$\qquad\qquad m_1 = \dfrac{1}{3} \qquad\qquad\qquad\qquad m_2 = -3$

Since

$$m_2 = -3 \quad \text{and} \quad -\frac{1}{m_1} = -3$$

we see that

$$m_2 = -\frac{1}{m_1}$$

and the lines are perpendicular.

✔ **Progress Check 6**

State whether each pair of lines is parallel, perpendicular, or neither.

(a) $4y - 6x = 11; 3y + 2x - 7 = 0$

(b) $9y - x + 16 = 0; 3y = 9x + 4$

(c) $5y = x - 4; 25y - 5x + 17 = 0$

Answers

(a) perpendicular   (b) neither   (c) parallel

Exercise Set 7.3

In Exercises 1−4 write an equation of the line satisfying the given conditions.

1. It is horizontal and passes through the point $(3, 2)$.

2. It is horizontal and passes through the point $(-2, 4)$.

3. It is vertical and passes through the point $(-2, 3)$.

4. It is vertical and passes through the point $(3, -2)$.

In Exercises 5−14 write an equation of (a) the horizontal line passing through the point, and (b) the vertical line passing through the point.

5. $(-6, 3)$ 6. $(-5, -2)$

7. $(4, -5)$ 8. $(11, -14)$

9. $(0, 0)$ 10. $(0, -4)$

11. $(-7, 0)$ 12. $(-1, -1)$

13. $(0, 5)$ 14. $(5, 0)$

In Exercises 15 and 16 write an equation of the line shown in each graph.

15.

16.

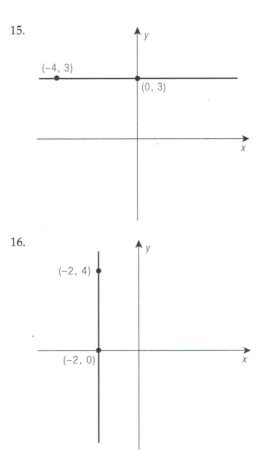

In Exercises 17–20 let L be the line determined by P_1 and P_2, and let L' be the line determined by P_3 and P_4. Determine whether L and L' are parallel, and sketch both L and L'.

17. $P_1(1, -1), P_2(3, 4); P_3(2, 3), P_4(-1, 8)$

18. $P_1(2, 1), P_2(4, 4); P_3(0, -2), P_4(-2, -5)$

19. $P_1(1, 3), P_2(0, 5); P_3(-4, 8), P_4(-2, 4)$

20. $P_1(4, 2), P_2(6, -1); P_3(4, 5), P_4(1, 8)$

In Exercises 21–24 find the slope of every line parallel to the given line.

21. $y = -\dfrac{2}{5}x + 4$

22. $x - 2y + 5 = 0$

23. $3x + 2y = 6$

24. $x = 3y - 2$

In Exercises 25–27 find the slope-intercept form of the line satisfying the given conditions.

25. It is parallel to the line $y = \frac{3}{2}x + 5$ and has y-intercept -2.

26. It is parallel to the line $y = -\frac{1}{2}x - 2$ and has y-intercept 3.

27. It passes through the point $(1, 3)$ and is parallel to the line $y = -3x + 2$.

28. Find an equation, of the form $Ax + By + C = 0$, of the line passing through the point $(-1, 2)$ and parallel to the line $3y + 2x = 6$.

In Exercises 29–32 find the slope of every line perpendicular to the line whose slope is given.

29. 2

30. -3

31. $-\dfrac{1}{2}$

32. $-\dfrac{3}{4}$

In Exercises 33 and 34 find an equation, of the form $Ax + By + C = 0$, of the line satisfying the given conditions.

33. It passes through the point $(-3, 2)$ and is perpendicular to the line $3x + 5y = 2$.

34. It passes through the point $(-1, -3)$ and is perpendicular to the line $3y + 4x - 5 = 0$.

35. State whether each pair of lines is parallel, perpendicular, or neither.
   (a) $3x + 2y = 7; 3y - 2x = 4$
   (b) $y - 3x + 1 = 0; 3y + x = 8$
   (c) $y = \dfrac{2}{3}x + 3; 6y - 4x + 8 = 0$

36. State whether each pair of lines is parallel, perpendicular, or neither.
   (a) $y - 3x + 1 = 0; x = \dfrac{y}{3} + 2$
   (b) $2x + 5y = 1; x + y = 2$
   (c) $3x + 2y = 6; 12y - 8x + 7 = 0$

*37. In the accompanying figure, lines L_1 and L_2 are parallel. Points A and D are selected on lines L_1 and L_2, respectively. Lines parallel to the x-axis are constructed connecting points A and D to points B and E, respectively, on the y-axis. Supply a reason for each of the steps in the following proof.

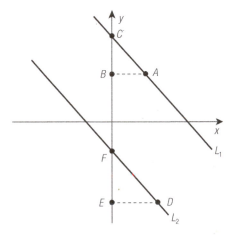

   (a) Angles ABC and DEF are equal.
   (b) Angles ACB and DFE are equal.
   (c) Triangles ABC and DEF are similar.
   (d) $\dfrac{\overline{CB}}{\overline{BA}} = \dfrac{\overline{FE}}{\overline{ED}}$
   (e) $m_1 = \dfrac{\overline{CB}}{\overline{BA}}, m_2 = \dfrac{\overline{FE}}{\overline{ED}}$
   (f) $m_1 = m_2$
   (g) Parallel lines have the same slope.

*38. Prove that if two lines have the same slope, they are parallel.

*39. In the accompanying figure, lines L_1 and L_2, perpendicular to each other, with slopes m_1 and m_2, respectively, intersect at a point Q. A perpendicular line from Q to the x-axis intersects the x-axis at the point C. Supply a reason for each of the steps in the following proof.

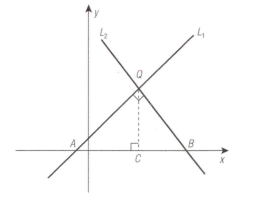

(a) Angles CAQ and BQC are equal.

(b) Triangles ACQ and BCQ are similar.

(c) $\dfrac{\overline{CQ}}{\overline{AC}} = \dfrac{\overline{CB}}{\overline{CQ}}$

(d) $m_1 = \dfrac{\overline{CQ}}{\overline{AC}}, m_2 = -\dfrac{\overline{CB}}{\overline{CQ}}$

(e) $m_2 = -\dfrac{1}{m_1}$

*40. Prove that if two lines have slopes m_1 and m_2 such that $m_2 = -1/m_1$, the lines are perpendicular.

41. Look back at Exercise 80 in the previous section. What do you now know about how the values of A and B affect the graph of the line $Ax + By = 0$? Why is a SQUARE viewing window needed to see this?

7.4 Linear Inequalities in Two Variables

When we draw the graph of a linear equation, say

$$y = 2x - 1$$

we can readily see that the graph of the line divides the set of points in the plane that are not on the line into two regions, which we call **half-planes**. (See Figure 15.) If, in the equation $y = 2x - 1$, we replace the equals sign with any of the symbols $<$, $>$, $\leq$, $\geq$, we have a **linear inequality in two variables**. By the **graph of a linear inequality** such as

$$y < 2x - 1$$

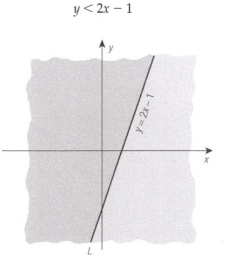

Figure 15 Graph of the Linear Inequality: $y < 2x - 1$

we mean the set of all points whose coordinates satisfy the inequality. Thus, the point $(4, 2)$ lies on the graph of $y < 2x - 1$, since

$$2 < (2)(4) - 1 = 7$$

shows that $x = 4$, $y = 2$ satisfies the inequality. However, the point $(1, 5)$ does *not* lie on the graph of $y < 2x - 1$, since

$$5 < (2)(1) - 1 = 1$$

is not true. Since the coordinates of every point on the line L in Figure 15 satisfy the *equation* $y = 2x - 1$, we readily see that the coordinates of those points in the half-plane below the line must satisfy the *inequality* $y < 2x - 1$. Similarly, the coordinates of those points in the half-plane above the line must satisfy the *inequality* $y > 2x - 1$. This leads to a straightforward method for graphing linear inequalities.

Example 1   Graphing a Linear Inequality
Sketch the graph of the inequality $x + y \geq 1$.

Solution

Graphing Linear Inequalities	
Step 1. Replace the inequality sign with an equals sign and plot the line. (a) If the inequality is $\leq$ or $\geq$, plot a solid line. (Points on the line will satisfy the inequality.) (b) If the inequality is $<$ or $>$, plot a dashed line. (Points on the line will not satisfy the inequality.)	*Step 1.* Graph $x + y = 1$.
Step 2. Choose any point that is not on the line as a test point. If the origin is not on the line, it is the most convenient choice.	*Step 2.* Choose $(0, 0)$ as a test point.
Step 3. Substitute the coordinates of the test point into the inequality. (a) If the test point satisfies the inequality, then the coordinates of every point in the half-plane that contains the test point will satisfy the inequality. (b) If the test point does not satisfy the inequality, then the points in the half-plane on the other side of the line will satisfy the inequality.	*Step 3.* Substituting $(0, 0)$ in $$x + y \geq 1$$ gives $$0 + 0 \geq 1 \quad (?)$$ $$0 \geq 1$$ which is false.

(continues)

Graphing Linear Inequalities *(continued)*

Since $(0, 0)$ is in the half-plane below the line and does not satisfy the inequality, all the points above the line will satisfy the inequality. Thus, the graph consists of the line together with the half-plane above the line. See Figure 16.

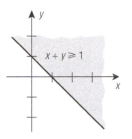

Figure 16   Graph of $x + y \geq 1$

✔ **Progress Check 1**

Sketch the graph of the inequality $4x + 3y \leq 12$.

Answer

See Figure 17.

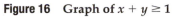

Figure 17   Graph of $4x + 3y \leq 12$

Example 2 Graphing a Linear Inequality

Sketch the graph of the inequality $2x - 3y > 6$.

Solution

We first graph the line $2x - 3y = 6$. We draw a dashed or broken line to indicate that $2x - 3y = 6$ is not part of the graph. (See Figure 18.) Since $(0, 0)$ is not on the line, we can use it as a test point.

$$2x - 3y > 6$$
$$2(0) - 3(0) > 6 \quad (?)$$
$$0 - 0 > 6 \quad (?)$$
$$0 > 6$$

is false. Since $(0, 0)$ is in the half-plane above the line, the graph consists of the half-plane below the line.

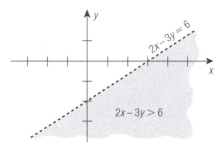

Figure 18 Graph of $2x - 3y > 6$

✔ **Progress Check 2**

Graph the inequalities

(a) $y \leq 2x + 1$ (b) $y + 3x > -2$ (c) $y \geq -x + 1$

Answers

(a)   (b)   (c)

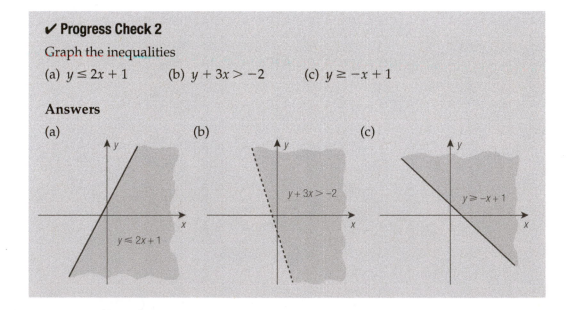

Select a test point far enough from the line for you to be certain it is above or below the line. If your graph is not accurately sketched, you might select a point that you think is above the line, but is actually below it, or vice versa.

Example 3   Graphs of Linear Inequalities

Graph the inequalities.

(a) $y < x$ (b) $2x \geq 5$

Solution

(a) Since the origin lies on the line $y = x$, we choose another test point, say, (0, 1), above the line. Since (0, 1) does not satisfy the inequality, the graph of the inequality is the half-plane below the line. See Figure 19a.

(b) The graph of $2x = 5$ is a vertical line, and the graph of $2x \geq 5$ consists of the line together with the half-plane to the right of the line. See Figure 19b.

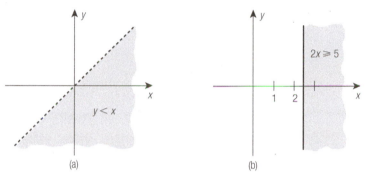

Figure 19   Diagrams for Example 3

✔ **Progress Check 3**

Graph the inequalities

(a) $2y \geq 7$ (b) $x < -2$ (c) $1 \leq y < 3$

Answers

(a)   (b)   (c)

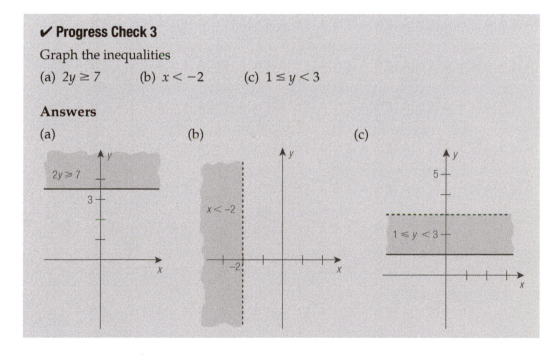

Exercise Set 7.4

In Exercises 1−28 graph the given inequality.

1. $y \le x + 2$

2. $y \ge x + 3$

3. $y > x - 4$

4. $y < x - 5$

5. $y \le 4 - x$

6. $y \ge 2 - x$

7. $y > x$

8. $y \le 2x$

9. $y \ge \frac{1}{2}x - 3$

10. $y \le 3 - \frac{2}{3}x$

11. $y < 1 - \frac{5}{2}x$

12. $y > \frac{1}{3}x + 2$

13. $3x - 5y > 15$

14. $2y - 3x < 12$

15. $3x + 8y + 24 \le 0$

16. $2x - 5y - 10 > 0$

17. $x \le 4$

18. $3x > -2$

19. $y > -3$

20. $5y \le 25$

21. $x < 0$

22. $y \ge 0$

23. $x > 0$

24. $y < 0$

25. $-2 \le x \le 3$

26. $-6 < y < -2$

27. $1 < y < 4$

28. $0 \le x \le 6$

In Exercises 29−34 give the linear inequality whose graph is shown.

29.

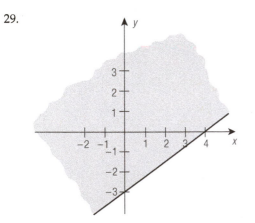

30.

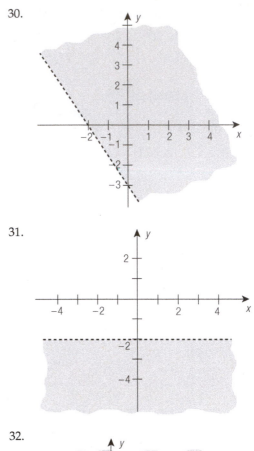

31.

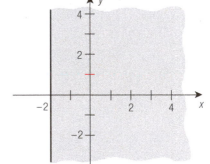

32.

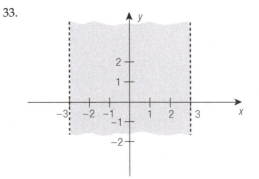

33.

34.

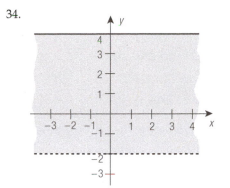

*35. A steel producer makes two types of steel: regular and special. A ton of regular steel requires 2 hours in the open-hearth furnace, and a ton of special steel requires 5 hours. Let x and y denote the numbers of tons of regular and special steel, respectively, made per day. If the open-hearth is available at most 15 hours per day, write an inequality that must be satisfied by x and y. Graph this inequality.

*36. A patient is placed on a diet that restricts caloric intake to 1500 calories per day. The patient plans to eat x ounces of cheese, y slices of bread, and z apples on the first day of the diet. If cheese contains 100 calories per ounce, bread 110 calories per slice, and apples 80 calories each, write an inequality that must be satisfied by x, y, and z.

7.5   Critical Thinking Problems

In this chapter we learned about linear equations. When given two points, we may find the equation of a line by computing its slope and y-intercept. Whenever two or more lines have the same slope, the lines are parallel.

A **parallelogram** is a quadrilateral (a figure that has 4 sides) in which opposite sides are parallel. Given a quadrilateral we may determine whether it is a parallelogram by finding the slopes of opposite sides.

Example 1   Is It a Parallelogram?
Verify that the figure below is a parallelogram.

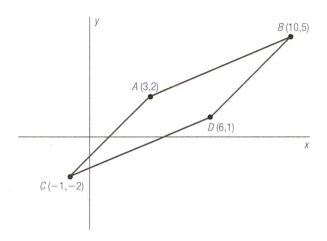

Solution
To show that this quadrilateral is a parallelogram, we need to show that opposite sides are parallel. Using four points $A(3,2)$, $B(10,5)$, $C(-1,-2)$, and $D(6,1)$, let's find the slope of each line containing two points.

Let

m_1 = The slope of a line containing points $A(3,2)$ and $B(10,5)$.

m_2 = The slope of a line containing points $C(-1,-2)$ and $D(6,1)$.

m_3 = The slope of a line containing points $A(3,2)$ and $C(-1,-2)$.

m_4 = The slope of a line containing points $B(10,5)$ and $D(6,1)$.

We need to show that $m_1 = m_2$ and $m_3 = m_4$ because we need to show that opposite sides are parallel, which means that both pairs of opposite sides have the same slope.

Using the points $A(3,2)$ and $B(10,5)$,

$$m_1 = \frac{y_2 - y_1}{x_2 - x_1} = \frac{5 - 2}{10 - 3} = \frac{3}{7}$$

Using the points $C(-1,-2)$ and $D(6,1)$,

$$m_2 = \frac{y_2 - y_1}{x_2 - x_1} = \frac{1 - (-2)}{6 - (-1)} = \frac{3}{7}$$

Since $m_1 = m_2$, the line containing the points $A(3,2)$ and $B(10,5)$ and the line containing the points $C(-1,-2)$ and $D(6,1)$ are parallel.

Using the points $A(3,2)$ and $C(-1,-2)$,

$$m_3 = \frac{y_2 - y_1}{x_2 - x_1} = \frac{-2 - 2}{-1 - 3} = \frac{-4}{-4} = 1$$

Using the points $B(10,5)$ and $D(6,1)$,

$$m_4 = \frac{y_2 - y_1}{x_2 - x_1} = \frac{1 - 5}{6 - 10} = \frac{-4}{-4} = 1$$

Since $m_3 = m_4$, the line containing the points $A(3,2)$ and $C(-1,-2)$ and the line containing the points $B(10,5)$ and $D(6,1)$ are parallel.

Therefore, this quadrilateral is a parallelogram.

✔ **Progress Check 1**

(a) Show that the triangle with vertices $A(0,2)$, $B(2,-1)$, and $C(3,4)$ is a right triangle by using the converse of the Pythagorean Theorem. Find the area of the triangle.

(b) Carpenters use the term *pitch* for the slope of a roof. Suppose a house is 40 feet wide and its roof is symmetrical. There are 20 feet on either side of the center line of the house. Now, suppose the pitch of the roof is $\frac{3}{16}$. Find the rise of the roof.

Answers

(a) The area of the right triangle is 6.5 square units.

(b) 3.75 feet

Example 2

A **rectangle** has four sides and four right angles. A quadrilateral has four points $A(0,4)$, $B(8,2)$, $C(-1,0)$, and $D(7,-2)$. Show that these four points form a rectangle.

Solution

Every rectangle is a parallelogram. To show that theses four points (vertices) form a rectangle we need to show that adjacent sides are perpendicular. In the previous section we learned that if two lines are perpendicular then the product of their slopes is -1. Using the definition of a parallelogram, we know that both pairs of opposite sides are parallel. That means the opposite sides have the same slopes, so it is not necessary to show that all four sides form a right angle.

Let

m_1 = The slope of a line containing points $A(0,4)$ and $B(8,2)$.

m_2 = The slope of a line containing points $C(-1,0)$ and $D(7,-2)$.

m_3 = The slope of a line containing points $A(0,4)$ and $C(-1,0)$.

m_4 = The slope of a line containing points $B(8,2)$ and $D(7,-2)$.

We need to show that $m_1 = m_2$ and $m_3 = m_4$ because we need to show that both pairs of opposite sides are parallel, which means that both pairs of opposite sides have the same slope.

Using the points $A(0,4)$ and $B(8,2)$,

$$m_1 = \frac{y_2 - y_1}{x_2 - x_1} = \frac{2 - 4}{8 - 0} = \frac{-2}{8} = -\frac{1}{4}$$

Using the points $C(-1,0)$ and $D(7,-2)$,

$$m_2 = \frac{y_2 - y_1}{x_2 - x_1} = \frac{-2 - 0}{7 - (-1)} = \frac{-2}{8} = -\frac{1}{4}$$

Since $m_1 = m_2$, the line containing the points $A(0,4)$ and $B(8,2)$ and the line containing the points $C(-1,0)$ and $D(7,-2)$ are parallel.

Using the points $A(0,4)$ and $C(-1,0)$,

$$m_3 = \frac{y_2 - y_1}{x_2 - x_1} = \frac{0 - (4)}{(-1) - 0} = \frac{-4}{-1} = 4$$

Using the points $B(8,2)$ and $D(7,-2)$,

$$m_4 = \frac{y_2 - y_1}{x_2 - x_1} = \frac{(-2) - 2}{7 - 8} = \frac{-4}{-1} = 4$$

Since $m_3 = m_4$, the line containing the points $A(0,4)$ and $C(-1,0)$ and the line containing the points $B(8,2)$ and $D(7,-2)$ are parallel. Thus, the four given points form a parallelogram.

Let's show that the line containing two points $A(0,4)$ and $B(8,2)$ and the line containing two points $C(-1,0)$ and $D(7,-2)$ are perpendicular. Since the product of these two slopes is

$$(m_1) \cdot (m_3) = \left(\frac{-1}{4}\right) \cdot (4) = -1$$

these two lines are perpendicular.

Let's show that the line containing the points $A(0,4)$ and $B(8,2)$ and the line containing the points $B(8,2)$ and $D(7,-2)$ are perpendicular. Since the product of these two slopes is

$$(m_1) \cdot (m_4) = \left(\frac{-1}{4}\right) \cdot (4) = -1$$

these two lines are perpendicular. Therefore, this is a rectangle.

✔ Progress Check 2

(a) Draw the rectangle with vertices $A(-2,3)$, $B(-2,-2)$, $C(3,-2)$, and $D(3,3)$ on a coordinate plane. Find the area of the rectangle.

(b) Show that the triangle with vertices $A(-2,4)$, $B(2,3)$, and $C(-1,0)$ is isosceles. (An isosceles triangle has at least two congruent sides.)

Answers

(a) 25 square units

(b) Since $d(A,B) = \sqrt{17}$, $d(A,C) = \sqrt{17}$ and $d(B,C) = 3\sqrt{2}$, the vertices form an isosceles triangle.

■ ■ ■

Terms and Symbols

constant function	horizontal line	point-slope form
decreasing function	increasing function	slope-intercept form
general first-degree equation	linear inequality in two variables	slope of a line
graph of a linear inequality in two variables	parallel lines	vertical line
half-plane	perpendicular lines	y-intercept

Key Ideas for Review

Topic	Key Idea
Linear function	A linear function is of the form $f(x) = ax + b$.
graph	The graph of a linear function is a nonvertical straight line.
Slope	Any two distinct points $P_1(x_1, y_1)$ and $P_2(x_2, y_2)$ on a line can be used to find the slope $$m = \frac{y_2 - y_1}{x_2 - x_1}.$$
positive and negative slope	Positive slope indicates that a line is rising; negative slope indicates that a line is falling.
Point-slope form	The point-slope form of the equation of a nonvertical line is $y - y_1 = m(x - x_1)$.
Slope-intercept form	The slope-intercept form of the equation of a nonvertical line is $y = mx + b$.

(continues)

Key Ideas for Review, *continued*

Topic	Key Idea
Horizontal and vertical lines	The slope of a horizontal line is 0; the slope of a vertical line is undefined. The equation of a horizontal line through the point (a, b) is $y = b$. The equation of a vertical line through the point (a, b) is $x = a$.
Parallel lines	Parallel lines have the same slope.
Perpendicular lines	The slopes of perpendicular lines are negative reciprocals of each other.
General first-degree equation	The graph of the general first-degree equation $Ax + By + C = 0$, where A and B are not both zero, is always a straight line.
Linear inequalities	The graph of a linear inequality in two variables is a half-plane.

Common Errors

1. When calculating the slope

$$m = \frac{y_2 - y_1}{x_2 - x_1}$$

by using two points, you must be consistent in labeling the points. For example, if we have $(x_1, y_1) = (2, 3)$ and $(x_2, y_2) = (4, 5)$, then

$$m = \frac{5 - 3}{4 - 2} = \frac{2}{2} = 1$$

Don't write

$$m = \frac{5 - 3}{2 - 4} = \frac{2}{-2} = -1$$

2. The equation of the horizontal line through (a, b) is $y = b$. The equation of the vertical line through (a, b) is $x = a$. *Don't reverse these.*

3. The equation $y - 6x + 2 = 0$ must be rewritten in the form $y = 6x - 2$ before you can determine the slope $m = 6$ and intercept $b = -2$. Notice also that the intercept includes the sign; that is, the intercept is -2, not 2.

4. If a line L as slope $-\frac{1}{3}$, then every line perpendicular to L has slope 3, *not* -3. For instance, the line $2y = x - 1$ has slope $\frac{1}{2}$; every line perpendicular to this line has slope -2, *not* 2.

5. Do not confuse "zero slope" and "no slope." A horizontal line has zero slope, but a vertical line has no slope.

Review Exercises

Solutions to exercises whose numbers are in bold are in the Solutions section in the back of the book.

7.1 In Exercises 1 and 2 find the slope of the line passing through the given points.

   1. $(-2, 3)$ and $(2, 5)$ **2.** $(3, -1)$ and $(-3, 3)$

In Exercises 3 and 4 state whether the line whose slope is given is rising or falling.

   3. $m = 3$ **4.** $m = -2$

In Exercises 5 and 6 state whether the line passing through the given points is rising or falling.

   5. $(-3, -2)$ and $(4, -5)$ **6.** $(2, 3)$ and $(3, -2)$

Exercises 7 and 8 refer to Figure 20. Indicate if the slope of the line is positive (P) or negative (N).

   7. L_1 **8.** L_2

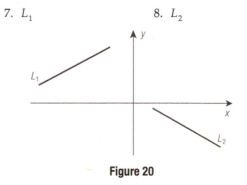

Figure 20

In Exercises 9 and 10 use Figure 21 to determine whether the given statement is true (T) or false (F).

9. The slope of L_1 is less than the slope of L_2.

10. The slope of L_4 is greater than the slope of L_3.

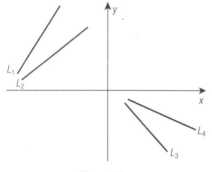

Figure 21

In Exercises 11 and 12 find the slope of the indicated line in Figure 22.

11. L_1 **12.** L_2

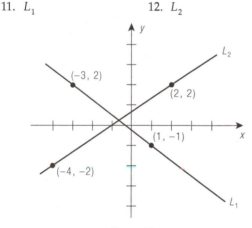

Figure 22

13. Find a real number c so that the straight line

$$3x + 2y = c$$

has y-intercept -3.

14. Find a real number c so that the point $(2, -3)$ is on the straight line

$$cx - 2y = 3$$

7.2   In Exercises 15 and 16 express the equation in the form $Ax + By = C$ and state the values of A, B, and C.

15. $3(x - 4) + 2(y + 1) = 4$

16. $x = -3y + 1$

17. Does the point $(2, -1)$ lie on the straight line $3x - 4y = 10$?

18. Show that the point $(5, -1)$ does not lie on the straight line $2x + 5y = 4$.

In Exercises 19 and 20 graph the line and label the x- and y- intercepts.

19. $3y - 2x = 12$ **20.** $x = -2y + 3$

In Exercises 21 and 22 find the point-slope form of the line satisfying the given conditions.

21. Its slope is -3 and its x-intercept is 4.

22. It passes through the points $(-2, 1)$ and $(0, 3)$.

In Exercises 23 and 24 find the slope-intercept form of the line satisfying the given conditions.

23. Its slope is 4 and its y-intercept is -2.

24. It passes through the points $(0, -3)$ and $(2, 4)$.

In Exercises 25 and 26 find the slope and the y-intercept of the line.

25. $x = \dfrac{3}{2}y - 2$ **26.** $2(x - 1) + y = 4$

In Exercises 27 and 28 determine whether the given line is rising or falling.

27. $2x - 3y = 6$ **28.** $x = -3y + 4$

7.3   In Exercises 29 and 30 write an equation of (a) the horizontal line passing through the point, and (b) the vertical line passing through the point.

29. $(2, -3)$ **30.** $(-3, 4)$

In Exercises 31 and 32 write an equation of the line shown in the graph.

31.

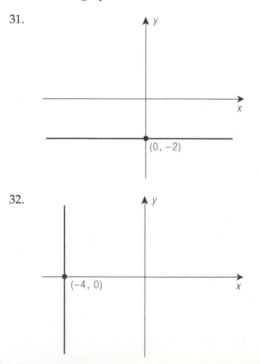

32.

In Exercises 33 and 34 let L be the line determined by P_1 and P_2, and let L' be the line determined by P_3 and P_4. Determine whether L and L' are parallel.

33. $P_1(4, 2)$, $P_2(-1, 5)$; $P_3(1, 2)$, $P_4(2, 3)$

34. $P_1(3, 2)$, $P_2(4, 3)$; $P_3(6, 2)$, $P_4(5, 1)$

In Exercises 35 and 36 find the slope-intercept form of the line satisfying the given conditions.

35. It is parallel to the line $3x - 2y = 4$ and has y-intercept 5.

36. It is parallel to the line $2x - 4y + 4 = 0$ and has x-intercept 3.

37. Find the point-slope form of the line passing through the point $(4, 1)$ and perpendicular to the line $5x - 2y = 4$.

38. Find the slope-intercept form of the line that is perpendicular to the line $3x + 4y = 6$ and whose y-intercept is 4.

In Exercises 39 and 40 state whether each pair of lines is parallel, perpendicular, or neither.

39. $2x - 3y = 4$; $2y + 3x = 6$

40. $3x - 2y = 6$; $x + 2y = 4$

7.4 In Exercises 41 and 42 graph the given inequality.

41. $y \geq 4 - 2x$ **42.** $-1 < y \leq 3$

In Exercises 43 and 44 give the linear inequality whose graph is shown.

43.

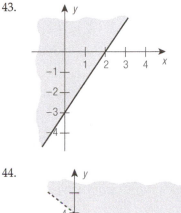

44.

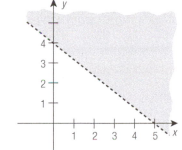

Progress Test 7A

1. Find the slope of the line passing through the points $(6, -3)$ and $(-6, -3)$.

2. Find the slope of the line passing through the points $\left(-1, \frac{3}{2}\right)$ and $\left(\frac{1}{2}, \frac{1}{2}\right)$.

3. Find an equation, of the form $Ax + By + C = 0$, of the line with slope -7 that passes through the point $(-1, 2)$.

4. Find an equation, of the form $Ax + By + C = 0$, of the line passing through the points $(6, 8)$ and $(-4, 7)$.

5. Find the slope and y-intercept of the line $2y + 5x - 6 = 0$.

6. Find the slope of the line $3y = 2x - 1$, and determine whether the line is rising or falling.

7. Find the slope of the line $2y + \frac{1}{2}x - 5 = 0$, and determine whether the line is rising or falling.

8. A telephone company charges 25 cents for the first minute and 20 cents for each additional minute. Write an equation relating the total cost C of a phone call and the number of minutes t the parties are connected.

9. Find an equation of the vertical line passing through the point $\left(-11, \frac{3}{4}\right)$.

10. Find an equation of the horizontal line passing through the point $\left(4, -\frac{7}{3}\right)$.

11. Find the slope-intercept form of the line passing through the point $(0, 2)$ and parallel to the line $y - 3x - 2 = 0$.

12. Find the slope of every line perpendicular to the line $2y + 7x - 6 = 0$.

13. Find an equation, of the form $Ax + By + C = 0$, of the line passing through the point $(-1, -2)$ and perpendicular to the line $3y = 4x - 1$.

14. Graph the inequality $y > x - 2$.

15. Graph the inequality $x \leq -3$.

Progress Test 7B

1. Find the slope of the line passing through the points $(-4, -2)$ and $(-4, 6)$.

2. Find the slope of the line passing through the points $\left(\frac{1}{3}, -\frac{4}{3}\right)$ and $\left(-\frac{1}{2}, \frac{1}{3}\right)$.

3. Find an equation, of the form $Ax + By + C = 0$, of the line with slope 5 that passes through the point $(-6, -7)$.

4. Find an equation, of the form $Ax + By + C = 0$, of the line passing through the points $(-9, 2)$ and $(3, -6)$.

5. Find the slope and y-intercept of the line $3y - 12x + 5 = 0$.

6. Find the slope of the line $2y - 7x + 10 = 0$, and determine whether the line is rising or falling.

7. Find the slope of the line $4y + 5x - 3 = 0$, and determine whether the line is rising or falling.

8. The U.S. Postal Service charges 22 cents for the first ounce and 17 cents for every additional ounce of a first class letter. Write an equation relating the total cost C of a mailing and the number of ounces n when n is a natural number.

9. Find an equation of the horizontal line passing through the point $\left(-1, \frac{5}{4}\right)$.

10. Find an equation of the vertical line passing through the point $\left(3, -\frac{2}{3}\right)$.

11. Find an equation, of the form $Ax + By + C = 0$, of the line passing through the point $(-5, -7)$ and parallel to the line $y - 2x = 6$.

12. Find the slope of every line perpendicular to the line $-3x + 5y - 2 = 0$

13. Find the slope-intercept form of the line passing through the point $\left(\frac{1}{2}, -\frac{3}{2}\right)$ and perpendicular to the line $3y - x = 0$.

14. Graph the inequality $2y + 3x \le 1$.

15. Graph the inequality $y > -1$.

Chapter 7 Project

To design a house, an architect must grasp some fundamental concepts of algebra, including many that we have studied in this chapter. A fundamental concept is the pitch, or slope, of a roof, which is usually expressed as a fraction with a denominator of 12. So a roofer might say, if a roof has a pitch of $\frac{5}{12}$, then for every 12 feet horizontally, the roof must rise 5 feet. (Refer back to the chapter opener.)

For this chapter's project, first do Exercises 23 and 24 in Section 7.1, and Exercises 83 and 84 in Section 7.2. Write a paragraph summarizing how the algebra of straight lines can help to put a roof over your head (literally and figuratively!)

Now, repeat the Exercises listed above with different values. Use your graphing calculator to visualize your results. If the graph below represents one side of a roof, what is its pitch?

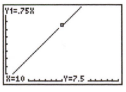

CHAPTER 8

Exponents, Radicals, and Complex Numbers

Mighty are numbers; joined with art, resistless.

—Euripides

Cosmologists like Stephen Hawking study the way the universe appears to us now, and use mathematics and physics to extrapolate what it may have been like billions of years ago. In particular, they look at two forces, gravitation and the electric force, which are both crucial to the way the galaxies formed after the Big Bang. But the electric force is much stronger than the gravitational force—one trillion times one trillion times one trillion times as strong, in fact! The force of gravity is hardly a factor with small masses like molecules, so chemists can ignore it. But with huge masses like galaxies and black holes, it is so important that it helps to determine the shape of the universe.

How can we express "one trillion times one trillion times one trillion?" We need rules for expressing large numbers with exponents, and for multiplying them together. In this chapter's project, we will see how mathematicians, manipulating large numbers using the rules of exponents, may help to determine the final fate of the universe.

■ ■ ■

We have previously worked with exponential notation such as x^n when n is a positive integer. We now seek to expand our capability to handle any exponent, whether zero, a positive integer, a negative integer, or a rational number. We will see that the same rules apply in all these cases.

Radicals are an alternate way of writing rational exponent forms. Since the solutions of polynomial equations frequently involve radicals, we will learn to manipulate and simplify radical forms, as background to our study of polynomial equations of degree greater than 1.

We will also see that the real number system is inadequate to provide solutions to all polynomial equations. It is necessary to create a new type of number, called a complex number, which we will explore at the end of the chapter.

8.1   Positive Integer Exponents

In Chapter 4 we defined a^n by

$$a^n = \underbrace{a \cdot a \cdot \cdots \cdot a}_{n \text{ factors}}$$

where n is a natural number and a is any real number. We then saw that if m and n are natural numbers and a is any real number,

$$a^m \cdot a^n = a^{m+n}$$

We shall now develop additional rules for exponents. We see that

$$(a^2)^3 = \underbrace{a^2 \cdot a^2 \cdot a^2}_{3 \text{ factors}} = a^6$$

and, in general, if m and n are any natural numbers and a is any real number, then

$$(a^m)^n = a^{mn}$$

Example 1   Simplifying Expressions with Exponents

Simplify.

(a) $(2^2)^3$

(b) $(x^4)^3$

(c) $(x^2 \cdot x^3)^4$

(d) $(a^2)^n$

(e) $(r^n)^{2n}$

(f) $[(x+2)^4]^2$

Solution

(a) $(2^2)^3 = 2^{2 \cdot 3} = 2^6$

(b) $(x^4)^3 = x^{4 \cdot 3} = x^{12}$

(c) $(x^2 \cdot x^3)^4 = (x^{2+3})^4 = (x^5)^4 = x^{5 \cdot 4} = x^{20}$

(d) $(a^2)^n = a^{2n}$

(e) $(r^n)^{2n} = r^{n \cdot 2n} = r^{2n^2}$

(f) $[(x+2)^4]^2 = (x+2)^{4 \cdot 2} = (x+2)^8$

✔ **Progress Check 1**

Simplify.

(a) $(x^3)^4$ (b) $(x^7)^7$ (c) $(x^2)^3 \cdot x^5$

(d) $(y^n)^2$ (e) $[(2a-2)^3]^5$ (f) $x^4(x^2)^3$

Answers

(a) x^{12} (b) x^{49} (c) x^{11} (d) y^{2n} (e) $(2a-2)^{15}$ (f) x^{10}

Now we turn to a^m/a^n. We will use our old friend, the cancellation principle, to simplify. We see that

$$\frac{a^4}{a^2} = \frac{\cancel{a} \cdot \cancel{a} \cdot a \cdot a}{\cancel{a} \cdot \cancel{a}} = \frac{a^2}{1} = a^2$$

and

$$\frac{a^2}{a^4} = \frac{\cancel{a} \cdot \cancel{a}}{\cancel{a} \cdot \cancel{a} \cdot a \cdot a} = \frac{1}{a^2}$$

We can conclude that the result depends upon which exponent is larger. If m and n are natural numbers and a is any nonzero real number, then

$$\frac{a^m}{a^n} = a^{m-n} \qquad \text{if } m > n$$

$$\frac{a^m}{a^n} = \frac{1}{a^{n-m}} \qquad \text{if } n > m$$

$$\frac{a^m}{a^n} = 1 \qquad \text{if } m = n$$

Example 2   Simplifying Expressions with Exponents

Simplify.

(a) $\dfrac{5^7}{5^4}$ (b) $\dfrac{(-3)^2}{(-3)^3}$ (c) $\dfrac{-x^{17}}{x^{11}}$

(d) $\dfrac{-(2y-1)^6}{(2y-1)^8}$ (e) $\dfrac{x^{2n+1}}{x^n}$ (f) $\dfrac{(x^3)^4}{x^7(x^2)^5}$

Solution

(a) $\dfrac{5^7}{5^4} = 5^{7-4} = 5^3 = 125$

(b) $\dfrac{(-3)^2}{(-3)^3} = \dfrac{1}{(-3)^{3-2}} = \dfrac{1}{-3} = -\dfrac{1}{3}$

(c) $\dfrac{-x^{17}}{x^{11}} = -x^{17-11} = -x^6$

(d) $\dfrac{-(2y-1)^6}{(2y-1)^8} = \dfrac{-1}{(2y-1)^{8-6}} = \dfrac{-1}{(2y-1)^2}$

(e) $\dfrac{x^{2n+1}}{x^n} = x^{2n+1-n} = x^{n+1}$

(f) $\dfrac{(x^3)^4}{x^7(x^2)^5} = \dfrac{x^{12}}{x^{17}} = \dfrac{1}{x^5}$

✔ Progress Check 2

Simplify, using only positive exponents.

(a) $\dfrac{6^3}{6^9}$

(b) $\dfrac{-2^4}{2^2}$

(c) $\dfrac{a^{14}}{a^8}$

(d) $\dfrac{b^{17}}{b^{25}}$

(e) $\dfrac{y^n}{y^{2n}}$

(f) $\dfrac{-2(x+1)^4}{(x+1)^{11}}$

Answers

(a) $\dfrac{1}{6^6}$ (b) -4 (c) a^6 (d) $\dfrac{1}{b^8}$ (e) $\dfrac{1}{y^n}$ (f) $\dfrac{-2}{(x+1)^7}$

Thus far, we have developed rules for multiplying and dividing exponents when there is a common base. It is also easy to develop rules for when there is a common exponent. For example,

$$(ab)^3 = (ab)(ab)(ab) = (a \cdot a \cdot a) \cdot (b \cdot b \cdot b)$$
$$= a^3 b^3$$

and, in general, if m is any natural number and a and b are any real numbers, then

$$(ab)^m = a^m b^m$$

Similarly,

$$\left(\frac{a}{b}\right)^3 = \left(\frac{a}{b}\right)\left(\frac{a}{b}\right)\left(\frac{a}{b}\right) = \frac{a \cdot a \cdot a}{b \cdot b \cdot b} = \frac{a^3}{b^3}$$

and, in general, if m is any natural number and a and b are any real numbers, $b \neq 0$, then

$$\left(\frac{a}{b}\right)^m = \frac{a^m}{b^m}$$

There is a helpful technique for keeping track of the sign. If we have $(-ab)^m$, we treat this as $[(-1)ab]^m$ and then have

$$(-ab)^m = [(-1)ab]^m = (-1)^m a^m b^m$$

The sign of the result will then depend upon whether m is even or odd. If m is even, $(-1)^m = 1$; and if m is odd, $(-1)^m = -1$. Thus, if m is even, the result is $a^m b^m$; if m is odd, the result is $-a^m b^m$. For example,

$$(-xy)^3 = -x^3 y^3 \qquad (-xy)^6 = x^6 y^6$$

Example 3   Simplifying Expressions with Exponents
Simplify.

(a) $\left(\dfrac{3}{2}\right)^2$ (b) $(xy)^6$ (c) $-(2x)^4$ (d) $(-2x)^4$

(e) $-\left(\dfrac{2}{x}\right)^3$ (f) $(2x^2 y)^4$ (g) $\left(\dfrac{-ab^2}{c^3}\right)^3$ (h) $\dfrac{(24y)^3}{(12x)^3}$

Solution

(a) $\left(\dfrac{3}{2}\right)^2 = \dfrac{3^2}{2^2} = \dfrac{9}{4}$ (b) $(xy)^6 = x^6 y^6$

(c) $-(2x)^4 = -2^4 x^4 = -16x^4$ (d) $(-2x)^4 = (-2)^4 x^4 = 16x^4$

(e) $-\left(\dfrac{2}{x}\right)^3 = -\dfrac{2^3}{x^3} = -\dfrac{8}{x^3}$ (f) $(2x^2 y)^4 = 2^4 (x^2)^4 \cdot y^4 = 16x^8 y^4$

(g) $\left(\dfrac{-ab^2}{c^3}\right)^3 = \dfrac{(-1)^3 a^3 \cdot (b^2)^3}{(c^3)^3} = \dfrac{-a^3 b^6}{c^9}$ (h) $\dfrac{(24y)^3}{(12x)^3} = \left(\dfrac{\overset{2}{\cancel{24}}y}{\cancel{12}x}\right)^3 = \left(\dfrac{2y}{x}\right)^3 = \dfrac{2^3 y^3}{x^3} = \dfrac{8y^3}{x^3}$

✔ Progress Check 3
Simplify.

(a) $\left(\dfrac{2}{3}\right)^3$ (b) $(2xy)^2$ (c) $\left(\dfrac{2x^2}{y^3}\right)^4$

(d) $\left(-\dfrac{2}{5}xy^2\right)^2$ (e) $(-xy)^3$ (f) $\left(\dfrac{x^5 y^2}{y}\right)^3$

Answers

(a) $\dfrac{8}{27}$ (b) $4x^2 y^2$ (c) $\dfrac{16x^8}{y^{12}}$ (d) $\dfrac{4}{25}x^2 y^4$ (e) $-x^3 y^3$ (f) $x^{15} y^3$

Exercise Set 8.1

In Exercises 1–4 evaluate the given expression. Identify the base and exponent.

1. $\left(\dfrac{1}{3}\right)^4$

2. $\left(\dfrac{2}{5}\right)^3$

3. $(-2)^5$

4. $(-0.2)^4$

In Exercises 5–8 rewrite the given expression, using exponents.

5. $(-5)(-5)(-5)(-5)$

6. $\left(\dfrac{1}{2}\right)\left(\dfrac{1}{2}\right)\left(\dfrac{1}{2}\right)\left(\dfrac{1}{3}\right)\left(\dfrac{1}{3}\right)$

7. $4 \cdot 4 \cdot x \cdot x \cdot y \cdot y \cdot y$

8. $3 \cdot x \cdot x \cdot x + 2 \cdot y \cdot y \cdot y \cdot y$

In Exercises 9–14 the right-hand side of each equation is incorrect. Correct that side.

9. $x^2 \cdot x^4 = x^8$

10. $(y^2)^5 = y^7$

11. $\dfrac{b^6}{b^2} = b^3$

12. $\dfrac{x^2}{x^6} = x^4$

13. $(2x)^4 = 2x^4$

14. $\left(\dfrac{4}{3}\right)^4 = \dfrac{4}{3^4}$

In Exercises 15–68 simplify, using the properties of exponents.

15. $\left(-\dfrac{1}{2}\right)^4\left(-\dfrac{1}{2}\right)^3$

16. $x^3 \cdot x^6$

17. $(x^m)^{3m}$

18. $(y^4)^{2n}$

19. $(x^{m+1})^m$

20. $(y^{2n})^{n-1}$

21. $\dfrac{3^6}{3^2}$

22. $\dfrac{(-4)^6}{(-4)^{10}}$

23. $-\left(\dfrac{x}{y}\right)^3$

24. $\left[\dfrac{(2x+1)^2}{(3x-2)^3}\right]^3$

25. $y^2 \cdot y^6$

26. $-3r^3 r^3$

27. $(x^3)^5 \cdot x^4$

28. $[(-2)^5]^4(-2)^3$

29. $-\left(\dfrac{a}{b}\right)^5$

30. $\dfrac{x^4}{x^8}$

31. $(-2x^2)^5$

32. $-(2x^2)^5$

33. $3^{2m} \cdot 3^m$

34. $(-2)^m(-2)^n$

35. $x^{3n} \cdot x^n$

36. $y^{2m-1} \cdot y^{m+2}$

37. $(3^2)^4$

38. $(x^6)^5$

39. $\dfrac{5^{2n}}{5^{n-1}}$

40. $\dfrac{7^{3m^2-m}}{7^{2m^2+2m}}$

41. $\dfrac{x^n}{x^{n+2}}$

42. $\dfrac{x^{3+n}}{x^n}$

43. $\left(\dfrac{3x^3}{y^2}\right)^5$

44. $\left(\dfrac{2x^4y^3}{y^2}\right)^3$

45. $-(-5x^3)(-6x^5)$

46. $-(-ab)^5$

47. $(x^2)^3(y^2)^4(x^3)^7$

48. $(a^3)^4(b^2)^5(b^3)^6$

49. $\dfrac{(r^2)^4}{(r^4)^2}$

50. $\dfrac{[(x+1)^3]^2}{[(x+1)^5]^3}$

51. $[(3b+1)^5]^5$

52. $[(2x+3)^3]^7$

53. $\dfrac{(2a+b)^4}{(2a+b)^6}$

54. $\dfrac{5(3x-y)^8}{(3x-y)^2}$

55. $-(3x^3y)^3$

56. $\left(\dfrac{3}{2}x^2y^3\right)^n$

57. $\left(\dfrac{2a^n}{b^{2n}}\right)^n$

58. $\left(\dfrac{1}{3}x^{2n}y^2\right)^n$

59. $\dfrac{(3x^2)^3}{(-2x)^3}$

60. $\dfrac{(-2a^2b)^4}{(-3ab^2)^3}$

61. $(2x+1)^3(2x+1)^7$

62. $(3x-2)^6(3x-2)^5$

63. $\dfrac{y^3(y^3)^4}{(y^4)^6}$

64. $\dfrac{2[(3x-1)^3]^5[(3x-1)^2]^4}{[(3x-1)^2]^7}$

65. $(-2a^2b^3)^{2n}$

66. $\left(-\dfrac{2}{3}a^2b^3c^2\right)^3$

67. $\left(\dfrac{-2a^2b^3}{c^2}\right)^3$

68. $\left(\dfrac{8x^3y}{6xy^4}\right)^3$

In Exercises 69–76 evaluate the expression.

69. $(1.27)^2(3.65)^2$

70. $(-4.73)^3(-0.22)^3$

71. $\dfrac{-(6.14)^2(2.07)^2}{(7.93)^2}$

72. $\dfrac{(1.77)^2}{(2.85)^2(8.19)^2}$

73. $(2x-1)^3(x+1)^3$ when $x = 1.73$

74. $\dfrac{(3-x)^2}{(x+3)^2}$ when $x = 2.25$

75. $(5.46^2)^2$

76. $(3.29^2)^2$

77. Does $\dfrac{a^m}{a^n} = a^{m-n}$ for all values of a? Investigate this question by setting up a TABLE in your graphing calculator. Let $m = 6$, $n = 4$, and $y1 = (x\char94 6)/(x\char94 4)$, $y2 = x\char94(6-4)$. (NOTE: "$\char94$" refers to the exponent key on your calculator.) Then set up a TABLE. (Make sure you set it up so that you can choose your own input values—see your manual for details.) Can you find any value of x for which $y1 \neq y2$? Explain.

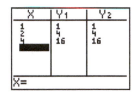

78. Perform the division: $10^{78}/(2 \times 10^9)$ using the rules of exponents.

(Hint: $\dfrac{10^{78}}{2(10^9)} = \dfrac{1}{2} \cdot \dfrac{10^{78}}{10^9}$)

Now perform the same operation in your calculator. Do the answers agree? Explain.

79. The ratio of the strength of the electric force (the force that holds electrons within atoms) to the gravitational force (which holds planets around the Sun) can be written as "one trillion times one trillion times one trillion." Write this number as the product of exponential expressions (base ten) and then find the product (as a larger power of ten).

8.2 Integer Exponents

Zero and Negative Exponents

We would like to expand our rules for exponents to include zero and negative exponents.

We begin with a^0, where $a \neq 0$. We will assume that the previous rules for exponents apply to a^0 and see if this leads us to a definition of a^0. For example, applying the rule $a^m a^n = a^{m+n}$ yields

$$a^m \cdot a^0 = a^{m+0} = a^m$$

Dividing both sides by a^m, we see that we must have

$$\boxed{a^0 = 1}$$

We *define* a^0 in this way. (We did not allow a to be zero, since 0^0 has no mathematical meaning.) The student can easily verify that the other rules for exponents also hold. For example, our *definition* tells us that $(a/b)^0 = 1$, which agrees with the rule for quotients, since

$$\left(\frac{a}{b}\right)^0 = \frac{a^0}{b^0} = \frac{1}{1} = 1$$

Example 1 Using an Exponent of Zero
Evaluate.

(a) 3^0

(b) $(-4)^0$

(c) $\left(\dfrac{2}{5}\right)^0$

(d) $4(xy)^0$

(e) $\dfrac{-2}{(t^2-1)^0}$

(f) -3^0

Solution

(a) $3^0 = 1$ (b) $(-4)^0 = 1$ (c) $\left(\dfrac{2}{5}\right)^0 = 1$

(d) $4(xy)^0 = 4(1) = 4$ (e) $\dfrac{-2}{(t^2 - 1)^0} = \dfrac{-2}{1} = -2$ (f) $-3^0 = -1$

✔ Progress Check 1

Simplify.

(a) $(-4x)^0$ (b) $-3(r^2 s)^0$ (c) $9\left(\dfrac{2}{7}\right)^0$

(d) $-4(x^2 - 5)^0$ (e) $5x^0 - 2xy^0$

Answers

(a) 1 (b) -3 (c) 9 (d) -4 (e) $5 - 2x$

The same approach will lead us to a meaning for negative exponents. For consistency, we must have, for $a \neq 0$,

$$a^m \cdot a^{-m} = a^{m-m} = a^0 = 1$$

Thus,

$$a^m \cdot a^{-m} = 1$$

If we divide both sides by a^m, we obtain

$$a^{-m} = \frac{1}{a^m}$$

Had we divided by a^{-m}, we would have obtained

$$a^m = \frac{1}{a^{-m}}$$

Thus, a^{-m} is the reciprocal of a^m, and a^m is the reciprocal of a^{-m}. Again, the student should verify that all the rules for exponents hold with this definition of a^{-m}. For example, if $a \neq 0$,

$$(a^{-m})^n = \left(\frac{1}{a^m}\right)^n = \frac{1}{a^{mn}} = a^{-mn}$$

The rules for negative exponents can be expressed in another way.

A factor moves from numerator to denominator (or from denominator to numerator) by changing the sign of the exponent.

Example 2 Working with Negative Exponents

Simplify, using positive exponents.

(a) 3^{-2} (b) $\dfrac{1}{2^{-3}}$ (c) $(-3)^{-2}$ (d) $-x^{-7}$

(e) $\dfrac{-2}{(a-1)^{-2}}$ (f) $(2x)^{-3}$ (g) $2x^{-3}$ (h) $a + b^{-5}$

Solution

(a) $3^{-2} = \dfrac{1}{3^2} = \dfrac{1}{9}$ (b) $\dfrac{1}{2^{-3}} = 2^3 = 8$

(c) $(-3)^{-2} = \dfrac{1}{(-3)^2} = \dfrac{1}{9}$ (d) $-x^{-7} = -(x^{-7}) = -\dfrac{1}{x^7}$

(e) $\dfrac{-2}{(a-1)^{-2}} = -2(a-1)^2$ (f) $(2x)^{-3} = \dfrac{1}{(2x)^3} = \dfrac{1}{8x^3}$

(g) $2x^{-3} = 2\left(\dfrac{1}{x^3}\right) = \dfrac{2}{x^3}$ (h) $a + b^{-5} = a + \dfrac{1}{b^5}$

✔ **Progress Check 2**

Simplify, using positive exponents.

(a) 4^{-2} (b) $\dfrac{1}{3^{-2}}$ (c) $\dfrac{r^{-6}}{s^{-2}}$ (d) $x^{-2}y^{-3}$

Answers

(a) $\dfrac{1}{16}$ (b) 9 (c) $\dfrac{s^2}{r^6}$ (d) $\dfrac{1}{x^2 y^3}$

Example 3 Simplifying Expressions with Exponents

Simplify, using only positive exponents in the answer.

(a) $\dfrac{4a^3}{6a^{-5}}$ (b) $(x^2 y^{-3})^{-5}$ (c) $a^{-3}\left(\dfrac{a^2}{b^{-2}}\right)^4$ (d) $(m^{-1} + n^{-1})^2$

Solution

(a) $\dfrac{4a^3}{6a^{-5}} = \dfrac{2}{3}a^3 a^5 = \dfrac{2}{3}a^8$

(b) $(x^2 y^{-3})^{-5} = (x^2)^{-5}(y^{-3})^{-5} = x^{-10} y^{15} = \dfrac{y^{15}}{x^{10}}$

(c) $a^{-3}\left(\dfrac{a^2}{b^{-2}}\right)^4 = a^{-3}\dfrac{(a^2)^4}{(b^{-2})^4} = a^{-3}\left(\dfrac{a^8}{b^{-8}}\right) = \dfrac{a^{-3+8}}{b^{-8}} = \dfrac{a^5}{b^{-8}} = a^5 b^8$

(d) $(m^{-1} + n^{-1})^2 = \left(\dfrac{1}{m} + \dfrac{1}{n}\right)^2 = \left(\dfrac{n+m}{mn}\right)^2 = \dfrac{(n+m)^2}{(mn)^2} = \dfrac{n^2 + 2nm + m^2}{m^2 n^2}$

✔ **Progress Check 3**

Simplify, using only positive exponents in the answer.

(a) $\dfrac{x^7}{x^{-5}}$ (b) $(x^{-4}y^{-3})^4$ (c) $a^2\left(\dfrac{a^{-4}}{b^3}\right)^{-3}$ (d) $(3+x)^{-1}$

Answers

(a) x^{12} (b) $\dfrac{1}{x^{16}y^{12}}$ (c) $a^{14}b^9$ (d) $\dfrac{1}{3+x}$

Warning

Don't confuse negative numbers and negative exponents.

(a) $2^{-4} = \dfrac{1}{2^4}$

Don't write
$$2^{-4} = -2^4$$

(b) $(-2)^{-3} = \dfrac{1}{(-2)^3} = \dfrac{1}{-8} = -\dfrac{1}{8}$

Don't write
$$(-2)^{-3} = \dfrac{1}{2^3} = \dfrac{1}{8}$$

(c) $-3^{-2} = -\dfrac{1}{3^2} = -\dfrac{1}{9}$

Don't write
$$-3^{-2} = 3^2 = 9$$

We can now summarize the laws of exponents.

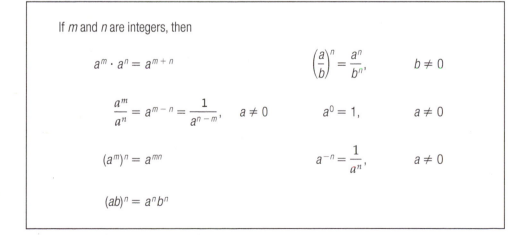

Laws of Exponents

If m and n are integers, then

$$a^m \cdot a^n = a^{m+n}$$

$$\left(\dfrac{a}{b}\right)^n = \dfrac{a^n}{b^n}, \qquad b \neq 0$$

$$\dfrac{a^m}{a^n} = a^{m-n} = \dfrac{1}{a^{n-m}}, \quad a \neq 0 \qquad a^0 = 1, \qquad a \neq 0$$

$$(a^m)^n = a^{mn} \qquad a^{-n} = \dfrac{1}{a^n}, \qquad a \neq 0$$

$$(ab)^n = a^n b^n$$

Scientific Notation

To represent very large or very small numbers, we can express numbers in scientific notation. In scientific notation, numbers are written in the form $a \times 10^n$, where n is an integer and a is written in decimal form, $1 \le |a| < 10$.

For example, the number 8,000,000,000 can be expressed in scientific notation as follows:

$$8,000,000,000 = 8 \times 1,000,000,000$$
$$= 8.0 \times 10^9$$

We can also express a very small number such as 0.0000000123 in scientific notation:

$$0.0000000123 = \frac{123}{10^{10}}$$
$$= \frac{123}{10} \cdot \frac{1}{10^9}$$
$$= 1.23 \times 10^{-9}$$

We convert a number from standard notation to scientific notation as follows.

> If the decimal is moved n places to the left, we multiply the decimal by 10^n.
> If the decimal is moved n places to the right, we multiply the decimal by 10^{-n}.

Let's practice expressing numbers in scientific notation and converting numbers from scientific notation to standard notation.

Example 1   Writing Numbers in Scientific Notation

Convert the following to scientific notation.

a. 2367
b. 30,929.3
c. −0.0079
d. 0.0000358

Solution

a. $2367 = 2.367 \times 1000 = 2.367 \times 10^3$

b. $30,929.3 = 3.09293 \times 10,000 = 3.09293 \times 10^4$

c. $-0.0079 = -7.9 \times 10^{-3}$

   because we move the decimal to the right by three places and multiply by 10^{-3}.

d. $0.0000358 = 3.58 \times 10^{-5}$

   because we move the decimal to the right by five places and multiply by 10^{-5}.

To convert a number in scientific notation to standard notation, we reverse the process.

> For $a \times 10^n$ where n is positive, move the decimal to the right by n digits.
> For $a \times 10^n$ where n is negative, move the decimal to the left by n digits.

Example 2   Writing in Standard Notation

Convert the following to standard notation.

a. 2.35×10^4

b. -4.093×10^2

c. 5.6×10^{-3}

d. 1.705×10^{-2}

Solution

a. $2.35 \times 10^4 = 23,500$

    because we move the decimal point four digits to the right.

b. $-4.093 \times 10^2 = -409.3$

    because we move the decimal point two digits to the right.

c. $5.6 \times 10^{-3} = 0.0056$

    because we move the decimal point three digits to the left.

d. $1.705 \times 10^{-2} = 0.01705$

    because we move the decimal point two digits to the left.

Example 3   Writing in Scientific Notation

A plane travels at 2500 miles per hour. Use scientific notation to express the number of miles traveled for 12 hours.

Solution

$$\begin{aligned} \text{Distance traveled for 12 hours} &= 2500 \times 12 \\ &= (2.5 \times 10^3)(1.2 \times 10) \\ &= (2.5 \times 1.2)(10^3 \times 10) \\ &= (3.0)(10^4) \\ &= 3.0 \times 10^4 \end{aligned}$$

The plane traveled 3.0×10^4 miles for 12 hours.

Exercise Set 8.2

In Exercises 1−72 use the rules for exponents to simplify. Write the answers using only positive exponents.

1. 2^0

2. $(-1.2)^0$

3. $(xy)^0$

4. $2(a^2 - 1)^0$

5. $\dfrac{3}{(2x^2 + 1)^0}$

6. -3^0

7. $-5xy^0$

8. 2^{-4}

9. $(-3)^{-3}$

10. $\dfrac{1}{3^{-4}}$

11. $\dfrac{2}{4^{-3}}$

12. x^{-5}

13. $(-x)^3$

14. $-x^{-5}$

15. -4^{-2}

16. $-2x^{-2}$

17. $\dfrac{1}{y^{-6}}$

18. $\dfrac{1}{x^{-7}}$

19. $(2a)^{-6}$

20. $-6(3x + 2y)^{-5}$

21. $\dfrac{-4}{(5a - 3b)^{-2}}$

22. 343^{-6}

23. $5^{-3}5^5$

24. $x^{-4}x^2$

25. $4y^5y^{-2}$

26. a^4a^{-4}

27. $x^{-4}x^{-5}x^2$

28. $-3a^{-3}a^{-6}a^4$

29. $(3^2)^{-3}$

30. $(4^{-2})^2$

31. $[(-2)^3]^3$

32. $(x^{-2})^4$

33. $(x^{-3})^{-3}$

34. $[(x + y)^{-2}]^2$

35. $\dfrac{2^2}{2^{-3}}$

36. $\dfrac{3^{-5}}{3^2}$

37. $\dfrac{x^8}{x^{-10}}$

38. $\dfrac{3x^{-7}}{x^4}$

39. $\dfrac{4x^{-3}}{x^{-2}}$

40. $\dfrac{2x^4y^{-2}}{x^2y^{-3}}$

41. $2x^3x^{-3}$

42. $(x^4y^{-2})^{-1}$

43. $(2a^2b^{-3})^{-3}$

44. $(ab^{-1})^{-1}$

45. $(a^{-1}b^{-1})^{-1}$

46. $\left(\dfrac{6}{9}x^{-3}y^2\right)^2$

47. $(3a^{-2}b^{-3})^{-2}$

48. $\dfrac{1}{(2xy)^{-2}}$

49. $\left(\dfrac{a^{-3}b^3}{c^{-2}}\right)^{-3}$

50. $\left(-\dfrac{1}{2}x^3y^{-4}\right)^{-3}$

51. $\dfrac{a^2b^{-4}}{c}$

52. $\dfrac{(x^{-2})^2}{(3y^{-2})^3}$

53. $\dfrac{3a^5b^{-2}}{9a^{-4}b^2}$

54. $\dfrac{8x^{-3}y^{-4}}{2x^{-4}y^{-3}}$

55. $\left(\dfrac{x^2}{x^3}\right)^{-1}$

56. $\left(\dfrac{x^3}{x^{-2}}\right)^2$

57. $\left(\dfrac{2a^2b^{-4}}{a^{-3}c^{-3}}\right)^2$

58. $\left(\dfrac{3xy^{-1}}{2x^{-1}y^2}\right)^{-2}$

59. $\dfrac{2x^{-3}y^2}{x^{-3}y^{-3}}$

60. $(a^{-2}b^2)^{-1}$

61. $\left(\dfrac{y^{-2}}{y^{-3}}\right)^{-1}$

62. $\left(\dfrac{8x^{-3}y}{6xy^{-4}}\right)^{-3}$

63. $\left(\dfrac{-2a^{-2}b^3}{c^{-2}}\right)^{-2}$

64. $\left(-\dfrac{3}{2}a^2b^{-2}c^{-2}\right)^{-3}$

65. $\left(\dfrac{x^3y^{-1}}{z^{-3}}\right)^3$

66. $\left(\dfrac{x^{-3}yz^{-4}}{x^2z}\right)^{-3}$

67. $\left(\dfrac{2a^{-2}b^3}{c^{-3}}\right)^2$

68. $\left(\dfrac{x^2y^{-3}}{2xz^{-2}}\right)^{-2}$

69. $\dfrac{(a+b)^{-1}}{(a-b)^{-2}}$

70. $(a^{-1}+b^{-1})^{-1}$

71. $\dfrac{(x+y)^{-1}}{x^{-1}+y^{-1}}$

72. $\dfrac{(a^{-1}+b)^{-1}}{(a+b^{-1})^{-1}}$

In Exercises 73−80 evaluate the expression.

73. $(1.20^2)^{-1}$

74. $(-3.67^2)^{-1}$

75. $\left(\dfrac{7.65^{-1}}{7.65^2}\right)^2$

76. $\left(\dfrac{4.46^2}{4.46^{-1}}\right)^{-1}$

77. $\dfrac{(1.7)^{-2}(2.1)^2}{(1.7)(2.1)^{-1}}$

78. $\dfrac{(3.42+2.01)^{-1}}{(3.42-2.01)^{-2}}$

79. $\dfrac{(2x+1)^{-1}}{(x-1)^{-2}}$ when $x = 8.65$

80. $\dfrac{(3x-1)(x+2)^2}{(4-x)^{-2}}$ when $x = 4.03$

81. The force of electrical repulsion (in Newtons) between two protons at a distance of one meter apart is given by $(8.9876 \times 10^9)(1.602 \times 10^{-19})$. Simplify this product.

   How strong is the gravitational force between two protons at a distance of one meter? (You must divide the product you just found by the ratio you found in Exercise 79.) (The ratio we used is rounded off, so this value is not exact. A better value is 1.876×10^{-64}).

Write the following in scientific notation.

82. 1230

83. −0.2459

84. 3,000,009

85. 0.00059

Write the following in standard notation.

86. 2.7×10^2

87. 3.99×10^5

88. 1.2×10^{-3}

89. 6.2×10^{-1}

90. Multiply the follwing and write the answer in scientfic notation: $(0.0000045)(0.307)$.

8.3 Rational Exponents and Radicals

Suppose a square whose sides are of length a has an area of 25 square inches (Figure 1). We can write the equation

$$a^2 = 25$$

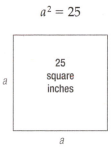

25
square
inches

a

a

Figure 1   Area of a Square

and seek a number a whose square is 25. We say that a is a **square root of b** if $a^2 = b$. Similarly, we say that a is a **cube root of b** if $a^3 = b$ and in general, if n is a natural number, we say that

a is an **nth root of b** if $a^n = b$.

Thus, 5 is a square root of 25, since $5^2 = 25$, and -2 is a cube root of -8, since $(-2)^3 = -8$.

Since $(-5)^2 = 25$, we conclude that -5 is also a square root of 25. More generally, if $b > 0$ and a is a square root of b, then $-a$ is also a square root of b. If $b < 0$, there is no real number a such that $a^2 = b$, since the square of a real number is always nonnegative. (We'll see in Section 8.5 that mathematicians have created an extended number system in which there is a root when $b < 0$ and n is even.)

Table 1 summarizes the different cases for the nth root of b. Note that when n is odd, the nth roots of b have the same sign as b.

Table 1   The nth Root of a Real Number b

b	n	Number of nth roots of b such that $a^n = b$	Form of nth roots	b	Examples
Positive	Even	2	$a, -a$	4	Square roots are 2, -2
Negative	Even	None	None	-1	No square roots
Positive	Odd	1	$a > 0$	8	Cube root is 2
Negative	Odd	1	$a < 0$	-8	Cube root is -2
0	All	1	0	0	Square root is 0

We would like to define rational exponents in a manner that will be consistent with the rules for integer exponents. If the rule $(a^m)^n = a^{mn}$ is to hold, then we must have

$$(b^{1/n}) = b^{n/n} = b$$

We also know that if $a^n = b$, then a is an nth root of b. If

$$a^n = b$$

and if we want

$$(b^{1/n})^n = b$$

to hold, then $b^{1/n}$ must be the same as a, so $b^{1/n}$ must be an nth root of b. Then for every natural number n, we say that

---

$b^{1/n}$ is an nth root of b.

Of course, when n is even we must also have $b \geq 0$.

Principal nth Root

If n is even and b is positive, Table 1 indicates that there are two numbers, a and $-a$, that are nth roots of b. For example

$$4^2 = 16 \quad \text{and} \quad (-4)^2 = 16$$

There are then two candidates for $16^{1/2}$, namely, 4 and -4. To avoid ambiguity we say that $16^{1/2} = 4$. That is, if n is even and b is positive, we always *choose* the positive number a such that $a^n = b$ to be the nth root and call a the **principal nth root** of b. Thus, $b^{1/n}$ denotes the principal nth root of b.

Example 1   Finding the Principal nth Root
Evaluate.

(a) $144^{1/2}$ (b) $(-8)^{1/3}$ (c) $(-25)^{1/2}$ (d) $-\left(\dfrac{1}{16}\right)^{1/4}$

Solution

(a) $144^{1/2} = 12$ (b) $(-8)^{1/3} = -2$

(c) $(-25)^{1/2}$ is not a real number   (d) $-\left(\dfrac{1}{16}\right)^{1/4} = -\dfrac{1}{2}$

✔ Progress Check 1

Evaluate.

(a) $(27)^{1/3}$ (b) $(-27)^{1/3}$ (c) $36^{1/2}$ (d) $(-36)^{1/2}$

(e) $-36^{1/2}$ (f) $-36^{-1/2}$ (g) $\left(\dfrac{1}{8}\right)^{1/3}$

Answers

(a) 3   (b) -3 (c) 6   (d) not a real number

(e) -6 (f) $-\dfrac{1}{6}$ (g) $\dfrac{1}{2}$

Warning

1. Note that

$$-36^{1/2} = -(36)^{1/2} = -6$$

but $(-36)^{1/2}$ is undefined.

2. *Don't* write $16^{1/2} = -4$. The definition of an nth root requires that you write $16^{1/2} = 4$ (the principal nth root).

Rational Exponents

Now we are prepared to define $b^{m/n}$, where m is an integer (positive, negative, or zero), n is a natural number, and $b > 0$ when n is even. We want the rules for exponents to hold for rational exponents as well. That is, we want to have

$$4^{3/2} = 4^{(1/2)(3)} = (4^{1/2})^3 = 2^3 = 8$$

and

$$4^{3/2} = 4^{(3)(1/2)} = (4^3)^{1/2} = (64)^{1/2} = 8$$

To achieve this consistency, we define $b^{m/n}$, for an integer m, a natural number n, and a real number b, by

$$b^{m/n} = (b^{1/n})^m = (b^m)^{1/n}$$

where b must be positive when n is even. With this definition, all the rules of exponents continue to hold when the exponents are rational numbers.

Example 2   Working with Rational Exponents

Simplify.

(a) $(-8)^{4/3}$ (b) $x^{1/2} \cdot x^{3/4}$ (c) $(x^{3/4})^2$ (d) $(3x^{2/3}y^{-5/3})^3$

Solution

(a) $(-8)^{4/3} = [(-8)^{1/3}]^4 = (-2)^4 = 16$

(b) $x^{1/2} \cdot x^{3/4} = x^{1/2+3/4} = x^{5/4}$

(c) $(x^{3/4})^2 = x^{(3/4)(2)} = x^{3/2}$

(d) $(3x^{2/3}y^{-5/3})^3 = 3^3 \cdot x^{(2/3)(3)}y^{(-5/3)(3)} = 27x^2 y^{-5} = \dfrac{27x^2}{y^5}, \; y \neq 0$

✔ Progress Check 2

Simplify. Assume all variables are positive real numbers.

(a) $27^{4/3}$ (b) $(a^{1/2}b^{-2})^{-2}$ (c) $\left(\dfrac{x^{1/3}y^{2/3}}{z^{5/6}}\right)^{12}$

Answers

(a) 81   (b) $\dfrac{b^4}{a}$ (c) $\dfrac{x^4 y^8}{z^{10}}$

Radicals

The symbol $\sqrt{b}$ is an alternative way of writing $b^{1/2}$; that is, $\sqrt{b}$ denotes the non-negative square root of b. The symbol $\sqrt{\;}$ is called a **radical sign**, and $\sqrt{b}$ is called the **principal square root of b**. Thus,

$$\sqrt{25} = 5 \qquad \sqrt{0} = 0 \qquad \sqrt{-25} \text{ is undefined}$$

In general, the symbol $\sqrt[n]{b}$ is an alternative way of writing $b^{1/n}$, the principal nth root of b. Of course, we must apply the same restrictions to $\sqrt[n]{b}$ that we established for $b^{1/n}$. In summary,

$$\sqrt[n]{b} = b^{1/n} = a, \quad \text{where } a^n = b$$

with these restrictions:

- If n is even and $b < 0$, $\sqrt[n]{b}$ is not a real number.
- If n is even and $b \geq 0$, $\sqrt[n]{b}$ is the *nonnegative* number a satisfying $a^n = b$.

Warning

Many students are accustomed to writing $\sqrt{4} = \pm 2$. This is incorrect, since the symbol $\sqrt{\;}$ indicates the *principal* square root, which is nonnegative. Get in the habit of writing $\sqrt{4} = 2$. If you want to indicate *all* the square roots of 4, write $\pm\sqrt{4} = \pm 2$.

When Is a Proof Not a Proof?

Books of mathematical puzzles love to include "proofs" that lead to false or contradictory results. Of course, there is always an incorrect step hidden somewhere in the proof. The error may be subtle, but a good grounding in the fundamentals of mathematics will enable you to catch it.

Examine the following "proof."

$$1 = 1^{1/2} \tag{1}$$
$$= [(-1)^2]^{1/2} \tag{2}$$
$$= (-1)^{2/2} \tag{3}$$
$$= (-1)^1 \tag{4}$$
$$= -1 \tag{5}$$

The result is obviously contradictory: we can't have $1 = -1$. Yet each step seems to be legitimate. Did you spot the flaw? The rule

$$(b^m)^{1/n} = b^{m/n}$$

used in going from (2) to (3) doesn't apply when n is even and b is negative. Any time the rules of algebra are abused the results are unpredictable!

In short, $\sqrt[n]{b}$ is the **radical form** of $b^{1/n}$. The quantity b is called the **radicand**, and the integer n is called the **index**. We can switch back and forth from one form to the other. For instance,

$$\sqrt[3]{7} = 7^{1/3} \quad (11)^{1/5} = \sqrt[5]{11}$$

Finally, we treat the radical form of $b^{m/n}$, where m is an integer and n is a natural number, as follows. We have already defined $b^{m/n}$ as $(b^m)^{1/n}$, so

$$b^{m/n} = (b^m)^{1/n} = \sqrt[n]{b^m}$$

Also, $b^{m/n}$ has been defined as $(b^{1/n})^m$, so

$$b^{m/n} = (b^{1/n})^m = (\sqrt[n]{b})^m$$

Of course, the radicand must be such that its radical form will be defined. Thus,

$$7^{2/3} = (7^2)^{1/3} = \sqrt[3]{7^2}$$
$$7^{2/3} = (7^{1/3})^2 = (\sqrt[3]{7})^2$$

Example 3   Radical Form and Rational Exponent Form

Change from radical form to rational exponent form, or vice versa. Simplify your answer and use only positive exponents. Assume all variables are nonzero.

(a) $(2x)^{-3/2}, \; x > 0$ (b) $\dfrac{1}{\sqrt[7]{y^4}}$ (c) $(-3a)^{3/7}$ (d) $\sqrt{x^2 + y^2}$

Solution

(a) $(2x)^{-3/2} = \dfrac{1}{(2x)^{3/2}} = \dfrac{1}{\sqrt{8x^3}}$ (b) $\dfrac{1}{\sqrt[7]{y^4}} = \dfrac{1}{y^{4/7}}$

(c) $(-3a)^{3/7} = \sqrt[7]{-27a^3}$ (d) $\sqrt{x^2 + y^2} = (x^2 + y^2)^{1/2}$

✔ Progress Check 3

Change from radical form to rational exponent form, or vice versa. Simplify your answer and use only positive exponents. Assume all variables are positive real numbers.

(a) $\sqrt[4]{2rs^3}$ (b) $(x + y)^{5/2}$ (c) $y^{-5/4}$ (d) $\dfrac{1}{\sqrt[4]{m^5}}$

Answers

(a) $(2r)^{1/4}s^{3/4}$ or $(2rs^3)^{1/4}$ (b) $\sqrt{(x+y)^5}$ (c) $\dfrac{1}{\sqrt[4]{y^5}}$ (d) $\dfrac{1}{m^{5/4}}$

Calculators with a "y^x" key can be used to evaluate expressions such as $(7.62)^{3/4}$. The following example illustrates the necessary keystrokes on most hand-held calculators.

Example 4   Rational Exponents and Calculators

Use a calculator to compute $(7.62)^{3/4}$.

Solution

The required keystrokes are as follows:

 7.62 $\boxed{y^x}$ .75 $\boxed{=}$

The displayed answer is

$$4.5863398$$

✔ Progress Check 4

Use a calculator to compute $(18.10)^{2/5}$.

Answer

3.1847213

Exercise Set 8.3

In Exercises 1−32 simplify, and write the answer using only positive exponents.

1. $16^{3/4}$

2. $4^{5/2}$

3. $(-125)^{-1/3}$

4. $(-64)^{-2/3}$

5. $\left(\dfrac{-8}{125}\right)^{2/3}$

6. $\left(\dfrac{-8}{27}\right)^{5/3}$

7. $c^{1/4}c^{-2/3}$

8. $x^{-1/2}x^{1/3}$

9. $\dfrac{2x^{1/3}}{x^{-3/4}}$

10. $\dfrac{y^{-2/3}}{y^{1/5}}$

11. $\left(\dfrac{x^{7/2}}{x^{2/3}}\right)^{-6}$

12. $\left(\dfrac{x^{3/2}}{x^{2/3}}\right)^{1/6}$

13. $\dfrac{125^{4/3}}{125^{2/3}}$

14. $\dfrac{32^{-1/5}}{32^{3/5}}$

15. $(x^2y^3)^{1/3}$

16. $(x^{1/3}y^2)^6$

17. $(16a^4b^2)^{3/2}$

18. $(x^6y^4)^{-1/2}$

19. $(a^{-3}b^2)^{-3/2}$

20. $(4a^{-4}b^{-5})^{-1/2}$

21. $(-64x^{6n})^{1/3}$

22. $(16^{8n}y^2)^{-1/4}$

23. $\left(\dfrac{x^{15}}{y^{10}}\right)^{3/5}$

24. $\left(\dfrac{x^8}{y^{12}}\right)^{3/4}$

25. $\left(\dfrac{x^{18}}{y^{-6}}\right)^{2/3}$

26. $\left(\dfrac{a^{-3/2}}{b^{-1/2}}\right)^{-5/2}$

27. $\left(\dfrac{x^3}{y^{-6}}\right)^{-4/3}$

28. $\left(\dfrac{x^9}{y^{-3/2}}\right)^{-2/3}$

29. $\left(\dfrac{-8x^9}{27y^{-3/2}}\right)^{5/3}$

30. $\left(\dfrac{-125x^{12}}{-y^{-3/2}}\right)^{-2/3}$

31. $\left(\dfrac{64x^6}{y^{12}}\right)^{1/4}$

32. $\left(-\dfrac{8}{27}\cdot\dfrac{x^6}{y^{-4}}\right)^{-2/3}$

In Exercises 33−40 write the expression in radical form.

33. $\left(\dfrac{1}{4}\right)^{2/5}$

34. $(-6)^{2/3}$

35. $x^{2/3}$

36. $(12y)^{-4/3}$

37. $(-8x^2)^{2/5}$

38. $(x^3y^3)^{1/6}$

39. $(x^2-1)^{2/3}$

40. $(3x^6+y^6)^{-3/4}$

In Exercises 41−48 write the expression in exponent form, using only positive exponents.

41. $\sqrt[4]{8^3}$

42. $\sqrt[4]{\left(\dfrac{1}{8}\right)^3}$

43. $\dfrac{1}{\sqrt[5]{(-8)^2}}$

44. $\dfrac{1}{\sqrt[3]{x^7}}$

45. $\dfrac{1}{\sqrt[4]{\dfrac{4}{9}a^3}}$

46. $\sqrt[6]{(3a^4b^6)^5}$

47. $\sqrt{(2x^{-4}y^3)^7}$

48. $\dfrac{1}{\sqrt[5]{(2a^2+3b^3)^3}}$

In Exercises 49−52 select the correct answer.

49. $\sqrt{121}=$

   (a) 12 (b) 10 (c) 11
   (d) ± 11 (e) not a real number

50. $\sqrt[3]{-27}=$

   (a) 3 (b) $\dfrac{1}{3}$ (c) $-\dfrac{1}{3}$
   (d) -3
   (e) not a real number

51. $-\sqrt[3]{-\dfrac{1}{8}}=$

   (a) -2 (b) 2 (c) $\dfrac{1}{2}$
   (d) $-\dfrac{1}{2}$ (e) not a real number

52. $\sqrt[4]{16}=$

   (a) 2 (b) -2 (c) $\dfrac{1}{2}$
   (d) $-\dfrac{1}{2}$ (e) not a real number

In Exercises 53−64 evaluate the expression.

53. $\sqrt{\dfrac{4}{9}}$

54. $\sqrt{\dfrac{25}{4}}$

55. $\sqrt{-36}$

56. $\sqrt[4]{-81}$

57. $\sqrt[3]{\dfrac{1}{27}}$

58. $\sqrt[3]{-\dfrac{1}{125}}$

59. $\sqrt{(-5)^2}$

60. $\sqrt{\left(-\dfrac{1}{3}\right)^2}$

61. $\sqrt{\left(\dfrac{1}{2}\right)^2}$ 62. $\sqrt{\left(\dfrac{5}{4}\right)^2}$

63. $\sqrt{\left(-\dfrac{7}{2}\right)^2}$ 64. $\sqrt{(-7)^2}$

In Exercises 65−72 use a calculator to evaluate the expression.

65. $(14.43)^{3/2}$ 66. $-(2.46)^{3/2}$

67. $(10.46)^{2/3}$ 68. $(8.97)^{4/3}$

69. $\dfrac{(6.47)^{1/3}}{(6.47)^{4/3}}$ 70. $\dfrac{(3.75)^{3/2}}{(3.75)^{1/2}}$

71. $\sqrt{3x^2 + 4y^3}$ when $x = 1.6, y = 5.7$

72. $\sqrt{(a^2 + b^4)^3}$ when $a = 2.5, b = 6.7$

8.4   Evaluating and Simplifying Radicals

Since radicals are just another way of writing exponents, the properties of radicals can be derived from the properties of exponents. By switching from radical to exponent form and back again, we can develop these properties of radicals.

If n is a natural number, a and b are real numbers, and all radicals denote real numbers, then

1. $\sqrt[n]{b^m} = (b^m)^{1/n} = (b^{1/n})^m = (\sqrt[n]{b})^m$ $\sqrt[3]{8^2} = (\sqrt[3]{8})^2$

2. $\sqrt[n]{a} \cdot \sqrt[n]{b} = a^{1/n} \cdot b^{1/n} = (ab)^{1/n} = \sqrt[n]{ab}$ $\sqrt{4}\sqrt{9} = \sqrt{36}$

3. $\dfrac{\sqrt[n]{a}}{\sqrt[n]{b}} = \dfrac{a^{1/n}}{b^{1/n}} = \left(\dfrac{a}{b}\right)^{1/n} = \sqrt[n]{\dfrac{a}{b}}, \; b \neq 0$ $\dfrac{\sqrt[3]{8}}{\sqrt[3]{27}} = \sqrt[3]{\dfrac{8}{27}}$

4. $\sqrt[n]{a^n} = \begin{cases} a & \text{if } n \text{ is odd} \\ |a| & \text{if } n \text{ is even} \end{cases}$ $\sqrt{(-4)^2} = |-4| = 4$

Properties of Radicals

Property 4 results from observing that

$$\sqrt[n]{a^n} = (a^n)^{1/n} = a^{n/n} = a$$

will result in a negative answer if $a < 0$ and n is even. Since we must choose the *principal* root, we must choose $|a|$, as shown in Property 4.

These properties can be used to evaluate and simplify radical forms. The key to the process is to think in terms of perfect squares when dealing with square roots, to think in terms of perfect cubes when dealing with cube roots, and so on. Here are some examples.

Example 1 Simplifying Radical Forms

Simplify.

(a) $\sqrt{72}$ (b) $\sqrt[3]{-54}$ (c) $2\sqrt[3]{8x^3y}$ (d) $\sqrt{\dfrac{16x}{9y^2}}$

Solution

(a) $\sqrt{72} = \sqrt{36 \cdot 2} = \sqrt{36}\sqrt{2} = 6\sqrt{2}$

(b) $\sqrt[3]{-54} = \sqrt[3]{(-27)(2)} = \sqrt[3]{-27}\sqrt[3]{2} = -3\sqrt[3]{2}$

(c) $2\sqrt[3]{8x^3y} = 2\sqrt[3]{8}\sqrt[3]{x^3}\sqrt[3]{y} = 2(2)(x)\sqrt[3]{y} = 4x\sqrt[3]{y}$

(d) $\sqrt{\dfrac{16x}{9y^2}} = \dfrac{\sqrt{16x}}{\sqrt{9y^2}} = \dfrac{\sqrt{16}\sqrt{x}}{\sqrt{9}\sqrt{y^2}} = \dfrac{4\sqrt{x}}{3|y|}$

✔ Progress Check 1

Simplify.

(a) $\sqrt{45}$ (b) $\sqrt[3]{-81}$ (c) $-3\sqrt[4]{x^3y^4}$

Answers

(a) $3\sqrt{5}$ (b) $-3\sqrt[3]{3}$ (c) $-3|y|\sqrt[4]{x^3}$

Warning

The properties of radicals state that

$$\sqrt{x^2} = |x|$$

It is a common error to write $\sqrt{x^2} = x$, but this leads to the conclusion that $\sqrt{(-6)^2} = -6$. Since the symbol $\sqrt{}$ represents the principal or nonnegative square root of a number, the result cannot be negative. It is therefore essential to write $\sqrt{x^2} = |x|$ (and, in fact, $\sqrt[n]{x^n} = |x|$ whenever n is even) unless we know that $x \geq 0$, in which case we can write $\sqrt{x^2} = x$.

Simplifying Radical Forms

There are other techniques we can use to simplify radical forms. If we have $\sqrt[3]{x^4}$, we can write this as

$$\sqrt[3]{x^4} = \sqrt[3]{x^3 \cdot x} = \sqrt[3]{x^3}\sqrt[3]{x} = x\sqrt[3]{x}$$

In general,

> $\sqrt[n]{x^m}$ can always be simplified so that the exponent within the radical is less than the index n, and x is prime (the only divisors of x are itself and 1).

Another possibility is illustrated by $\sqrt[4]{x^{10}}$, which can be written as

$$\sqrt[4]{x^{10}} = x^{10/4} = x^{5/2} = \sqrt{x^5}$$

In general,

> $\sqrt[n]{x^m}$ can always be simplified so that m and n have no common factors.

Example 2   Simplifying Radical Forms

Simplify. All variables represent positive real numbers.

(a) $\sqrt{x^3y^3}$ (b) $\sqrt{12x^5}$ (c) $\sqrt[3]{x^7y^6}$

Solution

(a) $\sqrt{x^3y^3} = \sqrt{(x^2 \cdot x)(y^2 \cdot y)} = \sqrt{x^2y^2}\sqrt{xy} = xy\sqrt{xy}$

(b) $\sqrt{12x^5} = \sqrt{(4 \cdot 3)(x^4 \cdot x)} = \sqrt{4x^4}\sqrt{3x} = 2x^2\sqrt{3x}$

(c) $\sqrt[3]{x^7y^6} = \sqrt[3]{x^6 \cdot x}\sqrt[3]{y^6} = \sqrt[3]{x^6}\sqrt[3]{y^6}\sqrt[3]{x} = x^2y^2\sqrt[3]{x}$

✔ Progress Check 2

Simplify. All variables represent positive real numbers.

(a) $\sqrt{4xy^5}$ (b) $\sqrt[3]{16x^4y^6}$ (c) $\sqrt[4]{16x^8y^5}$

Answers

(a) $2y^2\sqrt{xy}$ (b) $2xy^2\sqrt[3]{2x}$ (c) $2x^2y\sqrt[4]{y}$

It is always possible to rewrite a fraction so that the denominator is free of radicals, a process called **rationalizing the denominator**. The key to this process is to change the fraction so that the denominator is of the form $\sqrt[n]{a^n}$, which reduces to a if n is odd and to $|a|$ if n is even.

$$\frac{5}{\sqrt{7}} = \frac{5}{\sqrt{7}} \cdot \frac{\sqrt{7}}{\sqrt{7}}$$

$$= \frac{5\sqrt{7}}{\sqrt{7^2}} = \frac{5\sqrt{7}}{7}$$

Multiply numerator and denominator by $\sqrt{7}$ to form a perfect square under the radical sign in the denominator.

If we are given

$$\frac{1}{\sqrt[3]{2x^2}}$$

we seek a factor that will change the expression under the radical sign in the denominator into the perfect cube $\sqrt[3]{2^3x^3}$. The factor is $\sqrt[3]{2^2x}$ since $\sqrt[3]{2x^2} \cdot \sqrt[3]{2^2x} = \sqrt[3]{2^3x^3}$. Thus,

$$\frac{1}{\sqrt[3]{2x^2}} = \frac{1}{\sqrt[3]{2x^2}} \cdot \frac{\sqrt[3]{2^2x}}{\sqrt[3]{2^2x}} = \frac{\sqrt[3]{4x}}{\sqrt[3]{2^3x^3}} = \frac{\sqrt[3]{4x}}{2x}$$

Example 3 Rationalizing the Denominator

Rationalize the denominator. Every variable represents a positive real number.

(a) $\dfrac{1}{\sqrt{3}}$ (b) $\dfrac{6xy^2}{5\sqrt{2x}}$ (c) $\dfrac{-3x^5y^6}{\sqrt[4]{x^3y}}$

Solution

(a) $\dfrac{1}{\sqrt{3}} = \dfrac{1}{\sqrt{3}} \cdot \dfrac{\sqrt{3}}{\sqrt{3}} = \dfrac{\sqrt{3}}{3}$

(b) $\dfrac{6xy^2}{5\sqrt{2x}} = \dfrac{6xy^2}{5\sqrt{2x}} \cdot \dfrac{\sqrt{2x}}{\sqrt{2x}} = \dfrac{6xy^2\sqrt{2x}}{5 \cdot 2x} = \dfrac{3}{5}y^2\sqrt{2x}$

(c) $\dfrac{-3x^5y^6}{\sqrt[4]{x^3y}} = \dfrac{-3x^5y^6}{\sqrt[4]{x^3y}} \cdot \dfrac{\sqrt[4]{xy^3}}{\sqrt[4]{xy^3}}$ The multiplier $\sqrt[4]{xy^3}$ will produce $\sqrt[4]{x^4y^4}$ in the denominator

$$= \frac{-3x^5y^6\sqrt[4]{xy^3}}{\sqrt[4]{x^4y^4}}$$

$$= \frac{-3x^5y^6\sqrt[4]{xy^3}}{xy}$$

$$= -3x^4y^5\sqrt[4]{xy^3}$$

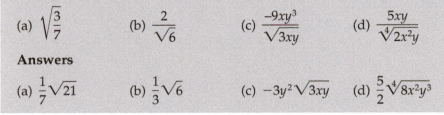

✔ **Progress Check 3**

Rationalize the denominator. Every variable represents a positive real number.

(a) $\sqrt{\dfrac{3}{7}}$ (b) $\dfrac{2}{\sqrt{6}}$ (c) $\dfrac{-9xy^3}{\sqrt{3xy}}$ (d) $\dfrac{5xy}{\sqrt[4]{2x^2y}}$

Answers

(a) $\dfrac{1}{7}\sqrt{21}$ (b) $\dfrac{1}{3}\sqrt{6}$ (c) $-3y^2\sqrt{3xy}$ (d) $\dfrac{5}{2}\sqrt[4]{8x^2y^3}$

A radical expression is said to be **simplified** when

(a) $\sqrt[n]{x^m}$ has $m < n$. (x is prime.)

(b) $\sqrt[n]{x^m}$ has no common factors between m and n.

(c) The denominator is rationalized.

Example 4   Radicals in Simplified Form

Write in simplified form. Every variable represents a positive real number.

(a) $\sqrt[4]{x^2y^5}$ (b) $\sqrt{\dfrac{8x^3}{y}}$ (c) $\sqrt[6]{\dfrac{x^3}{y^2}}$

Solution

(a) $\sqrt[4]{x^2y^5} = \sqrt[4]{x^2}\sqrt[4]{y^4 \cdot y} = \sqrt{x}\sqrt[4]{y^4}\sqrt[4]{y} = y\sqrt{x}\sqrt[4]{y}$

(b) $\sqrt{\dfrac{8x^3}{y}} = \dfrac{\sqrt{(4x^2)(2x)}}{\sqrt{y}} = \dfrac{\sqrt{4x^2}\sqrt{2x}}{\sqrt{y}} = \dfrac{2x\sqrt{2x}}{\sqrt{y}} = \dfrac{2x\sqrt{2x}}{\sqrt{y}} \cdot \dfrac{\sqrt{y}}{\sqrt{y}} = \dfrac{2x\sqrt{2xy}}{y}$

(c) $\sqrt[6]{\dfrac{x^3}{y^2}} = \dfrac{\sqrt[6]{x^3}}{\sqrt[6]{y^2}} = \dfrac{\sqrt{x}}{\sqrt[3]{y}} = \dfrac{\sqrt{x}}{\sqrt[3]{y}} \cdot \dfrac{\sqrt[3]{y^2}}{\sqrt[3]{y^2}} = \dfrac{\sqrt{x}\sqrt[3]{y^2}}{y}$

✔ Progress Check 4

Write in simplified form. Every variable represents a positive real number.

(a) $\sqrt{\dfrac{18x^6}{y}}$ (b) $\sqrt[3]{ab^4c^7}$ (c) $\dfrac{-2xy^3}{\sqrt[4]{32x^3y^5}}$

Answers

(a) $\dfrac{3x^3\sqrt{2y}}{y}$ (b) $bc^2\sqrt[3]{abc}$ (c) $-\dfrac{y}{2}\sqrt[4]{8xy^3}$

Exercise Set 8.4

In Exercises 1–69 simplify the expression. Every variable represents a positive real number.

1. $\sqrt{48}$

2. $\sqrt{100}$

3. $\sqrt[3]{54}$

4. $\sqrt{80}$

5. $\sqrt[3]{40}$

6. $\sqrt{\dfrac{8}{27}}$

7. $\sqrt[3]{\dfrac{8}{27}}$

8. $\sqrt[4]{16}$

9. $\sqrt[3]{\dfrac{8}{125}}$

10. $\sqrt{x^3}$

11. $\sqrt{x^8}$

12. $\sqrt[3]{y^7}$

13. $\sqrt[3]{a^{11}}$

14. $\sqrt[4]{b^{14}}$

15. $\sqrt{x^6}$

16. $\sqrt{48x^9}$

17. $\sqrt{98b^{10}}$

18. $\sqrt[3]{24x^8}$

19. $\sqrt[3]{108y^{16}}$

20. $\sqrt[4]{96x^{10}}$

21. $\sqrt{20x^4}$

22. $\sqrt{x^5y^4}$

23. $\sqrt{a^{10}b^7}$

24. $\sqrt{x^5y^3}$

25. $\sqrt[3]{x^6 y^8}$

26. $\sqrt[3]{x^{14} y^{17}}$

27. $\sqrt[4]{a^5 b^{10}}$

28. $\sqrt{9x^8 y^5}$

29. $\sqrt{72x^7 y^{11}}$

30. $\sqrt[3]{48x^6 y^9}$

31. $\sqrt[3]{24b^{10} c^{14}}$

32. $\sqrt[4]{16x^8 y^5}$

33. $\sqrt[4]{48b^{10} c^{12}}$

34. $\sqrt{20x^5 y^7 z^4}$

35. $\sqrt[3]{40a^8 b^4 c^5}$

36. $\sqrt[3]{72x^6 y^9 z^8}$

37. $\sqrt{\dfrac{1}{5}}$

38. $\dfrac{2}{\sqrt{5}}$

39. $\dfrac{4}{3\sqrt{11}}$

40. $\dfrac{3}{\sqrt{6}}$

41. $\dfrac{2}{\sqrt{12}}$

42. $\dfrac{1}{\sqrt{x}}$

43. $\dfrac{1}{\sqrt{3y}}$

44. $\sqrt{\dfrac{2}{y}}$

45. $\dfrac{4x^2}{\sqrt{2x}}$

46. $\sqrt{\dfrac{2}{x^2}}$

47. $\dfrac{6xy}{\sqrt{2x}}$

48. $\dfrac{8a^2 b^2}{2\sqrt{2b}}$

49. $\dfrac{-5x^4 y^5}{\sqrt[3]{x^2 y^2}}$

50. $\dfrac{-4a^8 b^6}{\sqrt[4]{a^3 b^2}}$

51. $\dfrac{5ab}{\sqrt[3]{2ab^2}}$

52. $\sqrt{\dfrac{12x^4}{y}}$

53. $\sqrt{\dfrac{20x^5}{y^3}}$

54. $\dfrac{\sqrt{8a^5}}{\sqrt{3b}}$

55. $\sqrt[3]{\dfrac{x^5}{y^2}}$

56. $\sqrt[3]{\dfrac{2a^2}{3b}}$

57. $\sqrt[4]{\dfrac{8x^2}{3y}}$

58. $\sqrt{a^3 b^5}$

59. $\sqrt{x^7 y^5}$

60. $\sqrt[3]{x^2 y^7}$

61. $\sqrt[4]{32x^8 y^6}$

62. $\sqrt{9x^7 y^5}$

63. $\sqrt[4]{48x^8 y^6 z^2}$

64. $\dfrac{xy}{\sqrt[3]{54x^2 y^4}}$

65. $\dfrac{7xy^2}{\sqrt[4]{48x^7 y^3}}$

66. $\dfrac{3a^3 b^3}{\sqrt[3]{2a^2 y^5}}$

67. $\dfrac{x}{\sqrt[4]{96x^6 y^9}}$

68. $\dfrac{xy}{\sqrt[3]{32x^6 y^4}}$

69. $\dfrac{4a^4 b^2}{\sqrt[3]{125a^9 b^4}}$

*70. Prove that $|ab| = |a||b|$. (*Hint:* Begin with $|ab| = \sqrt{(ab)^2}$.)

*71. Find the step in the following "proof" that is incorrect. Explain.

$$1 = \sqrt{1} = \sqrt{(-1)(-1)} = \sqrt{-1}\sqrt{-1} = -1$$

72. Enter the program below in your graphing calculator.

```
PROGRAM:RATIONAL
:Disp "X/Aⁿ√(Y)"
:Input "X? ",X
:Input "A? ",A
:Input "Y? ",Y
:Disp X/(A*Y)▶Fr
ac," ROOT ",Y
```

Run the program. Use it to do Exercises 38−41 above.

8.5   Operations with Radicals

We can add or subtract expressions involving radical forms that are exactly the same. For example,

$$2\sqrt{2} + 3\sqrt{2} = (2 + 3)\sqrt{2} = 5\sqrt{2}$$

$$3\sqrt[3]{x^2 y} - 7\sqrt[3]{x^2 y} = (3 - 7)\sqrt[3]{x^2 y} = -4\sqrt[3]{x^2 y}$$

(Note that in each example we displayed an intermediate step to show that the distributive law is really the key to the addition process.)

Example 1   Addition and Subtraction with Radical Forms

Simplify and combine terms.

(a) $\sqrt{27} - \sqrt{12} = \sqrt{9 \cdot 3} - \sqrt{4 \cdot 3} = 3\sqrt{3} - 2\sqrt{3} = \sqrt{3}$

(b) $7\sqrt{5} + 4\sqrt{3} - 9\sqrt{5} = (7 - 9)\sqrt{5} + 4\sqrt{3} = -2\sqrt{5} + 4\sqrt{3}$

(c) $\sqrt[3]{x^2 y} - \dfrac{1}{2}\sqrt{xy} - 3\sqrt[3]{x^2 y} + 4\sqrt{xy}$

$\quad = (1 - 3)\sqrt[3]{x^2 y} + \left(-\dfrac{1}{2} + 4\right)\sqrt{xy} = -2\sqrt[3]{x^2 y} + \dfrac{7}{2}\sqrt{xy}$

✔ **Progress Check 1**

Simplify and combine terms.

(a) $\sqrt{125} - \sqrt{80}$

(b) $\sqrt[3]{24} - \sqrt{8} - \sqrt[3]{81} + \sqrt{32}$

(c) $2\sqrt[5]{xy^3} - 4\sqrt[5]{x^3 y} - 5\sqrt[5]{xy^3} - 2\sqrt[5]{x^3 y}$

Answers

(a) $\sqrt{5}$ (b) $-\sqrt[3]{3} + 2\sqrt{2}$ (c) $-3\sqrt[5]{xy^3} - 6\sqrt[5]{x^3 y}$

Warning

Don't write

$$\sqrt{9} + \sqrt{16} = \sqrt{25}$$

You can perform addition only with identical radical forms. *This is one of the most common mistakes made by students in algebra!* You can easily verify that

$$\sqrt{9} + \sqrt{16} = 3 + 4 = 7$$

It is easy to simplify the product of $\sqrt[n]{a}$ and $\sqrt[m]{b}$ when $m = n$. Thus,

$$\sqrt[5]{x^2 y} \cdot \sqrt[5]{xy} = \sqrt[5]{x^3 y^2}$$

but $\sqrt[3]{x^2 y} \cdot \sqrt[5]{xy}$ cannot be simplified in this manner.

Products of the form

$$(\sqrt{2x} - 5)(\sqrt{2x} + 3)$$

can be handled by forming all four products and then simplifying.

$$(\sqrt{2x} - 5)(\sqrt{2x} + 3) = \sqrt{2x} \cdot \sqrt{2x} + 3\sqrt{2x} - 5\sqrt{2x} - 15$$

$$= 2x - 2\sqrt{2x} - 15$$

Example 2   Multiplication with Radical Forms

Multiply and simplify.

(a) $2\sqrt[3]{xy^2} \cdot \sqrt[3]{x^2y^2}$

(b) $(\sqrt{3} + 2)(\sqrt{3} - 2)$

(c) $(\sqrt{2} - \sqrt{5})(\sqrt{2} + \sqrt{5})$

(d) $(2\sqrt{x} + 3\sqrt{y})^2$

Solution

(a) $2\sqrt[3]{xy^2} \cdot \sqrt[3]{x^2y^2} = 2\sqrt[3]{x^3y^4} = 2xy\sqrt[3]{y}$

(b) $(\sqrt{3} + 2)(\sqrt{3} - 2) = \sqrt{3} \cdot \sqrt{3} - 2\sqrt{3} + 2\sqrt{3} - 4 = 3 - 4 = -1$

(c) $(\sqrt{2} - \sqrt{5})(\sqrt{2} + \sqrt{5}) = \sqrt{2} \cdot \sqrt{2} + \sqrt{2} \cdot \sqrt{5} - \sqrt{5} \cdot \sqrt{2} - \sqrt{5} \cdot \sqrt{5}$

$$= 2 - 5 = -3$$

(d) $(2\sqrt{x} + 3\sqrt{y})^2 = (2\sqrt{x})^2 + 2 \cdot 2\sqrt{x} \cdot 3\sqrt{y} + (3\sqrt{y})^2$

$$= 4x + 12\sqrt{xy} + 9y$$

✔ Progress Check 2

Multiply and simplify.

(a) $\sqrt[7]{a^3b^4} \cdot \sqrt[7]{3ab^3}$

(b) $\sqrt{3}(\sqrt{2} - 4)$

(c) $(\sqrt{2} - 5)(\sqrt{2} + 1)$

(d) $(\sqrt[3]{3x} - 4)(\sqrt[3]{3x} + 2)$

(e) $(\sqrt{x} - \sqrt{2y})^2$

Answers

(a) $b\sqrt[7]{3a^4}$

(b) $\sqrt{6} - 4\sqrt{3}$

(c) $-3 - 4\sqrt{2}$

(d) $\sqrt[3]{(3x)^2} - 2\sqrt[3]{3x} - 8$

(e) $x + 2y - 2\sqrt{2xy}$

Note that

$$(\sqrt{m} + \sqrt{n})(\sqrt{m} - \sqrt{n}) = m - n$$

That is, products of this form are free of radicals. This idea is used to rationalize denominators as in this example.

$$\frac{7}{\sqrt{2} + \sqrt{3}} = \frac{7}{\sqrt{2} + \sqrt{3}} \cdot \frac{\sqrt{2} - \sqrt{3}}{\sqrt{2} - \sqrt{3}} = \frac{7(\sqrt{2} - \sqrt{3})}{2 - 3}$$

$$= \frac{7(\sqrt{2} - \sqrt{3})}{-1} = -7(\sqrt{2} - \sqrt{3})$$

Example 3   Rationalizing the Denominator

Rationalize the denominator. Every variable represents a positive real number.

(a) $\dfrac{4}{\sqrt{5} - \sqrt{2}}$
(b) $\dfrac{5}{\sqrt{x} + 2}$
(c) $\dfrac{-1}{2 - \sqrt{3y}}$

Solution

(a) $\dfrac{4}{\sqrt{5} - \sqrt{2}} = \dfrac{4}{\sqrt{5} - \sqrt{2}} \cdot \dfrac{\sqrt{5} + \sqrt{2}}{\sqrt{5} + \sqrt{2}}$ Multiply numerator and denominator by $\sqrt{5} + \sqrt{2}$.

$$= \dfrac{4(\sqrt{5} + \sqrt{2})}{5 - 2} = \dfrac{4}{3}(\sqrt{5} + \sqrt{2})$$

(b) $\dfrac{5}{\sqrt{x} + 2} = \dfrac{5}{\sqrt{x} + 2} \cdot \dfrac{\sqrt{x} - 2}{\sqrt{x} - 2}$ Multiply numerator and denominator by $\sqrt{x} - 2$.

$$= \dfrac{5(\sqrt{x} - 2)}{x - 4}$$

(c) $\dfrac{-1}{2 - \sqrt{3y}} = \dfrac{-1}{2 - \sqrt{3y}} \cdot \dfrac{2 + \sqrt{3y}}{2 + \sqrt{3y}} = \dfrac{-2 - \sqrt{3y}}{4 - 3y}$

✔ **Progress Check 3**

Rationalize the denominator. Every variable represents a positive real number.

(a) $\dfrac{-6}{\sqrt{2} + \sqrt{6}}$
(b) $\dfrac{2}{\sqrt{3x} - 1}$
(c) $\dfrac{-4}{\sqrt{x} + \sqrt{5y}}$
(d) $\dfrac{4}{\sqrt{x} - \sqrt{y}}$

Answers

(a) $\dfrac{3}{2}(\sqrt{2} - \sqrt{6})$
(b) $\dfrac{2(\sqrt{3x} + 1)}{3x - 1}$

(c) $\dfrac{-4(\sqrt{x} - \sqrt{5y})}{x - 5y}$
(d) $\dfrac{4(\sqrt{x} + \sqrt{y})}{x - y}$

Exercise Set 8.5

In Exercises 1–28 simplify and combine terms. Every variable represents a positive real number.

1. $2\sqrt{3} + 5\sqrt{3}$

2. $3\sqrt{5} - 5\sqrt{5}$

3. $4\sqrt[3]{11} - 6\sqrt[3]{11}$

4. $\frac{1}{2}\sqrt[3]{7} - 2\sqrt[3]{7}$

5. $3\sqrt{x} + 4\sqrt{x}$

6. $3\sqrt[3]{a} - \frac{2}{5}\sqrt[3]{a}$

7. $3\sqrt{2} + 5\sqrt{2} - 2\sqrt{2}$

8. $\sqrt[3]{4} - 3\sqrt[3]{4} + \sqrt{6} - 2\sqrt{6}$

9. $3\sqrt{y} + 2\sqrt{y} - \frac{1}{2}\sqrt{y}$

10. $\frac{1}{2}\sqrt[3]{x} - 2\sqrt[4]{x} + \frac{1}{3}\sqrt[3]{x} - \frac{1}{2}\sqrt[4]{x}$

11. $\sqrt{24} + \sqrt{54}$

12. $\sqrt{75} - \sqrt{150}$

13. $2\sqrt{27} + \sqrt{12} - \sqrt{48}$

14. $\sqrt{20} - 4\sqrt{45} + \sqrt{80}$

15. $\sqrt[3]{40} + \sqrt{45} - \sqrt[3]{135} + 2\sqrt{80}$

16. $3\sqrt[3]{128} + \sqrt{128} - 2\sqrt{72} - \sqrt[3]{54}$

17. $3\sqrt[3]{xy^2} + 2\sqrt[3]{xy^2} - 4\sqrt[3]{x^2y}$

18. $\sqrt[4]{x^2y^2} + 2\sqrt[4]{x^2y^2} - \frac{2}{3}\sqrt{x^2y^2}$

19. $2\sqrt[3]{a^4b} + \frac{1}{2}\sqrt{ab} - \frac{1}{2}\sqrt[3]{a^4b} + 2\sqrt{ab}$

20. $\sqrt{\dfrac{xy}{3}} + \sqrt{6xy}$

21. $\sqrt[5]{2x^3y^2} - 3\sqrt[5]{2x^3y^2} + 4\sqrt[5]{2x^3y^2}$

22. $\sqrt{2abc} - 3\sqrt{8abc} + \sqrt{\dfrac{abc}{2}}$

23. $-\sqrt[3]{xy^4} - 2y\sqrt[3]{xy} - \frac{1}{2}\sqrt{xy^4}$

24. $\sqrt{xy} + xy - 3\sqrt{xy} - 2\sqrt{x^2y^2}$

25. $2\sqrt{5} - (3\sqrt{5} + 4\sqrt{5})$

26. $2\sqrt{18} - (3\sqrt{12} - 2\sqrt{75})$

27. $x\sqrt[3]{x^4y} - (\sqrt[3]{x^5y} - 2x\sqrt{x^4y})$

28. $2(\sqrt{x^3y^7} - xy\sqrt[3]{y}) - 3\sqrt[3]{x^3y^7}$

In Exercises 29–50 multiply and simplify.

29. $\sqrt{3}(\sqrt{3} + 4)$

30. $\sqrt{5}(2 - \sqrt{5})$

31. $\sqrt{6}(\sqrt{2} + 2\sqrt{3})$

32. $\sqrt{8}(\sqrt{2} - \sqrt{3})$

33. $3\sqrt[3]{x^2y} \cdot \sqrt[3]{x \cdot y^2}$

34. $2\sqrt[4]{a^2b^3} \cdot \sqrt[4]{a^3b^2}$

35. $-4\sqrt[5]{x^2y^3} \cdot \sqrt[5]{x^4y^2}$

36. $\sqrt[3]{3a^2b} \cdot \sqrt[3]{9a^3b^4}$

37. $(\sqrt{2} + 3)(\sqrt{2} - 2)$

38. $(\sqrt{7} + 5)(\sqrt{7} - 3)$

39. $(2\sqrt{3} - 3)(3\sqrt{2} + 2)$

40. $(\sqrt{5} - 1)(\sqrt{5} + 2)$

41. $(\sqrt{2} - \sqrt{3})^2$

42. $(\sqrt{3} + \sqrt{5})^2$

43. $(\sqrt{8} - 2\sqrt{2})(\sqrt{2} + 2\sqrt{8})$

44. $(\sqrt{x} + 2\sqrt{y})(\sqrt{x} - 3\sqrt{y})$

45. $(\sqrt{3x} + \sqrt{2y})(\sqrt{3x} - 2\sqrt{2y})$

46. $(\sqrt{2a} + \sqrt{b})(\sqrt{3ab} + 2)$

47. $(\sqrt[3]{2x} + 3)(\sqrt[3]{2x} - 3)$

48. $(\sqrt[3]{xy^2} - 3)(\sqrt[3]{x^2y} + 2)$

49. $(\sqrt[3]{a^4} + \sqrt[3]{b^2})(\sqrt[3]{a^2} - 2\sqrt[3]{b^4})$

50. $(\sqrt[4]{x^2y^3} + 2\sqrt[4]{x^5y})(\sqrt[4]{x^2} - \sqrt[4]{y^3})$

In Exercises 51–72 rationalize the denominator.

51. $\dfrac{3}{\sqrt{2} + 3}$

52. $\dfrac{2}{\sqrt{5} - 2}$

53. $\dfrac{-3}{\sqrt{7} - 9}$

54. $\dfrac{2}{\sqrt{3} - 4}$

55. $\dfrac{2}{\sqrt{x} + 3}$

56. $\dfrac{3}{\sqrt{x} - 5}$

57. $\dfrac{-3}{3\sqrt{a} + 1}$

58. $\dfrac{-4}{2\sqrt{x} - 2}$

59. $\dfrac{4}{2 - \sqrt{2y}}$

60. $\dfrac{-3}{5 + \sqrt{5y}}$

61. $\dfrac{\sqrt{8}}{\sqrt{2} + 2}$

62. $\dfrac{\sqrt{3}}{\sqrt{3} - 5}$

63. $\dfrac{\sqrt{2} + 1}{\sqrt{2} - 1}$

64. $\dfrac{\sqrt{5} - 1}{\sqrt{5} + 1}$

65. $\dfrac{\sqrt{5} + \sqrt{3}}{\sqrt{5} - \sqrt{3}}$

66. $\dfrac{\sqrt{6} + \sqrt{2}}{\sqrt{3} - \sqrt{2}}$

67. $\dfrac{\sqrt{x}}{\sqrt{x} + \sqrt{y}}$

68. $\dfrac{2\sqrt{a}}{\sqrt{2x} + \sqrt{y}}$

69. $\dfrac{\sqrt{a} + 1}{2\sqrt{a} - \sqrt{b}}$

70. $\dfrac{4\sqrt{x} - \sqrt{y}}{\sqrt{x} + \sqrt{y}}$

71. $\dfrac{2\sqrt{x} + \sqrt{y}}{\sqrt{2x} - \sqrt{y}}$

72. $\dfrac{3\sqrt{a} - \sqrt{3b}}{\sqrt{2a} + \sqrt{b}}$

In Exercises 73 and 74 demonstrate the result by providing real values for x and y and a positive integer value for n.

*73. $\sqrt{x} + \sqrt{y} \neq \sqrt{x + y}$

*74. $\sqrt[n]{x^n + y^n} \neq x + y$

8.6   Complex Numbers

One of the central problems in algebra is to find solutions to a given polynomial equation. A key difficulty is that even a simple polynomial equation such as

$$x^2 = -4$$

has no solution, since the square of a real number is always nonnegative.

To resolve this problem, mathematicians created a new number system built upon an "imaginary unit" i, defined by $i = \sqrt{-1}$. If we square both sides of the equation $i = \sqrt{-1}$, we have $i^2 = -1$, a result that cannot be obtained with real numbers. By definition,

$$i = \sqrt{-1}$$
$$i^2 = -1$$

We also assume that i behaves according to all the algebraic laws we have already developed (with the exception of the rules for inequalities for real numbers). This allows us to simplify higher powers of i by expressing the power as 1, -1, or $-i$.

$$i^3 = i^2 \cdot i = (-1)i = -i$$
$$i^4 = i^2 \cdot i^2 = (-1)(-1) = 1$$

Now it's easy to simplify i^n when n is any natural number. Since $i^4 = 1$, we simply seek the highest multiple of 4 that is less than or equal to n. For example,

$$i^5 = i^4 \cdot i = (1) \cdot i = i$$
$$i^{27} = i^{24} \cdot i^3 = (i^4)^6 \cdot i^3 = (1)^6 \cdot i^3 = i^3 = -1$$

Example 1   Working with the Imaginary Unit i
Simplify.

(a) i^{101} (b) $-i^{74}$ (c) i^{36} (d) i^{51}

Solution

(a) $i^{101} = i^{100} \cdot i = (i^4)^{25} \cdot i = i$

(b) $-i^{74} = -i^{72} \cdot i^2 = -(i^4)^{18} \cdot i^2 = -(1)^{18} \cdot i^2 = (-1)(-1) = 1$

(c) $i^{36} = (i^4)^9 = (1)^9 = 1$

(d) $i^{51} = i^{48} \cdot i^3 = (i^4)^{12} \cdot i^3 = (1)^{12} \cdot i^3 = i^3 = -i$

✔ **Progress Check 1**

Simplify.

(a) i^{22} (b) i^{15} (c) i^{29} (d) i^{200}

Answers

(a) -1 (b) $-i$ (c) i (d) 1

It is also easy to write square roots of negative numbers in terms of i. For example,

$$\sqrt{-25} = i\sqrt{25} = 5i$$

because $(5i)^2 = 5^2 i^2 = (25)(-1) = -25$, and, in general, we define

$$\sqrt{-a} = i\sqrt{a} \quad \text{for } a > 0$$

Any number in the form bi, where b is a real number, is called an **imaginary number**.

Warning

$$\sqrt{-4}\sqrt{-9} \neq \sqrt{36}$$

The rule $\sqrt{a} \cdot \sqrt{b} = \sqrt{ab}$ holds only when $a \geq 0$ and $b \geq 0$. Instead, write

$$\sqrt{-4}\sqrt{-9} = 2i \cdot 3i = 6i^2 = -6$$

Having created imaginary numbers, we next combine real and imaginary numbers. We say that $a + bi$, where a and b are real numbers, is a **complex number**. The number a is called the **real part** of $a + bi$, and b is called the **imaginary part**. The following are examples of complex numbers.

$3 + 2i$	$a = 3, b = 2$	$2 - i$	$a = 2, b = -1$
5	$a = 5, b = 0$	$-2i$	$a = 0, b = -2$
$2 - 3i$	$a = 2, b = -3$	$-5 - \dfrac{1}{2}i$	$a = -5, b = -\dfrac{1}{2}$
$-\dfrac{1}{3}$	$a = -\dfrac{1}{3}, b = 0$	$\dfrac{4}{5} + \dfrac{1}{5}i$	$a = \dfrac{4}{5}, b = \dfrac{1}{5}$

Note that every real number a can be written as a complex number by choosing $b = 0$. Thus,

$$a = a + 0i$$

We see that the real number system is a subset of the complex number system. The desire to find solutions to every quadratic equation has led mathematicians to create a more comprehensive number system, which incorporates all previous number systems.

Will you have to learn still more number systems? The answer, fortunately, is a resounding "No!" We will show in a later chapter that complex numbers are all that we need to provide solutions to any polynomial equation.

Example 2   Radicals and Complex Numbers
Write as a complex number.

(a) $-\dfrac{1}{2}$ (b) $\sqrt{-9}$ (c) $-1 - \sqrt{-4}$

Solution

(a) $-\dfrac{1}{2} = -\dfrac{1}{2} + 0i$

(b) $\sqrt{-9} = i\sqrt{9} = 3i = 0 + 3i$

(c) $-1 - \sqrt{-4} = -1 - i\sqrt{4} = -1 - 2i$

✔ Progress Check 2
Write as a complex number.

(a) 0.2 (b) $-\sqrt{-3}$ (c) $3 - \sqrt{-9}$

Answers
(a) $0.2 + 0i$ (b) $0 - i\sqrt{3}$ (c) $3 - 3i$

Operations with Complex Numbers

We say two complex numbers are **equal** if their real parts are equal and their imaginary parts are equal.

Equality of Complex Numbers

$$a + bi = c + di \text{ if } a = c \text{ and } b = d$$

Thus, $x + 3i = 6 - yi$ if $x = 6$ and $y = -3$.

We add and subtract the complex numbers $3 + 4i$ and $2 - i$ by combining like terms; that is, we combine the real parts and we combine the imaginary parts.

$$(3 + 4i) + (2 - i) = (3 + 2) + (4 - 1)i = 5 + 3i$$
$$(3 + 4i) - (2 - i) = (3 - 2) + (4 + 1)i = 1 + 5i$$

Addition and Subtraction of Complex Numbers

$$(a + bi) + (c + di) = (a + c) + (b + d)i$$
$$(a + bi) - (c + di) = (a - c) + (b - d)i$$

Note that the sum or difference of two complex numbers is again a complex number.

Example 3 Addition and Subtraction of Complex Numbers
Perform the indicated operations.

(a) $(7 - 2i) + (4 - 3i)$ (b) $3i + (-7 + 5i)$
(c) $(-11 + 5i) - (9 + i)$ (d) $14 - (3 - 8i)$

Solution
(a) $(7 - 2i) + (4 - 3i) = (7 + 4) + (-2 - 3)i = 11 - 5i$
(b) $3i + (-7 + 5i) = (0 - 7) + (3 + 5)i = -7 + 8i$
(c) $(-11 + 5i) - (9 + i) = (-11 - 9) + (5 - 1)i = -20 + 4i$
(d) $14 - (3 - 8i) = (14 - 3) + (0 + 8)i = 11 + 8i$

✔ **Progress Check 3**

Perform the indicated operations.

(a) $(-9 + 3i) + (6 - 2i)$ (b) $(-17 + i) + 15$
(c) $(2 - 3i) - (9 - 4i)$ (d) $7i - (-3 + 9i)$

Answers
(a) $-3 + i$ (b) $-2 + i$ (c) $-7 + i$ (d) $3 - 2i$

Multiplication of complex numbers is analogous to multiplication of polynomials. The distributive law is used to form all the products, and the substitution $i^2 = -1$ is used to simplify. For example,

$$5i(2 - 3i) = 5i(2) - (5i)(3i) = 10i - 15i^2$$
$$= 10i - 15(-1) = 15 + 10i$$
$$(2 + 3i)(3 - 5i) = 2(3 - 5i) + 3i(3 - 5i)$$
$$= 6 - 10i + 9i - 15i^2$$
$$= 6 - i - 15(-1)$$
$$= 21 - i$$

In general,

$$
\begin{aligned}
(a + bi)(c + di) &= a(c + di) + bi(c + di)\\
&= ac + adi + bci + bdi^2\\
&= ac + (ad + bc)i + bd(-1)\\
&= (ac - bd) + (ad + bc)i
\end{aligned}
$$

Thus,

Multiplication of Complex Numbers

$$
(a + bi)(c + di) = (ac - bd) + (ad + bc)i
$$

This result is significant because it demonstrates that the product of two complex numbers is again a complex number. It need not be memorized; simply use the distributive law to form all the products and the substitution $i^2 = -1$ to simplify.

Example 4   Multiplication of Complex Numbers
Find the product of $(2 - 3i)$ and $(7 + 5i)$.

Solution

$$
\begin{aligned}
(2 - 3i)(7 + 5i) &= 2(7 + 5i) - 3i(7 + 5i)\\
&= 14 + 10i - 21i - 15i^2\\
&= 14 - 11i - 15(-1)\\
&= 29 - 11i
\end{aligned}
$$

✔ Progress Check 4
Find the product.

(a) $(-3 - i)(4 - 2i)$ (b) $(-4 - 2i)(2 - 3i)$

Answers
(a) $-14 + 2i$ (b) $-14 + 8i$

Complex Conjugate

The complex number $a - bi$ is called the **conjugate** of the complex number $a + bi$. We see that

$$
\begin{aligned}
(a + bi)(a - bi) &= a(a - bi) + bi(a - bi)\\
&= a^2 - abi + abi - b^2i^2\\
&= a^2 - b^2(-1)\\
&= a^2 + b^2
\end{aligned}
$$

which is a real number. The following result will be helpful in the division of complex numbers.

The product of a complex number and its conjugate is a real number.
$$(a + bi)(a - bi) = a^2 + b^2$$

Example 5   Working with the Complex Conjugate

Multiply by the conjugate of the given complex number.

(a) $6 - i$ (b) $-3i$ (c) 4

Solution

(a) The conjugate of $6 - i$ is $6 + i$, and we have
$$(6 - i)(6 + i) = 36 - i^2 = 36 + 1 = 37$$

(b) The conjugate of $0 - 3i$ is $0 + 3i$. Thus,
$$(-3i)(3i) = -9i^2 = 9$$

(c) Since $4 = 4 + 0i$, the conjugate of $4 + 0i$ is $4 - 0i = 4$. Thus, the complex conjugate of a real number is the real number itself. Hence
$$(4)(4) = 16$$

✔ **Progress Check 5**

Multiply by the conjugate of the given complex number.

(a) $3 + 2i$ (b) $-\sqrt{2} - 3i$ (c) $4i$ (d) -7

Answers

(a) 13   (b) 11   (c) 16   (d) 49

We can now demonstrate that the quotient of two complex numbers is also a complex number. The quotient

$$\frac{q + ri}{s + ti}, \quad s + ti \neq 0$$

can be written in the form $a + bi$ by multiplying both numerator and denominator by $s - ti$, the conjugate of the denominator. We then have

$$\frac{q + ri}{s + ti} = \frac{q + ri}{s + ti} \cdot \frac{s - ti}{s - ti} = \frac{(qs + rt) + (rs - qt)i}{s^2 + t^2}$$

$$= \frac{qs + rt}{s^2 + t^2} + \frac{(rs - qt)}{s^2 + t^2} i$$

which is a complex number of the form $a + bi$. Thus, we have the following result:

Early Mathematicians' Views of Complex Numbers

When mathematicians in the middle of the sixteenth century tried to solve certain quadratic equations by completing the square, they found themselves, much to their distress, having to deal with the square root of a negative quantity. For example, in 1545 Girolamo Cardano (see also Section 10.3) solved the problem of dividing the number 10 into two parts whose product is 40. If one of the parts is x, then the other part is $10 - x$, and we must solve the equation $x(10 - x) = 40$. Using methods we will describe in Chapter 9, Cardano obtained the roots

$$5 + \sqrt{-15} \quad \text{and} \quad 5 - \sqrt{-15}$$

This frustrated him terribly since he had obtained an answer that was "nonsense." He wrote, "So progresses arithmetic subtlety the end of which, as is said, is as refined as it is useless." (See Morris Klein, *Mathematical Thought From Ancient to Modern Times*, Oxford Press, New York, 1972.)

Other famous mathematicians at that time also rejected complex numbers as worthless and fictitious objects, and in fact it was the philosopher and scientist René Descartes who called them "imaginary." It was not until the 1700s that these numbers began to be understood and used. Those earlier mathematicians would be very surprised to learn that complex numbers have been used in thousands of applications ranging from problems in aerodynamics to explanations of the inner workings of the atom.

Division of Complex Numbers

$$\frac{q + ri}{s + ti} = \frac{qs + rt}{s^2 + t^2} + \frac{(rs - qt)}{s^2 + t^2}i, \quad s + ti \neq 0$$

Example 6   Division of Complex Numbers

Write in the form $a + bi$.

(a) $\dfrac{-2 + 3i}{3 - i}$ (b) $\dfrac{2i}{2 + 5i}$ (c) $\dfrac{1 - i}{2i}$

Solution

(a) $\dfrac{-2 + 3i}{3 - i} = \dfrac{-2 + 3i}{3 - i} \cdot \dfrac{3 + i}{3 + i}$ Multiplying numerator and denominator by the conjugate $3 + i$ of the denominator

$\qquad = \dfrac{-6 - 2i + 9i + 3i^2}{9 + 3i - 3i - i^2} = \dfrac{-6 + 7i + 3(-1)}{9 - (-1)}$

$\qquad = \dfrac{-9 + 7i}{10} = -\dfrac{9}{10} + \dfrac{7}{10}i$

(b) $\dfrac{2i}{2 + 5i} = \dfrac{2i}{2 + 5i} \cdot \dfrac{2 - 5i}{2 - 5i}$ Multiplying numerator and denominator by the conjugate $2 - 5i$ of the denominator

$$= \frac{4i - 10i^2}{4 - 10i + 10i - 25i^2} = \frac{4i - 10(-1)}{4 - 25(-1)}$$

$$= \frac{10 + 4i}{29} = \frac{10}{29} + \frac{4}{29}i$$

(c) $\dfrac{1 - i}{2i} = \dfrac{1 - i}{2i} \cdot \dfrac{-2i}{-2i}$ Multiplying numerator and denominator by the conjugate $-2i$ of the denominator

$$= \frac{-2i + 2(-1)}{-4i^2} = \frac{-2i - 2}{4}$$

$$= -\frac{1}{2} - \frac{1}{2}i$$

✔ Progress Check 6

Write in the form $a + bi$.

(a) $\dfrac{4 - 2i}{5 + 2i}$ (b) $\dfrac{3}{2 - 3i}$ (c) $\dfrac{-3i}{3 + 5i}$

Answers

(a) $\dfrac{16}{29} - \dfrac{18}{29}i$ (b) $\dfrac{6}{13} + \dfrac{9}{13}i$ (c) $-\dfrac{15}{34} - \dfrac{9}{34}i$

The reciprocal of a nonzero complex number $s + ti$ can also be written in the form $a + bi$ by multiplying numerator and denominator by $s - ti$, the conjugate of the denominator. We will let the student verify that we obtain the following result.

The Reciprocal of a Complex Number

$$\frac{1}{s + ti} = \frac{s}{s^2 + t^2} - \frac{t}{s^2 + t^2}i, \quad s + ti \neq 0$$

Example 7   Finding the Reciprocal of a Complex Number

Write the reciprocal in the form $a + bi$.

(a) $2 - 2i$ (b) $3i$

Solution

(a) The reciprocal is

$$\frac{1}{2 - 2i}$$

Multiplying both numerator and denominator by the conjugate $2 + 2i$ of the denominator, we have

$$\frac{1}{2-2i} \cdot \frac{2+2i}{2+2i} = \frac{2+2i}{4-4i^2} = \frac{2+2i}{4+4}$$

$$= \frac{2+2i}{8} = \frac{1}{4} + \frac{1}{4}i$$

Verify that the product of the original complex number and its reciprocal equals 1, that is, $(2-2i)(\frac{1}{4} + \frac{1}{4}i) = 1 + 0i = 1$.

(b) The reciprocal is $\dfrac{1}{3i}$ and

$$\frac{1}{3i} = \frac{1}{3i} \cdot \frac{-3i}{-3i} = \frac{-3i}{-9i^2} = \frac{-3i}{9} = -\frac{1}{3}i$$

It is easy to see that $(3i)\left(-\dfrac{1}{3}i\right) = -i^2 = 1$.

✔ **Progress Check 7**

Write the reciprocal in the form $a + bi$.

(a) $3 - i$ (b) $1 + 3i$ (c) $-2i$

Answers

(a) $\dfrac{3}{10} + \dfrac{1}{10}i$ (b) $\dfrac{1}{10} - \dfrac{3}{10}i$ (c) $\dfrac{1}{2}i$

Why have mathematicians created complex numbers? In the next chapter we will show that complex numbers are indispensable in solving second-degree equations. Beyond that, advanced mathematics in science and engineering has many uses for complex numbers. The real number system simply isn't adequate.

Exercise Set 8.6

In Exercises 1–14 simplify.

1. i^{60}

2. i^{58}

3. i^{27}

4. i^{83}

5. $-i^{48}$

6. $-i^{54}$

7. $-i^{33}$

8. $-i^{95}$

9. i^{-15}

10. i^{-84}

11. $-i^{-26}$

12. $-i^{39}$

13. $-i^{-25}$

14. $i^{8/3}$ [*Hint:* $(i^8)^{1/3}$]

In Exercises 15–30 write each complex number in the form $a + bi$.

15. 2

16. -4

17. $-\dfrac{1}{2}$

18. -0.3

19. $\sqrt{-16}$

20. $\sqrt{-25}$

21. $-\sqrt{-5}$

22. $\sqrt{-8}$

23. $-\sqrt{-36}$

24. $-\sqrt{-18}$

25. $2 + \sqrt{-16}$

26. $3 - \sqrt{-49}$

27. $-\dfrac{1}{3} - \sqrt{-72}$

28. $-2 + \sqrt{-128}$

29. $0.3 - \sqrt{-98}$

30. $-0.5 + \sqrt{-32}$

In Exercises 31−60 perform the indicated operations and write the answer in the form $a + bi$.

31. $2i + (3 - i)$

32. $-3i + (2 - 5i)$

33. $2 + (6 - i)$

34. $3 - (2 - 3i)$

35. $2 + 3i + (3 - 2i)$

36. $(3 - 2i) - \left(2 + \dfrac{1}{2}i\right)$

37. $-3 - 5i - (2 - i)$

38. $\left(\dfrac{1}{2} - i\right) + \left(1 - \dfrac{2}{3}i\right)$

39. $(2i)(4i)$

40. $(-3i)(6i)$

41. $-2i(3 + i)$

42. $3i(2 - i)$

43. $i\left(-\dfrac{1}{2} + i\right)$

44. $\dfrac{i}{2}\left(\dfrac{4 - i}{2}\right)$

45. $(2 + 3i)(2 + 3i)$

46. $(1 + i)(-3 + 2i)$

47. $(2 - i)(2 + i)$

48. $(5 + i)(2 - 3i)$

49. $(-2 - 2i)(-4 - 3i)$

50. $(2 + 5i)(1 - 3i)$

51. $(3 - 2i)(2 - i)$

52. $(4 - 3i)(2 + 3i)$

53. $(3 + 2i)^2$

54. $(2 - 5i)^2$

55. $(3 - i)^2$

56. $(5 + 3i)^2$

57. $2i^2$

58. $(2i)^2$

59. $-4i^2$

60. $(-4i)^2$

In Exercises 61−66 multiply by the conjugate and simplify.

61. $2 - i$

62. $3 + i$

63. $3 + 4i$

64. $2 - 3i$

65. $-4 - 2i$

66. $5 + 2i$

In Exercises 67−76 perform the indicated division and write the answer in the form $a + bi$.

67. $\dfrac{2 + 5i}{1 - 3i}$

68. $\dfrac{1 + 3i}{2 - 5i}$

69. $\dfrac{3 - 4i}{3 + 4i}$

70. $\dfrac{4 - 3i}{4 + 3i}$

71. $\dfrac{3 - 2i}{2 - i}$

72. $\dfrac{2 - 3i}{3 - i}$

73. $\dfrac{2 + 5i}{3i}$

74. $\dfrac{5 - 2i}{-3i}$

75. $\dfrac{4i}{2 + i}$

76. $\dfrac{-2i}{3 - i}$

In Exercises 77−84 find the reciprocal and write it in the form $a + bi$.

77. $3 + 2i$

78. $4 + 3i$

79. $\dfrac{1}{2} - i$

80. $1 - \dfrac{1}{3}i$

81. $-7i$

82. $-5i$

83. $\sqrt{2} - i$

84. $2 - \sqrt{3}i$

*85. Show that the reciprocal of $s + ti$ is

$$\dfrac{s}{s^2 + t^2} - \dfrac{t}{s^2 + t^2}i$$

*86. Show that the commutative law of addition holds for the set of complex numbers.

*87. Show that the commutative law of multiplication holds for the set of complex numbers.

*88. Show that $0 + 0i$ is the additive identity and $1 + 0i$ is the multiplicative identity for the set of complex numbers.

*89. Show that $-a - bi$ is the additive inverse of the complex number $a + bi$.

*90. Demonstrate the distributive property for the set of complex numbers.

*91. For what values of x is $\sqrt{x - 3}$ a real number?

*92. For what values of y is $\sqrt{2y - 10}$ a real number?

93. Your graphing calculator probably has an "i" key. Use it to find the following product (see the graphic below for an example).

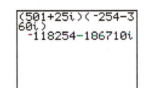

94. Use your graphing calculator to find the quotient:

$$\dfrac{10^6 - 14^{-2}i}{10^9 - 13^{-2}i}$$

95. Use your graphing calculator to find the quotient:

$$\dfrac{1000 + 1000i}{1001 - 1001i}$$

8.7   Critical Thinking Problems

In this section we will work with some interesting problems that you may enjoy "playing" with your peers. One type involves reading minds. Like a magician, you ask your friends to choose a number but not tell you what that number is. Then you ask them to do some mathematical operations. In the end you will "guess" (know) what the original number is.

Let's do an example and see how this fun trick works.

Example 1   Mind Reading

I ask you to pick any number. Then you double it, add 1, and square the result. Now you subtract 1 and divide by 4. Finally, subtract the square of the number you started with. The result is the number you started with.

Solution

Did I get the right answer? How do I know?

Well, the trick is behind the math. We may translate these steps in algebraic expressions. Let's translate these sentences into algebraic expressions.

I don't know what number you chose; how will I find it? Let x represent the number you chose.

Then you double it:	$2x$
Add 1:	$(2x + 1)$
Square the result:	$(2x + 1)^2$
Subtract 1:	$(2x + 1)^2 - 1$
Divide by 4:	$\dfrac{(2x + 1)^2 - 1}{4}$
Subtract the square of the number you started with:	$\dfrac{(2x + 1)^2 - 1}{4} - x^2$

Let's simplify this expression.

$$\frac{(2x + 1)^2 - 1}{4} - x^2 = \frac{(4x^2 + 4x + 1) - 1}{4} - x^2 \quad \text{By squaring } (2x + 1)^2 = 4x^2 + 4x + 1$$

$$= \frac{4x^2 + 4x}{4} - x^2 \quad \text{Simplifying the numerator}$$

$$= \frac{4(x^2 + x)}{4} - x^2 \quad \text{Factoring out 4 in the numerator}$$

$$= (x^2 + x) - x^2 \quad \text{4 is canceled}$$

$$= x \quad \text{Simplifying the expression}$$

We see that if we simplify the expression

$$\frac{(2x + 1)^2 - 1}{4} - x^2$$

CHAPTER 8 ■ Exponents, Radicals, and Complex Numbers **339**

we get x, which is the number we started with. It doesn't matter what number is chosen—you will always get x (the number you start with).

Now, develop your own mind-reading trick.

✔ Progress Check 1

(a) Choose a nonzero number and then add 2. Multiply the result by a number 2 less than the number you started with. Now add 4 and divide by the square of the number you started with. The result is 1.

(b) Choose two nonzero numbers. Add these two numbers and square the result. Subtract the square of each number. Now divide the result by twice the product of the two numbers. The result is 1.

Answers

(a) $\dfrac{(x+2)(x-2)+4}{x^2} = 1$ (b) $\dfrac{(x+y)^2 - x^2 - y^2}{2xy} = 1$

In the next example, we will learn how to find the average value. We use the word average in many different contexts. One type of average is the **arithmetic mean.** The arithmetic mean of the numbers of $x_1, x_2, x_3, x_4, \ldots x_n$ is given by

$$\text{(Arithmetic) Mean: } \bar{x} = \frac{x_1 + x_2 + \ldots + x_n}{n}$$

(We often use $\bar{x}$ to represent the mean.)

If your math exam scores are 78, 86, 70, and 96, then your average for these four exams is

$$\frac{78 + 86 + 70 + 96}{4} = \frac{330}{4} = 82.5$$

There is another type of average called the **weighted mean.** The weighted mean of the n numbers of $x_1, x_2, x_3, x_4, \ldots x_n$ that are weighted by the respective factors $w_1, w_2, w_3, w_4, \ldots w_n$ is given by

$$weighted\ mean = \frac{x_1 \cdot w_1 + x_2 \cdot w_2 + x_3 \cdot w_3 + x_4 \cdot w_4 + \ldots + x_n \cdot w_n}{w_1 + w_2 + w_3 + w_4 + \ldots + w_n} = \frac{\sum_{i=1}^{i=n}(x_i \cdot w_i)}{100}$$

Suppose your three exam scores are 78, 80, and 62 and your final exam is 94. If each exam counts 20% and the final exam counts 40%, then your weighted average is

$$= \frac{78 \cdot 20 + 76 \cdot 20 + 62 \cdot 20 + 94 \cdot 40}{100}$$

$$= \frac{1{,}560 + 1{,}520 + 1{,}240 + 3{,}760}{100}$$

$$= \frac{8{,}080}{100}$$

$$= 80.8$$

Since the final exam counts 40%, your weighted average is higher than the other exam scores.

Example 2   Find the Mean

In this example you will determine what grade you need on a final exam in order to achieve a specific overall class grade.

(a) Suppose there are four exams and one comprehensive final exam in Algebra 1 class. Each exam is 100 points and the final is 200 points. In order to get an A grade you need to have at least 90%, at least 80% to get a B, and at least 70% to get a C. If your exam scores are 78, 85, 68, and 95, find the minimum scores that you need on the final exam in order to get a passing grade of A, B, or C. Is it possible to get a passing grade?

(b) Jamie's three exam scores are 80, 75, and 62 in biology class. Her grade in class is determined by three exams and one comprehensive final exam. If each exam counts 18%, what does she need to get on the final exam in order to pass this class with a B grade? (The range 80–89% equals a B.)

Solution

(a) There are four exams worth 100 points each and one comprehensive final exam worth 200 points. The possible total points is 600 points.

In order to get an A grade, you need to get at least 90%.

$$90\% \text{ of } 600 \text{ points} = (0.9)(600) = 540 \qquad \text{Convert } \% \text{ into a decimal and "of" represents "product"}$$

In order to get a B grade, you need to get at least 80%.

$$80\% \text{ of } 600 \text{ points} = (0.8)(600) = 480 \qquad \text{Convert } \% \text{ into a decimal and "of" represents "product"}$$

In order to get a C grade, you need to get at least 70%.

$$70\% \text{ of } 600 \text{ points} = (0.7)(600) = 420 \qquad \text{Convert } \% \text{ into a decimal and "of" represents "product"}$$

Before the final exam you have $78 + 85 + 68 + 95 = 326$ points. In order to get an A grade, you must get at least $540 - 326 = 214$ points on the final exam. That is not possible since the final exam is only worth 200 points total.

In order to get a B grade, you must get at least $480 - 326 = 154$ points on the final exam.

In order to get a C grade, you must get at least $420 - 326 = 94$ points on the final exam.

Therefore, it is possible to get a B grade if you get at least 154 points on the final exam, and a C grade if you get at least 94 points on the final exam.

(b) Let x = the minimum final exam score Jamie must get.

Since each exam counts 18%, $3 \cdot (18\%) = 54\%$. Thus, the final exam counts $100\% - 54\% = 46\%$. Then the weighted mean is

$$\frac{(80) \cdot (18) + (75) \cdot (18) + (62) \cdot (18) + (x) \cdot (46)}{100} = 80$$

Solving this equation for x,

$$\frac{3{,}906 + 46x}{100} = 80$$

$$3{,}906 + 46x = (80)(100)$$

$$3{,}906 + 46x = 8{,}000 \qquad \text{Multiplying both sides by 100}$$

$$46x = 4{,}094$$

$$\frac{46x}{46} = \frac{4{,}094}{46} \qquad \text{Dividing both sides by 46}$$

$$x = 89$$

Therefore, Jamie must get at least 89 points on the final exam in order to get a B grade.

Now try the following problems to check whether you understand the concepts of mean and weighted mean.

✔ Progress Check 2

(a) You surveyed 10 local high school students to find out how many hours they spend on the internet per day. Given the number of hours shown below, find the average number of hours the students spent on the internet per day.

2.5	4.2	1.2	2.0	3.6	2.4	5.1	0.5	1.0	2.5

(b) In beginning algebra class, your midterm scores are 82 and 76. Your quiz score is 90, your homework score is 84, and your final exam score is 78. Each midterm counts 25%, the quiz counts 10%, homework counts 10%, and the final exam counts 30%. Find the weighted mean.

Answers

(a) 2.5 hours   (b) 80.3

Example 3   Finding the Length of a Pendulum

The period of the pendulum varies directly as the square root of the length of the pendulum. Find the change in the length of the pendulum if the period is tripled.

Solution

The period of the pendulum is T and the length of the pendulum is l. The relationship between the period and the length of the pendulum can be expressed as

$$T = k \cdot \sqrt{l},\, (k \neq 0)$$

We want to know the change in the length of the pendulum when the period is tripled. So, let's solve the equation for l.

$$T = k \cdot \sqrt{l}$$

$$\frac{T}{k} = \frac{k \cdot \sqrt{l}}{k}$$

$$\frac{T}{k} = \sqrt{l}$$

$$\left(\frac{T}{k}\right)^2 = \left(\sqrt{l}\right)^2$$

$$l = \left(\frac{T}{k}\right)^2 = \frac{T^2}{k^2}$$

If we triple the period of the pendulum then we can write $period = 3T$. By substituting $period = 3T$ into the equation,

$$l_{new} = \left(\frac{3T}{k}\right)^2 = \frac{(3T)^2}{(k)^2}$$

$$= \frac{9T^2}{k^2}$$

$$= 9\left(\frac{T^2}{k^2}\right)$$

$$= 9 \cdot l$$

If we triple the period of the pendulum, we need to multiply the length of the pendulum by 9.

✔ Progress Check 3

The period of the pendulum is proportional to the square root of the length of the pendulum.

(a) If the period is multiplied by $\frac{1}{2}$, what happens to the length of the pendulum?

(b) If the period is doubled, what happens to the length of the pendulum?

(c) If the period is multiplied by $\frac{1}{4}$, what happens to the length of the pendulum?

Answers

(a) $l_{new} = \frac{1}{4} \cdot l$

(b) $l_{new} = 4 \cdot l$

(c) $l_{new} = \frac{1}{16} \cdot l$

■ ■ ■

Terms and Symbols

complex number, $a + bi$

conjugate of a complex number

cube root, $\sqrt[3]{a}$

imaginary number

imaginary part

imaginary unit, i

index

nth root, $\sqrt[n]{a}$

principal nth root

principal square root

radical form

radical sign, $\sqrt{}$

radicand

rationalizing the denominator

real part

reciprocal of a complex number

simplified radical

square root, $\sqrt{a}$

Key Ideas for Review

Topic	Key Idea
Exponents	The laws of exponents hold for all rational exponents.
zero exponent	Zero as an exponent produces a result of 1. Thus, $a^0 = 1$, for $a \neq 0$.
negative exponents	Since $$a^{-m} = \frac{1}{a^m} \quad \text{and} \quad a^m = \frac{1}{a^{-m}}, \qquad a \neq 0$$ we can change the sign of the exponent by moving the factor from numerator to denominator or from denominator to numerator.
Radicals	Radicals are an alternate means of writing rational exponent forms. Thus, $$a^{m/n} = \sqrt[n]{a^m} = (\sqrt[n]{a})^m, \qquad \text{if } a \geq 0$$
identities	The identities $$(\sqrt[n]{a})^n = \sqrt[n]{a^n} = \begin{cases} a & \text{if } n \text{ is odd} \\ |a| & \text{if } n \text{ is even} \end{cases}$$ $$\sqrt[n]{ab} = \sqrt[n]{a}\,\sqrt[n]{b}$$ $$\sqrt[n]{\frac{a}{b}} = \frac{\sqrt[n]{a}}{\sqrt[n]{b}}, \qquad b \neq 0$$ are useful in simplifying expressions with radicals when all radicals denote real numbers.
simplified form	A radical expression is in simplified form if (a) $\sqrt[n]{x^m}$ has $m < n$, x prime, (b) $\sqrt[n]{x^m}$ has no common factors between m and n, and (c) the denominator does not contain a radical.
addition and subtraction	Addition and subtraction of radical expressions can be performed only if exactly the same radical form is involved.
product	The product $(\sqrt[n]{a})(\sqrt[m]{b})$ can be easily simplified if $m = n$.
Imaginary unit i	The identities $i = \sqrt{-1}$ and $i^2 = -1$ can be used to simplify an expression of the form i^n and to rewrite $\sqrt{-a}$ as $i\sqrt{a}$, $a > 0$.
Complex numbers	Every complex number can be written in the form $a + bi$, where a and b are real numbers.
operations	The sum, difference, product, and quotient of two complex numbers can always be expressed in the form $c + di$. (Of course, we cannot divide by zero.)
subsets	The real number system is a subset of the complex number system, since any real number a can be written as $a + 0i$.

Common Errors

1. *Don't* perform intermediate steps on any polynomial, no matter how complicated, that is raised to the zero power, since 1 is the answer.

$$(y^2 + x^2 - 2y + 4)^0 = 1$$

2. Don't confuse negative *numbers* and negative *exponents*. *Don't* write

$$(-2)^{-3} = \frac{1}{2^3} = \frac{1}{8}$$

When the factor is moved to the denominator, only the sign of the exponent changes.

$$(-2)^{-3} = \frac{1}{(-2)^3} = \frac{1}{-8} = -\frac{1}{8}$$

$$-2^{-3} = -\frac{1}{2^3} = -\frac{1}{8}$$

3. *Don't* write

$$\sqrt{4} + \sqrt{60} = \sqrt{64}$$

You can add only if the radical forms are identical:

$$\sqrt{2x} + 5\sqrt{2x} = 6\sqrt{2x}$$

4. *Don't* write

$$\sqrt{-2} \cdot \sqrt{-8} = \sqrt{16} = 4$$

When dealing with negative numbers under the radical sign, first write the expressions in terms of the imaginary unit i:

$$\sqrt{-2} \cdot \sqrt{-8} = (i\sqrt{2})(i\sqrt{8})$$

$$= i^2\sqrt{16} = (-1)(4) = -4$$

5. *Don't* write

$$\sqrt{25} = \pm 5$$

The number indicated by $\sqrt{25}$ is the *positive* square root of 25. Thus,

$$\sqrt{25} = 5 \quad \text{and} \quad -\sqrt{25} = -5$$

6. Remember that

$$\sqrt{x^2} = |x|$$

Don't write

$$\sqrt{x^2} = x$$

unless you know that $x \geq 0$.

Review Exercises

Solutions to exercises whose numbers are in bold are in the Solutions section in the back of the book.

8.1   In Exercises 1–8 simplify, using the properties of exponents.

1. $(x^2)^{3n}$

2. $y^4 y^5$

3. $\left(-\dfrac{a}{b}\right)^5$

4. $(x^3)^4(x^2)^5$

5. $\dfrac{(b^2)^3(b^3)^2}{(b^4)^2}$

6. $[(2a - 1)^2]^5$

7. $(2x + y)^2(2x + y)^3$

8. $\dfrac{(3a^3b^2)^3}{(-2a^4b^3)^4}$

8.2   In Exercises 9–16 use the rules for exponents to simplify. Write the answers using only positive exponents.

9. $(-2)^{-5}$

10. $\dfrac{3}{x^{-3}}$

11. $2y^2y^{-4}$

12. $a^{-4}a^4a^2$

13. $(-3x^3y^{-2})^0$

14. $\dfrac{12a^{-4}b^{-2}}{3a^{-2}b^{-5}}$

15. $\left(\dfrac{2xy^{-2}}{3x^{-2}y^{-3}}\right)^{-4}$

16. $\left(\dfrac{-3x^{-2}y^{-3}}{2x^{-3}y^{-4}}\right)^{-3}$

8.3   In Exercises 17–24 simplify, and write the answer using only positive exponents. Every variable represents a positive real number.

17. $32^{2/5}$

18. $(x^2)^{1/6}$

19. $a^{1/4}a^{2/3}$

20. $\dfrac{81^{1/4}}{81^{5/4}}$

21. $(x^3y^4)^{1/6}$

22. $(x^4y^{2/5})^{-1/2}$

23. $\left(\dfrac{x^{2/3}}{x^{4/3}}\right)^{1/4}$

24. $\left(\dfrac{x^2}{y^{-2/5}}\right)^{-3/2}$

8.4 In Exercises 25−30 write the expression in simplified form. Every variable represents a positive real number.

25. $\sqrt{60}$

26. $\sqrt[3]{\dfrac{125}{27}x^8}$

27. $\dfrac{2}{\sqrt{4x}}$

28. $\dfrac{4ab}{\sqrt[3]{3a^2b}}$

29. $\dfrac{6a^7}{\sqrt{3b}}$

30. $\sqrt[4]{\dfrac{16x^8}{5y^2}}$

8.5 In Exercises 31−34 simplify, and combine terms. Every variable represents a positive real number.

31. $5\sqrt{5} - 2\sqrt{5}$

32. $\sqrt[4]{x^2y^2} + 2\sqrt[4]{x^2y^2}$

33. $\sqrt[3]{3xy^2} + \sqrt[3]{5xy^2}$

34. $\sqrt{\dfrac{xy}{2}} + 2\sqrt{xy}$

In Exercises 35−38 rationalize the denominator.

35. $\dfrac{-3}{3 - \sqrt{x}}$

36. $\dfrac{\sqrt{3x} - 1}{\sqrt{3x} + 1}$

37. $\dfrac{2}{\sqrt{x - y}}$

38. $\dfrac{\sqrt{2ab}}{\sqrt{a} - \sqrt{b}}$

8.6 In Exercises 39−50 perform the indicated operations and write the answer in the form $a + bi$.

39. i^{68}

40. $-i^{29}$

41. $\sqrt{-20}$

42. $2 + \sqrt[3]{-54}$

43. $3i - (4 - 5i)$

44. $(3 + 4i)(3 - 4i)$

45. $(5i)(3 - 2i)$

46. $(4 - 3i)^2$

47. $\dfrac{1}{\sqrt{3} + 2i}$

48. $\dfrac{2 - 3i}{1 + i}$

49. $\dfrac{1}{i}$

50. $\dfrac{i}{1 - i}$

Progress Test 8A

In Problems 1−7 simplify, and write the answer using only positive exponents.

1. $\dfrac{(x + 1)^{2n-1}}{(x + 1)^{n+1}}$

2. $\left(\dfrac{1}{2}x^3y^2\right)^4$

3. $\left(\dfrac{-2xy^3}{5x^2y}\right)^3$

4. $\dfrac{5(a^2 - 2a + 1)^0}{(x^{-2})^3}$

5. $(2x^{2/5} \cdot 4x^{2/5})^{-2}$

6. $\dfrac{x^{-2/3}y^{1/2}}{x^{-2}y^{-3/2}}$

7. $\left(\dfrac{27x^{-6}z^0}{125y^{-3/2}}\right)^{-2/3}$

8. Write $(2y - 1)^{5/2}$ in radical form.

9. Write $\sqrt[3]{6y^5}$ in rational exponent form.

10. Simplify $-\sqrt{32x^4y^9}$.

11. Simplify $\sqrt{\dfrac{x}{5}}$.

12. Simplify $\dfrac{-4a^2b\sqrt[3]{a^7b^6}}{\sqrt[3]{a}}$.

13. Simplify $\sqrt[3]{24} - 3\sqrt[3]{81}$.

14. Simplify $2\sqrt{xy^2} - 6\sqrt{x^2y} + 3\sqrt{xy^2} - 2\sqrt{x^2y}$.

15. Multiply and simplify $3(2\sqrt{x} - 3\sqrt{y})(2\sqrt{x} + 3\sqrt{y})$.

16. Write in the form $a + bi$: $4 - \sqrt{-4}$.

17. Compute $2 + \sqrt{-27} - 3\sqrt{-3}$.

18. Simplify $-i^{47}$.

19. Write in the form $a + bi$: $(-4 - 2i) \div (3 - 4i)$.

20. Write the reciprocal of $4 + 3i$ in the form $a + bi$.

Progress Test 8B

In Problems 1−7 simplify, and write the answer using only positive exponents.

1. $(x^{3n-1})^2$

2. $\left(\dfrac{1}{3}a^2b\right)^3$

3. $\left(\dfrac{-3y^{-2}}{x^{-3}}\right)^{-3}$

4. $\dfrac{4(x+1)^5(2x+1)^0}{(x+1)^6}$

5. $(-2y^{1/3}\cdot 3y^{1/6})^{-3}$

6. $\dfrac{x^{1/2}y^{-1/5}}{x^{-2}y^{3/5}}$

7. $\left(\dfrac{27x^{-3/2}y^{4/5}}{x^{5/2}y^{1/5}}\right)^{-2/5}$

8. Write $(3x+1)^{2/3}$ in radical form.

9. Write $\sqrt[5]{4x^3}$ in rational exponent form.

10. Simplify $-3\sqrt[4]{16x^6z^2}$.

11. Simplify $\sqrt{\dfrac{2x^3}{y}}$.

12. Simplify $\dfrac{-2x^3y^2\sqrt{x^5y^6}}{\sqrt{xy}}$.

13. Simplify $2\sqrt[3]{54}-4\sqrt[3]{16}$.

14. Simplify:

$$-\sqrt{(a-1)b^2}+2\sqrt{(a-1)^3b}-2\sqrt{(a-1)b^2}$$
$$-3\sqrt{(a-1)^3b}$$

15. Multiply and simplify $-2(3\sqrt{a}-\sqrt{b})(2\sqrt{a}-3\sqrt{b})$.

16. Write in the form $a+bi$: $2+\sqrt{-8}$.

17. Compute $-3-3\sqrt{-8}+2\sqrt{-18}$.

18. Simplify $-3i^{25}$.

19. Write in the form $a+bi$: $(2-i)\div(2-3i)$.

20. Write the reciprocal of $3-5i$ in the form $a+bi$.

Chapter 8 Project

Physicists are accustomed to dealing with very large numbers! Without exponents, they would have no convenient way to express or deal with these quantities. For instance, there are about 10^{78} atoms in the observable universe. If all of these atoms contained one proton each (and most of them do) and if there are about 2×10^9 times as many photons in the universe as protons, how many photons are there? You must use the laws of exponents to answer this question.

Look at Exercises 78 and 79 in Section 7.1, and Exercise 81 in Section 8.2.

What will the final fate of the universe be? Some scientists think it will probably keep expanding forever—the galaxies getting farther and farther away from each other. Some, however, think that there may be a "Big Crunch," a sort of reverse Big Bang in which gravitational forces will cause the galaxies to stop moving outward and collapse toward each other again.

Do some research on cosmology, and determine how many atoms of "dark matter" there may be in the universe. What is the ratio of dark matter to bright matter, and how do the laws of exponents help to calculate it? How does this ratio help cosmologists to think about the possibility of a "Big Crunch?"

CHAPTER 9

Second-Degree Equations and Inequalities

*All the effects of nature are only the mathematical conse-
quences of a small number of immutable laws.*

—Pierre-Simon de Laplace

Number theory is a classic area of mathematical investigation. Number theorists hunt for formulas that reveal interesting properties of positive integers. Sometimes, these formulas are arrived at after lengthy study; at other times, they may appear in a flash of insight. Such flashes often happened to the brilliant mathematical prodigy Srinivasa Ramanujan (1887–1920), who is famous for providing remarkably complicated mathematical formulas. No one else has ever been able to derive some of these formulas!

Second-degree equations like the ones we will study in this chapter often play a role in number-theoretic formulas. For instance, how do you find the product of two numbers without multiplying them directly? One way is with the "quarter squares rule," which we will look at in this chapter's project.

■ ■ ■

The function

$$f(x) = ax^2 + bx + c, \quad a \neq 0$$

is called a **quadratic function**. We are interested in finding the **zeros** of the function, that is, the values of x for which $f(x) = 0$. This is equivalent to finding the roots of the equation

$$ax^2 + bx + c = 0, \quad a \neq 0$$

which we call a **quadratic equation** or **second-degree equation in one variable**. We will look at techniques for solving quadratic equations and at applications that lead to this algebraic form. We will also study methods of attacking second-degree inequalities in one variable.

9.1   Solving Quadratic Equations

The Form $ax^2 + c = 0$

When the quadratic equation $ax^2 + bx + c = 0$ has the coefficient $b = 0$, we have an equation of the form

$$2x^2 - 10 = 0$$

which is easily solved. We begin by isolating x^2.

$$2x^2 - 10 = 0$$
$$2x^2 = 10$$
$$x^2 = 5$$

At this point we ask: Is there a number whose square is 5? There are actually two such numbers: $\sqrt{5}$ and $-\sqrt{5}$.

$$x^2 = 5$$
$$x = \pm\sqrt{5}$$

(Note that we have used the shorthand notation, $\pm\sqrt{5}$, as a way of indicating $\sqrt{5}$ and $-\sqrt{5}$. We will see that a quadratic equation always has two solutions.)

Example 1   Solving "Simple" Quadratic Equations
Solve the equation.

(a) $3x^2 - 8 = 0$ (b) $4x^2 + 11 = 0$ (c) $(x - 5)^2 + 9 = 0$

Solution

(a) We isolate and solve for x.

$$3x^2 - 8 = 0$$

$$3x^2 = 8$$

$$x^2 = \frac{8}{3}$$

$$x = \pm\sqrt{\frac{8}{3}} = \pm\frac{2\sqrt{2}}{\sqrt{3}}$$

To attain simplest radical form, we must rationalize the denominator.

$$x = \pm\frac{2\sqrt{2}}{\sqrt{3}} \cdot \frac{\sqrt{3}}{\sqrt{3}} = \pm\frac{2\sqrt{6}}{3} \text{ or } \pm\frac{2}{3}\sqrt{6}$$

(b) We isolate and solve for x.

$$4x^2 + 11 = 0$$

$$4x^2 = -11$$

$$x^2 = -\frac{11}{4}$$

$$x = \pm\sqrt{\frac{-11}{4}} = \pm\frac{i\sqrt{11}}{2}$$

We see that the solutions to a quadratic equation may be complex numbers.

(c) Although this equation is not strictly of the form $ax^2 + c = 0$, we can use the same approach. We see that

$$(x - 5)^2 + 9 = 0$$
$$(x - 5)^2 = -9$$

which implies that

$$x - 5 = \pm\sqrt{-9}$$
$$x - 5 = \pm 3i \qquad \text{Since } (3i)^2 = (-3i)^2 = -9$$
$$x = 5 \pm 3i \qquad \text{Add 5 to both sides.}$$

Thus, the solutions of the given equation are the complex numbers

$$x = 5 + 3i \quad \text{and} \quad x = 5 - 3i$$

Note that the solutions are complex conjugates; we will see that this situation applies in general.

✔ **Progress Check 1**

Solve each equation.

(a) $4x^2 - 9 = 0$ 　　　(b) $2x^2 - 15 = 0$
(c) $5x^2 + 13 = 0$ 　　　(d) $(2x - 7)^2 + 5 = 0$

Answers

(a) $\pm\dfrac{3}{2}$ 　　(b) $\pm\dfrac{\sqrt{30}}{2}$ 　　(c) $\pm\dfrac{i\sqrt{65}}{5}$ 　　(d) $\dfrac{7 \pm i\sqrt{5}}{2}$

Solving by Factoring

Under what circumstances can the product of two numbers be 0? Stated more formally, if $ab = 0$, what must be true of a and b? A little thought will convince you that at least one of the numbers must be zero! In fact, this result is very easy to prove. If we assume that $a \neq 0$, then we can divide both sides by a.

$$ab = 0$$
$$\frac{ab}{a} = \frac{0}{a}$$
$$b = 0$$

Similarly, if we assumed $b \neq 0$, we would conclude that $a = 0$.

> If $ab = 0$, then $a = 0$ or $b = 0$ (or both $a = 0$ and $b = 0$).

This simple theorem provides us with a means for solving quadratic equations whenever we can factor the quadratic into linear factors.

Example 2　Solving a Quadratic Equation by Factoring

Solve by factoring.

(a) $x^2 - 2x - 3 = 0$ 　　　(b) $2x^2 - 3x - 2 = 0$
(c) $3x^2 - 4x = 0$ 　　　(d) $x^2 + x + 1 = 0$

Solution

(a) Factoring, we have

$$x^2 - 2x - 3 = 0$$
$$(x - 3)(x + 1) = 0$$

But the product of two real numbers can equal 0 only if at least one of them is 0. Thus, either

$$x - 3 = 0 \qquad \text{or} \qquad x + 1 = 0$$

So

$$x = 3 \qquad \text{or} \qquad x = -1$$

You can verify that 3 and -1 are both roots of the equation by substituting each of these values back into the original equation.

(b) Factoring, we have

$$2x^2 - 3x - 2 = 0$$
$$(2x + 1)(x - 2) = 0$$

Either

$$2x + 1 = 0 \qquad \text{or} \qquad x - 2 = 0$$

Therefore,

$$x = -\frac{1}{2} \qquad \text{or} \qquad x = 2$$

(c) Factoring, we have

$$3x^2 - 4x = 0$$
$$x(3x - 4) = 0$$

Either

$$x = 0 \qquad \text{or} \qquad 3x - 4 = 0$$

Thus,

$$x = 0 \qquad \text{or} \qquad x = \frac{4}{3}$$

(d) If we attempt to factor $x^2 + x + 1$, we see that the only possible factors with integer coefficients are $(x + 1)$ and $(x - 1)$. However, trying all the possible combinations of these—$(x + 1)(x + 1)$ or $(x - 1)(x - 1)$ or $(x + 1)(x - 1)$—we find that none of them works. We will look at methods for handing this situation, following the progress check.

✔ Progress Check 2

Solve by factoring.

(a) $x^2 + 3x - 10 = 0$ (b) $3x^2 - 11x - 4 = 0$

(c) $4x^2 - x = 0$ (d) $2x^2 + 4x + 1 = 0$

Answers

(a) $-5, 2$ (b) $-\frac{1}{3}, 4$ (c) $0, \frac{1}{4}$ (d) cannot be factored

Completing the Square

We saw in Example 2d that the method of factoring doesn't always work if we restrict ourselves to integer coefficients. However, the following method will enable us to find solutions to *any* quadratic equation. Given an expression such as

$$x^2 + 10x$$

we seek a constant k such that the addition of k^2 will "complete" a perfect square on the left-hand side.

$$x^2 + 10x + k^2 = (x + k)^2 = x^2 + 2kx + k^2$$

Then we must have

$$10x = 2kx$$

from which we see that the constant k that we seek is exactly $\frac{1}{2}$ of the coefficient of x. Thus, in our example, $k = \frac{10}{2} = 5$ and $k^2 = 25$ so

$$x^2 + 10x + 25 = (x + 5)^2$$

This procedure is called **completing the square**.

Example 3   Completing the Square
Complete the square for each of the following.

(a) $x^2 - 6x$ 　　　　　　(b) $x^2 + 3x$

Solution
(a) The coefficient of x is -6 so $k^2 = \left(-\frac{6}{2}\right)^2 = 9$. Then
$$x^2 - 6x + 9 = (x - 3)^2$$

(b) The coefficient of x is 3 and $k^2 = \left(\frac{3}{2}\right)^2 = \frac{9}{4}$. Then
$$x^2 + 3x + \frac{9}{4} = \left(x + \frac{3}{2}\right)^2$$

✔ Progress Check 3

Complete the square for each of the following.

(a) $x^2 + 8x$ 　　　　　　(b) $x^2 - 7x$

Answers

(a) $x^2 + 8x + 16 = (x + 4)^2$

(b) $x^2 - 7x + \dfrac{49}{4} = \left(x - \dfrac{7}{2}\right)^2$

When the coefficient of x^2 in a quadratic equation is 1, the process of completing the square can be used to solve the quadratic.

Example 4 Solving a Quadratic Equation by Completing the Square

Solve the quadratic equation

$$x^2 + 8x - 1 = 0$$

by completing the square.

Solution

Procedure	Example
Step 1. Isolate the constant on one side of the equation.	*Step 1.* $$x^2 + 8x = 1$$
Step 2. Compute k, which is equal to half the coefficient of x.	*Step 2.* $$k = \frac{1}{2}(8) = 4$$
Step 3. Complete the square by adding k^2 to both sides of the equation.	*Step 3.* $$x^2 + 8x + 16 = 1 + 16$$ $$(x + 4)^2 = 17$$
Step 4. Solve for x.	*Step 4.* $$x + 4 = \pm\sqrt{17}$$ $$x = -4 \pm \sqrt{17}$$

✔ Progress Check 4

Solve $x^2 - 3x + 2 = 0$ by completing the square.

Answer

1, 2

By modifying the procedure for completing the square to include the case where the coefficient of x^2 is *not* equal to 1, we can solve any quadratic equation. We now outline and explain each step of the process.

Example 5   Solving a Quadratic Equation by Completing the Square

Solve the quadratic equation $2x^2 - 5x + 4 = 0$ by completing the square.

Solution

Solving $ax^2 + bx + c = 0$ by Completing the Square

Procedure	Example
Step 1. Isolate the constant on one side of the equation.	*Step 1.* $$2x^2 - 5x = -4$$
Step 2. Factor out the coefficient a of x^2.	*Step 2.* $$2\left(x^2 - \frac{5}{2}x\right) = -4$$
Step 3. Complete the square for the quadratic expression in parentheses $$x^2 + dx + k^2 = (x + k)^2$$ where $k = d/2$. Balance the equation by adding ak^2 to both sides. Simplify.	*Step 3.* $$k = \frac{1}{2}\left(-\frac{5}{2}\right) = -\frac{5}{4}$$ $$2\left(x^2 - \frac{5}{2}x + \frac{25}{16}\right) = -4 + 2\left(\frac{25}{16}\right)$$ $$\left(x - \frac{5}{4}\right)^2 = -\frac{7}{16}$$
Step 4. Solve for x.	*Step 4.* $$x - \frac{5}{4} = \pm\sqrt{\frac{-7}{16}} = \frac{\pm i\sqrt{7}}{4}$$ $$x = \frac{5}{4} \pm \frac{i\sqrt{7}}{4} = \frac{5 \pm i\sqrt{7}}{4}$$

✔ Progress Check 5

Solve by completing the square.

(a) $x^2 - 3x + 2 = 0$ (b) $3x^2 - 4x + 2 = 0$

Answers

(a) $1, 2$ (b) $\dfrac{2 \pm i\sqrt{2}}{3}$

Warning

In the equation

$$x^2 + 8x = -2$$

completing the square on the left-hand side produces $(x + 4)^2$. But this is $4^2 = 16$ more than the original left-hand side. *Don't* forget to balance the equation by adding 16 to the right-hand side.

$$x^2 + 8x + 16 = -2 + 16$$

$$(x + 4)^2 = 14$$

Exercise Set 9.1

In Exercises 1–20 solve the given equation.

1. $3x^2 - 27 = 0$
2. $4x^2 - 64 = 0$
3. $4x^2 - 25 = 0$
4. $49y^2 - 9 = 0$
5. $5y^2 - 25 = 0$
6. $6x^2 - 12 = 0$
7. $(x - 3)^2 = -2$
8. $(s + 3)^2 = 4$
9. $(2r + 5)^2 = 8$
10. $(3x - 4)^2 = -6$
11. $(2y + 4)^2 + 3 = 0$
12. $(3p - 2)^2 + 6 = 0$
13. $(3x - 5)^2 - 8 = 0$
14. $(4t + 1)^2 - 3 = 0$
15. $2x^2 + 8 = 0$
16. $6y^2 + 96 = 0$
17. $9x^2 + 64 = 0$
18. $81x^2 + 25 = 0$
19. $2y^2 + 12 = 0$
20. $9x^2 + 45 = 0$

In Exercises 21–34 solve by factoring.

21. $x^2 - 3x + 2 = 0$
22. $x^2 - 6x + 8 = 0$
23. $x^2 + x - 2 = 0$
24. $3r^2 - 4r + 1 = 0$
25. $x^2 + 6x = -8$
26. $x^2 + 6x + 5 = 0$
27. $y^2 - 4y = 0$
28. $2x^2 - x = 0$
29. $2x^2 - 5x = -2$
30. $2s^2 - 5s - 3 = 0$
31. $t^2 - 4 = 0$
32. $4x^2 - 9 = 0$
33. $6x^2 - 5x + 1 = 0$
34. $6x^2 - x = 2$

In Exercises 35–46 solve by completing the square.

35. $x^2 - 2x = 8$
36. $t^2 - 2t = 15$
37. $2r^2 - 7r = 4$
38. $9x^2 + 3x = 2$
39. $3x^2 + 8x = 3$
40. $2y^2 + 4y = 5$
41. $2y^2 + 2y = -1$
42. $3x^2 - 4x = -3$
43. $4x^2 - x = 3$
44. $2x^2 + x = 2$
45. $3x^2 + 2x = -1$
46. $3u^2 - 3u = -1$

In Exercises 47–60 solve by any method.

47. $x^2 + x - 12 = 0$
48. $x^2 - 2x - 8 = 0$
49. $3y^2 + y = 0$
50. $4x^2 - 4x - 3 = 0$
51. $2x^2 + 2x - 5 = 0$
52. $2t^2 + 2t + 3 = 0$
53. $3x^2 + 4x - 4 = 0$
54. $x^2 + 2x = 0$
55. $2x^2 + 5x + 4 = 0$
56. $2r^2 - 3r + 2 = 0$
57. $4u^2 - 1 = 0$
58. $x^2 + 2 = 0$
59. $4x^2 + 2x + 3 = 0$
60. $4s^2 + 4s - 15 = 0$

In Exercises 61–64 solve by completing the square, and verify the answer by substitution.

*61. $2x^2 + 3x - 1 = 0$
*62. $3x^2 - 4x - 4 = 0$
*63. $2x^2 - 3x - 9 = 0$
*64. $4x^2 + 4x - 3 = 0$

65. Find the solutions of $(3x - 1)^2 = 4$ by graphing both sides and looking for points of intersection. (See the figures below.)

 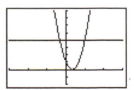

66. Find the solutions of $(1 - 5x)^2 = 1$ by graphing both sides and finding points of intersection.

67. Are there any solutions to $(0.2x + 2)^2 = -(0.3x - 1)^2$? Explain why or why not. Refer to the graphs of both sides of the equation.

68. Are there any solutions to $(0.2x + 1)^2 = (0.3x - 1)^2$? Explain why or why not. Refer to the graphs of both sides of the equation.

69. The following equation is an example of the "quarter squares rule" for finding the product of two numbers.

In this case, 5 is one of the numbers and 3 is the other. Solve the equation below for x.

$$\left(\frac{x + 3}{2}\right)^2 - \left(\frac{5 - 3}{2}\right)^2 = 5(3)$$

(The chapter project reveals the complete formula.)

70. Solve for x:

$$\left(\frac{x + 7}{2}\right)^2 - \left(\frac{11 - 7}{2}\right)^2 = 7x$$

How does this equation provide a formula for finding the product of two integers?

9.2   The Quadratic Formula

Let's apply the method of completing the square to the general quadratic equation

$$ax^2 + bx + c = 0, \quad a > 0$$

where a, b, and c are real numbers. Following the steps we illustrated in the last section, we have

$$ax^2 + bx = -c$$

$$a\left(x^2 + \frac{b}{a}x\right) = -c$$

$$a\left[x^2 + \frac{b}{a}x + \left(\frac{b}{2a}\right)^2\right] = a\left(\frac{b}{2a}\right)^2 - c$$

$$a\left(x + \frac{b}{2a}\right)^2 = \frac{b^2}{4a} - c$$

$$\left(x + \frac{b}{2a}\right)^2 = \frac{b^2}{4a^2} - \frac{c}{a} = \frac{b^2 - 4ac}{4a^2}$$

$$x + \frac{b}{2a} = \pm\sqrt{\frac{b^2 - 4ac}{4a^2}} = \frac{\pm\sqrt{b^2 - 4ac}}{2a}$$

$$x = -\frac{b}{2a} \pm \frac{\sqrt{b^2 - 4ac}}{2a}$$

$$x = \frac{-b \pm \sqrt{b^2 - 4ac}}{2a}$$

By applying the method of completing the square to the standard form of the quadratic equation, we have derived a *formula* that gives us the roots, or solutions, of *any* quadratic equation in one variable.

If $ax^2 + bx + c = 0$, $a > 0$, then

$$x = \frac{-b \pm \sqrt{b^2 - 4ac}}{2a}$$

That is, the roots of the quadratic equation $ax^2 + bx + c = 0$ are

$$\frac{-b + \sqrt{b^2 - 4ac}}{2a} \quad \text{and} \quad \frac{-b - \sqrt{b^2 - 4ac}}{2a}$$

Example 1   Applying the Quadratic Formula

Solve by the quadratic formula.

(a) $2x^2 - 3x - 3 = 0$ (b) $-5x^2 + 3x = 2$

Solution

(a) We begin by identifying a, b, and c.

$$a = 2$$
$$b = -3$$
$$c = -3$$

We can now write the quadratic formula and substitute.

$$x = \frac{-b \pm \sqrt{b^2 - 4ac}}{2a}$$

$$= \frac{-(-3) \pm \sqrt{(-3)^2 - 4(2)(-3)}}{2(2)}$$

$$= \frac{3 \pm \sqrt{33}}{4}$$

(b) We first rewrite the given equation as $5x^2 - 3x + 2 = 0$ so that $a > 0$ and the right-hand side equals 0. Now we can identify a, b, and c.

$$a = 5$$
$$b = -3$$
$$c = 2$$

Determining the Golden Ratio

When a point divides a line segment of length L into two parts of lengths a and b so that

$$\frac{L}{a} = \frac{a}{b}$$

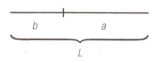

then a/b is called the "golden ratio." (See Section 5.6.) To determine the golden ratio ϕ, assume that $b = 1$. Then we see from the accompanying figure that

$$L = a + 1$$

In addition, the above proportion will simplify to

$$L = a^2$$

Equating the expressions for L, we have

$$a^2 = a + 1$$
$$a^2 - a - 1 = 0$$

The length a satisfies this quadratic equation. Using the quadratic formula, we have

$$a = \frac{1 \pm \sqrt{5}}{2}$$

You can use a calculator to verify that $(1 + \sqrt{5})/2$ yields an approximate value for the golden ratio ϕ of 1.61803. The negative number $(1 - \sqrt{5})/2$ is rejected because the segment has a positive length.

We write the quadratic formula and substitute.

$$x = \frac{-b \pm \sqrt{b^2 - 4ac}}{2a}$$

$$= \frac{-(-3) \pm \sqrt{(-3)^2 - 4(5)(2)}}{2(5)}$$

$$= \frac{3 \pm \sqrt{-31}}{10} = \frac{3 \pm i\sqrt{31}}{10}$$

✔ Progress Check 1

Solve by the quadratic formula.

(a) $x^2 - 8x = -10$ (b) $4x^2 - 2x + 1 = 0$

(c) $2x^2 - x - 1 = 0$ (d) $x^2 + \frac{5}{2}x + 1 = 0$

Answers

(a) $4 \pm \sqrt{6}$ (b) $\dfrac{1 \pm i\sqrt{3}}{4}$ (c) $1, -\dfrac{1}{2}$ (d) $-2, -\dfrac{1}{2}$

Warning

There are a number of errors that students make in using the quadratic formula.

(a)   To solve $x^2 - 3x = -4$, you must write the equation in the form

$$x^2 + (-3)x + 4 = 0$$

to properly identify a, b, and c.

(b)   Since a, b, and c are coefficients, you must include the sign. If

$$x^2 - 3x + 4 = 0$$

then $b = -3$. *Don't write $b = 3$.*

(c)   The quadratic formula is

$$x = \frac{-b \pm \sqrt{b^2 - 4ac}}{2a}$$

Don't write

$$x = -b \pm \frac{\sqrt{b^2 - 4ac}}{2a}$$

The term $-b$ must also be divided by $2a$.

Now that you have a formula that works for any quadratic equation, you may be tempted to use it all the time. However, if you see an equation of the form

$$x^2 = 15$$

it is certainly easier to immediately supply the answer: $x = \pm\sqrt{15}$. Similarly, if you are faced with

$$x^2 + 3x + 2 = 0$$

it is faster to solve if you see that

$$x^2 + 3x + 2 = (x + 1)(x + 2)$$

The method of completing the square is generally not used for solving quadratic equations once you have learned the quadratic formula. However, we will need to use this technique when we graph second-degree equations in Chapter 12. The technique of completing the square is occasionally helpful in a variety of areas of applications.

Exercise Set 9.2

In Exercises 1−4, a, b, and c denote the coefficients of the general quadratic equation $ax^2 + bx + c = 0$. Select the correct answer.

1. $2x^2 + 3x - 4 = 0$

    (a) $a = 2, b = 3, c = 4$

    (b) $a = 3, b = 2, c = 4$

    (c) $a = -2, b = 4, c = 3$

    (d) $a = 2, b = 3, c = -4$

2. $3x^2 - 2x = 5$

    (a) $a = 3, b = 2, c = 5$

    (b) $a = 2, b = 3, c = 5$

    (c) $a = 3, b = -2, c = -5$

    (d) $a = -3, b = 2, c = -5$

3. $r = 5r^2 - \frac{2}{3}$

    (a) $a = 1, b = 5, c = -\frac{2}{3}$

    (b) $a = -1, b = 5, c = \frac{2}{3}$

    (c) $a = 5, b = -1, c = -\frac{2}{3}$

    (d) $a = 5, b = 1, c = \frac{2}{3}$

4. $2r^2 + r = 0$

    (a) $a = -2, b = 1, c = 0$

    (b) $a = 0, b = 2, c = 1$

    (c) $a = 2, b = -1, c = 0$

    (d) $a = 2, b = 1, c = 0$

In Exercises 5−10 identify a, b, and c in the general quadratic equation $ax^2 + bx + c = 0$.

5. $3x^2 - 2x + 5 = 0$

6. $2x^2 + x = 4$

7. $s = 2s^2 + 5$

8. $2x^2 + 5 = 0$

9. $3x^2 - \frac{1}{3}x = 0$

10. $4y^2 = 2y + 1$

In Exercises 11−32 solve, using the quadratic equation.

11. $x^2 + 5x + 6 = 0$

12. $x^2 + 2x - 8 = 0$

13. $x^2 - 8x = -15$

14. $6r^2 - r = 1$

15. $2x^2 + 3x = 0$

16. $2x^2 + 3x + 3 = 0$

17. $5x^2 - 4x + 3 = 0$

18. $2x^2 - 3x - 2 = 0$

19. $5y^2 - 4y + 5 = 0$

20. $x^2 - 5x = 0$

21. $x^2 + x = 12$

22. $2x^2 + 5x - 6 = 0$

23. $-3x^2 - x + 2 = 0$

24. $-2x^2 - 4x + 3 = 0$

25. $x^2 - 9 = 0$

26. $5x^2 + 2 = 0$

27. $3y^2 - 4 = 0$

28. $2x^2 + 2x + 5 = 0$

29. $x^2 + \frac{7}{2}x - 2 = 0$

30. $x^2 - \frac{4}{3}x + \frac{1}{3} = 0$

31. $4u^2 + 3u = 0$

32. $4x^2 - 1 = 0$

*33. Show that if r_1 and r_2 are the roots of the equation $ax^2 + bx + c = 0$, then

    (a) $r_1 r_2 = c/a$, and

    (b) $r_1 + r_2 = -b/a$

    This result provides a quick check of the correctness of the roots.

*34. Show that if $b^2 - 4ac = 0$, then the two roots of the quadratic equation $ax^2 + bx + c = 0, a \neq 0$, are equal.

35.−36. Verify the answers you found to Exercises 1−32 by graphing. (See Exercise 65 in the last section for an example.)

9.3   Roots of a Quadratic Equation: The Discriminant

By analyzing the quadratic formula

$$x = \frac{-b \pm \sqrt{b^2 - 4ac}}{2a}$$

we can learn a great deal about the roots of the quadratic equation $ax^2 + bx + c = 0$. The key to the analysis is the **discriminant** $b^2 - 4ac$ found under the radical sign.

- If $b^2 - 4ac$ is negative, then we have the square root of a negative number and both values of x will be complex numbers; in fact, they will be complex conjugates of each other.

- If $b^2 - 4ac$ is positive, then we have the square root of a positive number and both values of x will be real.

- If $b^2 - 4ac$ is 0, then $x = -b/2a$, which we call a **double root** or **repeated root** of the quadratic equation. For example, if $x^2 - 10x + 25 = 0$, then $b^2 - 4ac = 0$ and $x = -b/2a = 10/2 = 5$. Moreover,

$$x^2 - 10x + 25 = (x - 5)(x - 5) = 0$$

We call $x = 5$ a double root because the factor $(x - 5)$ is a double factor of $x^2 - 10x + 25 = 0$.

If the roots of the quadratic equation are real and a, b, and c are rational numbers, the discriminant enables us to determine whether the roots are rational or irrational. Since $\sqrt{k}$ is a rational number only if k is a perfect square, we see that the quadratic formula produces a rational result only if $b^2 - 4ac$ is a perfect square. We summarize these results.

The quadratic equation $ax^2 + bx + c = 0$, $a > 0$, has exactly two roots, the nature of which is determined by the discriminant $b^2 - 4ac$.

Discriminant	Roots
Negative	Two conjugate complex roots
0	A double root (two equal roots)
Positive	Two real roots
a, b, c rational $\begin{cases} \text{A perfect square} \\ \text{Not a perfect square} \end{cases}$	Two rational roots Two irrational roots

---

Example 1 Using the Discriminant of a Quadratic Equation

Without solving, determine the nature of the roots of the quadratic equation.

(a) $3x^2 - 4x + 6 = 0$ (b) $2x^2 - 7x = -1$ (c) $4x^2 + 12x + 9 = 0$

Solution

(a) We evaluate $b^2 - 4ac$ using $a = 3$, $b = -4$, $c = 6$.

$$b^2 - 4ac = (-4)^2 - 4(3)(6) = 16 - 72 = -56$$

The discriminant is negative and the equation has two conjugate complex roots.

(b) Rewrite the equation in the standard form.

$$2x^2 - 7x + 1 = 0$$

and then substitute $a = 2, b = -7, c = 1$ in the discriminant. Thus,

$$b^2 - 4ac = (-7)^2 - 4(2)(1) = 49 - 8 = 41$$

The discriminant is positive and is not a perfect square; thus, the roots are real and irrational.

(c) Setting $a = 4, b = 12, c = 9$, we evaluate the discriminant:

$$b^2 - 4ac = (12)^2 - 4(4)(9) = 144 - 144 = 0$$

The discriminant is 0, so there is a double real root.

✔ Progress Check 1

Without solving, determine the nature of the roots of the quadratic equation by using the discriminant.

(a) $4x^2 - 20x + 25 = 0$ (b) $5x^2 - 6x = -2$

(c) $10x^2 = x + 2$ (d) $x^2 + x - 1 = 0$

Answers

(a) double real root   (b) two conjugate complex roots

(c) two real, rational roots   (d) two real, irrational roots

---

Graph of a Quadratic Function

If we seek the zeros of the quadratic function

$$f(x) = ax^2 + bx + c, \quad a \neq 0 \tag{1}$$

we need only set $f(x) = 0$ and solve the resulting quadratic equation

$$ax^2 + bx + c = 0 \tag{2}$$

It is important to recognize that the solutions to Equation (2) are the same as the x-intercepts of the graph of the function in Equation (1), since these points have coordinates of the form $(x_1, 0)$.

In Section 6.3 we saw that the graph of a second-degree function is a parabola. The discriminant of the quadratic equation (2) therefore tells us the number of x-intercepts of the parabola. The possibilities are two real roots (Figure 1a), a double root (Figure 1b), and two complex roots (Figure 1c). We can now summarize.

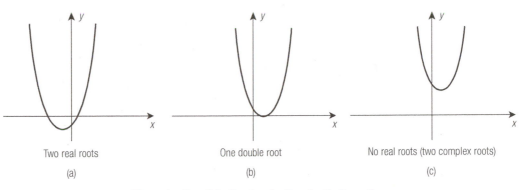

Figure 1   Possible Roots of a Quadratic Equation

The x-intercepts of the graph of a quadratic function are the real zeros of the function. The number of x-intercepts is related to the discriminant as follows:

Discriminant	Graph of the Function
Positive	Meets the x-axis at two distinct points
0	Meets the x-axis at one point
Negative	Does not meet the x-axis

Exercise Set 9.3

In Exercises 1−14 select the correct answer.

1. In $3x^2 - 2x + 4 = 0$, the discriminant is

   (a) 52   (b) 44   (c) $\sqrt{44}$
   (d) −52   (e) −44

2. In $x^2 - 6x + 9 = 0$, the discriminant is

   (a) 72   (b) −72   (c) −36
   (d) 0   (e) $\sqrt{72}$

3. In $3y^2 = 2y - 1$, the discriminant is

   (a) $\sqrt{8}$ (b) −8   (c) 4
   (d) $\sqrt{-8}$ (e) $-2\sqrt{3}$

4. In $3x^2 + 4x = 0$, the discriminant is

   (a) 4   (b) −4   (c) 0
   (d) 16   (e) 7

5. In $r = 5r^2 + 3$, the discriminant is

   (a) −61   (b) 59   (c) 61
   (d) −59   (e) $\sqrt{61}$

6. In $2t = -4t^2 - 3$, the discriminant is

   (a) 44   (b) $2\sqrt{11}$ (c) −44
   (d) −23   (e) 41

7. In $4x^2 - 8 = 0$, the discriminant is

   (a) −64   (b) 64   (c) −128
   (d) 128   (e) $\sqrt{128}$

8. In $4y^2 + 9 = 0$, the discriminant is

   (a) 65   (b) −144   (c) −65
   (d) 144   (e) 12

9. $4x^2 - 3x + 5 = 0$ has

   (a) two real roots   (b) a double root
   (c) two complex roots

10. $y^2 - 10y + 25 = 0$ has

    (a) two real roots   (b) a double root
    (c) two complex roots

11. $5x^2 = x + 1$ has

    (a) two real roots   (b) a double root
    (c) two complex roots

12. $4r^2 - 2r = 0$ has

 (a) two real roots (b) a double root
 (c) two complex roots

13. $x = 2x^2 - 2$ has

 (a) two real roots (b) a double root
 (c) two complex roots

14. $8x^2 + 24 = 0$ has

 (a) two real roots (b) a double root
 (c) two complex roots

In Exercises 15–30 determine, without solving, the nature of the roots of each quadratic equation.

15. $x^2 - 2x + 3 = 0$ 16. $3x^2 + 2x - 5 = 0$

17. $4x^2 - 12x + 9 = 0$ 18. $2x^2 + x + 5 = 0$

19. $-3x^2 + 2x + 5 = 0$ 20. $-3y^2 + 2y - 5 = 0$

21. $3x^2 + 2x = 0$ 22. $4x^2 + 20x + 25 = 0$

23. $2r^2 = r - 4$ 24. $3x^2 = 5 - x$

25. $3x^2 + 6 = 0$ 26. $4x^2 - 25 = 0$

27. $6r = 3r^2 + 1$ 28. $4x = 2x^2 + 3$

29. $12x = 9x^2 + 4$ 30. $4s^2 = -4s - 1$

In Exercises 31–38 determine the number of x-intercepts of the graph of the function.

31. $f(x) = 3x^2 + 4x - 1$ 32. $f(x) = 2x^2 - 3x + 2$

33. $f(x) = x^2 + x + 3$ 34. $f(x) = 2x^2 - 6x + 1$

35. $f(x) = 4x^2 - 12x + 9$ 36. $f(x) = 9x^2 + 12x + 4$

37. $f(x) = 4x^2 + 3$ 38. $f(x) = -x^2 + 1$

*39. Show that if a, b, and c are rational numbers, and the discriminant of the equation $ax^2 + bx + c = 0$ is positive, then the quadratic has either two rational roots or two irrational roots.

9.4   Applications of Quadratic Equations

In earlier chapters we carefully avoided those work problems, number problems, business problems, geometric problems, and other applications that resulted in second-degree equations. Now that you can solve quadratic equations, we can look at these applications.

Example 1   A Work Problem Leading to a Quadratic Equation

Working together, two cranes can unload a ship in 4 hours. The slower crane, working alone, requires 6 hours more than the faster crane to do the job. How long does it take each crane to do the job by itself?

Solution

Let x = number of hours required by faster crane to do the job. Then $x + 6$ = number of hours required by slower crane to do the job.

 Displaying the information in a table, we have

	Rate	×	Time	=	Fractional Part of the Work
Faster crane	$\dfrac{1}{x}$		4		$\dfrac{4}{x}$
Slower crane	$\dfrac{1}{x+6}$		4		$\dfrac{4}{x+6}$

Since the job is completed in 4 hours when the two cranes work together, we must have

| fractional part of the work done by faster crane | + | fractional part of the work done by slower crane | = | 1 whole job (sum of fractional parts) |

or

$$\frac{4}{x} + \frac{4}{x+6} = 1$$

To solve, we multiply by the LCD, which is $x(x+6)$.

$$x(x+6)\left(\frac{4}{x} + \frac{4}{x+6}\right) = x(x+6)$$

$$4(x+6) = 4x = x^2 + 6x$$

$$0 = x^2 - 2x - 24$$

$$0 = (x+4)(x-6)$$

$$x = -4 \quad \text{or} \quad x = 6$$

The solution $x = -4$ is rejected, because it makes no sense to speak of negative hours of work. Thus,

$x = 6$ is the number of hours in which the faster crane can do the job alone.

$x + 6 = 12$ is the number of hours in which the slower crane can do the job alone.

To check our answer, we find that the rate of the faster crane is $\frac{1}{6}$ while that of the slower one is $\frac{1}{12}$. In 4 hours the sum of the fractional parts of the work done by the cranes is

$$\frac{4}{6} + \frac{4}{12} = \frac{12}{12} = 1$$

✔ Progress Check 1

A storage tank can be filled in 6 hours when two pipes are used. The larger-diameter pipe, used alone, requires 5 hours less to fill the tank than the smaller-diameter pipe. How many hours does each pipe require to fill the tank when working alone?

Answer
The larger pipe requires 10 hours. The smaller pipe requires 15 hours.

Example 2   A Problem in Area Leading to a Quadratic Equation
The length of a pool is 3 times its width, and the pool is surrounded by a grass walk 4 feet wide. If the area of the region consisting of the pool and the walk is 684 square feet, find the dimensions of the pool.

Solution

A diagram is useful in solving geometric problems (see Figure 2). If we let x = width of pool, then $3x$ = length of pool, and the region consisting of the pool and the walk has length $3x + 8$ and width $x + 8$. The area is then

$$\text{length} \times \text{width} = \text{area}$$
$$(3x + 8)(x + 8) = 984$$
$$3x^2 + 32x + 64 = 684$$
$$3x^2 + 32x - 620 = 0$$
$$(3x + 62)(x - 10) = 0$$
$$x = 0 \qquad \text{Reject } x = -\frac{62}{3}$$
$$3x = 30$$

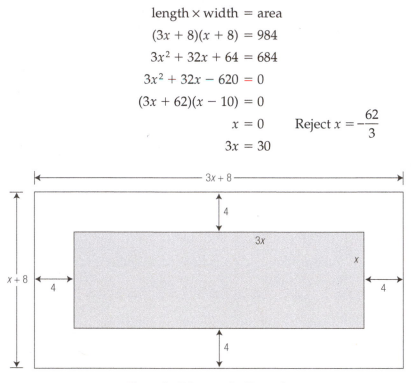

Figure 2 Diagram for Example 2

The dimensions of the pool are 10 feet by 30 feet.

To check our answer, we see that the dimensions of the region consisting of the pool and the walk are 18 feet by 38 feet, and the area is $(18)(38) = 684$ square feet.

✔ Progress Check 2

The altitude of a triangle is 2 centimeters less than the base. If the area of the triangle is 24 square centimeters, find the base and altitude of the triangle.

Answers
base = 8 cm; altitude = 6 cm

Example 3 A Number Problem Leading to a Quadratic Equation

The larger of two numbers exceeds the smaller by 2. If the sum of the squares of the two numbers is 74, find the two numbers.

Solution

If we let

$$x = \text{the smaller number}$$

then

$$x + 2 = \text{the larger number}$$

The sum of the squares is then

$$x^2 + (x + 2)^2 = 74$$
$$x^2 + x^2 + 4x + 4 = 74$$
$$2x^2 + 4x - 70 = 0$$
$$x^2 + 2x - 35 = 0$$
$$(x - 5)(x + 7) = 0$$
$$x = 5 \quad \text{or} \quad x = -7$$

The numbers are then 5 and 7, or -7 and -5. Verify that the sum of the squares is indeed 74.

✔ Progress Check 3

The sum of a number and its reciprocal is $\frac{17}{4}$. Find the number.

Answer

$4 \text{ or } \dfrac{1}{4}$

Example 4 An Investment Problem Leading to a Quadratic Equation

An investor purchased a number of shares of stock for a total of $600. If the investor had paid $2 less per share, the number of shares that could have been purchased for the same amount of money would have increased by 10. How many shares were bought?

Solution

Let

$$n = \text{the number of shares purchased}$$

and

$$p = \text{the price paid per share}$$

Since

number of shares	×	price per share	=	total dollars invested

we must have

$$n \cdot p = 600 \qquad \text{Actual situation}$$

and

$$(n + 10)(p - 2) = 100 \qquad \text{Hypothetical situation}$$

Substituting $p = 600/n$ we obtain

$$(n + 10)\left(\frac{600}{n} - 2\right) = 600$$

$$600 + \frac{6000}{n} - 2n - 20 = 600$$

$$6000 - 2n^2 - 20n = 0 \qquad \text{Multiply by } n$$

$$n^2 + 10n - 3000 = 0 \qquad \text{Divide by } -2$$

$$(n - 50)(n + 60) = 0$$

$$n = 50 \qquad \text{Reject } n = -60$$

The investor purchased 50 shares of stock.

✔ **Progress Check 4**

A business machine dealer purchased a number of used printing calculators at an auction for a total expenditure of $240. After giving one of the calculators to his daughter, he sold the remaining calculators at a profit of $15 each, for a profit of $35 on the entire transaction. How many printing calculators did he buy?

Answer

6 calculators

Exercise Set 9.4

1. Working together, computers A and B can complete a data-processing job in 2 hours. Computer A working alone can do the job in 3 hours less than computer B working alone. How long does it take each computer to do the job by itself?

2. A graphic designer and her assistant working together can complete an advertising layout in 6 days. The assistant working alone could complete the job in 16 more days than the designer working alone. How long would it take each person to do the job alone?

3. A roofer and his assistant working together can finish a roofing job in 4 hours. The roofer working alone could finish the job in 6 hours less than the assistant working alone. How long would it take each person to do the job alone?

4. A mounting board 16 inches by 20 inches is used to mount a photograph. How wide is the uniform border if the photograph occupies $\frac{3}{5}$ of the area of the mounting board?

5. The length of a rectangle exceeds twice its width by 4 feet. If the area of the rectangle is 48 square feet, find the dimensions.

6. The length of a rectangle is 4 centimeters less than twice its width. Find the dimensions if the area of the rectangle is 96 square centimeters.

7. The area of a rectangle is 48 square centimeters. If the length and width are each increased by 4 centimeters, the area of the larger rectangle is 120 square centimeters. Find the dimensions of the original rectangle.

8. The base of a triangle is 2 feet more than twice its altitude. If the area is 12 square feet, find the base and altitude.

9. Find the width of a strip that has been mowed around a rectangular lawn 60 feet by 80 feet if $\frac{1}{2}$ of the lawn has not yet been mowed.

10. The sum of the reciprocals of two consecutive numbers is $\frac{7}{12}$. Find the numbers.

11. The sum of a number and its reciprocal is $\frac{26}{5}$. Find the numbers.

12. The difference between a number and its reciprocal is $\frac{35}{6}$. Find the number. (*Hint:* There are two answers.)

13. The smaller of the two numbers is 4 less than the larger. If the sum of their squares is 58, find the numbers.

14. The sum of the reciprocals of two consecutive odd numbers is $\frac{8}{15}$. Find the numbers.

15. The sum of the reciprocals of two consecutive even numbers is $\frac{7}{24}$. Find the numbers.

16. A number of students rented a car for a one-week camping trip for $160. If another student had joined the original group, each person's share of expenses would have been reduced by $8. How many students were in the original group?

17. An investor placed an order totaling $1200 for a certain number of shares of a stock. If the price of each share of stock were $2 more, the investor would get 30 shares less for the same amount of money. How many shares did the investor buy?

18. A fraternity charters a bus for a ski trip at a cost of $360. When 6 more students join the trip, each person's cost decreases by $2. How many students were in the original group of travelers?

19. A salesman worked a certain number of days to earn $192. If he had been paid $8 more per day, he would have earned the same amount of money in 2 fewer days. How many days did he work?

20. A freelance photographer worked a certain number of days for a newspaper to earn $480. If she had been paid $8 less per day, she would have earned the same amount in 2 more days. What was her daily rate of pay?

21. The square of one-half of the difference between eight and x is subtracted from the square of one-half of the sum of eight and x, and the result is equal to the product of eight and x. For what values of x is this true?

9.5   Forms Leading to Quadratics

Radical Equations

Certain types of equations that do not appear to be quadratic can be transformed into quadratic equations that can be solved by the methods discussed in this chapter. One such form that leads to a quadratic equation is the **radical equation**. To solve an equation such as

$$x = \sqrt{x + 12}$$

it seems natural to square both sides of the equation.

$$x^2 = x + 12$$

We now have a quadratic equation that is easily solved.

$$x^2 - x - 12 = 0$$
$$(x + 3)(x - 4) = 0$$
$$x = -3 \quad \text{or} \quad x = 4$$

Checking these solutions by substituting in the original equation, we have

$$-3 \overset{?}{=} \sqrt{-3 + 12} \qquad 4 \overset{?}{=} \sqrt{4 + 12}$$

$$-3 \overset{?}{=} \sqrt{9} \qquad 4 \overset{?}{=} \sqrt{16}$$

$$-3 \neq 3 \qquad 4 \overset{\checkmark}{=} 4$$

(Remember: $\sqrt{9}$ is the principal square root of 9, which is 3.) Thus, 4 is a solution and -3 is not a solution of the original equation. We say that -3 is an **extraneous solution**, which was introduced when we raised each side of the original equation to the second power. This is an illustration of the following general theorem:

The solution set of the equation

$$f(x) = g(x)$$

is a subset of the solution set of the equation

$$[f(x)]^n = [g(x)]^n$$

where n is a natural number.

This suggests that we can solve radical equations if we observe a precaution.

If both sides of an equation are raised to the same power, the solutions of the resulting equation must be checked to see that they satisfy the original equation.

Example 1 Solving a Radical Equation

Solve $x - \sqrt{x - 2} = 4$.

Solution

Isolate the radical on one side of the equation before solving.

$$x - 4 = \sqrt{x - 2}$$
$$x^2 - 8x + 16 = x - 2 \qquad \text{Square both sides}$$
$$x^2 - 9x + 18 = 0$$
$$(x - 3)(x - 6) = 0$$
$$x = 3 \quad \text{or} \quad x = 6$$

Checking by substituting in the original equation, we have

$$3 - \sqrt{3 - 2} \overset{?}{=} 4 \qquad\qquad 6 - \sqrt{6 - 2} \overset{?}{=} 4$$

$$3 - 1 \overset{?}{=} 4 \qquad\qquad 6 - \sqrt{4} \overset{?}{=} 4$$

$$2 \neq 4 \qquad\qquad\qquad 4 \overset{\checkmark}{=} 4$$

We conclude that 6 is a solution of the original equation, and 3 is rejected as an extraneous solution.

✔ **Progress Check 1**

Solve $x - \sqrt{1 - x} = -5$.

Answer

-3

Example 2   Solving a Radical Equation

Solve $\sqrt{2x - 4} - \sqrt{3x + 4} = -2$.

Solution

The algebraic manipulations are simpler if, before squaring, we rewrite the equation so that a radical is on each side of the equation.

$$\sqrt{2x - 4} = \sqrt{3x + 4} - 2$$

$$2x - 4 = (3x + 4) - 4\sqrt{3x + 4} + 4 \quad \text{Square both sides}$$

$$\text{(don't forget the middle term)}$$

$$-x - 12 = -4\sqrt{3x + 4}$$

$$x^2 + 24x + 144 = 16(3x + 4)$$

$$x^2 - 24x + 80 = 0 \qquad\qquad\qquad\qquad \text{Isolate the radical}$$

$$(x - 20)(x - 4) = 0 \qquad\qquad\qquad\qquad \text{Square both sides}$$

$$x = 20 \quad \text{or} \quad x = 4$$

Verify that both 20 and 4 are solutions of the original equation.

✔ **Progress Check 2**

Solve $\sqrt{5x - 1} - \sqrt{x + 2} = 1$.

Answer

2

Substitution of Variable

Although the equation

$$x^4 - x^2 - 2 = 0$$

is not a quadratic equation with respect to the variable x, it is a quadratic equation with respect to the variable x^2.

$$(x^2)^2 - (x^2) - 2 = 0$$

This may be seen more clearly by replacing x^2 with a new variable $u = x^2$, which gives us

$$u^2 - u - 2 = 0$$

a quadratic equation with respect to the variable u. Solving, we have

$$(u + 1)(u - 2) = 0$$

$$u = -1 \quad \text{or} \quad u = 2$$

Since $x^2 = u$, we must next solve the equations

$$x^2 = -1 \qquad x^2 = 2$$
$$x = \pm i \qquad x = \pm\sqrt{2}$$

The original equation has four solutions: i, $-i$, $\sqrt{2}$, and $-\sqrt{2}$.

The technique we have used is called a **substitution of variable**. Although simple in concept, it is a powerful method that is commonly used in calculus. We will apply this technique to a variety of examples.

Example 3   Choosing an Appropriate Substitution of Variable

Indicate an appropriate substitution of variable that will lead to a quadratic equation.

(a) $2x^6 + 7x^3 - 4 = 0$ (b) $y^{2/3} - 3y^{1/3} - 10 = 0$

Solution

(a) The substitution $u = x^3$ results in the quadratic equation $2u^2 + 7u - 4 = 0$.

(b) The substitution $u = y^{1/3}$ results in the equation $u^2 - 3u - 10 = 0$.

✔ Progress Check 3

Indicate an appropriate substitution of variable that will lead to a quadratic equation.

(a) $3x^4 - 10x^2 - 8 = 0$ (b) $4x^{2/3} + 7x^{1/3} - 2 = 0$

Answers

(a) $u = x^2; 3u^2 - 10u - 8 = 0$ (b) $u = x^{1/3}; 4u^2 + 7u - 2 = 0$

Example 4   Using a Substitution of Variable

Indicate an appropriate substitution of variable that will lead to a quadratic equation, and solve each of the equations.

(a) $\dfrac{2}{z^2} - \dfrac{4}{z} + 1 = 0$ (b) $\left(\dfrac{1}{x} - 1\right)^2 + 6\left(\dfrac{1}{x} - 1\right) - 7 = 0$

Solution

(a) Substituting $u = \dfrac{1}{z}$, we obtain $2u^2 - 4u + 1 = 0$.

Solving this quadratic equation by the quadratic formula, we have

$$u = \frac{4 \pm \sqrt{(-4)^2 - 4(2)(1)}}{2(2)} = \frac{4 \pm \sqrt{16 - 8}}{4}$$

$$= \frac{4 \pm 2\sqrt{2}}{4} = \frac{2 \pm \sqrt{2}}{2}$$

The solutions to the given equation are obtained by writing

$$u = \frac{2 \pm \sqrt{2}}{2} = \frac{1}{z}$$

and solving for z to get

$$z = \frac{2}{2 \pm \sqrt{2}}$$

which can be simplified as

$$z = 2 + \sqrt{2} \quad \text{and} \quad z = 2 - \sqrt{2}.$$

(b) Substituting $u = \dfrac{1}{x} - 1$, we have $u^2 + 6u - 7 = 0$.

Factoring this quadratic equation, we have

$$(u + 7)(u - 1) = 0$$
$$u = -7 \quad \text{and} \quad u = 1$$

The solutions to the given equation are obtained by solving the equations

$$u = -7 = \frac{1}{x} - 1 \quad \text{and} \quad u = 1 = \frac{1}{x} - 1$$

for x, yielding

$$x = -\frac{1}{6} \quad \text{and} \quad x = \frac{1}{2}.$$

✔ Progress Check 4

Indicate an appropriate substitution of variable, and solve each of the following equations.

(a) $\dfrac{2}{x^2} + \dfrac{1}{x} - 10 = 0$ (b) $\left(1 + \dfrac{2}{x}\right)^2 - 8\left(1 + \dfrac{2}{x}\right) + 15 = 0$

Answers

(a) $u = \dfrac{1}{x}; -\dfrac{2}{5}, \dfrac{1}{2}$ (b) $u = 1 + \dfrac{2}{x}; 1, \dfrac{1}{2}$

Exercise Set 9.5

In Exercises 1–14 solve for x.

1. $x + \sqrt{x + 5} = 7$

2. $x - \sqrt{13 - x} = 1$

3. $x + \sqrt{2x - 3} = 3$

4. $x - \sqrt{4 - 3x} = -8$

5. $2x + \sqrt{x + 1} = 8$

6. $3x - \sqrt{1 + 3x} = 1$

7. $\sqrt{3x + 4} - \sqrt{2x + 1} = 1$

8. $\sqrt{4x + 1} - \sqrt{x + 4} = 3$

9. $\sqrt{2x - 1} + \sqrt{x - 4} = 4$

10. $\sqrt{5x + 1} + \sqrt{4x - 3} = 7$

11. $\sqrt{x + 3} + \sqrt{2x - 3} = 6$

12. $\sqrt{x - 1} - \sqrt{3x - 2} = -1$

13. $\sqrt{8x + 20} - \sqrt{7x + 11} = 1$

14. $\sqrt{6x + 12} - \sqrt{5x + 5} = 1$

In Exercises 15–24 indicate an appropriate substitution that will lead to a quadratic equation. Do not attempt to solve.

15. $3x^4 + 5x^2 - 5 = 0$

16. $-8y^8 + 5y^6 + 4 = 0$

17. $3x^{4/3} + 5x^{2/3} + 3 = 0$

18. $-3y^{6/5} + y^{3/5} - 8 = 0$

19. $\dfrac{5}{y^4} + \dfrac{2}{y^2} - 3 = 0$

20. $\dfrac{2}{z^6} + \dfrac{5}{z^3} + 6 = 0$

21. $\dfrac{2}{x^{4/3}} + \dfrac{1}{x^{2/3}} + 4 = 0$

22. $\dfrac{4}{x^{8/5}} - \dfrac{3}{x^{4/5}} + 2 = 0$

23. $\left(2 + \dfrac{3}{x}\right)^2 - 5\left(2 + \dfrac{3}{x}\right) - 5 = 0$

24. $\left(1 - \dfrac{2}{x}\right)^4 + 3\left(1 - \dfrac{2}{x}\right)^2 - 8 = 0$

In Exercises 25–32 indicate an appropriate substitution of variable, and solve the equation.

25. $3x^4 + 5x^2 - 2 = 0$

26. $2x^6 + 15x^3 - 8 = 0$

27. $\dfrac{6}{x^2} + \dfrac{1}{x} - 2 = 0$

28. $\dfrac{2}{x^4} - \dfrac{3}{x^2} - 9 = 0$

29. $2x^{2/5} + 5x^{1/5} + 2 = 0$

30. $3x^{4/3} - 4x^{2/3} - 4 = 0$

31. $2\left(\dfrac{1}{x} + 1\right)^2 - 3\left(\dfrac{1}{x} + 1\right) - 20 = 0$

32. $3\left(\dfrac{1}{x} - 2\right)^2 + 2\left(\dfrac{1}{x} - 2\right) - 1 = 0$

9.6 Second-Degree Inequalities

To solve a second-degree inequality such as

$$x^2 - 2x > 15$$

we rewrite it as

$$x^2 - 2x - 15 > 0$$

When the left-hand side is factored as

$$(x + 3)(x - 5) > 0$$

we can solve the given inequality by determining under what circumstances the product of the factor $(x + 3)$ and the factor $(x - 5)$ will be positive. By the rules of algebra, a product of two real numbers is positive only if both factors have the same sign.

Let's form a table of the values of the linear factor $(x + 3)$.

x	-50	-10	-5	-4	-3	-2	0	5	10	50
$(x + 3)$	-47	-7	-2	-1	0	1	3	8	13	53

Something interesting has happened at $x = -3$: The factor $(x + 3)$ is negative when $x < -3$ and positive when $x > -3$. Similarly, the factor $(x - 5)$ is negative when $x < 5$ and positive when $x > 5$. In general,

Critical Value

> The linear factor $ax + b$ equals 0 at the **critical value** $x = -b/a$ and has opposite signs depending on whether x is to the left or right of the critical value on a number line.

Displaying these results for $(x + 3)$ and $(x - 5)$, using a real number line, we have

```
x + 3    –   –   –   –   0   +   +   +   +   +   +   +   +   +
x – 5    –   –   –   –   –   –   –   –   –   –   0   +   +   +
        ─────────────────┼───────────────────┼──────────────▶
                        –3                    5
(x + 3)(x – 5)  +  +  +  +  0  –   –   –   –   –   0   +   +   +
```

Recall that we want the values of x for which

$$(x + 3)(x - 5) > 0$$

that is, the values of x for which both factors have the same sign. From the graph we see that $(x + 3)$ and $(x - 5)$ have the same sign when $x < -3$ or $x > 5$. The solution of $x^2 - 2x > 15$ is the set

$$\{x \mid x < -3 \quad \text{or} \quad x > 5\}$$

Warning

Don't write the above solution as

$$\{x \mid 5 < x < -3\}$$

since it states that x is simultaneously greater than 5 *and* less than -3, which is impossible.

Example 1   Solving a Quadratic Inequality

Solve the inequality $x^2 \leq -3x + 4$, and then graph the solution set on a real number line.

Solution

We rewrite the inequality and factor.

$$x^2 \leq -3x + 4$$
$$x^2 + 3x - 4 \leq 0$$
$$(x - 1)(x + 4) \leq 0$$

The critical values are found by setting each factor equal to 0.

$$x - 1 = 0 \qquad x + 4 = 0$$
$$x = 1 \qquad\quad x = -4$$

We mark the critical values on a real number line and analyze the *sign* of each factor to the left and to the right of each critical value.

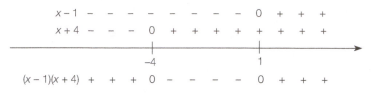

Since we are interested in values of x for which $(x - 1)(x + 4) \leq 0$, we seek values of x for which the factors $(x - 1)$ and $(x + 4)$ have opposite signs or are 0. From the graph, we see that when $-4 \leq x \leq 1$, the conditions are satisfied. Graphing the result, we have

✔ Progress Check 1

Solve the inequality $2x^2 \geq 5x + 3$, and graph the solution set on a real number line.

Answer

$\left\{ x \mid x \leq -\dfrac{1}{2} \text{ or } x \geq 3 \right\}$

Although

$$\frac{ax + b}{cx + d} < 0$$

is not a second-degree inequality, the solution to this inequality is the same as the solution to the inequality $(ax + b)(cx + d) < 0$, since both expressions are negative (<0) when $(ax + b)$ and $(cx + d)$ have opposite signs.

Example 2   Solving an Inequality

Solve the inequality $\dfrac{y + 1}{2 - y} \leq 0$.

Solution

The factors equal 0 at the critical value $y = -1$ and $y = 2$. Analyzing the signs of $y + 1$ and $2 - y$ we have

Since

$$\frac{y + 1}{2 - y}$$

can be negative (<0) only if the factors $(y + 1)$ and $(2 - y)$ have opposite signs, the solution set is $\{y \mid y \leq -1 \text{ or } y > 2\}$. Note that $y = 2$ would result in division by 0 and is therefore excluded from the solution set.

✔ Progress Check 2

Solve the inequality $\dfrac{2x - 3}{1 - 2x} \geq 0$.

Answers

$\left\{ x \,\middle|\, \dfrac{1}{2} < x \leq \dfrac{3}{2} \right\}$

Example 3   Solving an Inequality

Solve the inequality $(x - 2)(2x + 5)(3 - x) < 0$.

Solution

Although this is a third-degree inequality, the same approach will work. The critical values are $x = 2$, $x = -\frac{5}{2}$, and $x = 3$. Graphing, we have

The product of three factors is negative when one of the factors is negative or when all three factors are negative. The solution set is then

$$\{x \mid -\tfrac{5}{2} < x < 2 \text{ or } x > 3\}$$

✔ Progress Check 3

Solve the inequality $(2y - 9)(6 - y)(y + 5) \geq 0$.

Answers

$\left\{ y \,\middle|\, y \leq -5 \text{ or } \dfrac{9}{2} \leq y \leq 6 \right\}$

Exercise Set 9.6

In Exercises 1–6 select the values that are solutions to the given inequality.

1. $x^2 - 3x - 4 > 0$

   (a) $x = 3$ (b) $x = 5$ (c) $x = 0$
   (d) $x = -2$ (e) $x = 6$

2. $x^2 - 7x + 12 \le 0$

   (a) $x = 3$ (b) $x = 3.5$ (c) $x = 5$
   (d) $x = 3.8$ (e) $x = 4$

3. $x^2 + 7x + 10 \ge 0$

   (a) $x = -2$ (b) $x = -3$ (c) $x = 0$
   (d) $x = -6$ (e) $x = 4$

4. $2x^2 - 3x - 2 < 0$

   (a) $x = 0$ (b) $x = -3$ (c) $x = 2$
   (d) $x = -1$ (e) $x = 3$

5. $2x^2 - x > 0$

   (a) $x = 0$ (b) $x = \dfrac{1}{2}$ (c) $x = -1$

   (d) $x = \dfrac{1}{4}$ (e) $x = 2$

6. $3x^2 + x \le 0$

   (a) $x = 0$ (b) $x = 2$ (c) $x = -2$
   (d) $x = -4$ (e) $x = 1$

In Exercises 7–18 find the critical values of the factors in each given inequality. Do not solve.

7. $x^2 + 5x + 6 > 0$

8. $x^2 + 3x + 4 \le 0$

9. $2x^2 - x - 1 < 0$

10. $3x^2 - 4x - 4 \ge 0$

11. $4x - 2x^2 < 0$

12. $r^2 + 4r \ge 0$

13. $\dfrac{x + 5}{x + 3} < 0$

14. $\dfrac{x - 6}{x + 4} \ge 0$

15. $\dfrac{2r + 1}{r - 3} \le 0$

16. $\dfrac{x - 1}{2x - 3} > 0$

17. $\dfrac{3s + 2}{2s - 1} > 0$

18. $\dfrac{4x + 5}{x^2} < 0$

In Exercises 19–46 solve, and graph the solution set of the given inequality.

19. $x^2 + x - 6 > 0$

20. $x^2 - 3x - 10 \ge 0$

21. $2x^2 - 3x - 5 < 0$

22. $3x^2 - 4x - 4 \le 0$

23. $2x^2 + 7x + 6 > 0$

24. $2y^2 + 3y + 1 < 0$

25. $\dfrac{2r + 3}{1 - 2r} < 0$

26. $\dfrac{3x + 2}{3 - 2x} \ge 0$

27. $\dfrac{x - 1}{x + 1} > 0$

28. $\dfrac{2x - 1}{x + 2} \le 0$

29. $6x^2 + 8x + 2 \ge 0$

30. $2x^2 + 5x + 2 \le 0$

31. $\dfrac{2x + 2}{x + 1} \ge 0$

32. $\dfrac{3s + 1}{2s + 4} < 0$

33. $3x^2 - 5x + 2 \le 0$

34. $2x^2 - 9x + 10 > 0$

35. $\dfrac{5y - 2}{2 - 3y} \le 0$

36. $\dfrac{4x - 3}{3 - x} > 0$

37. $x^2 - 2x + 1 > 0$

38. $4r^2 - 4r + 1 < 0$

39. $\dfrac{2x + 1}{2x - 3} \ge 0$

40. $\dfrac{4x - 2}{2x} < 0$

41. $(x + 2)(3x - 2)(x - 1) > 0$

42. $(x - 4)(2x + 5)(2 - x) \le 0$

43. $(y - 3)(2 - y)(2y + 4) \ge 0$

44. $(2x + 5)(3x - 2)(x + 1) < 0$

45. $(x - 3)(1 + 2x)(3x + 5) > 0$

46. $(1 - 2x)(2x + 1)(3 - x) \le 0$

*47. $\dfrac{(x - 4)(2x - 3)}{x + 1} < 0$ *48. $\dfrac{(x + 1)(1 - 2x)}{x - 1} < 0$

*49. A manufacturer of solar heaters finds that when x units are made and sold per week, its profit (in thousands of dollars) is given by $x^2 - 50x - 5000$.

   (a) What is the minimum number of units that must be manufactured and sold each week to make a profit?

   (b) For what values of x is the firm losing money?

*50. Repeat Exercise 49, with the profit given by $x^2 - 180x - 4000$.

*51. A ball is thrown directly upward from level ground with an initial velocity such that the height d attained after t seconds is given by $d = 40t - 16t^2$. For what values of t is the ball at a height of at least 16 feet?

9.7 Critical Thinking Problems

In this chapter we learned about polynomial equations and inequalities. We can use these equations and inequalities to solve problems in everyday life. We can find the length of sidewalks, areas of gardens, and maximum or minimum values. After mastering this chapter, we can apply mathematics at work, in daily life, and even in the arts.

The first example involves finding the dimensions of a sidewalk.

Example 1   Computing Dimensions

Suppose that you have a nice, big rectangular garden in front of your house. The area of this garden is 1008 yd². You'd like to surround this rectangular garden with a brick walk of uniform width. If the dimensions of the garden plus the walk are 30 yards by 48 yards, find the width of the walk. Find the area the of walk. (See the figure below).

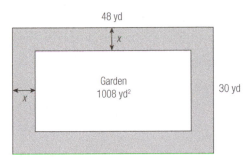

Solution

What is the width of the walk? We don't know, so we let x = the width of the walk.

The dimension of this entire garden plus the walk is 30 yd by 48 yd, and the area of the garden inside the walk is 1008 yd².

If we subtract the width (twice) from 48, then we get the length of this garden:

$$48 - x - x = 48 - 2x$$

If we subtract the width (twice) from 30, then we get the width of this garden:

$$30 - x - x = 30 - 2x$$

To find the area of a rectangle we multiply width by length, so

$$\text{area of garden} = (48 - 2x) \cdot (30 - 2x)$$

By substituting the area of the garden, we get this equation.

$$1008 \text{ yd}^2 = (48 - 2x) \cdot (30 - 2x)$$

We notice that x must be

$$0 < x < 30$$

Let's solve this equation for x.

$$1008 \text{ yd}^2 = (48 - 2x) \cdot (30 - 2x)$$

$$1008 = 1440 - 96x - 60x + 4x^2 \qquad \text{Multiply } (48 - 2x)(30 - 2x)$$

$$1008 = 1440 - 156x + 4x^2 \qquad \text{By simplifying the right-hand side}$$

$$1008 - 1008 = 1440 - 156x + 4x^2 - 1008$$

$$0 = 4x^2 - 156x + 432 \qquad \text{By subtracting 1008 from both sides}$$

$$0 = 4(x^2 - 39x + 108) \qquad \text{By factoring out 4}$$

$$0 = 4(x - 36)(x - 3) \qquad \text{By factoring } x^2 - 39x + 108$$

By setting each factor equal to 0,

$$x - 36 = 0 \qquad \text{or} \qquad x - 3 = 0$$

$$x = 36 \qquad \text{or} \qquad x = 3$$

Since $0 < x < 30$, $x = 36$ can't be a solution. The only solution is $x = 3$. The width of the brick walk is 3 yards.

Let's find the area of the walk. We need to find the area of the rectangle that is 48 yd by 30 yd and subtract the area of the garden from this rectangle. The area of the walk is

$$(48 \text{ yd} \cdot 30 \text{ yd}) - 1008 \text{ yd}^2$$

$$= (1440 \text{ yd}^2 - 1008 \text{ yd}^2)$$

$$= 432 \text{ yd}^2$$

The width of the walk is 3 yards, and the area of the walk is 432 yd².

✔ Progress Check 1

(a) The length of a rectangle is 5 more than its width and the area is 204 square units. Find the dimensions of this rectangle.

(b) You have a rectangular swimming pool in your backyard. The width of the swimming pool is 16 feet and the length is 20 feet. You would like to surround the swimming pool with a uniform walk. If you want the total area of the swimming pool plus the walk to be 480 ft², find the width of the walk.

Answers

(a) length: 17 units; width: 12 units

(b) 2 feet

Example 2   Minimizing Walking Distance

In some big cities, some traffic lights are set up to permit crossing from one street corner to a diagonally opposite corner by walking along a diagonal path. In the figure on the next page, there are traffic lights at the corners labeled A, B, and C. The distance between B and C is 5 feet and the distance between A and C is 25 feet.

You can get from A to C in one of two ways: cross from A to B, and then from B to C; or, when the traffic lights at A and C give a certain signal, cross along the diagonal directly from A to C. Compare the distance walked along each path.

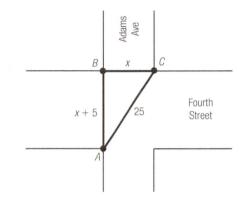

Solution

Let the distance between points B and C be x. Then, the distance between points A and B is $x + 5$. The distance between points A and C is 25 feet.

Since the points A, B, and C form a right triangle, we can use the Pythagorean Theorem to find the distances between B and C and between A and B.

Thus, we have

$$x^2 + (x + 5)^2 = (25)^2$$

Solve the equation for x.

$$x^2 + (x + 5)^2 = (25)^2$$
$$x^2 + x^2 + 10x + 25 = 625$$

$2x^2 + 10x + 25 = 625$	By simplifying the left-hand side
$2x^2 + 10x + -600 = 0$	By subtracting 625 from both sides
$2(x^2 + 5x - 300) = 0$	By factoring out 2
$2(x - 15)(x + 20) = 0$	By factoring

Setting each factor equal to 0,

$$x - 15 = 0 \qquad \text{or} \qquad x + 20 = 0$$
$$x = 15 \qquad \text{or} \qquad x = -20$$

Since the dimension must be greater than 0, the only solution is $x = 15$. The distance from point B to C is 15 feet and the distance from point A to B is $15 + 5 = 20$ feet.

If you take the path from A to B and then from B to C, you will walk

$$15 + 20 = 35 \text{ feet}$$

If you take the diagonal path from A to C, you will walk 25 feet.

✔ Progress Check 2

(a) An isosceles triangle has two equal legs. Find the length of each leg if the hypotenuse is 18 cm.

(b) The diagonal of a rectangular baseball field is 50 feet. The length of the field is 10 feet longer than its width. If you walk across the field diagonally rather than along one leg and then the next, what distance do you save?

Answers

(a) $9\sqrt{2}$ cm   (b) 20 feet

Given a quadratic equation $f(x) = ax^2 + bx + c$, $(a \neq 0)$ we can find the maximum value or the minimum value at its vertex. We find the vertex of the quadratic function using the vertex formula

$$V = \left(\frac{-b}{2a}, \frac{4ac - b^2}{4a} \right)$$

We can also write the quadratic function $f(x) = ax^2 + bx + c$, $(a \neq 0)$ in the form $f(x) = a(x - h)^2 + k$, $(a \neq 0)$. The vertex is (h, k). If the coefficient of x^2, a, is positive, then the graph of the quadratic function is a parabola that faces upward. Then the function has its minimum value at its vertex. If the coefficient of x^2, a, is negative, then the graph of the quadratic function is a parabola that faces downward. Then the function has its maximum value at its vertex. The next example shows how we find the maximum function value.

Example 3   Find the Maximum Height

A baseball is thrown upward from the top of a 96-foot tall building with an initial velocity of 80 feet per second. The height, h, of the baseball after t seconds is given by the equation

$$h = -16t^2 + 80t + 96$$

(a) Find the height of the baseball after 2 seconds.

(b) Find the time when the baseball hits its maximum height.

(c) Find its maximum height.

(d) Find the time when the baseball hits the ground.

Solution

(a) At time $t = 2$, the height is

$$h = -16(2)^2 + 80(2) + 96 \qquad \text{By substituting } t = 2$$
$$h = -16(4) + 160 + 96$$
$$h = 192 \text{ feet}$$

The baseball reaches the height of 192 feet after 2 seconds.

(b) To find the time when the baseball hits the maximum height we need to find the x-coordinate of the vertex. Using the vertex formula,

$$x\text{-coordinate} = \frac{-b}{2a}$$

By substituting $a = -16$ and $b = 80$,

$$x = \frac{-(80)}{2(-16)} = \frac{5}{2} = 2.5 \text{ seconds}$$

The baseball hits the maximum height after 2.5 seconds.

(c) To find the maximum height, we need to find the y-coordinate at the vertex. We may use the vertex formula, or we may substitute $t = \frac{5}{2}$ into the function to find the y-coordinate. By substituting $t = \frac{5}{2}$ into the function,

$$h = -16\left(\frac{5}{2}\right)^2 + 80\left(\frac{5}{2}\right) + 96$$

$$h = -16\left(\frac{25}{4}\right) + 40(5) + 96$$

$$h = -100 + 200 + 96$$

$$h = 196$$

The baseball reaches the maximum height of 196 feet.

(d) When the baseball hits the ground, the height of the baseball is 0. By substituting $h = 0$, we solve for time t.

$$h = -16t^2 + 80t + 96$$
$$0 = -16t^2 + 80t + 96$$
$$0 = -16(t^2 - 5t - 6) \qquad \text{By factoring out } -16$$
$$0 = -16(t - 6)(t + 1) \qquad \text{By factoring } t^2 - 5t - 6 = (t - 6)(t + 1)$$

Setting each factor equal to 0,

$$t - 6 = 0 \qquad \text{or} \qquad t + 1 = 0$$
$$t = 6 \qquad \text{or} \qquad t = -1$$

Since we can't have negative time, $t = -1$ is not a solution. The only solution is $t = 6$ seconds.

Therefore, the baseball hits the ground after $t = 6$ seconds.

✔ Progress Check 3

(a) The sum of two numbers is 80. Find two numbers that yield the maximum product.

(b) The difference of two numbers is 24. Find two numbers that yield the minimum product.

(c) You throw a rock upward from the ground. Its height in feet above the ground after t seconds is given by the function $f(t) = -12t^2 + 16t$. Find the time and height when the rock reaches the maximum height.

Answers

(a) 40 and 40

(b) 12 and -12

(c) The rock reaches its maximum height of $\frac{16}{3} = 5\frac{1}{3}$ feet in $\frac{2}{3}$ seconds.

■ ■ ■

Terms and Symbols

completing the square	quadratic formula	second-degree inequality
critical value	quadratic function	solving by factoring
discriminant	radical equation	substitution of variable
double root	repeated root	zeros of a function
extraneous solution	second-degree equation in	
quadratic equation	one variable	

Key Ideas for Review

Topic	Key Idea
Zero product rule	If the product of two real numbers is 0, at least one of the numbers must be 0. Thus, $ab = 0$ only if $a = 0$ or $b = 0$, or both $a = 0$ and $b = 0$.
Quadratic equation	A quadratic equation has the form $$ax^2 + bx + c = 0, a \neq 0$$
solving when $b = 0$	When $b = 0$, the resulting quadratic equation $$ax^2 + c = 0$$ has solutions $x = \pm\sqrt{-c / a}$.
solving by factoring	If a quadratic equation can be written as a product of linear factors $$(rx + s)(ux + v) = 0$$ then $$x = -\frac{s}{r} \quad \text{and} \quad x = -\frac{v}{u}$$ are the roots of the quadratic equation.
Quadratic formula	The quadratic formula $$x = \frac{-b \pm \sqrt{b^2 - 4ac}}{2a}$$ provides us with a pair of solutions to the quadratic equation $ax^2 + bx + c = 0, a > 0$.
discriminant	The expression $b^2 - 4ac$ found under the radical in the quadratic formula is called the discriminant and determines the nature of the roots of the quadratic equation.
Power rule	If both sides of an equation are raised to the same power, then the resulting equation may have extraneous roots that are not solutions of the original equation.
Radical equations	Certain forms, such as radical equations, can be solved by raising both sides of the equation to a power. The solutions of the resulting equation must be checked to see that they satisfy the original equation.

(continues)

Key Ideas for Review

Topic	Key Idea
Substitution of variable	The method of substitution of variable can be used to convert certain nonquadratic equations to quadratic equations.
Second-degree inequalities	
critical value	The linear factor $ax + b$ equals 0 at the critical value $$x = -\frac{b}{a}$$ and has opposite signs depending on whether x is to the left or right of the critical value on a number line.
solution process	To solve an inequality, write it as a product of linear factors with the right-hand side equal to 0. Analyze the signs to the left and right of each critical value. The product and quotient of linear factors can be negative (<0) only if an odd number of factors is negative; they can be positive (>0) only if an even number of factors is negative.

Common Errors

1. The equation $2x^2 = 10$ has as its solutions $x = \pm\sqrt{5}$. Remember to write $\pm$ before the radical when solving a quadratic.

2. The quadratic equation $3x^2 + x = 0$ can be factored as
$$x(3x + 1) = 0$$
The solutions are then $x = 0$ and $x = -\frac{1}{3}$. Remember that each linear factor yields a root; in particular, the factor x yields the root $x = 0$.

3. When solving by factoring make sure that one side of the equation is zero. Note that
$$(x + 1)(x - 2) = 2$$
does *not* imply that $x + 1 = 2$ or $x - 2 = 2$.

4. To complete the square for
$$4(x^2 + 6x \quad) = 7$$
we must add $\left(\frac{6}{2}\right)^2 = 3^2 = 9$ within the parentheses. To balance the equation, we must add $4 \cdot 9 = 36$ to the right-hand side.
$$4(x^2 + 6x + 9) = 7 + 36$$

Don't write
$$4(x^2 + 6x + 9) = 7 + 9$$

5. The quadratic formula is
$$x = \frac{-b \pm \sqrt{b^2 - 4ac}}{2a}$$

Don't use the formula as
$$x = -b \pm \frac{\sqrt{b^2 - 4ac}}{2a}$$

6. Proper use of the quadratic formula requires that the equation be written in the form $ax^2 + bx + c = 0$. Remember that a, b, and c are coefficients and therefore include the sign.

7. To solve an inequality such as
$$x^2 + 2x \geq 3$$
you must make one side of the equation zero:
$$x^2 + 2x - 3 \geq 0$$
and then factor. *Don't* write
$$x(x + 2) \geq 3$$
and then attempt to analyze the signs. The inequality does *not* imply that $x \geq 3$ or that $x + 2 \geq 3$.

8. When solving

$$(x + 3)(2x - 1) < 0$$

   don't write

$$(x + 3) < 0 \quad \text{or} \quad 2x - 1 < 0$$

   You must analyze the linear factors $(x + 3)$ and $(2x - 1)$ and find the values of x for which the factors have opposite signs.

9. If both sides of an equation are raised to a power, some of the solutions of the resulting equation may be extraneous, that is, they may not satisfy the original equation. Always substitute all answers in the original equation to see if the answers are or are not solutions.

Review Exercises

Solutions to exercises whose numbers are in bold are in the Solutions section in the back of the book.

9.1 In Exercises 1–4 solve the given equation.

1. $8x^2 - 200 = 0$
2. $4y^2 - 144 = 0$
3. $(x - 2)^2 = 9$
4. $(2t + 1)^2 + 4 = 0$

In Exercises 5–8 solve the given equation by factoring.

5. $x^2 + x - 6 = 0$
6. $2y^2 - 3y - 2 = 0$
7. $3r^2 - r = 0$
8. $8x^2 - 50 = 0$

In Exercises 9 and 10 solve by completing the square.

9. $x^2 - 5x = 3$
10. $3x^2 + 12x = 4$

9.2 In Exercises 11–16 solve by the quadratic formula.

11. $x^2 + 2x - 3 = 0$
12. $6x^2 + 4x - 2 = 0$
13. $2x^2 + 4x + 1 = 0$
14. $-3x^2 - 2x + 3 = 0$
15. $2x^2 - x + 1 = 0$
16. $4x^2 + 2x + 3 = 0$

9.3 In Exercises 17–22 determine the nature of the roots of each quadratic equation.

17. $-4x^2 + x - 2 = 0$
18. $3y^2 + y = 4$
19. $9r^2 + 1 = 6r$
20. $3x^2 + 4 = 0$
21. $2y^2 = y$
22. $2s^2 + s - 2 = 0$

In Exercises 23–26 determine the number of x-intercepts of the graph of the given function.

23. $f(x) = x^2 - 2x + 6$
24. $f(x) = 3x^2 - x - 2$
25. $f(x) = x^2 - x + \dfrac{1}{4}$
26. $f(x) = 6x^2 - x - 2$

9.4 27. The width of a rectangular field is 3 feet less than twice its length. If the area of the field is 54 square feet, find the dimensions of the field.

28. A charitable organization rented an auditorium at a cost of $420 and split the cost among the attendees. If 10 additional persons had attended the meeting, the cost per person would have decreased by $1. How many attendees were there in the original group?

9.5 In Exercises 29 and 30 solve for x.

29. $x + \sqrt{x + 10} = 10$

30. $\sqrt{5x + 6} - \sqrt{2x + 4} = 2$

In Exercises 31 and 32 indicate an appropriate substitution of variable that will change the given equation to a quadratic equation, and solve the given equation.

31. $2x^4 + x^2 - 6 = 0$
32. $\dfrac{2}{x^4} - \dfrac{9}{x^2} + 10 = 0$

9.6 In Exercises 33 and 34 find the critical values for the given inequality.

33. $x^2 - 2x - 8 < 0$
34. $\dfrac{x - 3}{x - 5} \geq 0$

In Exercises 35 and 36 solve, and graph the solution set of the given inequality.

35. $2x^2 - x - 3 \leq 0$
36. $\dfrac{2s - 1}{3s + 2} > 0$

Progress Test 9A

1. Solve $3x^2 + 7 = 0$.

2. Solve $x - \sqrt{12 - 2x} = 2$.

3. Solve $(2x - 3)^2 = 16$.

4. Solve $\left(\dfrac{x}{2} - 1\right)^2 = -15$.

5. Solve $2x^2 - 7x = 4$ by factoring.

6. Solve $3x^2 - 5x = 2$ by factoring.

7. Solve $3x^2 - 6x = 8$ by completing the square.

8. Use the discriminant to determine the nature of the roots of the equation $3x^2 - 2x - 5 = 0$.

9. Use the discriminant to determine the nature of the roots of the equation $2x^2 - 4x = -7$.

10. Solve $2x^2 + 3x - \frac{1}{2} = 0$ by the quadratic formula.

11. Solve $3x^2 = -2x$ by the quadratic formula.

12. Solve $2x^2 + 5x \le 3$.

13. Solve $\dfrac{x + 1}{x - 1} \le 0$.

14. Solve $\dfrac{2x - 3}{4 - x} > 0$.

15. The length of a rectangle is 5 meters greater than its width. If the area of the rectangle is 546 square meters, find the dimensions of the rectangle.

16. A faster assembly line can fill an order in 6 fewer hours than it takes a slower assembly line to fill the same order. Working together, they can fill the order in 3 hours. How long would it take each assembly line to fill the order alone?

Progress Test 9B

1. Solve $4x^2 - 9 = 0$.

2. Solve $x - \sqrt{11 - 2x} = 4$.

3. Solve $\left(\dfrac{x}{3} - 2\right)^2 = 25$.

4. Solve $(3x + \frac{1}{2})^2 = -10$.

5. Solve $x^2 - x - 12 = 0$ by factoring.

6. Solve $2x^2 = -3x - 1$ by factoring.

7. Solve $2x^2 - 6x + 5 = 0$ by completing the square.

8. Use the discriminant to determine the nature of the roots of the equation $4x^2 - 12x + 9 = 0$.

9. Use the discriminant to determine the nature of the roots of the equation $3x^2 - 4x = -3$.

10. Solve $2x^2 - 5x + 4 = 0$ by the quadratic formula.

11. Solve $3x^2 = -5$ by the quadratic formula.

12. Solve $2x^2 + x \ge 10$.

13. Solve $\dfrac{2x - 1}{2x + 1} \ge 0$.

14. Solve $\dfrac{3x + 1}{x - 2} < 0$.

15. The length of one leg of a right triangle exceeds the length of the other by 3 meters. If the hypotenuse is 15 meters long, find the lengths of the legs of the triangle.

16. The formula
$$s = \frac{n(n + 1)}{2}$$
gives the sum of the first n natural numbers 1, 2, 3, ... How many consecutive natural numbers, starting with 1, must be added to obtain a sum of 325?

Chapter 9 Project

In the chapter opener, you were asked the question "how do you find the product of two numbers without multiplying them directly?"

One answer is, by using the "quarter squares rule."

Look at Exercises 69 and 70 in section 5.1, and Exercise 21 in section 9.4.

Here is the formula:

$$\left(\frac{a + b}{2}\right)^2 - \left(\frac{a - b}{2}\right)^2 = ab$$

Try it! Find the product of $a = 501$ and $b = 299$.

Now see if you can prove that this formula always works. Expand the two squared terms on the left-hand side, and combine like terms.

Make a list of pairs a and b for which you think it might be easier to use the quarter squares rule, rather than evaluating the product directly.

CHAPTER 10

Practice Problems

The most beautiful experience we can have is the mysterious. It is the fundamental emotion that stands at the cradle of true art and science.

—Albert Einstein

Problem Solving Strategies

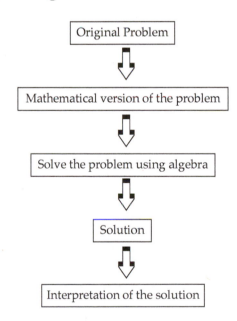

Problems

1. Magic square:

   Fill in each square with a number 1 through 9 so that the sum of the numbers in each row, each column, and the two diagonals is the same.

2. A rectangular flower garden is 30 ft wide and 20 ft long. The owner wants to surround the garden with a grass border of uniform width that extends all the way around the edge of the garden. He has 600 square feet of grass for the border. How wide can the border be?

3. A lot has the shape of a right triangle with the hypotenuse that is 3 ft less than twice the length of the shorter leg. The longer leg is 3 ft longer than the shorter leg. Find the area of the right triangle.

4. An oval athletic field consists of a square and semicircles at opposite ends. The total area of the field is 1400 square feet.

   (a) Sketch the field.

   (b) Find the length of the square.

5. Nafisa walks 100 meters due south, then 100 meters due west, and then 20 meters due north. How far is she from her starting point?

6. An investment of $3,000 is made by Zini at an annual simple interest rate of 6%. How much additional money must she invest at 9% interest so that the total interest earned will be 8% of the total investment?

7. Anisa invests $6,000 in two simple interest accounts. In one account the annual simple interest rate is 5% and in the second account it is 7%. How much did she invest in each account if both accounts earn the same amount of interest?

8. The formula for the period of a simple pendulum is

$$T = 2\pi \sqrt{\frac{l}{g}}$$

   where T = period of oscillation, π = 3.14, l = length of the string in feet, and g = acceleration due to gravity (32 feet per second per second). Find the length of a simple pendulum if T = 2.52 seconds.

9. How many liters of pure orange juice need to be added to 10 liters of a fruit drink that is originally 10% orange juice in order to make an orange drink that is 20% orange juice?

10. Jiyoung purchases 20 apples and 30 oranges for a total cost of $40. A second purchase, at the same prices, included 30 apples and 10 oranges for a total cost of $25. Find the cost of an apple and an orange.

Answers to Odd-Numbered Exercises, Review Exercises, and Progress Tests

Chapter 1
Exercise Set 1.1

1. a, b, c, d

3. a, c

5. a, b, c, d

7. a, c, d

9. c, e

11. c, e

13. F

15. F

17. F

19. T

21. T

23.
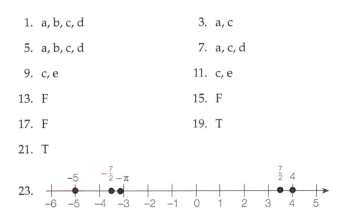

25. (a) 10   (b) -20 (c) 20   (d) -5

27. 0

29. -4

31. -5

33. 3

35. 0

37. 5

39.
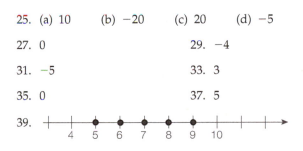

41. Although pi is irrational, the calculator rounds it off in order to display an appxoimate value.

Exercise Set 1.2

1. 4

3. 27

5. 0

7. 8/33

9. 10/3

11. 4/3

13. 3/2

15. 12

17. 7

19. 25

21. 60

23. 180

25. 17/12

27. 5/12

29. 8/23

31. 20/39

33. 1/5, 0.2

35. 131/200, 0.655

37. 6/125, 0.048

39. 6/5, 1.2

41. 1/500, 0.002

43. 5%

45. 42.5%

47. 628%

49. 60%

51. 225%

53. 28.57%

55. 21

57. 42

59. 0.2

61. 5/32

63. 125/144

65. 52/89

67. 850/304

69. $58

71. $6480

73. $115,200

75. $32.20

77. 8%

79. $8649.60

81. $399,000

83. $\dfrac{3}{100,000}$

85. $32\dfrac{37}{100}$

87. $-54\dfrac{2}{100}$

89. 0.1

91. 121.0007

93. 79.03

Exercise Set 1.3

1. T

3. T

5. 11

7. 2

9. 64

11. 1/11

13. 10

15. 5

17. 33

19. 1/2

21. 12

23. 8/3

25. 5/4

27. 1/3

29. 18.84

31. 9.4

33. 3.76

35. 1.06

37. (a) $2160   (b) $2480   (c) $2080   (d) $2106.67

39. $3(1.25) + 2(1.10) + 1.5(2.29)$

41. $0.85d + 1.35h + 0.8f$

43. -0.358; approximately -0.343

Exercise Set 1.4

1. 8

3. -7

5. 2

7. -2

9. 3

11. 2

13. 8

15. -5

17. -13

19. -2

21. -3

23. 10

25. $-1/2$

27. 4

29. -3

31. $-3/5$

33. 18

35. $-9/2$

37. 6

39. 0

41. 0

43. -3

45. -4

47. -12

49. $2x - 3y$

51. x/y

53. $-4/x$

55. -7

57. 2/3

59. 1

61. -1

63. 216

65. 8/125

67. 625/81

69. -8

71. 3

73. 12°C

75. $1200

77. $y - x$

79. average profit = $500

Exercise Set 1.5

1. commutative (addition)

3. commutative (multiplication)

5. distributive

7. distributive

9. associative (addition)

11. commutative (addition)

13. associative (multiplication)

15. commutative and associative (multiplication)

17. commutative and associative (addition)

19. $1 - 2 \neq 2 - 1; 1 - (3 - 2) \neq (1 - 3) - 2$

21. $2(a + 2) = 2a + 4$

23. $(a - b)2 = 2a - 2b$

25. $(2a + 3) + a = 3(a + 1)$ 27. $4 - x$

29. $-x - 5$ 31. $12x$

33. $6abc$ 35. $6 + 8a - 4b$

37. $-\dfrac{1}{2x}$ 39. $-\dfrac{4}{3}xy$

41. $2ab$ 43. $\dfrac{5}{4}x - \dfrac{1}{4}y$

45. $3a - \dfrac{5}{2}b + \dfrac{15}{2}c$

47. $4x + 4y - 2z + 4w$ 49. $x + 2y + 2u - 8$

51. 1.31 53. 2.01

55. $a = 2, b = 3, c = 4$ 57. $a = 3, b = 2, c = 5$

Exercise Set 1.6

1. 2   3. 1.5

5. −2   7. 1

9. 4   11. 2

13. 1/5   15. −1

17. 6   19. −7

21. 1   23. 0.31

25. 3   27. 2

29. 8/5   31. $4 > 1$

33. $2 \leqslant 3$ 35. $3 \geqslant 0$

37. $<$ 39. $>$

41. $<$ 43. $<$

45. $>$ 47. $<$

49. $>$ 51. $<$

53. $>$ 55. $>$

57. $>$ 59. $x \geqslant -1$

61. $-3 \leqslant x < 4$

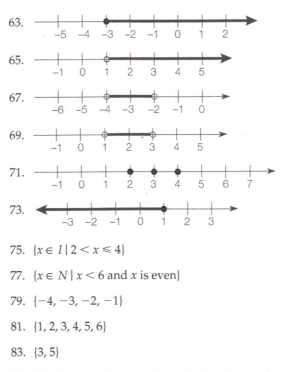

63.

65.

67.

69.

71.

73.

75. $\{x \in I \mid 2 < x \leqslant 4\}$

77. $\{x \in N \mid x < 6 \text{ and } x \text{ is even}\}$

79. $\{-4, -3, -2, -1\}$

81. $\{1, 2, 3, 4, 5, 6\}$

83. $\{3, 5\}$

85. The distance from a to b equals the distance from b to a.

Review Exercises

1. $\{1, 2, 3, 4\}$ 2. $\{-3, -2, -1\}$

3. $\{2\}$ 4. T

5. F   6. F

7. F

8.

9. 3   10. −4

11. 0   12. 14

13. $-5/2$ 14. $16/35$

15. $6/5$ 16. $6/5$

17. $-15/23$ 18. $7/100, 0.07$

19. 9/400, 0.0225

20. 452%

21. 2.1%

22. 2%

23. T

24. F

25. F

26. T

27. $51

28. −2

29. −2

30. −8

31. −1

32. 1

33. 8

34. 11

35. $y - x + 1000$

36. distributive

37. associative (addition), commutative (addition)

38. distributive, commutative (multiplication), commutative (addition)

39. associative (multiplication), commutative (multiplication)

40. $2(a + 3) = 2a + 6$

41. $\dfrac{4 + a}{2} = 2 + a/2$

42. $-2(a - 3) = -2a + 6$

43. $2(ab) = (2b)a$

44. $-1/7$

45. $3/2$

46. $a = 3, b = -3$

47. 5

48. 4

49. $x \geq -1$

50. $x < 2$

51.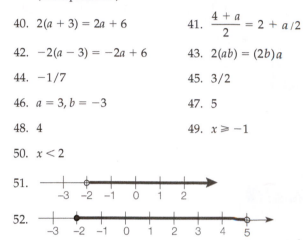

52.

Progress Test 1A

1. b

2. c

3.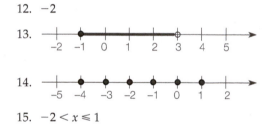

4. 1/4

5. 4

6. 2

7. $-x - 2y$

8. b

9. 3/5

10. −6

11. 9

12. −2

13.

14.

15. $-2 < x \leq 1$

Progress Test 1B

1. c

2. c

3.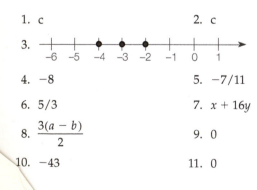

4. −8

5. −7/11

6. 5/3

7. $x + 16y$

8. $\dfrac{3(a - b)}{2}$

9. 0

10. −43

11. 0

12. −140

13.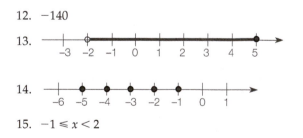

14.

15. $-1 \leq x < 2$

Chapter 2

Exercise Set 2.1

1. T	3. F	33. 3	35. 5
5. T	7. T	37. $-7/2$	39. -7
9. 4	11. $-5/4$	41. 1	43. $8/(5-k)$
13. -2	15. 1	45. $(6+k)/5$	47. C
17. $-4/3$	19. 2	49. I	51. C
21. 6	23. 3	53. 4	55. 20
25. 4	27. $3/2$	57. $41/4$	
29. $-10/3$	31. -2		

61. $x = 2050$. x represents the number of calories the man should eat each day to lose one pound per week.

Exercise Set 2.2

1. $250	3. 50	29. 16, 28	31. 8
5. 8.5 cents	7. 260	33. 5, 13	35. 68°F
9. 80	11. no	37. $12.30	39. 4 m and 8 m
13. $1.20	15. 8	41. 9/2 m by 27/2 m	43. 9 cm
17. $-10, 38$	19. 6	45. 65°, 65°, and 50°	47. $W = 5, L = 15$
21. 9 and 12	23. 11, 3	49. $W = 27, L = 43$	51. 5, 8, 11
25. 24, 27	27. 15, 45		

Exercise Set 2.3

1. $\dfrac{C}{2\pi}$

3. $\dfrac{S}{2\pi r}$

21. $\dfrac{A-c}{b}$

23. $-\dfrac{2kt}{5A+3bt}$

5. $\dfrac{2A}{h} - b'$

7. $\dfrac{A-p}{Pr}$

25. (a) $\dfrac{A-P}{Pt}$ (b) $\dfrac{A-P}{Pr}$

9. $\dfrac{a_n - a_1}{d} + 1$

11. $\dfrac{S-a_1}{S}$

27. $\dfrac{a(1+A)}{1-A}$

13. $\dfrac{A}{2\pi r} - r$

15. $\dfrac{3V}{\pi r^2}$

29. $\dfrac{a-St}{t-S}$

17. $\dfrac{2s}{t^2}$

19. $\dfrac{S}{(1+r)^t}$

Exercise Set 2.4

1. c, d, e

3. a, c, d, e

5. $x < 4$

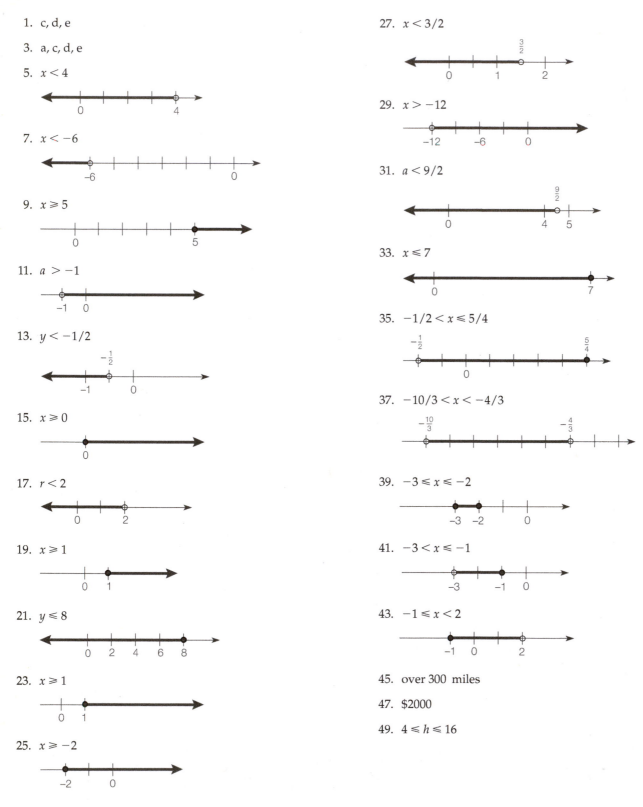

7. $x < -6$

9. $x \geqslant 5$

11. $a > -1$

13. $y < -1/2$

15. $x \geqslant 0$

17. $r < 2$

19. $x \geqslant 1$

21. $y \leqslant 8$

23. $x \geqslant 1$

25. $x \geqslant -2$

27. $x < 3/2$

29. $x > -12$

31. $a < 9/2$

33. $x \leqslant 7$

35. $-1/2 < x \leqslant 5/4$

37. $-10/3 < x < -4/3$

39. $-3 \leqslant x \leqslant -2$

41. $-3 < x \leqslant -1$

43. $-1 \leqslant x < 2$

45. over 300 miles

47. $2000

49. $4 \leqslant h \leqslant 16$

Exercise Set 2.5

1. b, d

3. b, d

5. b, c

7. e

9. 1, −5

11. 11/2, 9/2

13. 1, −2

15. 2, −2/3

17. 2, −4/3

19. −5/2, 1/2

21. −5 < x < 5

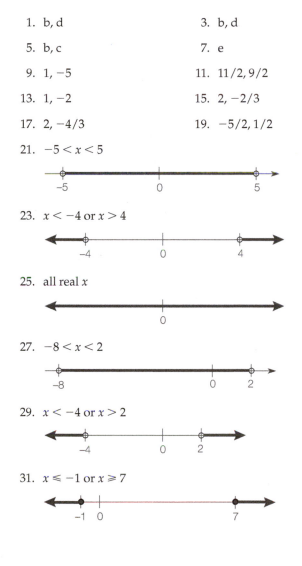

23. x < −4 or x > 4

25. all real x

27. −8 < x < 2

29. x < −4 or x > 2

31. x ≤ −1 or x ≥ 7

33. −6 ≤ x ≤ 2

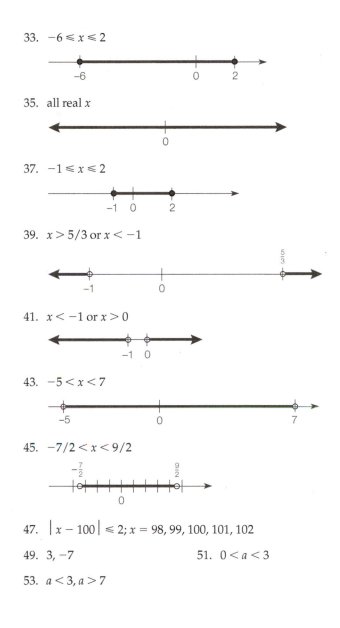

35. all real x

37. −1 ≤ x ≤ 2

39. x > 5/3 or x < −1

41. x < −1 or x > 0

43. −5 < x < 7

45. −7/2 < x < 9/2

47. $|x - 100| \leq 2; x = 98, 99, 100, 101, 102$

49. 3, −7

51. 0 < a < 3

53. a < 3, a > 7

Review Exercises

1. 5/3

2. 3

3. 6

4. 2

5. 1/2

6. 1/2

7. The domestic profit is 14 million dollars; the foreign profit is 5 million dollars.

8. One book costs $25; the other costs $19.

9. 20 sec

10. 12 in by 11 in

11. $\dfrac{r - 2s}{4t}$

12. $\dfrac{2B + C + D}{3}$

13. $\dfrac{3A + C - D}{2}$

14. $\dfrac{ef - g - 2a}{3d}$

15. x < 3

16. x ≤ 6

17. x > 1

18. x ≥ 5/3

19. x > 7

20. no real x

21. 3/2 < x < 3

22. −5/3 < x ≤ 2/3

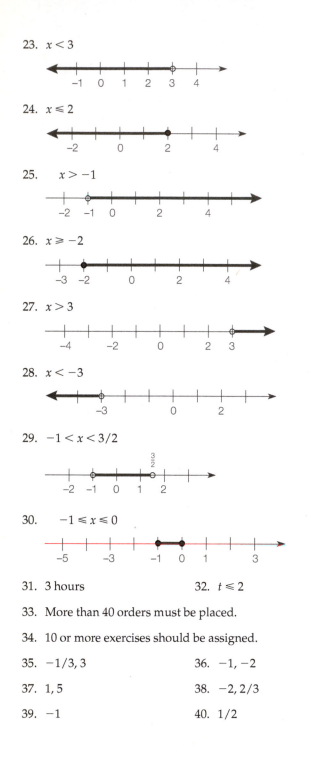

23. $x < 3$

24. $x \leq 2$

25. $x > -1$

26. $x \geq -2$

27. $x > 3$

28. $x < -3$

29. $-1 < x < 3/2$

30. $-1 \leq x \leq 0$

31. 3 hours   32. $t \leq 2$

33. More than 40 orders must be placed.

34. 10 or more exercises should be assigned.

35. $-1/3, 3$ 36. $-1, -2$

37. $1, 5$ 38. $-2, 2/3$

39. -1 40. $1/2$

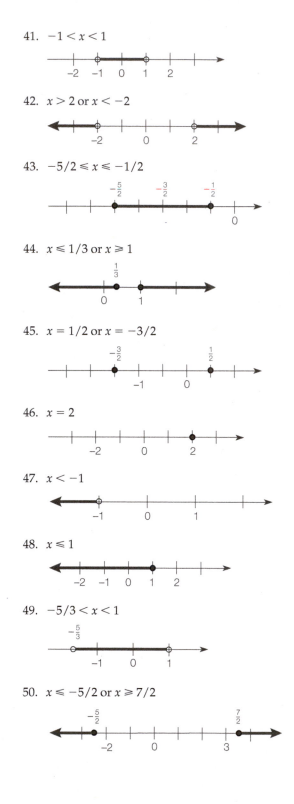

41. $-1 < x < 1$

42. $x > 2$ or $x < -2$

43. $-5/2 \leq x \leq -1/2$

44. $x \leq 1/3$ or $x \geq 1$

45. $x = 1/2$ or $x = -3/2$

46. $x = 2$

47. $x < -1$

48. $x \leq 1$

49. $-5/3 < x < 1$

50. $x \leq -5/2$ or $x \geq 7/2$

Progress Test 2A

1. $15/4$

2. -4

3. F

4. $h = V/\pi r^2$

5. $x = \dfrac{-1}{k+2}$

6. 70

7. 3200

8. $L = 21/2, W = 15/2$

9. 14, 16, 18

10. $3000 at 6%, $2000 at 7%

11. $x > -2$

12. $x \geqslant 1$

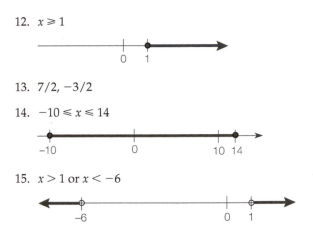

13. $7/2, -3/2$

14. $-10 \leqslant x \leqslant 14$

15. $x > 1$ or $x < -6$

Progress Test 2B

1. -2

2. 5

3. F

4. $\dfrac{1}{h}(2A - ch) = b$

5. $\dfrac{1}{2(k-1)}$

6. 40

7. 80

8. $W = 7, L = 4$

9. 25, 21

10. $4000 at 5%, $4000 at 8%

11. $x < -5/2$

12. $x \leqslant -1$

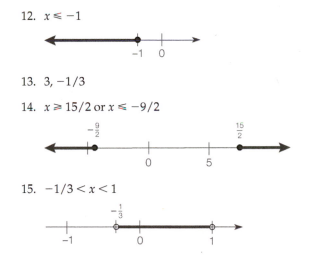

13. $3, -1/3$

14. $x \geqslant 15/2$ or $x \leqslant -9/2$

15. $-1/3 < x < 1$

Chapter 3

Exercise Set 3.1

1. 10 nickels, 25 dimes

3. 14 10-dollar bills, 8 20-dollar bills, 32 5-dollar bills

5. 300 children, 400 adults

7. 28 5-cent stamps, 26 10-cent stamps, 18 15-cent stamps

9. 61 3-dollar tickets, 40 5-dollar tickets, 20 6-dollar tickets

11. 20 quart jugs, 40 pint jugs, 12 gallon jugs

Exercise Set 3.2

1. $5000 at 7%, $3000 at 8%

3. $5806.45 at 8.5%, $4193.55 at 7%

5. $3000 in black-and-white, $1000 in color

7. $32,000

9. $3400 at 6%, $3700 at 8%, $13,600 at 10%

11. $4.80

13. Goya: $24,900; Monet: $10,800

Exercise Set 3.3

1. 20 hr

3. 50 mph, 54 mph

5. 40 mi

7. 40 km per hour, 80 km per hour

9. 4 hr

Exercise Set 3.4

1. 20 lb

3. 30 kg of 40%, 90 kg of 80%

5. 15 gal

7. 5 qt

9. 20 lb

Review Exercises

1. 3 quarters, 6 dimes, 8 half-dollars

2. 4 16-transistor components, 2 48-transistor components, 5 64-transistor components

3. 29 2-ton slabs, 9 5-ton slabs, 59 8-ton slabs

4. 4 20-cent stamps, 7 40-cent stamps, 2 1-dollar stamps

5. $15,000 at 10%, $25,000 at 8%

6. $4000 in classical, $8000 in popular

7. $4500 at 10% profit, $2500 at 5% loss

8. $5000 to the AB company, $5500 to the CD company, $4000 to the EF company

9. 200 mph, 100 mph

10. 12 hr

11. 2 lb

12. 5 lb

13. 0.6 hr

14. 400 mph, 500 mph

15. 20 gal

16. 5 lb

17. 0.0000013%

18. 0.08755 mL

19. There are 172 L of gas in the mixture, and 17% is the final concentration of the mixture.

Progress Test 3A

1. $C = 4T - 3$

2. 17, 23

3. $L = 10/3$ cm, $W = 8/3$ cm

4. 3 quarters, 10 dimes, 17 nickels

5. six 30-pound, six 50-pound, eleven 60-pound crates

6. $8000

7. $6000 at 6.5%, $6200 at 7.5%, $12,300 at 9%

8. moped: 15 mph; car: 45 mph

9. 240 miles

10. 30 oz of 60%, 90 oz of 80%

11. 37.5 cm^3

Progress Test 3B

1. $D = \frac{1}{3}R + 4$

2. 16, 23

3. first side: 3.6 cm; second side: 5.8 cm; third side: 5.6 cm

4. fourteen $1, four $5, two $10 coupons

5. six 1-oz, five 2-oz, three 3-oz samples

6. $3000 at 6%, $15,000 at 7.2%

7. $8000 at 6%, $6000 at 8%

8. 6 P.M.

9. 12 hr

10. 3.75 lb

11. 20 gal

Chapter 4

Exercise Set 4.1

1. base: 2; exponent: 5

3. base: t; exponent: 4

5. bases: 3, y; exponents: 1, 5

7. bases: 3, x, y; exponents: 1, 2, 3

9. 3^3

11. $\left(\dfrac{1}{3}\right)^4$

13. $3y^4$

15. (a) 36   (b) -36

17. b^7

19. $6x^6$

21. $-20y^9$

23. $\dfrac{20}{21}v^8$

25. $-3x^4$

27. c, d

29.

Term	$4x^4$	$-2x^2$	x	-3
Coefficient	4	-2	1	-3

31.

Term	$\frac{2}{3}x^3y$	$\frac{1}{2}xy$	$-y$	2
Coefficient	$\frac{2}{3}$	$\frac{1}{2}$	-1	2

33.

Term	$\frac{1}{3}x^3$	$\frac{1}{2}x^2y$	$-2x$	y	7
Coefficient	$\frac{1}{3}$	$\frac{1}{2}$	-2	1	7

35.

Term	$3x^3$	$-2x^2$	3
Degree	3	2	0

37.

Term	$4x^4$	$-5x^3$	$2x^2$	$-5x$	1
Degree	4	3	2	1	0

39.

Term	$\frac{3}{2}x^4$	$2xy^2$	y^3	$-y$	2
Degree	4	3	3	1	0

41. 3

43. 3

45. 4

47. b

49. 13

51. 11

53. 176.2

55. πr^2

57. (a) the area of the field
    (b) the perimeter of the rectangle
    (c) the perimeter of the square
    (d) the total amount of fencing

Exercise Set 4.2

1. $7x$

3. $3x^3 - 6x^2$

5. $4x^2 - x + 4$

7. $7x^2 + 3$

9. $-3rs$

11. $\dfrac{6}{5}rs^3 - 2r^2s^2 - r^2s + 2r^2 + 7$

13. $-x^2 - 4x + 14$

15. $y^2 - 2x^2 - xy + 7y$

17. $24y$

19. $6x^2 - 3$

21. $x^2y^2 + 3xy - 3y - x - 3$

23. $\dfrac{19}{10}x^3 - 3x^2 + x + 2$

25. $3rs^3 - 2rs + r - s + 3$

27. $2x^2 - 6x + 9$

29. $4xy + 2y + 3$

31. $5r^2s^2 + rs^2 - r^2s - rs + r + s + 1$

33. $2s^2t^3 - 3s^2t^2 + 2s^2t + 3st^2 + st - s + 2t - 3$

35. $-2a^2bc + ab^2c - 2ab^3 + 3$

37. $-110x + 13y + 17z$

Exercise Set 4.3

1. $6x^5$

3. $6a^2b^3$

45. $6x^5 - 4x^4 - 8x^3 + 14x^2 - 12x + 4$

5. $2x^3 + 6x^2 - 10x$

7. $-4s^4t^2 + 4s^4t - 12s^3$

47. $6a^3 + 2a^2 + 3a^2b - 2a^2b^2 + 3ab^2 - ab^3 + ab + b^2 - b^4$

9. $8a^4b^2 + 4a^3b^3 - 4a^2b^4$

11. $x^2 - x - 6$

49. $20x^2 - 60x + 45$

51. $2x^3 + 3x^2 - 2x$

13. $y^2 + 7y + 10$

15. $x^2 + 6x + 9$

53. $x^3 + 4x^2 + x - 6$

55. (a) -3 (b) 5

17. $s^2 - 9$

19. $3x^2 - x - 2$

57. (a) 1 (b) 6

59. $4x^3y + 2x^2y$

21. $2a^2 + a - 10$

23. $6y^2 + 13y + 6$

61. $2x - 3$

63. $-2x^2 - 6x + 16$

25. $4a^2 + 12a + 9$

27. $4y^2 - 25$

65. $4x - 20$

67. c

29. $9x^2 - 16$

31. $x^4 + 4x^2 + 4$

69. $1.56x^2 - 9.18x + 13.5$

33. $x^4 - 4$

35. $x^3 + 3x^2 - x - 3$

71. $22.73y^4 - 4.57y^2 - 3.24$

37. $2s^4 - 3s^3 - 2s^2 + 7s - 6$

39. $3a^3 + 5a^2 + 3a + 10$

73. $21.68x^3 - 2.90x^2 - 6.88x + 0.28$

41. $2x^4 - x^3 + 8x^2 - 3x + 6$

75. no

77. $a = 1, b = 2$

43. $2x^4 + x^3 - 6x^2 + 7x - 2$

Exercise Set 4.4

1. $2(x + 3)$

3. $3(x - 3y)$

53. $(5rs + 2t)(2rs + t)$

55. $(3 + 4x)(2 - x)$

5. $-2(x + 4y)$

7. $2(2x^2 + 4y - 3)$

57. $25r^2 + 4s^2$

59. $2(x - 3)(x + 2)$

9. $5b(c + 5)$

11. $y(1 - 3y^2)$

61. $2(5x - 2)(3x + 4)$

63. $2b^2(3x - 4)(2x + 3)$

13. $-y^2(3 + 4y^3)$

15. $3bc(a + 4)$

65. $3m(3x + 1)(2x + 3)$

67. $5m^2n(5n^2 - 1)$

17. $5r^3s^3(s - 8rt)$

19. $4(2a^3b^5 - 3a^5b^2 + 4)$

69. $xy\left(1 + \frac{1}{4}x^2y^2\right)$

71. $(x^2 + y^2)(x^2 + y^2)$

21. $(x + 1)(x + 3)$

23. $(y - 5)(y - 3)$

73. $(b^2 + 4)(b^2 - 2)$

75. $(3b^2 - 1)(2b^2 + 3)$

25. $(a - 3b)(a - 4b)$

27. $(y + 3)(y + 3)$

77. $(x - 1)(2x + 7)$

79. $3(x + 1)(y - 2)$

29. $(5 - x)(5 - x)$

31. $(x - 7)(x + 2)$

81. $(x^2 - y)(2xy - 3)$

33. $(2 + y)(2 - y)$

35. $(x - 3)^2$

83. $(2x - 1)^2(x + 2)^2[4(x + 2)(x + 1) - 3(2x - 1)^3(x + 3)]$

37. $(x - 10)(x - 2)$

39. $(x + 8)(x + 3)$

85. $10(5x)(7 - 5x)(7 - 2x)^2$ 89. $(2x - 3)(x + 4)$

41. $(2x + 1)(x - 2)$

43. $(3a - 2)(a - 3)$

91. $(3x + 1)(2x - 3)$

45. $(3x + 2)(2x + 3)$

47. $(2m - 3)(4m + 3)$

49. $(2x - 3)(5x + 1)$

51. $(2a - 3b)(3a + 2b)$

Exercise Set 4.5

1. $8x^3 + y^3$

3. $x^3 - 8y^3$

5. $27r^3 + 8s^3$

7. $8m^3 - 125n^3$

9. $\frac{1}{8}x^3 - 8y^3$

11. $(x - 7)(x + 7)$

13. $\left(y + \frac{1}{3}\right)\left(y - \frac{1}{3}\right)$

15. $(2b + a)(2b - a)$

17. $(xy + 3)(xy - 3)$

19. $(x + 3y)(x^2 - 3xy + 9y^2)$

21. $(3x - y)(9x^2 + 3xy + y^2)$

23. $(a + 2)(a^2 - 2a + 4)$

25. $\left(\frac{1}{2}m - 2n\right)\left(\frac{1}{4}m^2 + mn + 4n^2\right)$

27. $(x + y - 2)(x^2 + 2xy + y^2 + 2x + 2y + 4)$

29. $(2x^2 - 5y^2)(4x^4 + 10x^2y^2 + 25y^4)$

31. $(x^3 - y^3)(x^3 + y^3); (x^2 - y^2)(x^4 + x^2y^2 + y^4)$

Exercise Set 4.6

1. $2x + 5$

3. $4x - \frac{4}{3}$

5. $4x^2 - 2x + 1$

7. $6x - 4$

9. $-3a^2 + \frac{5}{2}$

11. $x^2 - 3x + 4$

13. $x - 4$

15. $a - \frac{8}{a - 2}$

17. $x - 2 + \frac{2}{x - 5}$

19. $x + 2 + \frac{1}{2x + 1}$

21. $3a + 2 + \frac{1}{2a - 1}$

23. $2x - \frac{1}{5} - \frac{14}{25x + 5}$

25. $2s - 3$

27. $2s - 3 + \frac{18}{2s + 3}$

29. $3y^2 - 1$

31. $x^2 - 2x + 4 - \frac{16}{x + 2}$

33. $(x - 1)^2$

35. $-a - 3 + \frac{14}{4 - a^2}$

37. $1.27x + \frac{19.88x + 3.05}{x^2 - 2}$

39. c

Review Exercises

1. yes

2. yes

3. no

4. yes

5.

Term	$3x^3$	$-4x$	2
Coefficient	3	-4	2

6.

Term	$4x^4$	$-x^2$	$2x$	-3
Coefficient	4	-1	2	-3

7.

Term	$-4x^2y^2$	$3x^2y$	$-xy^2$	xy	-1
Coefficient	-4	3	-1	1	-1

8.

Term	$2xy^2$	$-3xy$	x	3
Coefficient	2	-3	1	3

9. 7

10. 5

11. 2

12. 4

13. 35

14. 8

15. 17

16. 63

17. $5x^3 + 2x^2 - 3x - 2$

18. $2a^3b^3 + 3a^2b^3 - 2a^2b - ab^2 + 3ab - a - b$

19. $x^2y + 2xy^2 - x + y + 2$

20. $4x^4 - 5x^3 + x^2 - x + 2$ 21. $6x^2 - x - 2$

22. $4x^3 - 4x^2 + x$ 23. $6y^2 + 4y - 2$

24. $6y^3 - 2y^2 + 6y - 2$ 25. $a^4b + 3a^3b - 4ab$

26. $a^4 + a^3 - 5a - 3$

27. $x^4 - 2x^3 - x^2 + 8x - 12$

28. $4b^4 + 4b^3 - 3b^2 - 2b + 1$

29. 3 30. 0

31. -12 32. 0

33. $x(x + 2)(x - 1)$ 34. $y^2(y - 3)(y + 2)$

35. $x(x + 3)(x - 1)$ 36. $(2x + 1)(x - 3)$

37. $(2x - 1)(3x - 2)$ 38. $(4x + y)(4x - y)$

39. $6(3x - 1)(x - 1)$ 40. $(2r + 1)(s - 1)$

41. $(3a^2 + 1)^2$ 42. $(2x - y)(x + y)$

43. $\left(y + \dfrac{1}{2}x\right)\left(y - \dfrac{1}{2}x\right)$ 44. $(3a + 2b)(a - 1)$

45. $(a - 1)(2b + c)$ 46. $(a^2 - 1)^2$

47. $\left(a + \dfrac{1}{2}b\right)\left(a - \dfrac{1}{2}b\right)$ 48. $(xy + 3)(xy - 3)$

49. $(2a + 3b)(4a^2 - 6ab + 9b^2)$

50. $(2x + 5y)(4x^2 - 10xy + 25y^2)$

51. $(2a - 3b)(4a^2 + 6ab + 9b^2)$

52. $(2x - 5y)(4x^2 + 10xy + 25y^2)$

53. $4x - 2$ 54. $2 - 6x^2$

55. $2y^3 - 3y^2 + y$ 56. $4y - 20 + \dfrac{75}{y + 5}$

57. $x^2 - 3x + 9$ 58. $x^2 - 3x + 9 - \dfrac{54}{x + 3}$

59. $y^2 + 2y + 1 + \dfrac{4}{y - 2}$ 60. $a - 3 + \dfrac{-4a + 12}{a^2 + 2}$

Prorress Test 4A

1. base: $-1/5$; exponent: 4   2. 5

3. 31 4. s^3

5. $-3x^3 + 3x^2 + x - 2$ 6. $2x^2y - x + 6y - 2$

7. $-x^3 + x^2 - 6x + 3$

8. $3x^2y + 3xy^2 - x^2 + 4y - 2$

9. $4x^2 - 20xy + 25y^2$

10. $3x^4 - 2x^3 + 11x^2 - 4x + 10$

11. $(x + 6)(x - 2)$ 12. $2y(x - 3)(x - 1)$

13. $(2a + 7)(2a - 7)$ 14. $(x - 5y)(3x + 2y)$

15. $\left(\dfrac{x}{5} - 5y\right)\left(\dfrac{x^2}{25} + xy + 25y^2\right)$ 16. $x^2 + 4x + 6 + \dfrac{13}{x - 2}$

17. $2a^2 - 3a - 4$ 18. 7

Progress Test 4B

1. base: $-2/3$; exponent: 5   2. 5

3. 2 4. $\dfrac{1}{2}s^2$

5. $6x^5 + 4x^4 + 2x^3 - x^2 + 1$ 6. $x^2y + 6x^2 - 3y^2 - 10$

7. $-5x^3 + 2x^2 + 3x - 8$ 8. $4x^2y^2 - xy^2 + xy + 2$

9. $9x^2 - 24x + 16$

10. $2x^2 - 3y^2 - xy - 2x - 2y$

Chapter 5

Exercise Set 5.1

1. $\dfrac{1}{8}$

3. -7

5. $-\dfrac{2}{7}$

7. $\dfrac{3}{13}$

9. -3

11. $3b^2$

13. $-\dfrac{2(z+3)}{3x}$

15. $-\dfrac{8s(r+4)}{3(s-1)}$

17. $-\dfrac{y^2+z^2}{4}$

19. $\dfrac{2(z^2+z+1)}{17}$

21. $-\dfrac{1}{3}x$

23. $\dfrac{1}{3}x^2$

25. $2x^2$

27. $\dfrac{1}{5}b$

29. $\dfrac{1}{2}(x-1)$

31. $\dfrac{t^2-t+1}{t}$

33. $\dfrac{2a-3}{a-3}$

35. 4

37. $\dfrac{3}{2}t(t+3)$

39. $a(3b+1)$

41. $-\dfrac{2x+3}{x-3}$

43. $3-a$

45. -4

47. $-\dfrac{2}{3t+1}$

49. $\dfrac{x+3}{x}$

Exercise Set 5.2

1. T

3. F

5. T

7. F

9. $2x+1$

11. $\dfrac{3x+2}{3}$

13. $\dfrac{1}{2x^2-3}$

15. $a^2/5$

17. $\dfrac{1}{x-4}$

19. $x-4$

21. $\dfrac{3x+1}{x+2}$

23. $\dfrac{2x^2+5x+3}{12}$

25. $\dfrac{3(a^2-16)}{b}$

27. $a/2$

29. $4/9$

31. $\dfrac{2(3x+1)}{(x+2)^2}$

33. $-2b(5+a)$

35. $\dfrac{x+3}{3x(x-3)}$

37. $\dfrac{-x(2y+3)}{x+1}$

39. $\dfrac{2(x+2)(x-2)^2}{(x+1)(2x+3)}$

41. $\dfrac{5y}{x-4}$

43. $\dfrac{(2x+1)(x-2)}{(x-1)(x+1)}$

45. $\dfrac{(x-2)^2}{(x+3)(x-3)}$

47. $\dfrac{(x+2)(2x+3)}{x+4}$

49. $b(b+1)$

51. $\dfrac{(x+3)(x^2+1)}{x-2}$

53. $\dfrac{x+4}{(x+1)(x-5)}$

55. $x(x-3)$

Exercise Set 5.3

1. xy

3. $2a$

5. $(b-1)^2$

7. $(x-2)(x+3)$

9. $x(x+1)(x-1)$

11. $7/x$

13. $3x/y$

15. 1

17. $x-3$

19. $\dfrac{y-14}{(y-4)(y+4)}$

21. $\dfrac{4}{a-2}$

23. $\dfrac{14y}{3(2-y)}$

25. 2

27. $\dfrac{10+x}{5x}$

29. $\dfrac{5x-2}{x}$

31. $\dfrac{3x-4}{(x-1)(x-2)}$

33. $\dfrac{3a^2-2b^2}{24ab}$

35. $\dfrac{8x-1}{6x^3}$

37. $\dfrac{2(x+1)}{3(x-3)}$

39. $\dfrac{x^2+y^2}{x^2-y^2}$

41. $\dfrac{x^2 + 2xy - y^2}{x^2 - y^2}$

43. $\dfrac{r + 8}{r(r + 2)}$

51. $-\dfrac{x^3 - 4x^2 + 3x - 1}{x(x - 2)(x + 2)(x - 1)}$

45. $\dfrac{3x^2 - 4x - 1}{(x - 1)(x - 2)(x + 1)}$

47. $-\dfrac{2a^3 - 3a^2 - 3a - 2}{a(a - 1)(a + 1)}$

53. $\dfrac{17x + 26}{(x + 2)(x - 2)(x + 3)}$

49. $\dfrac{3x^2 - 4x - 12}{(x - 2)(x + 2)(x - 3)}$

55. $\dfrac{2y^2 + y + 1}{y(y + 1)(y - 1)}$

57. $\dfrac{x + 3}{x - 1}$

1. $\dfrac{x + 2}{x - 3}$

3. $\dfrac{3x - 4}{5x^2}$

Exercise Set 5.4

5. $\dfrac{x(x + 1)}{x - 1}$

7. $4x(x + 4)$

17. $\dfrac{1 - x}{2}$

19. $\dfrac{a^3 - a^2 + 1}{a - 1}$

9. $\dfrac{a + 2}{a + 1}$

11. $\dfrac{x + 3}{(3x - 7)(x + 2)}$

21. $\dfrac{(y - 2)(y + 1)}{(y - 1)(y + 2)}$

23. $\dfrac{x + 1}{2x + 1}$

13. $a - b$

15. $\dfrac{x - 2}{x}$

Exercise Set 5.5

1. $10/3$

3. 1

21. $12/7$

23. $x < 7$

5. $9/2$

7. 4

25. $x \le -1$

27. $x \ge 1$

9. 4

11. no solution

29. no solution

31. $\dfrac{3a - 14}{3a - 2}$

13. $1/4$

15. 12

33. $r \le \dfrac{a + 2}{a - 2}$

17. $5/19$

19. 2

Exercise Set 5.6

1. 18

3. $3/8, 3/4$

17. 9 hr

19. 8 hr

5. $3/4$

7. 4

21. 25 km per hour

9. 6/5 hr

11. 12/13 hr

23. 100 km per hour, 120 km per hour

13. 6 hr

15. 60/7 hr

Exercise Set 5.7

1. $\dfrac{5.08\ cm}{2\ in}$ or 5.08 cm:2 in

3. $\dfrac{16}{5}$ or 8:2.5

17. $500

19. 60 ft

5. 3/4 or 3:4

7. 20 cm, 16 cm

21. 55,000

23. 962

9. 18/5

11. 3/10

25. 24 cm^3

27. $\dfrac{3a + 4}{4}$

13. 5

15. 9, 21

Review Exercises

1. $x + 2$

2. $\dfrac{2x - 3}{2}$

3. $x - 4$

4. $2x^2 - x + 3$

5. $\dfrac{x^2 - 3x + 2}{6}$

6. $\dfrac{4x^2 - 1}{6}$

7. $\dfrac{2x - 2}{x^2 + x}$

8. $\dfrac{2x^2 + 2x - 4}{x - 4}$

9. $\dfrac{4x^2 + 4x - 3}{6x^2 - x - 2}$

10. $\dfrac{x^2 - 3x + 2}{x^2 + 5x + 6}$

11. $x^2 - 4$

12. $(x - 2)^2$

13. $y^3 - 4y$

14. $3y^2(y - 1)$

15. $\dfrac{10 - x^2}{3x}$

16. $\dfrac{4a^2 - a - 1}{a^2 - 1}$

17. $\dfrac{a - 6}{a - 2}$

18. $\dfrac{3y - yx + x - 1}{2x^2 + x - 3}$

19. $\dfrac{-4x^2 + 21x - 15}{6(x^2 - 9)}$

20. $\dfrac{6x^2 - 7x - 1}{2(x^2 - 1)}$

21. $\dfrac{2x - 1}{x + 5}$

22. $\dfrac{a^2 - a - 1}{3a^2 - 3a - 1}$

23. $\dfrac{x^2 - 4}{2x + 3}$

24. $\dfrac{3(10 - y^2)(y + 2)}{2(y + 3)}$

25. $\dfrac{a^2 + 3a - 6}{a - 2}$

26. $\dfrac{(x + 1)(x + 3)}{x + 9}$

27. 4/7

28. $x = 3/2$

29. $a = -5/8$

30. $y = -2$

31. $x = -1/10$

32. $r = -5$

33. 5/3

34. 3, −3

35. 2

36. 6 days

37. 7.5 hr

38. 12 mo

39. 24/13 hr

40. 16 km per hour

41. Computer A carries out 25 million operations; computer B carries out 15 million operations.

42. 30 mph

43. $x = 2$

44. $y = 3$

45. $r = 1/2$

46. $r = -13$

47. 10 smokers

48. $3.125

49. $800.00

50. 19.5 oz

Progress Test 5A

1. $\dfrac{12x^2(x + 2)}{y}$

2. $-\dfrac{(2x + 3)(3x - 1)}{(x + 4)^2}$

3. $-\dfrac{(2x - 1)(x - 2)(x - 1)}{3x}$

4. $5y^2(x - 1)^2$

5. $\dfrac{13}{x - 5}$

6. $\dfrac{7 - 5y^2}{2y(y + 1)}$

7. $3x$

8. $\dfrac{(x + 4)(x - 2)}{x - 3}$

9. -2

10. $x \leqslant -33/5$

11. 2 hr

12. 4

13. $291.67

Progress Test 5B

1. $\dfrac{-6(y - 1)}{y^2(x - y)}$

2. $-\dfrac{(2x - 1)}{(3x - 1)(x + 1)}$

3. $-\dfrac{2x(x + 1)}{x + 2}$

4. $4x^2(y + 1)^2(y - 1)$

5. $\dfrac{2}{3 - x}$

6. $\dfrac{-2v^3 + 3v^2 + 6v + 8}{4v^2(v - 1)}$

7. $-2x$

8. $\dfrac{(x - 1)(x - 3)}{2(2 - x)}$

9. 11/12

10. $x \leqslant 24/5$

11. 7/3 hr

12. 7

Chapter 6

Exercise Set 6.1

1. $A(2, 3)$, $B(-2, -1)$, $C(4, -1)$, $D(0, 5)$, $E(-4, 0)$, $\dot{F}(-3, 4)$, $G(1, 1/2)$, $H(-1, 7/2)$

3.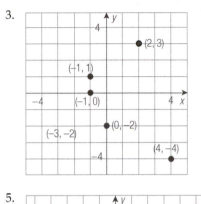

5.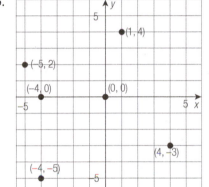

7.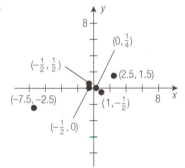

9. (a) $(-4, 0)$ (b) $(6, -2)$

11. I

13. IV

15. III

17. I

19. III

21. I

23. a, d

25. a, c

27.

x	1	$\frac{9}{2}$	0	3	-3	$\frac{3}{2}$
y	$\frac{8}{3}$	-2	4	0	8	2

29.

31.

33.

35.

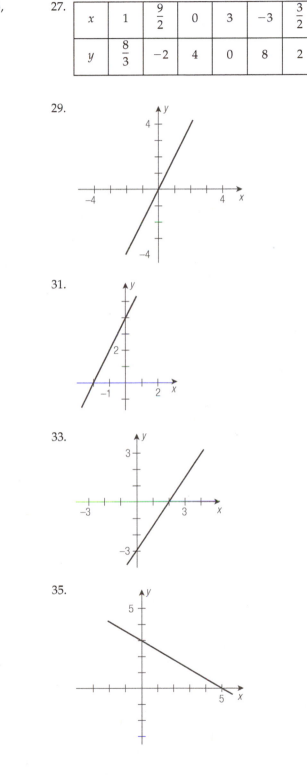

37.

39.

41.

43.

45.

47.

49.

51.

53.

55.

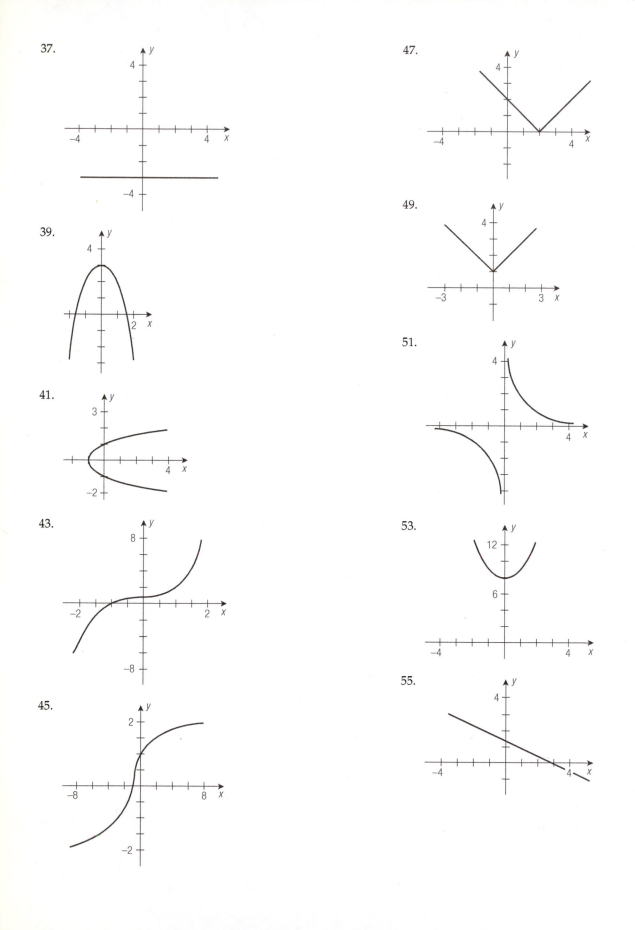

57.

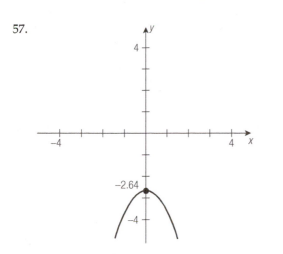

59.

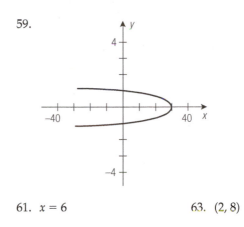

61. $x = 6$ 63. $(2, 8)$

Exercise Set 6.2

1.

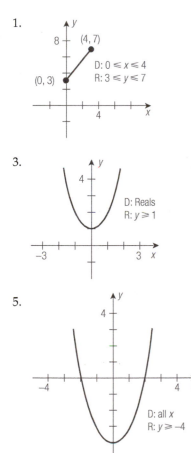

D: $0 \leqslant x \leqslant 4$
R: $3 \leqslant y \leqslant 7$

3.

D: Reals
R: $y \geqslant 1$

5.

D: all x
R: $y \geqslant -4$

7.

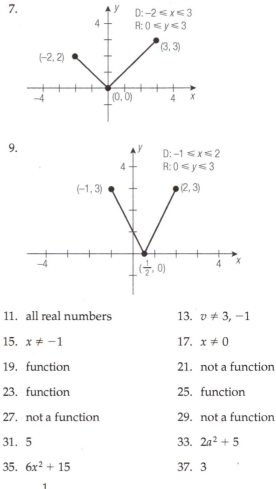

D: $-2 \leqslant x \leqslant 3$
R: $0 \leqslant y \leqslant 3$

9.

D: $-1 \leqslant x \leqslant 2$
R: $0 \leqslant y \leqslant 3$

11. all real numbers   13. $v \neq 3, -1$

15. $x \neq -1$ 17. $x \neq 0$

19. function   21. not a function

23. function   25. function

27. not a function   29. not a function

31. 5   33. $2a^2 + 5$

35. $6x^2 + 15$ 37. 3

39. $\dfrac{1}{x^2 + 2x}$

41. $a^2 + h^2 + 2ah + 2a + 2h$

43. -0.92

45. $\dfrac{3x - 1}{x^2 + 1}$

47. $\dfrac{8x^2 + 2}{6x - 1}$

49. -0.21

51. $\dfrac{2(a - 1)}{4a^2 + 4a - 3}$

53. $\dfrac{a - 1}{a(a + 4)}$

55. $R(x) = \begin{cases} 300x, & 0 \leqslant x \leqslant 100 \\ 30{,}000 + 250(x - 100), & 100 < x < 150 \end{cases}$

57. $A(x) = 1.07x$

59. (a) 1001   (b) 16,004

61. (a) even   (b) odd   (c) neither   (d) even

63. $d = \dfrac{c}{\pi}$

Exercise Set 6.3

1.

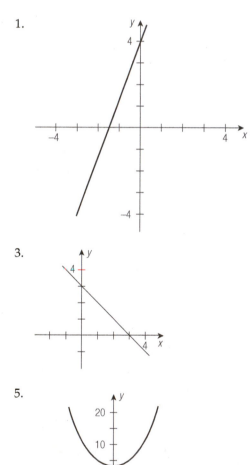

3.

5.

7.

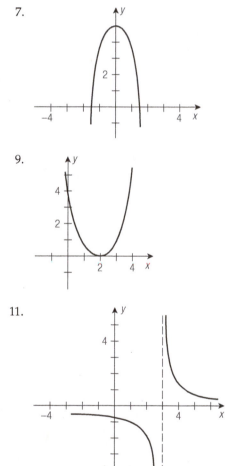

9.

11.

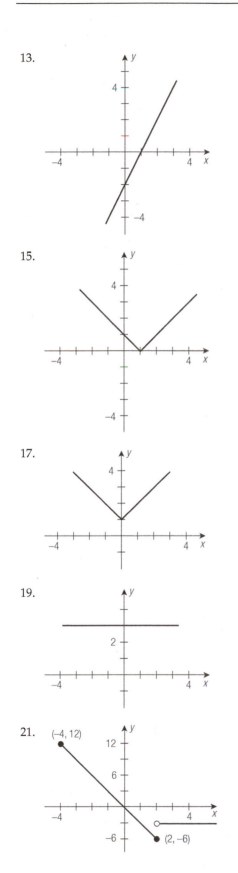

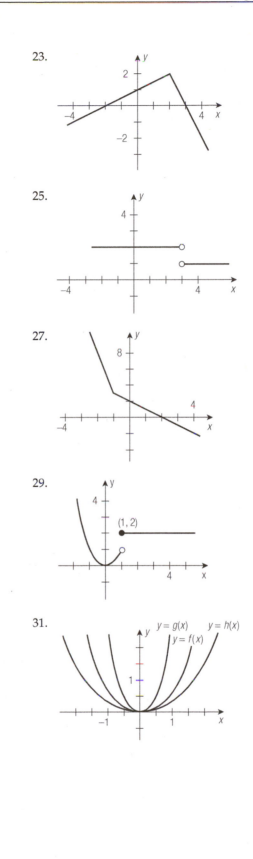

33.

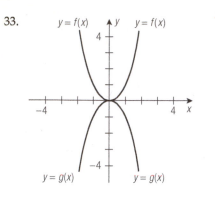

35.

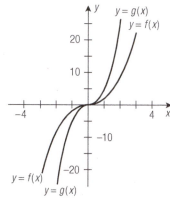

37.

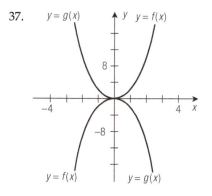

39.

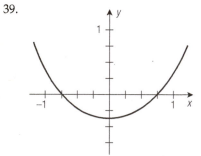

41.

43.

45. $C(x) = \begin{cases} 6.50, & 0 \le x \le 100 \\ 0.50 + 0.06x, & 100 < x \le 200 \\ 2.50 + 0.05x, & x > 200 \end{cases}$

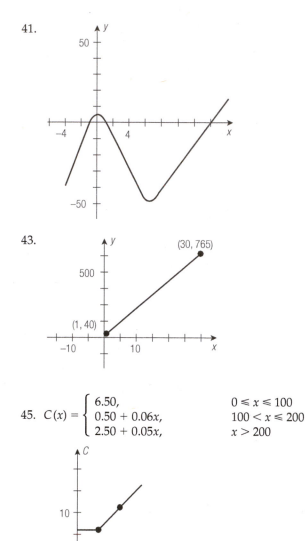

Exercise Set 6.4

1. always increasing

3. decreasing for $x \leq 0$; increasing for $x \geq 0$

5. decreasing for $x \geq 0$; increasing for $x \leq 0$

7. decreasing for $x \geq 2$; increasing for $x \leq 2$

9. decreasing for $x \leq 0$; increasing for $x \geq 0$

11. decreasing for $x \leq 2$; increasing for $x \geq 2$

13. decreasing for $x \leq -1/2$; increasing for $x \geq -1/2$

15. decreasing for $x \leq -1$; increasing for $x > -1$

17. always increasing

19. always increasing

21. decreasing for $x \leq 1$; increasing for $x \geq 1$

23. decreasing for all $x \neq 1$

25. decreasing for $x \geq 40$; increasing for $x \leq 40$

27. decreasing for $2 \leq x \leq 5$; increasing for $0 \leq x \leq 2$, $5 \leq x \leq 6$

Exercise Set 6.5

1. (a) 4   (b) $y = 4x$ (c)

x	8	12	20	30
y	32	48	80	120

3. (a) $-1/32$ (b) $-3/8$

5. (a) $1/10$ (b) $5/2$

7. (a) -3 (b) $-1/4$

9. (a) 512   (b) $512/125$

11. (a) $M = r^2/s^2$ (b) $36/25$

13. (a) $T = 16pv^3/u^2$ (b) $2/3$

15. (a) 256 ft   (b) 5 sec

17. $40/3$ ohms

19. (a) $800/9$ candlepower   (b) 8 ft

21. 6

23. 120 candlepower/ft^2

Review Exercises

1. $(-2, -4)$

2. $(-3, 1)$

3. II

4. a, d

5. d

6.

x	2	$\dfrac{25}{2}$	0	10	3	0
y	$\dfrac{16}{5}$	-1	4	0	$\dfrac{14}{5}$	4

7.

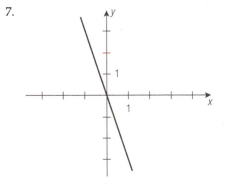

8.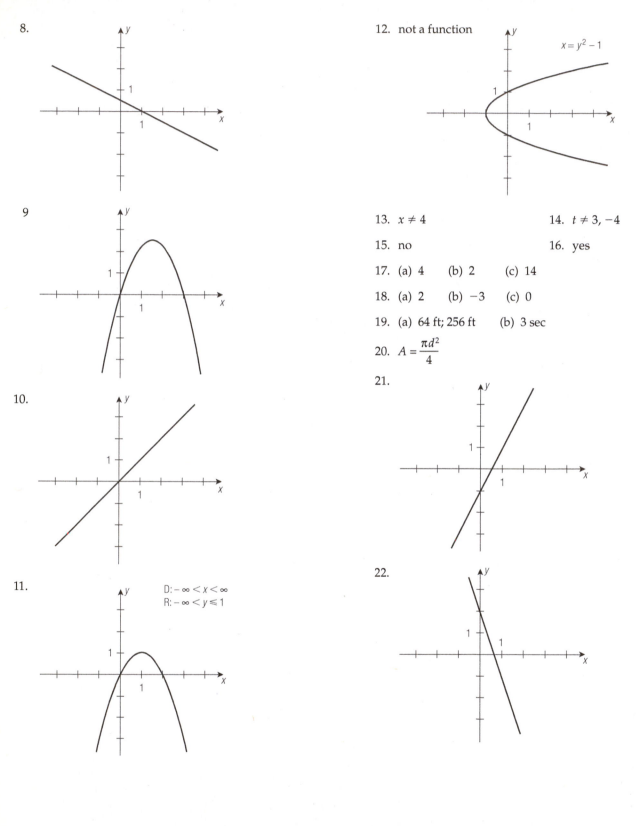

9

10.

11.

D: $-\infty < x < \infty$
R: $-\infty < y \leqslant 1$

12. not a function

$x = y^2 - 1$

13. $x \neq 4$ 14. $t \neq 3, -4$

15. no   16. yes

17. (a) 4   (b) 2   (c) 14

18. (a) 2   (b) −3   (c) 0

19. (a) 64 ft; 256 ft   (b) 3 sec

20. $A = \dfrac{\pi d^2}{4}$

21.

22.

23.

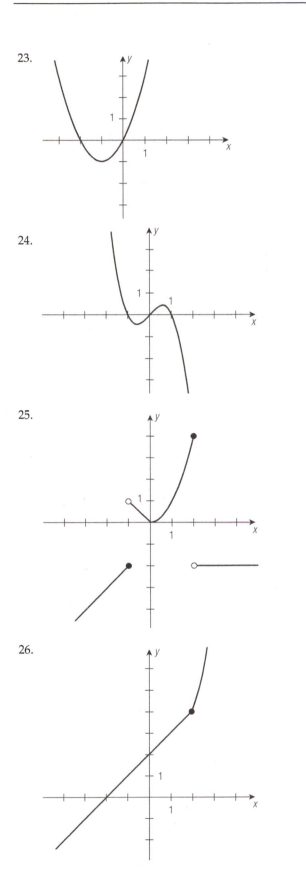

24.

25.

26.

27.

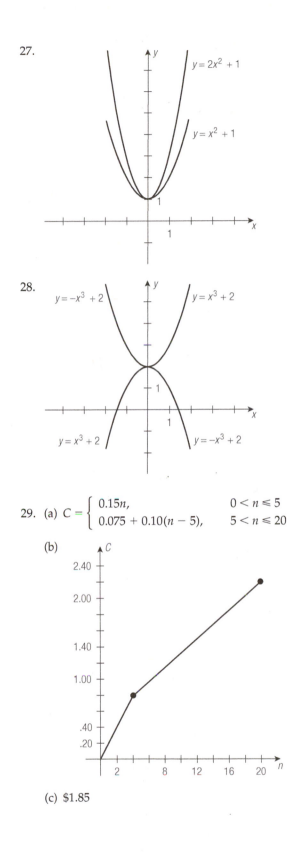

$y = 2x^2 + 1$

$y = x^2 + 1$

28.

$y = -x^3 + 2$ $y = x^3 + 2$

$y = x^3 + 2$ $y = -x^3 + 2$

29. (a) $C = \begin{cases} 0.15n, & 0 < n \leqslant 5 \\ 0.075 + 0.10(n - 5), & 5 < n \leqslant 20 \end{cases}$

(b)

(c) $1.85

30. (a) $C = \begin{cases} 2.20n, & 0 < n \leq 10 \\ 22 + 2.15(n-10), & 10 < n \leq 25 \\ 54.25 + 2.05(n-25), & n > 25 \end{cases}$

    (b) $68.60

31. decreasing for all x

32. increasing for $x \geq 1/2$; decreasing for $x \leq 1/2$

33. increasing for $x \geq 0$; decreasing for $x \leq 0$

34. increasing for $x \geq -1/2$; decreasing for $x \leq -1/2$

35. increasing for $x \geq 1$; decreasing for $x \leq 1$

36. increasing for $x \geq -2$; decreasing for $x \leq -2$

37. increasing for $x < 1$; constant for $1 < x \leq 3$

38. increasing for $x < -2$, $0 \leq x < 4$; constant for $x \geq 4$; decreasing for $-2 \leq x \leq 0$

39. increasing for $x \geq 10$; decreasing for $x \leq 10$

40. decreasing for $x \geq 2$; increasing for $x \leq 2$

41. (a) $y = \frac{1}{2}t^2$ (b) 1/2

    (c)

t	1	2	3	4	5
y	1/2	2	9/2	8	25/2

42. (a) $M = K/n^3$ (b) 2/3

    (c)

n	2	3	4	5
M	1/2	2/81	1/96	2/375

43. (a) 2/3   (b) $F = 24$

44. (a) 3/2   (b) $A = 3/128$

45. 3   46. 3/16

47.

x	2	3	4	2	4
y	3	5	2	5	3
z	9	45/2	12	15	18

48.

r	2	3	4	5	3
s	3	2	5	2	3
t	$\frac{8}{27}$	1	$\frac{16}{75}$	$\frac{5}{3}$	$\frac{4}{9}$

49. 30 items per hour

50. 30 min

51. $1,250,000

Progress Test 6A

1.

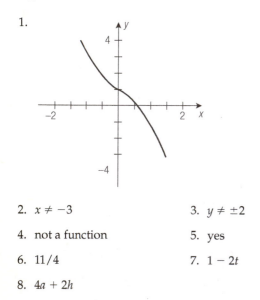

9.

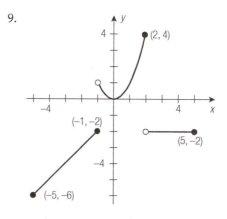

2. $x \neq -3$ 3. $y \neq \pm 2$

4. not a function   5. yes

6. 11/4   7. $1 - 2t$

8. $4a + 2h$

10.

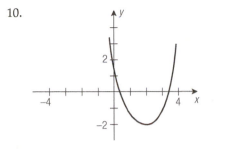

11. 160

12. 1

13. −1/4

14. increasing for $x > 1$; decreasing for $x < 1$

15. increasing for $1 < x < 3$; decreasing for $x < 1$; constant for $x \geq 3$

Progress Test 6B

1.

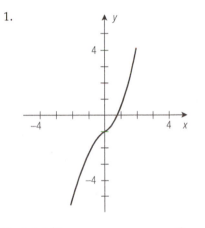

2. $t \neq 1/2$

3. $x \neq \pm 1$

4. function

5. yes

6. −3

7. $1 + a + \dfrac{a^2}{4}$

8. $-2a - h$

9.

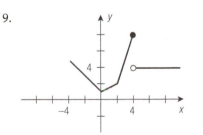

10.

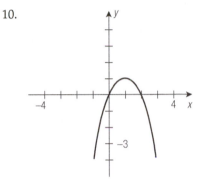

11. −1024

12. −32/9

13. 65,536

14. increasing for $x > 2$; decreasing for $x < 2$

15. increasing for $0 < x < 3$; decreasing for $-1 < x < 0$; constant for $x < -1$ and $x > 3$

13. 81

Chapter 7
Exercise Set 7.1

1. 2; rising

3. −1; falling

5. −3/2; falling

7. 0

9. P

11. N

13. T

15. F

17. 1

19. undefined

21. $C = -2$

Exercise Set 7.2

1. a, d

3. $2x - y - 3 = 0; A = 2, B = -1, C = -3$

5. $0x + y - 3 = 0; A = 0, B = 1, C = -3$

7. $3x - 2y - 7 = 0; A = 3, B = -2, C = -7$

9. $x + 0y - 1/2 = 0; A = 1, B = 0, C = -1/2$

11. yes

13.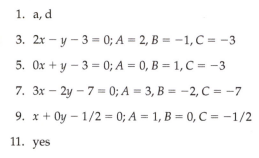

15.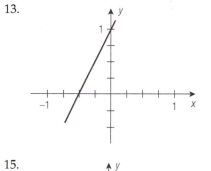

17.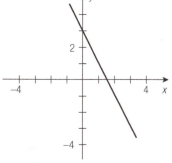

19.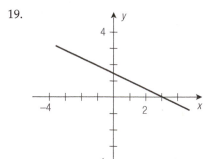

21.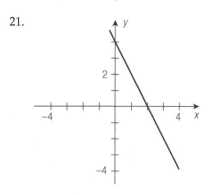

23.

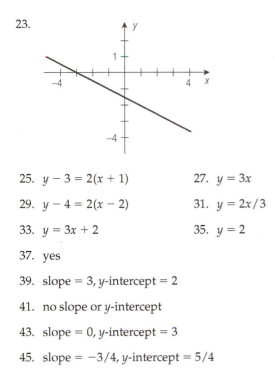

25. $y - 3 = 2(x + 1)$ 27. $y = 3x$

29. $y - 4 = 2(x - 2)$ 31. $y = 2x/3$

33. $y = 3x + 2$ 35. $y = 2$

37. yes

39. slope $= 3$, y-intercept $= 2$

41. no slope or y-intercept

43. slope $= 0$, y-intercept $= 3$

45. slope $= -3/4$, y-intercept $= 5/4$

47. slope $= 2/5$, y-intercept $= 3/5$

49. slope $= 3/2$, y-intercept $= -3$

51. rises   53. falls

55. rises   57. $y = \dfrac{3}{4}x + \dfrac{11}{4}$

59. $y = -0.98x + 14.57$ 61. $y = 0.83x - 7.04$

63. $y = -\dfrac{3}{4}x + \dfrac{5}{2}$

65. $c = 8 + 1.5h$; $c =$ charge in dollars, $h =$ hours

67. $c = 25 + 0.12s$; $c =$ charge in dollars, $s =$ number of shares

69. (a) $F = \dfrac{9}{5}C + 32$ (b) 68°F

71. $\$1,000,000$ 73. 5

75. $f(x) = 8x + 13$

Exercise Set 7.3

1. $y = 2$ 3. $x = -2$

5. (a) $y = 3$ (b) $x = -6$

7. (a) $y = -5$ (b) $x = 4$

9. (a) $y = 0$ (b) $x = 0$

11. (a) $y = 0$ (b) $x = -7$

13. (a) $y = 5$ (b) $x = 0$

15. $y = 3$

17.

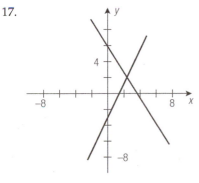

19.

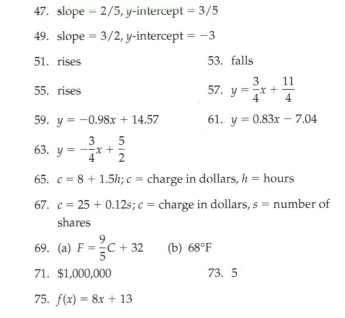

21. $-2/5$ 23. $-3/2$

25. $y = \dfrac{3}{2}x - 2$ 27. $y = -3x + 6$

29. $-1/2$ 31. 2

33. $-5x + 3y - 21 = 0$

35. (a) perpendicular   (b) perpendicular   (c) parallel

Exercise Set 7.4

1.

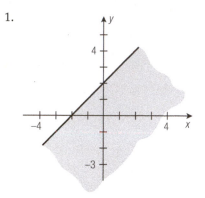

3.

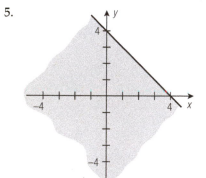

5.

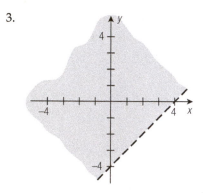

7.

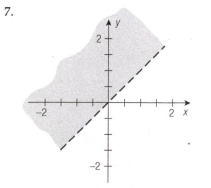

9.

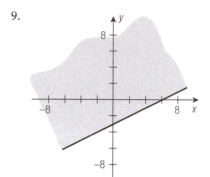

11.

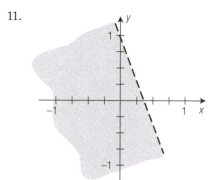

13.

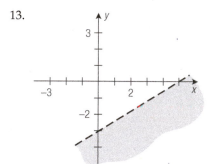

15.

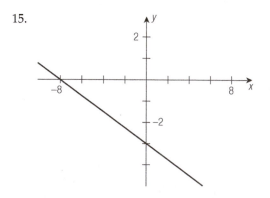

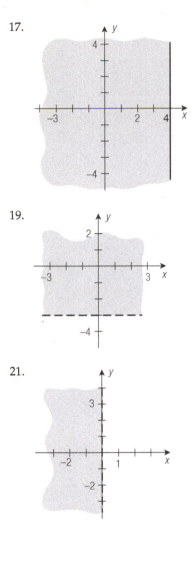

17.

19.

21.

23.

25.

27.

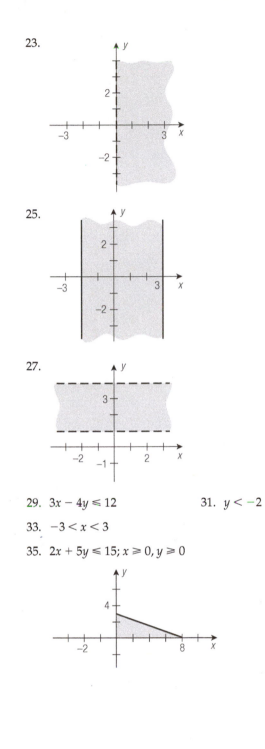

29. $3x - 4y \leq 12$ 31. $y < -2$

33. $-3 < x < 3$

35. $2x + 5y \leq 15; x \geq 0, y \geq 0$

Review Exercises

1. 1/2

2. −2/3

3. rising

4. falling

5. falling

6. falling

7. P

8. N

9. F

10. T

11. −3/4

12. 2/3

13. −6

14. −3/2

15. $3x + 2y = 14; A = 3, B = 2, C = 14$

16. $x + 3y = 1; A = 1, B = 3, C = 1$

17. yes

19.

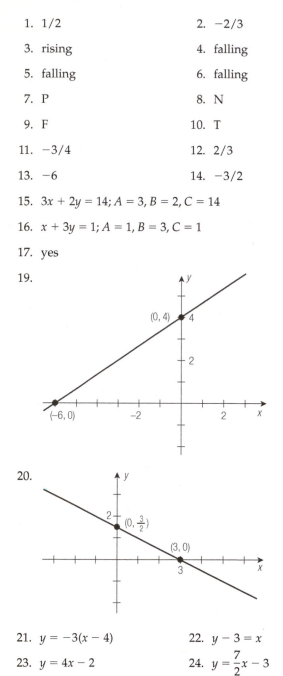

20.

21. $y = -3(x - 4)$

22. $y - 3 = x$

23. $y = 4x - 2$

24. $y = \dfrac{7}{2}x - 3$

25. $m = 2/3, b = 4/3$

26. $m = 2, b = 6$

27. rising

28. falling

29. (a) $y = -3$ (b) $x = 2$

30. (a) $y = 4$ (b) $x = -3$

31. $y = -2$

32. $x = -4$

33. no

34. yes

35. $y = \dfrac{3}{2}x + 5$

36. $y = \dfrac{1}{2}x - 3/2$

37. $y - 1 = -\dfrac{2}{5}(x - 4)$

38. $y = \dfrac{4}{3}x + 4$

39. perpendicular

40. neither

41.

42.

43. $y > -\dfrac{4}{5}x + 4$

44. $y \geq \dfrac{3}{2}x - 3$

Progress Test 7A

1. 0

2. $-2/3$

3. $7x + y + 5 = 0$

4. $x - 10y + 74 = 0$

5. slope $= -5/2$, y-intercept $= 3$

6. slope $= 2/3$; rising

7. slope $= -1/4$; falling

8. $c = 20t + 5$

9. $x = -11$

10. $y = -7/3$

11. $y = 3x + 2$, same line

12. $2/7$

13. $3x + 4y + 11 = 0$

14.

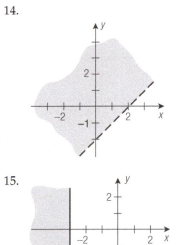

15.

Progress Test 7B

1. no slope

2. -2

3. $y - 5x - 23 = 0$

4. $2x + 3y + 12 = 0$

5. slope $= 4$, y-intercept $= -5/3$

6. slope $= 7/2$; rising

7. slope $= -5/4$; falling

8. $C = 17n + 5$

9. $y = 5/4$

10. $x = 3$

11. $y - 2x - 3 = 0$

12. $-5/3$

13. $y = -3x$

14.

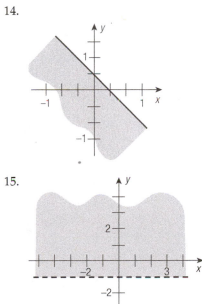

15.

Chapter 8

Exercise Set 8.1

1. $1/81$, base $= 1/3$, exponent $= 4$
3. -32, base $= -2$, exponent $= 5$
5. $(-5)^4$
7. $4^2 x^2 y^3$
9. x^6
11. b^4
13. $16x^4$
15. $-1/128$
17. x^{3m^2}
19. $x^{(m^2 + m)}$
21. 81
23. $-x^3/y^3$
25. y^8
27. x^{19}
29. $-a^5/b^5$
31. $-32x^{10}$
33. 3^{3m}
35. x^{4n}
37. 3^8
39. 5^{n+1}
41. $1/x^2$
43. $3^5 x^{15}/y^{10}$
45. $-30x^8$
47. $x^{27} y^8$
49. 1
51. $(3b + 1)^{25}$
53. $1/(2a + b)^2$
55. $-27x^9 y^3$
57. $2^n a^{n^2}/b^{2n^2}$
59. $-27x^3/8$
61. $(2x + 1)^{10}$
63. $1/y^9$
65. $2^{2n} a^{4n} b^{6n}$
67. $-8a^6 b^9/c^6$
69. 21.49
71. -2.57
73. 302.90
75. 888.73
79. $10^{12} \times 10^{12} \times 10^{12}$; 10^{36}

Exercise Set 8.2

1. 1
3. 1
5. 3
7. $-5x$
9. $-1/3^3$
11. $2 \cdot 4^3$ or 2^7
13. $-x^3$
15. $-1/16$
17. y^6
19. $1/2^6 a^6$
21. $-4(5a - 3b)^2$
23. 25
25. $4y^3$
27. $1/x^7$
29. $1/3^6$
31. -2^9
33. x^9
35. 32
37. x^{18}
39. $4/x$
41. 2
43. $b^9/8a^6$
45. ab
47. $a^4 b^6/9$
49. $a^9/b^9 c^6$
51. $a^2/b^4 c$
53. $a^9/3b^4$
55. x
57. $4a^{10} c^6/b^8$
59. $2y^5$
61. $1/y$
63. $a^4/4b^6 c^4$
65. $x^9 z^9/y^3$
67. $4b^6 c^6/a^4$
69. $(a - b)^2/a + b$
71. $xy/(x + y)^2$
73. 0.69
75. 0.00000499
77. 1.9
79. 3.20
83. -2.459×10^{-1}
85. 5.9×10^{-4}
87. $399,000$
89. 0.62

Exercise Set 8.3

1. 8
3. $-1/5$
5. $4/25$
7. $1/c^{5/12}$
9. $2x^{13/12}$
11. $1/x^{17}$
13. 25
15. $x^{2/3} y$
17. $64a^6 b^3$
19. $a^{9/2}/b^3$
21. $-4x^{2n}$
23. x^9/y^6
25. $x^{12} y^4$
27. $1/x^4 y^8$
29. $-32x^{15} y^{5/2}/243$
31. $64^{1/4} x^{3/2}/y^3$
33. $\sqrt[5]{1/16}$
35. $\sqrt[3]{x^2}$
37. $\sqrt[5]{64x^4}$
39. $\sqrt[3]{(x^2 - 1)^2}$

41. $8^{3/4}$

43. $1/(-8)^{2/5}$

45. $1/(\frac{4}{9}a^3)^{1/4}$

47. $(2y^3)^{7/2}/x^{14}$

49. c

51. c

53. $2/3$

55. not real

57. $1/3$

59. 5

61. $1/2$

63. $7/2$

65. 54.82

67. 4.78

69. 0.15

71. 27.4

Exercise Set 8.4

1. $4\sqrt{3}$

3. $3\sqrt[3]{2}$

5. $2\sqrt[3]{5}$

7. $2/3$

9. $2/5$

11. x^4

13. $a^3\sqrt[3]{a^2}$

15. x^3

17. $7b^5\sqrt{2}$

19. $3y^5\sqrt[3]{4y}$

21. $2x^2\sqrt{5}$

23. $a^5b^3\sqrt{b}$

25. $x^2y^2\sqrt[3]{y^2}$

27. $ab^2\sqrt[4]{ab^2}$

29. $6x^3y^5\sqrt{2xy}$

31. $2b^3c^4\sqrt[3]{3bc^2}$

33. $2b^2c^3\sqrt[4]{3}\sqrt{b}$

35. $2a^2bc\sqrt[3]{5a^2bc^2}$

37. $\sqrt{5}/5$

39. $4\sqrt{11}/33$

41. $\sqrt{3}/3$

43. $\sqrt{3y}/3y$

45. $2x\sqrt{2x}$

47. $3y\sqrt{2x}$

49. $-5x^3y^4\sqrt[3]{xy}$

51. $5\sqrt[3]{4a^2b}/2$

53. $2x^2\sqrt{5xy}/y^2$

55. $x\sqrt[3]{x^2y}/y$

57. $\sqrt[4]{216x^2y^3}/3y$

59. $x^3y^2\sqrt{xy}$

61. $2x^2y\sqrt[4]{2y^2}$

63. $2x^2y\sqrt[4]{3y^2z^2}$

65. $7y\sqrt[4]{27xy}/6x$

67. $\sqrt[4]{216x^2y^3}/12xy^3$

69. $\frac{4}{5}a\sqrt[3]{b^2}$

Exercise Set 8.5

1. $7\sqrt{3}$

3. $-2\sqrt[3]{11}$

5. $7\sqrt{x}$

7. $6\sqrt{2}$

9. $\frac{9}{2}\sqrt{y}$

11. $5\sqrt{6}$

13. $4\sqrt{3}$

15. $11\sqrt{5}-\sqrt[3]{5}$

17. $5\sqrt[3]{xy^2}-4\sqrt[3]{x^2y}$

19. $\frac{3}{2}a\sqrt[3]{ab}+\frac{5}{2}\sqrt{ab}$

21. $2\sqrt[5]{2x^3y^2}$

23. $-3y\sqrt[3]{xy}-\frac{1}{2}y^2\sqrt{x}$

25. $-5\sqrt{5}$

27. $x(x\sqrt[3]{xy}-\sqrt[3]{x^2y}+2x^2\sqrt{y})$

29. $3+4\sqrt{3}$

31. $2\sqrt{3}+6\sqrt{2}$

33. $3xy$

35. $-4xy\sqrt[5]{x}$

37. $\sqrt{2}-4$

39. $6\sqrt{6}+4\sqrt{3}-9\sqrt{2}-6$

41. $5-2\sqrt{6}$

43. 0

45. $3x-4y-\sqrt{6xy}$

47. $\sqrt[3]{4x^2}-9$

49. $a^2-2b^2-2ab\sqrt[3]{ab}+\sqrt[3]{a^2b^2}$

51. $\frac{3}{7}(3-\sqrt{2})$

53. $\dfrac{3(9+\sqrt{7})}{74}$

55. $\dfrac{2(\sqrt{x}-3)}{x-9}$

57. $\dfrac{3(1-3\sqrt{a})}{9a-1}$

59. $\dfrac{2(2+\sqrt{2y})}{2-y}$

61. $2(\sqrt{2}-1)$

63. $3+2\sqrt{2}$

65. $4+\sqrt{15}$

67. $\dfrac{x-\sqrt{xy}}{x-y}$

69. $\dfrac{2a+\sqrt{ab}+2\sqrt{a}+\sqrt{b}}{4a-b}$

71. $\dfrac{2x\sqrt{2}+2\sqrt{xy}+\sqrt{2xy}+y}{2x-y}$

Exercise Set 8.6

1. 1

3. $-i$

5. -1

7. $-i$

9. i

11. 1

13. i

15. $2 + 0i$

17. $-\dfrac{1}{2} + 0i$

19. $0 + 4i$

21. $0 - \sqrt{5}\,i$

23. $0 - 6i$

25. $2 + 4i$

27. $-\dfrac{3}{2} - 6i\sqrt{2}$

29. $0.3 - 7i\sqrt{2}$

31. $3 + i$

33. $8 - i$

35. $5 + i$

37. $-5 - 4i$

39. $-8 + 0i$

41. $2 - 6i$

43. $-1 - \dfrac{1}{2}i$

45. $-5 + 12i$

47. $5 + 0i$

49. $2 + 14i$

51. $4 - 7i$

53. $5 + 12i$

55. $8 - 6i$

57. $-2 + 0i$

59. $4 + 0i$

61. $5 + 0i$

63. 25

65. 20

67. $-\dfrac{13}{10} + \dfrac{11}{10}i$

69. $-\dfrac{7}{25} - \dfrac{24}{25}i$

71. $\dfrac{8}{5} - \dfrac{1}{5}i$

73. $\dfrac{5}{3} - \dfrac{2}{3}i$

75. $\dfrac{4}{5} + \dfrac{8}{5}i$

77. $\dfrac{3}{13} - \dfrac{2}{13}i$

79. $\dfrac{2}{5} + \dfrac{4}{5}i$

81. $0 + \dfrac{1}{7}i$

83. $\dfrac{\sqrt{2}}{3} + \dfrac{1}{3}i$

85. $\dfrac{1}{s + ti} = \dfrac{1}{s + ti} \cdot \dfrac{s - ti}{s - ti} = \dfrac{s - ti}{s^2 + t^2} = \dfrac{s}{s^2 + t^2} - \dfrac{t}{s^2 + t^2}i$

Review Exercises

1. x^{6n}

2. y^9

3. $-a^5/b^5$

4. x^{22}

5. b^4

6. $(2a - 1)^{10}$

7. $(2x + y)^5$

8. $27/16a^7b^6$

9. $-1/32$

10. $3x^3$

11. $2/y^2$

12. a^2

13. 1

14. $4b^3/a^2$

15. $16x^{12}y^4/81$

16. $-8/27x^3y^3$

17. 4

18. $x^{1/3}$

19. $a^{11/12}$

20. $1/81$

21. $x^{1/2}y^{2/3}$

22. $1/x^2y^{1/5}$

23. $1/x^{1/6}$

24. $1/x^3y^{1/5}$

25. $2\sqrt{15}$

26. $5x^2\sqrt[3]{x^2}/3$

27. $\dfrac{\sqrt{x}}{x}$

28. $4\sqrt[3]{3^2ab^2}/3$

29. $2a^7\sqrt{3b}/b$

30. $2x^2\sqrt[4]{5^3}\sqrt{y}/5y$

31. $3\sqrt{5}$

32. $3\sqrt{xy}$

33. $\sqrt[3]{xy^2}(\sqrt[3]{3} + \sqrt[3]{5})$

34. $(\sqrt{2} + 2)\sqrt{xy}$

35. $(-9 - 3\sqrt{x})/(9 - x)$

36. $(\sqrt{3x} - 1)^2/(3x - 1)$

37. $2\sqrt{x - y}/(x - y)$

38. $(a\sqrt{2ab} + b\sqrt{2a})/(a - b)$

39. 1

40. $0 - i$

41. $0 + 2\sqrt{5}\,i$

42. $2 - 3\sqrt[3]{2} + 0i$

43. $-4 + 8i$

44. 25

45. $10 + 15i$

46. $7 - 24i$

47. $\dfrac{\sqrt{3}}{7} - \dfrac{2}{7}i$

48. $-\dfrac{1}{2} - \dfrac{5}{2}i$

49. $0 - i$

50. $-\dfrac{1}{2} + \dfrac{1}{2}i$

Progress Test 8A

1. $(x + 1)^{n-2}$

2. $x^{12}y^8/16$

3. $-8y^6/125x^3$

4. $5x^6$

5. $1/64x^{8/5}$

6. $x^{4/3}y^2$

7. $25x^4/9y$

8. $\sqrt{(2y-1)^5}$

9. $(6y^5)^{1/3}$

10. $-4x^2y^4\sqrt{2y}$

11. $\sqrt{5x}/5$

12. $-4a^4b^3$

13. $-7\sqrt[3]{3}$

14. $5y\sqrt{x} - 8x\sqrt{y}$

15. $3(4x - 9y)$

16. $4 - 2i$

17. 2

18. i

19. $\dfrac{-4}{25} - \dfrac{22}{25}i$

20. $\dfrac{4}{25} - \dfrac{3}{25}i$

Progress Test 8B

1. x^{6n-2}

2. $-a^6b^3/27$

3. $-y^6/27x^9$

4. $4/(x + 1)$

5. $-1/216y^{3/2}$

6. $x^{5/2}/y^{4/5}$

7. $x^{8/5}/27^{2/5}y^{6/25}$

8. $\sqrt[3]{(3x + 1)^2}$

9. $(4x^3)^{1/5}$

10. $-6x\sqrt{xz}$

11. $x\sqrt{2xy}/y$

12. $-2x^5y^4\sqrt{y}$

13. $-2\sqrt[3]{2}$

14. $-3b\sqrt{a-1} - (a-1)\sqrt{b(a-1)}$

15. $-2(6a + 3b - 11\sqrt{ab})$

16. $2 + 2\sqrt{2}i$

17. -3

18. $-3i$

19. $\dfrac{7}{13} + \dfrac{4}{13}i$

20. $\dfrac{3}{34} + \dfrac{5}{34}i$

Chapter 9

Exercise Set 9.1

1. ± 3

3. $\pm 5/2$

5. $\pm\sqrt{5}$

7. $3 \pm i\sqrt{2}$

9. $-5/2 \pm \sqrt{2}$

11. $-2 \pm \dfrac{\sqrt{3}}{2}i$

13. $(5 \pm 2\sqrt{2})/3$

15. $\pm 2i$

17. $\pm\dfrac{8}{3}i$

19. $\pm i\sqrt{6}$

21. $1, 2$

23. $-2, 1$

25. $-4, -2$

27. $0, 4$

29. $1/2, 2$

31. ± 2

33. $1/3, 1/2$

35. $4, -2$

37. $-1/2, 4$

39. $1/3, -3$

41. $-\dfrac{1}{2} \pm \dfrac{1}{2}i$

43. $1, -3/4$

45. $-\dfrac{1}{3} \pm \dfrac{\sqrt{2}}{3}i$

47. $3, -4$

49. $0, -1/3$

51. $(-1 \pm \sqrt{11})/2$

53. $-2, 2/3$

55. $-\dfrac{5}{4} \pm \dfrac{\sqrt{7}}{4}i$

57. $\pm 1/2$

59. $-\dfrac{1}{4} \pm \dfrac{\sqrt{11}}{4}i$

61. $-\dfrac{3}{4} \pm \dfrac{\sqrt{17}}{4}$

63. $3, -3/2$

65. $1, -1/3$

69. $x = 5$

Exercise Set 9.2

1. d   3. c

5. $a = 3, b = -2, c = 5$ 7. $a = 2, b = -1, c = 5$

9. $a = 3, b = -1/3, c = 0$ 11. $-2, -3$

13. $3, 5$ 15. $0, -3/2$

17. $\dfrac{2}{5} \pm \dfrac{\sqrt{11}}{5} i$ 19. $\dfrac{2}{5} \pm \dfrac{\sqrt{21}}{5} i$

21. $3, -4$ 23. $2/3, -1$

25. ± 3 27. $\pm 2\sqrt{3}/3$

29. $1/2, -4$ 31. $u = 0, u = -\dfrac{3}{4}$

Exercise Set 9.3

1. e   3. b

5. d   7. d

9. c   11. a

13. a   15. two complex roots

17. a double root   19. two real roots

21. two real roots   23. two complex roots

25. two complex roots   27. two real roots

29. a double root   31. 2

33. 0   35. 1

37. 0

Exercise Set 9.4

1. A: 3 hr; B: 6 hr

3. roofer: 6 hr; assistant: 12 hr

5. $L = 12$ ft, $W = 4$ ft   7. $L = 8$ cm, $W = 5$ cm

9. 10 ft   11. 5 or 1/5

13. 3, 7 or $-3, -7$ 15. 6, 8

17. 150   19. 8

21. true for all x

Exercise Set 9.5

1. 4   3. 2

5. 3   7. 0, 4

9. 5   11. 6

13. 2, 10   15. $u = x^2$

17. $u = x^{2/3}$ 19. $u = 1/y^2$

21. $u = 1/x^{2/3}$ 23. $u = 2 + 3/x$

25. $u = x^2; \pm \sqrt{3}/3, \pm i\sqrt{2}$ 27. $u = 1/x; -3/2, 2$

29. $u = x^{1/5}; -1/32, -32$ 31. $u = 1 + 1/x; -2/7, 1/3$

Exercise Set 9.6

1. b, d, e   3. a, c, d, e

5. c, e   7. $-2, -3$

9. $-1/2, 1$ 11. 0, 2

13. $-5, -3$ 15. $-1/2, 3$

17. $-2/3, 1/2$

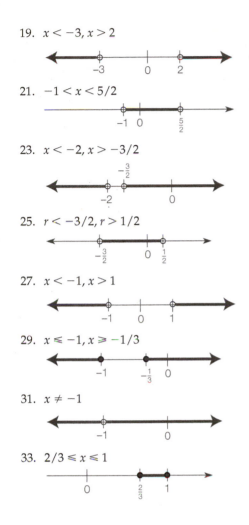

19. $x < -3, x > 2$

21. $-1 < x < 5/2$

23. $x < -2, x > -3/2$

25. $r < -3/2, r > 1/2$

27. $x < -1, x > 1$

29. $x \leq -1, x \geq -1/3$

31. $x \neq -1$

33. $2/3 \leq x \leq 1$

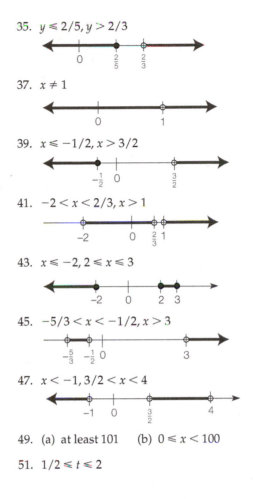

35. $y \leq 2/5, y > 2/3$

37. $x \neq 1$

39. $x \leq -1/2, x > 3/2$

41. $-2 < x < 2/3, x > 1$

43. $x \leq -2, 2 \leq x \leq 3$

45. $-5/3 < x < -1/2, x > 3$

47. $x < -1, 3/2 < x < 4$

49. (a) at least 101   (b) $0 \leq x < 100$

51. $1/2 \leq t \leq 2$

Review Exercises

1. $x = \pm 5$

2. $y = \pm 6$

3. $x = -1, 5$

4. $t = -\dfrac{1}{2} \pm i$

5. $x = -3, 2$

6. $y = 2, -1/2$

7. $r = 0, 1/3$

8. $x = \pm 5/2$

9. $x = (\sqrt{37} + 5)/2, (-\sqrt{37} + 5)/2$

10. $x = -2 + 4\sqrt{3}/3, -2 - 4\sqrt{3}/3$

11. $x = -3, 1$

12. $x = -1, 1/3$

13. $x = -1 + \sqrt{2}/2, -1 - \sqrt{2}/2$

14. $x = -1 + \sqrt{10}/3, -1 - \sqrt{10}/3$

15. $x = \dfrac{1}{4} \pm \dfrac{\sqrt{7}}{4}i$

16. $x = -\dfrac{1}{4} \pm \dfrac{\sqrt{11}}{4}i$

17. 2 complex roots

18. 2 real roots

19. double real root

20. 2 complex roots

21. 2 real roots

22. 2 real roots

23. no x-intercepts

24. 2 x-intercepts

25. 1 x-intercept

26. 2 x-intercepts

27. length = 6 ft; width = 9 ft

28. 60

29. $x = 6$

30. $x = 6$

31. $x = \pm \sqrt{2}\,i, \pm \sqrt{6}/2$

32. $x = \pm \sqrt{2}/2, \pm \sqrt{40}/2$ 33. $x = 4, -2$ 36. $s > 1/2, s < -2/3$

34. $x = 3, 5$

35. $-1 \leqslant x \leqslant 3/2$

$$\begin{array}{c} -\frac{2}{3} \\ \longleftarrow \! \\ -1 \quad 0 \quad \frac{1}{2} \quad 1 \end{array}$$

Progress Test 9A

1. $\pm \dfrac{\sqrt{21}}{3} i$

2. 4

3. $7/2, -1/2$

4. $2 \pm 2\sqrt{15}i$

5. $4, -1/2$

6. $2, -1/3$

7. $(3 \pm \sqrt{33})/3$

8. two real roots

9. two complex roots

10. $(-3 \pm \sqrt{13})/4$

11. $0, -2/3$

12. $-3 \leqslant x \leqslant 1/2$

13. $-1 \leqslant x < 1$

14. $3/2 < x < 4$

15. $L = 26$ m, $W = 21$ m

16. $3\sqrt{2}, 3\sqrt{2} + 6$ hr

Progress Test 9B

1. $\pm 3/2$

2. 5

3. $-9, 21$

4. $-\dfrac{1}{6} \pm \dfrac{\sqrt{10}}{3}$

5. $4, -3$

6. $-1/2, -1$

7. $\dfrac{3}{2} \pm \dfrac{1}{2} i$

8. a double root

9. two complex roots

10. $(5 \pm i\sqrt{7})/4$

11. $\pm \dfrac{\sqrt{15}}{3} i$

12. $x \leqslant -5/2, x \geqslant 2$

13. $x < -1/2, x \geqslant 1/2$

14. $-1/3 < x < 2$

15. 9 m, 12 m

16. 25

Solutions to Selected Review Exercises

Chapter 1

1. The set of natural numbers between -5 and 4 inclusive is $\{1, 2, 3, 4\}$, since the set of natural numbers is $\{1, 2, 3, \ldots\}$.

4. T. $\sqrt{7}$ is irrational and thus real.

6. F. -14 is a negative integer and therefore an integer.

19. $2.25\% = \dfrac{2.25}{100} = \dfrac{225}{10,000} = \dfrac{9}{400} = 0.0225$

23. T. $2(3) + 4 = 10$.

25. F. $3(1) - 4(2) = -5$.

34. $2 - 3(-3) = 2 + 9 = 11$

37. $a + (b + c) = (a + b) + c$ associative (addition)
$= c + (a + b)$ commutative (addition)

39. $3(ab) = (3a)b$ associative (multiplication)
$= b(3a)$ commutative (multiplication)

41. $\dfrac{4 + a}{2} = \dfrac{4}{2} + \dfrac{a}{2} = 2 + \dfrac{a}{2}$

42. $-2(a - 3) = -2a + (-2)(-3) = -2a + 6$

43. $2(ab) = 2(ba) = (2b)a$

45. $\dfrac{|2 - 2(3)| + |-2 - 3|}{|(-2)3|} = \dfrac{|-4| + |-5|}{|-6|} = 9/6 = 3/2$

47. $\overline{AB} = |2 - (-3)| = |2 + 3| = |5| = 5$

49. $x \geq -1$

Chapter 2

5. $2(x - 1) = 4x - 3$
$2x - 2 = 4x - 4$
$-2 + 3 = 4x - 2x$
$1 = 2x$
$x = \dfrac{1}{2}$

7. Let f = annual profit of the foreign division. Then the annual profit of the domestic division was

$$2f + 4$$

Since the total annual profit was $19 million,

$$f + 2f + 4 = 19$$
$$3f = 15$$
$$f = 5$$

The foreign profit was $5 million; the domestic profit is $2f + 4 = 2(5) + 4 = 14$ million dollar.

9. Let x = exposure time for the fourth test print. Then

$$\frac{5 + 12 + 15 + x}{4} = 13$$

$$5 + 12 + 15 + x = 4(13) = 52$$

$$32 + x = 52$$

$$x = 20 \text{ seconds}$$

11.
$$r = 2s + 4tu$$

$$r - 2s = 4tu$$

$$\frac{r - 2s}{4t} = u$$

17.
$$2x + 3 > 5$$

$$2x > 5 - 3$$

$$2x > 2$$

$$x > 1$$

19.
$$2(x + 2) < 3(x - 1)$$

$$2x + 4 < 3x - 3$$

$$4 + 3 < 3x - 2x$$

$$7 < x \quad \text{or} \quad x > 7$$

21.
$$3 < 2x < 6$$

$$3/2 < x < 3$$

25.
$$3x - 2 > -5$$

$$3x > -5 + 2$$

$$3x > -3$$

$$x > -1$$

29.
$$-1 < 2x + 1 < 4$$

$$-1 - 1 < 2x < 4 - 1$$

$$-2 < 2x < 3$$

$$-1 < x < 3/2$$

33. Let x = number of orders placed.

$$120 + 1.5x > 180$$

$$1.5x > 180 - 120$$

$$1.5x > 60$$

$$x > 40$$

More than 40 orders must be placed.

37.
$$|-y + 3| = 2$$

$$-y + 3 = 2 \qquad \text{or} \qquad -(-y + 3) = 2$$

$$-y = 2 - 3 \qquad\qquad\qquad y - 3 = 2$$

$$-y = -1 \qquad\qquad\qquad\qquad y = 2 + 3$$

$$y = 1 \qquad\qquad\qquad\qquad y = 5$$

Check: $|-1 + 3| \overset{?}{=} 2 \qquad |-5 + 3| \overset{?}{=} 2$

$$|2| \overset{✔}{=} 2 \qquad\qquad |-2| \overset{✔}{=} 2$$

39.
$$|3r + 3| = 0$$

$$3r + 3 = 0$$

$$3r = -3$$

$$r = -3/3 = -1$$

Check: $|3(-1) + 3| \overset{?}{=} |-3 + 3| = |0| \overset{✔}{=} 0$

43.
$$|2x + 3| \leq 2$$

$$-2 \leq 2x + 3 \leq 2$$

$$-5 \leq 2x \leq -1$$

$$-5/2 \leq x \leq -1/2$$

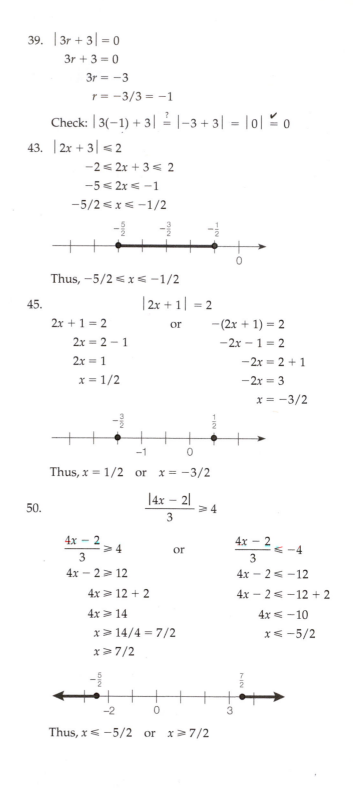

Thus, $-5/2 \leq x \leq -1/2$

45.
$$|2x + 1| = 2$$

$$2x + 1 = 2 \qquad \text{or} \qquad -(2x + 1) = 2$$

$$2x = 2 - 1 \qquad\qquad\qquad -2x - 1 = 2$$

$$2x = 1 \qquad\qquad\qquad\qquad -2x = 2 + 1$$

$$x = 1/2 \qquad\qquad\qquad\qquad -2x = 3$$

$$x = -3/2$$

Thus, $x = 1/2 \quad \text{or} \quad x = -3/2$

50.
$$\frac{|4x - 2|}{3} \geq 4$$

$$\frac{4x - 2}{3} \geq 4 \qquad \text{or} \qquad \frac{4x - 2}{3} \leq -4$$

$$4x - 2 \geq 12 \qquad\qquad\qquad 4x - 2 \leq -12$$

$$4x \geq 12 + 2 \qquad\qquad\qquad 4x - 2 \leq -12 + 2$$

$$4x \geq 14 \qquad\qquad\qquad\qquad 4x \leq -10$$

$$x \geq 14/4 = 7/2 \qquad\qquad\qquad x \leq -5/2$$

$$x \geq 7/2$$

Thus, $x \leq -5/2 \quad \text{or} \quad x \geq 7/2$

Chapter 3

4. Let t = number of 20-cent stamps. We can arrange the given information as follows.

		× Denomination =	Value
20-cent	t	20	$20t$
40-cent	$t + 3$	40	$40(t + 3)$
1-dollar	$t - 3$	100	$100(t + 2)$
Total			560

Since

$$\text{total value} = \begin{pmatrix} \text{value of} \\ \text{20-cent} \\ \text{stamps} \end{pmatrix}$$
$$+ \begin{pmatrix} \text{value of} \\ \text{40-cent} \\ \text{stamps} \end{pmatrix} + \begin{pmatrix} \text{value of} \\ \text{1-dollar} \\ \text{stamps} \end{pmatrix}$$

we have

$$560 = 20t + 40(t + 3) + 100(t - 2)$$
$$560 = 20t + 40t + 120 + 100t - 200$$
$$560 = 160t - 80$$
$$640 = 160t$$
$$t = 4$$

Thus,

$$t = \text{number of 20-cent stamps} = 4$$
$$t + 3 = \text{number of 40-cent stamps} = 7$$
$$t - 2 = \text{number of 1-dollar stamps} = 2$$

6. Let

$$c = \text{amount in classical music inventory}$$

then

$$12,000 - c = \text{amount in popular music inventory}$$

Displaying the information we have

	Amount	× Profit =	Rate of Return
Classical music	c	0.15	$0.15c$
Popular music	$12,000 - c$	0.20	$0.20(12,000 - c)$

Then

$$0.15c = 0.20 (12,000 - c) - 1000$$
$$0.15c = 2400 - 0.20c - 1000$$
$$0.35c = 1400$$
$$c = \$4000 = \text{amount in classical}$$
$$\text{music inventory}$$
$$12,000 - 4000 = \$8000 = \text{amount in popular}$$
$$\text{music inventory}$$

9. Let

$$x = \text{average speed of slower aircraft}$$

then

$$2x = \text{average speed of faster aircraft}$$

	Rate	× Time	= Distance
Slower aircraft	x	5	$5x$
Faster aircraft	$2x$	5	$10x$

Since after 5 hours the planes are 1500 miles apart,

$$5x + 10x = 1500$$
$$15x = 1500$$
$$x = 100 = \text{average speed of}$$
$$\text{slower aircraft}$$
$$2x = 200 = \text{average speed of}$$
$$\text{faster aircraft}$$

12. Let

$$x = \text{average speed of first aircraft}$$

then

$$x + 100 = \text{average speed of second aircraft}$$

	Rate	× Time	= Distance
First aircraft	x	3.5	$3.5x$
Second aircraft	$x + 100$	3.5	$(3.5x + 100)$

After 3.5 hours the total distance covered is 3150 miles, so

$$3.5x + 3.5(x + 100) = 3150$$
$$3.5x + 3.5 + 350 = 3150$$
$$7x = 2800$$
$$x = 400 = \text{average speed of}$$
$$\text{first aircraft}$$
$$x + 100 = 500 = \text{average speed of}$$
$$\text{second aircraft}$$

16. Let
$$x = \text{number of pounds of Colombian coffee}$$

Since the mixture is to consist of 25 pounds, we must have $25 - x$ pounds of Jamaican coffee.

Type of Coffee	Number of pounds	×	Price per pound	=	Value in cents
Colombian	x		400		$400x$
Jamaican	$25 - x$		500		$500(25 - x)$
Mixture	25		480		12,000

Since the value of the mixture is the sum of the two components, we have

$$12,000 = 400x + 500(25 - x)$$
$$12,000 = 400x + 12,500 - 500x$$
$$100x = 500$$
$$x = 5 = \text{number of pounds of Colombian coffee to be used}$$
$$25 - x = 20 = \text{number of pounds of Colombian coffee to be used}$$

Chapter 4

3. No, since x appears to the power of $-\frac{1}{2}$, which is not a nonnegative integer.

4. Yes, since all the exponents are nonnegative integers.

9. The degrees of the terms are 7, 3, and 0, so the degree of the polynomial is 7.

10. The degrees of the terms are 2, 4, and 5, so the degree of the polynomial is 5.

15. $-3(1)^3(-2) + (1)(-2)^2 - 2(1)(-2) + 3 = 17$

17. $(2x^3 - 3x + 1) + (3x^3 + 2x^2 - 3)$
$$= (2 + 3)x^3 + (0 + 2)x^2 + (-3 + 0)x + (1 - 3)$$
$$= 5x^3 + 2x^2 - 3x - 2$$

18. $(3a^2b^3 - 2a^2b + ab - a) - (-2a^3b^3 + ab^2 - 2ab + b)$
$$= (0 + 2)a^3b^3 + (3 - 0)a^2b^3 + (-2 - 0)a^2b + (0 - 1)ab^2 + (1 + 2)ab + (-1 - 0)a + (0 - 1)b$$
$$= 2a^3b^3 + 3a^2b^3 - 2a^2b - ab^2 + 3ab - a - b$$

22. $x(2x - 1)^2 = x(2x - 1)(2x - 1)$
$$= x(4x^2 - 4x + 1)$$
$$= 4x^3 - 4x^2 + x$$

26. $(a^2 + 2a + 3)(a^2 - a - 1)$
$$= a^2(a^2 - a - 1) + 2a(a^2 - a - 1) + 3(a^2 - a - 1)$$
$$= a^4 - a^3 - a^2 + 2a^3 - 2a^2 - 2a + 3a^2 - 3a - 3$$
$$= a^4 + a^3 - 5a - 3$$

28. $(b + 1)^2(2b - 1)^2$
$$= (b + 1)(b + 1)(2b - 1)(2b - 1)$$
$$= (b^2 + 2b + 1)(4b^2 - 4b + 1)$$
$$= b^2(4b^2 - 4b + 1) + 2b(4b^2 - 4b + 1) + 1(4b^2 - 4b + 1)$$
$$= 4b^4 - 4b^3 + b^2 + 8b^3 - 8b^2 + 2b + 4b^2 - 4b + 1$$
$$= 4b^4 + 4b^3 - 3b^2 - 2b + 1$$

31. $x^2(2x - 3)^2 = x^2(2x - 3)(2x - 3)$
$$= x^2(4x^2 - 12x + 9)$$

The x^3 term comes from $x^2(-12x)$, so the coefficient of x^3 is -12.

38. $16x^2 - y^2 = (4x)^2 - y^2$ (the difference of two squares)
$$= (4x + y)(4x - y)$$

39. $18x^2 - 24x + 6 = 6(3x^2 - 4x + 1)$
$$= 6(3x + a)(x + b)$$
so
$$ab = 1 \quad \text{and} \quad a + 3b = -4$$
The only integer factors satisfying $ab = 1$ are $a = 1$, $b = 1$ and $a = -1, b = -1$. We quickly see that $a = 1$, $b = 1$ does not satisfy $a + 3b = -4$ but that $a = -1$, $b = -1$ is a satisfactory choice. Thus,
$$18x^2 - 24x + 6 = 6(3x - 1)(x - 1)$$

40. $2rs + s - 2r - 1 = 2rs - 2r + s - 1$
$$= (2r)(s - 1) + (s - 1)$$
$$= (2r + 1)(s - 1)$$

44. $3a^2 + 2ab - 2b - 3a = 3a^2 - 3a + 2ab - 2b$
$$= 3a(a - 1) + 2b(a - 1)$$
$$= (3a + 2b)(a - 1)$$

46. $a^4 - 2a^2 + 1 = (a^2)^2 - 2a^2 + 1$
$$= (a^2 - 1)^2$$

50. $8x^3 + 125y^3$
$$= (2x)^3 + (5y)^3$$
$$= (2x + 5y)(4x^2 - 10xy + 25y^2) \quad \text{Sum of cubes}$$

52. $8x^3 - 125y^3$
$$= (2x)^3 - (5y)^3$$
$$= (2x - 5y)(4x^2 + 10xy + 25y^2) \quad \text{Difference of cubes}$$

56.
$$
\begin{array}{r}
4y \phantom{{}^2} - 20 \\
y + 5 \, \overline{\smash{)}\, 4y^2 - 25} \\
\underline{4y^2 + 20y} \\
-20y - 25 \\
\underline{-20y - 100} \\
75
\end{array}
$$

$$\frac{4y^2 - 25}{y + 5} = 4y - 20 + \frac{75}{y + 5}$$

60.
$$
\begin{array}{r}
a \phantom{{}^2} - 3 \\
a^2 + 2 \, \overline{\smash{)}\, a^3 - 3a^2 - 2a + 6} \\
\underline{a^3 \phantom{{}^2000} + 2a} \\
-3a^3 - 4a + 6 \\
\underline{-3a^2 \phantom{{}^20} - 6} \\
-4a + 12
\end{array}
$$

$$\frac{a^3 - 3a^2 - 2a + 6}{a^2 + 2} = a - 3 + \frac{12 - 4a}{a^2 + 2}$$

Chapter 5

1. $\dfrac{5x + 10}{5} = \dfrac{\cancel{5}(x + 2)}{\cancel{5}} = x + 2$

3. $\dfrac{x^2 - 2x - 8}{x + 2} = \dfrac{(x + 2)(x - 4)}{x + 2} = x - 4$

7. $\dfrac{4x}{x + 1} \div \dfrac{2x^2}{x - 1} = \dfrac{4x}{x + 1} \cdot \dfrac{x - 1}{2x^2} = \dfrac{2(x - 1)}{x(x + 1)} = \dfrac{2x - 2}{x^2 + x}$

13. First we write the fractions
$$\frac{3y}{y^2 - 4} \qquad \frac{2}{y + 2} \qquad \frac{4y^2}{y^2 - 2y}$$

with factored denominators:
$$\frac{3y}{(y - 2)(y + 2)} \qquad \frac{2}{y + 2} \qquad \frac{4y^2}{y(y - 2)}$$

Then we fill in the following table to discover the factors of the LCD:

Factor	Highest power	Final factor
$y - 2$	1	$y - 2$
$y + 2$	1	$y + 2$
y	1	y

Thus, the LCD is $y(y - 2)(y + 2) = y(y^2 - 4) = y^3 - 4y$.

15. $\dfrac{2 - x^2}{x} + \dfrac{4 + 2x^2}{3x}$

The LCD is $3x$; thus, we have
$$\frac{3(2 - x^2)}{3x} + \frac{4 + 2x^2}{3x} = \frac{6 - 3x^2 + 4 + 2x^2}{3x} = \frac{10 - x^2}{3x}$$

18. $\dfrac{2y}{(2x + 3)(x - 1)} - \dfrac{y - 1}{2x + 3}$

The LCD is $(2x + 3)(x - 1)$. Thus, we have
$$\frac{2y}{(2x + 3)(x - 1)} - \frac{(y - 1)(x - 1)}{(2x + 3)(x - 1)}$$
$$= \frac{2y - (y - 1)(x - 1)}{(2x + 3)(x - 1)}$$
$$= \frac{2y - (yx - y - x + 1)}{(2x + 3)(x - 1)}$$
$$= \frac{2y - yx + y + x - 1}{(2x + 3)(x - 1)}$$
$$= \frac{3y - yx + x - 1}{(2x + 3)(x - 1)}$$

21. $$\dfrac{2-\dfrac{1}{x}}{1+\dfrac{5}{x}}$$

Multiply numerator and denominator by the LCD, x. Thus, we have

$$\frac{\left(2-\dfrac{1}{x}\right)x}{\left(1+\dfrac{5}{x}\right)x} = \frac{2x-1}{x+5}$$

23. $$\dfrac{x-2}{2-\dfrac{1}{x+1}}$$

Combining as one fraction in the denominator, we have

$$\frac{x-2}{\dfrac{2(x+2)-1}{x+2}} = \frac{x-2}{\dfrac{2x+4-1}{x+2}} = \frac{x-2}{\dfrac{2x+3}{x+2}}$$

$$= (x-2)\cdot\frac{x+2}{2x+3} = \frac{x^2-4}{2x+3}$$

31. $\dfrac{2x+1}{2x-1} = -\dfrac{2}{3}$

Multiplying both sides by $3(2x-1)$ to clear fractions, we obtain

$$3(2x+1) = -2(2x-1)$$
$$6x+3 = -4x+2$$
$$6x+4x = 2-3$$
$$10x = -1$$
$$x = -1/10$$

35. Let x = the number. Then $1/x$ is its reciprocal.

$$\frac{1}{2} + 3\left(\frac{1}{x}\right) = 2$$

$$\frac{1}{2} + \frac{3}{x} = 2$$

$$2x\left(\frac{1}{2} + \frac{3}{x}\right) = 2x(2) \qquad \text{Multiply both sides by } 2x$$

$$\frac{2x}{2} + \frac{6x}{x} = 4x$$

$$x + 6 = 4x$$
$$6 = 3x$$
$$x = 2$$

37.

	Time alone	Rate	× Time =	Work done
Senior photographer	5	1/5	3	3/5
Junior photographer	x	$1/x$	3	$3/x$

Since

$$\left(\begin{array}{c}\text{work done by} \\ \text{senior photographer}\end{array}\right) + \left(\begin{array}{c}\text{work done by} \\ \text{junior photographer}\end{array}\right)$$

$$= 1 \text{ whole job}$$

we have

$$\frac{3}{5} + \frac{3}{x} = 1$$

$$5x\left(\frac{3}{5} + \frac{3}{x}\right) = 1$$

$$5x\left(\frac{3}{5}\right) + 5x\left(\frac{3}{x}\right) = 5x$$

$$3x + 15 = 5x$$

$$15 = 2x$$

$$x = \frac{15}{2} = 7.5 \text{ hours}$$

Thus, the junior photographer would take 7.5 hours to complete the job alone.

40. Let s = speed of the canoe in sill water.

	Rate	× Time	= Distance
upstream	$s-4$	$\dfrac{30}{s-4}$	30
downstream	$s+4$	$\dfrac{50}{s+4}$	50

$$\frac{30}{s-4} = \frac{50}{s+4}$$

Multiply both sides of the equation by the LCD $(s-4)(s+4)$:

$$30(s+4) = 50(s-4)$$
$$30s + 120 = 50s - 200$$
$$20s = 320$$
$$s = 16$$

Thus, the speed of the canoe in still water is 16 km per hour.

45. $\dfrac{2}{2r+3} = \dfrac{1}{2}$

After clearing fractions by multiplying both sides by $2(2r+3)$, we have

$$2(2) = 1(2r+3)$$
$$4 = 2r+3$$
$$1 = 2r$$
$$r = \dfrac{1}{2}$$

46. $\dfrac{3}{r-2} = \dfrac{2}{r+3}$

Multiply both sides by $(r-2)(r+3)$:

$$3(r+3) = 2(r-2)$$
$$3r+9 = 2r-4$$
$$3r-2r = -4-9$$
$$r = -13$$

49. Let x = cost of a 240-square-foot carpet. Since cost is proportioned to square footage,

$$\dfrac{600}{180} = \dfrac{x}{240}$$
$$600(240) = x(180)$$
$$144{,}000 = 180x$$
$$x = 800$$

Thus, the carpet costs $800.

Chapter 6

1. $B = (2-4, -3-1) = (-2, -4)$

3. II, since x is negative and y is positive

4. a and d, since

$$2(2)^2 - 5(3) = 8 - 15 = -7$$
$$2(-2)^2 - 5(3) = 8 - 15 = -7$$

14. $g(t) = \dfrac{3}{t^2 + t - 12} = \dfrac{3}{(t+4)(t-3)}$

Since the denominator cannot be zero, we must exclude the values $t = -4$ and $t = 3$ from the domain of g.

15. Not a function by the vertical line test.

18. (a) $g(-5) = \dfrac{-5-3}{-5+1} = \dfrac{-8}{-4} = 2$

(b) $g(0) = \dfrac{0-3}{0+1} = -3$

(c) $g(3) = \dfrac{3-3}{3+1} = 0$

19. (a) When $t = 2$ seconds, $s = 16(2)^2 = 64$ feet
   When $t = 4$ seconds, $s = 16(4)^2 = 256$ feet

(b) With $s = 144$, solve

$$144 = 16t^2$$
$$t^2 = \dfrac{144}{16} = 9$$
$$t = 3 \quad (\text{reject } t = -3)$$

It takes 3 seconds to fall 144 feet.

29. (a) $C = \begin{cases} 0.15n, & 0 < n \leqslant 5 \\ 0.075 + 0.10(n-5), & 5 < n \leqslant 20 \end{cases}$

(c) $C = 0.75 + 0.10(16 - 5) = 0.75 + 1.10 = 1.85$

It costs $1.85.

37.

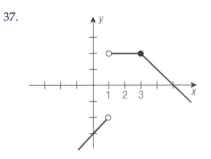

42. (a) $M = k/n^3$

   (b) $\dfrac{1}{12} = \dfrac{k}{8}$, so $k = 2/3$

   Hence,
   $$M = \frac{2}{3n^3}$$

   (c) When $n = 4$, $M = \dfrac{2}{3 \cdot 4^3} = \dfrac{1}{96}$;

   when $n = 5$, $M = \dfrac{2}{3 \cdot 5^3} = \dfrac{2}{375}$.

n	2	3	4	5
M	1/2	2/81	1/96	2/375

45. $S = ktu^2$

   Substituting $S = 18$, $t = 4$, and $u = 9$, we have
   $$18 = k \cdot 4 \cdot 9^2$$

   Then $k = 18/324 = 1/18$. When $t = 6$ and $u = 3$,
   $$S = \frac{1}{18}tu^2$$
   $$= \frac{1}{18}(6)(3)^2$$
   $$= \frac{1}{18} \cdot 6 \cdot 9 = 3$$

51. Let

   a = the amount (in dollars) spent on advertising
   L = the length (in pages) of the manual
   R = revenue
   K = constant of proportionality

   Then
   $$R = k \cdot \frac{A}{L}$$

   Substituting the given values, we have
   $$1{,}000{,}000 = k \cdot \frac{50{,}000}{100}$$

   $$k = \frac{1{,}000{,}000(100)}{50{,}000} = 2000$$

   Thus,
   $$R = 2000\frac{A}{L}$$

   When $L = 120$ and $A = 75{,}000$,
   $$R = 2000\left(\frac{75{,}000}{120}\right)$$
   $$= 1{,}250{,}000$$

   The firm would have received \$1,250,000.

Chapter 7

1. $P_1(-2, 3)$, $P_2(2, 5)$
   $$m = \frac{y_2 - y_1}{x_2 - x_1} = \frac{5 - 3}{2 - (-2)} = \frac{2}{4} = \frac{1}{2}$$

4. falling, since $m < 0$

9. false, since L_1 is steeper than L_2

13. Solving for y:
   $$2y = c - 3x$$
   $$y = -\frac{3}{2}x + \frac{c}{2}$$
   Then $c/2 = -3$, so $c = -6$.

17. yes, since $3(2) - 4(-1) = 10$

21. The line has slope $m = -3$ and passes through the point $(4, 0)$. Thus,
   $$y - 0 = -3(x - 4)$$
   $$y = -3(x - 4)$$

23. Since $m = 4$ and $b = -2$, $y = 4x - 2$.

25. Solving for y, we have
   $$2x = 3y - 4$$
   $$y = \frac{2}{3}x + \frac{4}{3}$$
   Then $m = 2/3$, $b = 4/3$.

29. (a) $y = -3$ (b) $x = 2$

33. The slope of L is
   $$m_1 = \frac{5 - 2}{-1 - 4} = -\frac{3}{5}$$

   The slope of L' is
   $$m_2 = \frac{3 - 2}{2 - 1} = 1$$

   Since the slopes are unequal, the lines are not parallel.

35. Solving $3x - 2y = 4$ for y, we obtain

$$y = \frac{3}{2}x - 2$$

so $m = 3/2$. Thus, the equation of the line parallel to the given line is

$$y = \frac{3}{2}x + 5$$

37. Solving $5x - 2y = 4$ for y, we obtain

$$y = \frac{5}{2}x - 2$$

so $m = 5/2$. The slope of any line perpendicular to the given line is then $-2/5$. Since the line passes through $(4, 1)$,

$$y - 1 = -\frac{2}{5}(x - 4)$$

39. The slope of the line $2x - 3y = 4$ is $m_1 = 2/3$, and the slope of the line $2y + 3x = 6$ is $m_2 = -3/2$. Since $m_1 m_2 = -1$, the lines are perpendicular.

Chapter 8

3. $\left(-\frac{a}{b}\right)^5 = \left(\frac{-a}{b}\right)^5 = \frac{(-a)^5}{b^5} = \frac{(-1)^5 a^5}{b^5} = \frac{-a^5}{b^5}$

8. $\frac{(3a^3 b^2)^3}{(-2a^4 b^3)^4} = \frac{3^3 a^9 b^6}{(-2)^4 a^{16} b^{12}} = \frac{27 a^9 b^6}{16 a^{16} b^{12}} = \frac{27}{16 a^7 b^6}$

12. $a^{-4} a^4 a^2 = a^{-4+4+2} = a^2$

15. $\left(\frac{2xy^{-2}}{3x^{-2}y^{-3}}\right)^4 = \frac{2^4 x^4 y^{-8}}{3^4 x^{-8} y^{-12}} = \frac{16 x^{12} y^4}{81}$

17. $32^{2/5} = (2^5)^{2/5} = 2^2 = 4$

20. $\frac{81^{1/4}}{81^{5/4}} = \frac{1}{81^{5/4-1/4}} = \frac{1}{81^{4/4}} = \frac{1}{81}$

23. $\left(\frac{x^{2/3}}{x^{4/3}}\right)^{1/4} = \frac{x^{1/6}}{x^{1/3}} = x^{1/16-1/3} = x^{-1/6} = \frac{1}{x^{1/6}}$

25. $\sqrt{60} = \sqrt{4 \cdot 15} = 2\sqrt{15}$

29. $\frac{6a^7}{\sqrt{3b}} = \frac{6a^7}{\sqrt{3b}} \cdot \frac{\sqrt{3b}}{\sqrt{3b}} = \frac{6a^7 \sqrt{3b}}{3b} = \frac{2a^7 \sqrt{3b}}{b}$

33. $\sqrt[3]{3xy^2} + \sqrt[3]{5xy^2} = \sqrt[3]{3}\sqrt[3]{xy^2} + \sqrt[3]{5}\sqrt[3]{xy^2}$
$$= \sqrt[3]{xy^2}(\sqrt[3]{3} + \sqrt[3]{5})$$

36. $\frac{\sqrt{3x} - 1}{\sqrt{3x} + 1} = \frac{(\sqrt{3x} - 1)(\sqrt{3x} - 1)}{(\sqrt{3x} + 1)(\sqrt{3x} - 1)} = \frac{(\sqrt{3x} - 1)^2}{3x - 1}$

37. $\frac{2}{\sqrt{x - y}} = \frac{2}{\sqrt{x - y}} \cdot \frac{\sqrt{x - y}}{\sqrt{x - y}} = \frac{2\sqrt{x - y}}{x - y}$

40. $-i^{29} = -(i^{28} \cdot i) = -i = 0 - i$

41. $\sqrt{-20} = \sqrt{-5(2)^2} = 2\sqrt{5}i = 0 + 2\sqrt{5}i$

46. $(4 - 3i)^2 = 16 - 24i + 9i^2 = 16 - 24i - 9 = 7 - 24i$

47. $\frac{1}{\sqrt{3} + 2i} = \frac{1}{\sqrt{3} + 2i} \cdot \frac{\sqrt{3} - 2i}{\sqrt{3} - 2i} = \frac{\sqrt{3} - 2i}{3 - 4i^2}$

Chapter 9

$$= \frac{\sqrt{3} - 2i}{7} = \frac{\sqrt{3}}{7} - \frac{2}{7}i$$

3. $(x - 2)^2 = 9$

$$x - 2 = \pm 3$$
$$x = 2 \pm 3$$
$$x = 5 \quad x = -1$$

6. $2y^2 - 3y - 2 = 0$

$$(2y + 1)(y - 2) = 0$$
$$y = -\frac{1}{2} \quad y = 2$$

9. $x^2 - 5x = 3$

$$x^2 - 5x + \left(\frac{5}{2}\right)^2 = 3 + \left(\frac{5}{2}\right)^2$$
$$\left(x - \frac{5}{2}\right)^2 = 3 + \frac{25}{4} = \frac{37}{4}$$
$$x - \frac{5}{2} = \pm\frac{\sqrt{37}}{2}$$
$$x = \frac{5}{2} \pm \frac{\sqrt{37}}{2}$$
$$x = \frac{5 + \sqrt{37}}{2} \quad x = \frac{5 - \sqrt{37}}{2}$$

15. $a = 2, b = -2, c = 1$

$$x = \frac{-b \pm \sqrt{b^2 - 4ac}}{2a}$$
$$= \frac{1 \pm \sqrt{1 - 8}}{4}$$
$$= \frac{1 \pm \sqrt{-7}}{4}$$
$$= \frac{1}{4} \pm \frac{\sqrt{7}}{4}i$$

19. $9r^2 - 6r + 1 = 0$

$$b^2 - 4ac = 36 - 4(9)(1)$$
$$= 36 - 36$$
$$= 0 \text{ Since the discriminant is zero, there is a double real root}$$

29. $x + \sqrt{x + 10} = 10$

$$\sqrt{x + 10} = 10 - x$$
$$x + 10 = (10 - x)^2$$
$$x + 10 = 100 - 20x + x^2$$
$$x^2 - 21x + 90 = 0$$
$$(x - 6)(x - 15) = 0$$
$$x = 6 \quad x = 15$$

Test both answers:

$$6 + \sqrt{6 + 10} \overset{?}{=} 10 \qquad 15 + \sqrt{15 + 10} \overset{?}{=} 10$$
$$6 + 4 \overset{\checkmark}{=} 10 \qquad\qquad 15 + 5 \overset{\checkmark}{\neq} 10$$

31. $2x^4 + x^2 - 6 = 0$

Substitute $y = x^2$:

$$2y^2 + y - 6 = 0$$
$$(2y - 3)(y + 2) = 0$$
$$y = -2 \quad y = \frac{3}{2}$$

Then

$$x^2 = -2 \quad \text{or} \quad x^2 = \frac{3}{2}$$
$$x = \pm\sqrt{2}i \quad x = \pm\sqrt{\frac{3}{2}} = \pm\frac{\sqrt{6}}{2}$$

34. $\dfrac{x - 3}{x - 5} \geq 0$

The critical values occur where

$$x - 3 = 0$$
$$x - 5 = 0$$

So critical values are at

$$x = 3, 5$$

(Note: At $x = 5$ we have division by zero.)

Index